CONCRETE PIPE
DESIGN MANUAL

Prepared by
AMERICAN CONCRETE PIPE ASSOCIATION
8320 Old Courthouse Road
Vienna, Virginia 22180

$22.50

Library of Congress catalog number 78-58624
Printed in the United States of America

First printing February, 1970
15,000 copies
Second printing July, 1970
15,000 copies
Third printing (revised) February, 1974
15,000 copies
Fourth printing (revised) June 1978
10,000 copies
Fifth printing (revised) June 1980
15,000 copies

Technical programs of the American Concrete Pipe Association, since its founding in 1907, have been designed to compile engineering data on the hydraulics, loads and supporting strengths and design of concrete pipe. Information obtained is disseminated to producers and consumers of concrete pipe through technical literature and promotional handbooks. Other important activities of the Association include development of product specifications, government relations, participation in related trade and professional societies, advertising and promotion, an industry safety program and educational training. These services are made possible by the financial support of member companies located throughout the United States, Canada, and in almost 40 foreign countries. A directory of member companies is available on request.

FOREWORD

The principal objective in compiling the material for this **CONCRETE PIPE DESIGN MANUAL** was to present data and information on the design of concrete pipe systems in a readily usable form. The Design Manual is a companion volume to the **CONCRETE PIPE HANDBOOK** which provides an up-to-date compilation of the concepts and theories which form the basis for the design and installation of precast concrete pipe sewers and culverts and explanations for the charts, tables and design procedures summarized in the Design Manual.

Special recognition is acknowledged for the contribution of the staff of the American Concrete Pipe Association and the technical review and assistance of the engineers of the member companies of the Association in preparing this Design Manual. Also acknowledged is the development work of the American Association of State Highway and Transportation Officials, American Society of Civil Engineers, U. S. Army Corps of Engineers, U. S. Federal Highway Administration, U. S. Water and Power Resources Service, Iowa State University, U. S. Soil Conservation Service, Water Pollution Control Federation, and many others. Credit for much of the data in this Manual goes to the engineers of these organizations and agencies. Every effort has been made to assure accuracy, and technical data are considered reliable, but no guarantee is made or liability assumed.

AMERICAN CONCRETE PIPE ASSOCIATION
June 1980

CONTENTS

INDEX OF CONTENTS

Chapter 5. Supplemental Data

FIGURES

APPENDIX

CHAPTER 1

INTRODUCTION

The design and construction of sewers and culverts are among the most important areas of public works engineering and, like all engineering projects, they involve various stages of development. The information presented in this manual does not cover all phases of the project, and the engineer may need to consult additional references for the data required to complete preliminary surveys.

This manual is a compilation of data on concrete pipe, and it was planned to provide all design information needed by the engineer when he begins to consider the type and shape of pipe to be used. All equations used in developing the figures and tables are shown along with limited supporting theory. A condensed bibliography of literature references is included to assist the engineer who wishes to further study the development of these equations.

Chapters have been arranged so the descriptive information can be easily followed into the tables and figures containing data which enable the engineer to select the required type and size concrete pipe without the lengthy computations previously required. All of these design aids are presently published in engineering textbooks or represent the computer analysis of involved equations. Supplemental data and information are included to assist in completing this important phase of the project, and illustrative example problems are presented in Chapters 2 through 4. A review of these examples will indicate the relative ease with which this manual can be used.

CHAPTER 2

HYDRAULICS OF SEWERS

The hydraulic design procedure for sewers requires:

1. Determination of Sewer System Type
2. Determination of Design Flow
3. Selection of Pipe Size
4. Determination of Flow Velocity

SANITARY SEWERS

DETERMINATION OF SEWER SYSTEM TYPE

Sanitary sewers are designed to carry domestic, commercial and industrial sewage with consideration given to possible infiltration of ground water. All types of flow are designed on the basis of having the flow characteristics of water.

DETERMINATION OF DESIGN FLOW

In designing sanitary sewers, average, peak and minimum flows are considered. Average flow is determined or selected, and a factor applied to arrive at the peak flow which is used for selecting pipe size. Minimum flows are used to determine if specified velocities can be maintained to prevent deposition of solids.

Average Flow. The average flow, usually expressed in gallons per day, is a hypothetical quantity which is derived from past data and experience. With adequate local historical records, the average rate of water consumption can be related to the average sewage flow from domestic, commercial and industrial sources. Without such records, information on probable average flows can be obtained from other sources such as state or national agencies. Requirements for minimum average flows are usually specified by local or state sanitary authorities or local, state and national public

3

health agencies. Table 1 lists design criteria for domestic sewage flows for various municipalities. Commercial and industrial sewage flows are listed in Table 2. These tables were adapted from the "Design and Construction of Sanitary and Storm Sewers," published by American Society of Civil Engineers and Water Pollution Control Federation. To apply flow criteria in the design of a sewer system, it is necessary to determine present and future zoning, population densities and types of business and industry.

Peak Flow. The actual flow in a sanitary sewer is variable, and many studies have been made of hourly, daily and seasonal variations. Typical results of one study are shown in Figure 1 adapted from "Design and Construction of Sanitary Storm Sewers," published by the American Society of Civil Engineers and Water Pollution Control Federation. Maximum and minimum daily flows are used in the design of treatment plants, but the sanitary sewer must carry the peak flow that will occur during its design life. This peak flow is defined as the mean rate of the maximum flow occurring during a 15-minute period for any 12-month period and is determined by multiplying average daily flow by an appropriate factor. Estimates of this factor range from 4.0 to 5.5 for design populations of one thousand, to a factor of 1.5 to 2.0 for design population of one million. Tables 1 and 2 list minimum peak loads used by some municipalities as a basis for design.

Minimum Flow. A minimum velocity of 2 feet per second, when the pipe is flowing full or half full, will prevent deposition of solids. The design should be checked using the minimum flow to determine if this self-cleaning velocity is maintained.

SELECTION OF PIPE SIZE

After the design flows have been calculated, pipe size is selected using Manning's formula. The formula can be solved by selecting a pipe roughness coefficient, and assuming a pipe size and slope. However, this trial and error method is not necessary since nomographs, tables, graphs and computer programs provide a direct solution.

Manning's Formula. Manning's formula for selecting pipe size is:

$$Q = \frac{1.486}{n} AR^{2/3}S^{1/2} \tag{1}$$

A constant $C_1 = \dfrac{1.486}{n} AR^{2/3}$ which depends only on the geometry and

characteristics of the pipe enables Manning's formula to be written as:

$$Q = C_1 S^{1/2} \tag{2}$$

Tables 3, 4, 5 and 6 list full flow values of C_1 for circular pipe, elliptical pipe, arch pipe, and box sections. Table A-1 in the Appendix lists values of $S^{1/2}$.

Manning's "n" Value. Results of numerous test programs have established values for the roughness coefficient of concrete pipe from 0.009 to 0.011. Higher values of 0.012 and 0.013 are used to account for the possibility of slime or grease build-up in sanitary sewers. When this build-up can be prevented by higher velocities or effluent characteristics, lower values of "n" should be used.

Full Flow Graphs. Graphical solutions of Manning's formula are presented for circular pipe in Figures 2 through 5 and for horizontal elliptical pipe, vertical elliptical pipe, arch pipe and box sections in Figures 6 through 19. When flow, slope and roughness coefficient are known, pipe size and the resulting velocity for full flow can be determined.

Partially Full Flow Graphs. Velocity, hydraulic radius and quantity and area of flow vary with the depth of flow. These values are proportionate to full flow values and for any depth of flow are plotted for circular pipe, horizontal elliptical pipe, vertical elliptical pipe, arch pipe, and box sections in Figures 20 through 24.

DETERMINATION OF FLOW VELOCITY

Minimum Velocity. Slopes required to maintain a velocity of 2 feet per second under full flow conditions with various "n" values are listed in Table 7 for circular pipe. The slopes required to maintain velocities other than 2 feet per second under full flow conditions can be obtained by multiplying the tabulated values by one-fourth of the velocity squared or by solving Manning's formula using Figures 2 through 19.

Maximum Velocity. Maximum design velocities for clear effluent in concrete pipe can be very high. Unless governed by topography or other restrictions, pipe slopes should be set as flat as possible to reduce excavation costs and consequently velocities are held close to the minimum.

STORM SEWERS

DETERMINATION OF SEWER SYSTEM TYPE

Storm sewers are designed to carry precipitation runoff, surface waters and, in some instances, ground water. Storm water flow is analyzed on the basis of having the flow characteristics of water.

DETERMINATION OF DESIGN FLOW

The Rational Method is widely used for determining design flows in urban and small watersheds. The method assumes that the maximum rate of runoff for a given intensity occurs when the duration of the storm is such that all parts of the watershed are contributing to the runoff at the interception point. The formula used is an empirical equation that relates the quantity of runoff from a given area to the total rainfall falling at a uniform rate on the same area and is expressed as:

$$Q = CiA \qquad (3)$$

The runoff coefficient "C" and the drainage area "A" are both constant for a given area at a given time. Rainfall intensity "i", however, is determined by using an appropriate storm frequency and duration which are selected on the basis of economics and engineering judgment. Storm sewers are designed on the basis that they will flow full during storms occurring at certain intervals. Storm frequency is selected through consideration of the size of drainage area, probable flooding, possible flood damage and projected development schedule for the area.

Runoff Coefficient. The runoff coefficient "C" is the ratio of the average rate of rainfall on an area to the maximum rate of runoff. Normally ranging between zero and unity, the runoff coefficient can exceed unity in those areas where rainfall occurs in conjunction with melting snow or ice. The soil characteristics, such as porosity, permeability and whether or not it is frozen are important considerations. Another factor to consider is ground cover, such as paved, grassy or wooded. In certain areas, the coefficient depends upon the slope of the terrain. Duration of rainfall and shape of area are also important factors in special instances. Average values for different areas are listed in Table 8.

Rainfall Intensity. Rainfall intensity "i" is the amount of rainfall measured in inches per hour that would be expected to occur during a storm of a certain duration. The storm frequency is the time in years in which a certain storm would be expected again and is determined statistically from available rainfall data.

Several sources, such as the U.S. Weather Bureau, have published tables and graphs for various areas of the country which show the relationship between rainfall intensity, storm duration and storm frequency. To illustrate these relationships, the subsequent figures and tables are presented as examples only, and specific design information is available for most areas. For a 2-year frequency storm of 30-minute duration, the expected rainfall intensities for the United States are plotted on the map in Figure 25. These intensities could be converted to storms of other durations and frequencies by using factors as listed in Tables 9 and 10 and an intensity-duration-frequency curve constructed as shown in Figure 26.

Time of Concentration. The time of concentration at any point in a sewer system is the time required for runoff from the most remote portion of the drainage area to reach that point. The most remote portion provides the longest time of concentration but is not necessarily the most distant point in the drainage area. Since a basic assumption of the Rational Method is that all portions of the area are contributing runoff, the time of concentration is used as the storm duration in calculating the intensity. The time of concentration consists of the time of flow from the most remote portion of the drainage area to the first inlet (called the inlet time) and the time of flow from the inlet through the system to the point under consideration (called the flow time). The inlet time is affected by the rainfall intensity, topography and ground conditions. Many designers use inlet times ranging from a minimum of 5 minutes for densely developed areas with closely spaced inlets to a maximum of 30 minutes for flat residential areas with widely spaced inlets. If the inlet time exceeds 30 minutes, then a detailed analysis is required because a very small inlet time will result in an overdesigned system while conversely for a very long inlet time the system will be underdesigned.

Runoff Area. The runoff area "A" is the drainage area in acres served by the storm sewer. This area can be accurately determined from topographic maps or field surveys.

SELECTION OF PIPE SIZE

Manning's Formula. Manning's formula for selecting pipe size is:

$$Q = \frac{1.486}{n} AR^{2/3}S^{1/2} \tag{1}$$

A constant $C_1 = \dfrac{1.486}{n}AR^{2/3}$ which depends only on the geometry and characteristics of the pipe enables Manning's formula to be written as:

$$Q = C_1 S^{1/2} \tag{2}$$

Tables 3, 4, 5 and 6 for circular pipe, elliptical pipe, arch pipe, and box sections with full flow and Table A-1 in the Appendix for values of C_1 and $S^{1/2}$ respectively are used to solve formula (2). Graphical solutions of Manning's formula (1) are presented in Figures 2 through 5 for circular pipe, and Figures 6 through 19 for horizontal elliptical pipe, vertical elliptical pipe, arch pipe and box sections under full flow conditions.

Partial flow problems can be solved with the proportionate relationships plotted in Figure 20 through 24.

Manning's "n" Value. In Manning's formula, "n" values of 0.010 to 0.012 are used for concrete pipe storm sewers. These lower values are used because slime or grease deposits are not prevalent in storm sewers.

DETERMINATION OF FLOW VELOCITY

Minimum Velocity. The debris entering a storm sewer system will generally have a higher specific gravity than sanitary sewage, therefore a minimum velocity of 3 feet per second is usually specified. The pipe slopes required to maintain this velocity can be calculated from Table 7 or by solving Manning's formula using Figures 2 through 19.

Maximum Velocity. Tests have indicated that concrete pipe can carry clear water of extremely high velocities without eroding. Actual performance records of storm sewers on grades up to 45 percent and carrying high percentages of solids indicate that erosion is seldom a problem with concrete pipe.

EXAMPLE PROBLEMS

EXAMPLE 2 - 1
STORM SEWER FLOW

Given: The inside diameter of a circular concrete pipe storm sewer is 48 inches, "*n*" = 0.012 and slope is 0.006 feet per foot.

Find: The full flow capacity, "*Q*".

Solution: The problem can be solved using Figure 4 or Table 3.

Figure 4 The slope for the sewer is 0.006 feet per foot or 0.60 feet per 100 feet. Find this slope on the horizontal axis. Proceed vertically along the 0.60 line to the intersection of this line and the curve labelled 48 inches. Proceed horizontally to the vertical axis and read $Q = 121$ cubic feet per second.

Table 3 Enter Table 3 under the column $n = 0.012$ for a 48-inch diameter pipe and find $C_1 = 1556$. For $S = 0.006$, find $S^{1/2} = 0.07746$ in Table A-1. Then $Q = 1556 \times 0.07746$ or 121 cubic feet per second.

Answer: $Q = 121$ cubic feet per second.

EXAMPLE 2 - 2
REQUIRED SANITARY SEWER SIZE

Given: A concrete pipe sanitary sewer with "*n*" = 0.013, slope of 0.6 percent and required full flow capacity of 110 cubic feet per second.

Find: Size of circular concrete pipe required.

Solution: This problem can be solved using Figure 5 or Table 3.

Figure 5 Find the intersection of a horizontal line through $Q = 110$ cubic feet per second and a slope of 0.60 feet per 100 feet. The minimum size sewer is 48 inches.

Table 3 For $Q = 110$ cubic feet per second and $S^{1/2} = 0.07746$

$$C_1 = \frac{Q}{S^{1/2}} = \frac{110}{0.07746} = 1420$$

In the table, 1436 is the closest value of C_1 equal to or larger than 1420, so the minimum size sewer is 48 inches.

Answer: A 48-inch diameter circular pipe would have more than adequate capacity.

EXAMPLE 2 - 3
STORM SEWER MINIMUM SLOPE

Given: A 48-inch diameter circular concrete pipe storm sewer, *"n"* = 0.012 and flowing one-third full.

Find: Slope required to maintain a minimum velocity of 3 feet per second.

Solution: Enter Figure 20 on the vertical scale at Depth of Flow = 0.33 and project a horizontal line to the curved line representing velocity. On the horizontal scale directly beneath the point of intersection read a value of 0.81 which represents the proportional value to full flow.

$$\frac{V}{V_{full}} = 0.81$$

$$V_{full} = \frac{V}{0.81}$$

$$= \frac{3}{0.81}$$

$$= 3.7$$

Enter Figure 4 and at the intersection of the line representing 48-inch diameter and the interpolated velocity line of 3.7 read a slope of 0.088 percent on the horizontal scale.

Answer: The slope required to maintain a minimum velocity of 3 feet per second at one-third full is 0.088 percent.

EXAMPLE 2 - 4
SANITARY SEWER DESIGN

General: A multi-family housing project is being developed on 350 acres of rolling to flat ground. Zoning regulations establish a population density of 30 persons per acre. The state Department of Health specifies 100 gallons per capita per day as the average and 500 gallons per capita per day as the peak domestic sewage flow, and an infiltration allowance of 500 gallons per acre per day.

Circular concrete pipe will be used, *"n"* = 0.013, designed to flow full at peak load with a minimum velocity of 2 feet per second at one-third peak flow. Maximum spacing between manholes will be 400 feet.

Given:
Population Density	= 30 persons per acre
Average Flow	= 100 gallons per capita per day
Peak Flow	= 500 gallons per capita per day

Infiltration   = 500 gallons per acre per day
Manning's Roughness = 0.013 (*See discussion of Manning's*
  Coefficient   *"n" Value*)
Minimum Velocity   = 2 feet per second @ ⅓ peak flow

Find: Design the final 400 feet of pipe between manhole Nos. 20 and 21, which serves 58 acres in addition to carrying the load from the previous pipe which serves the remaining 292 acres.

Solution: 1. *Design Flow*
Population-Manhole   1 to 20 = 30 × 292 = 8760
Population-Manhole 20 to 21 = 30 × 58   = 1740

Total population   10,500 persons
Peak flow-Manhole
       1 to 20 = 500 × 8760 = 4,380,000 gallons per day
Infiltration-Manhole
       1 to 20 = 500 × 292   = 146,000 gallons per day
Peak flow-Manhole
       20 to 21 = 500 × 1740 = 870,000 gallons per day
Infiltration-Manhole
       20 to 21 = 500 × 58   =   29,000 gallons per day

Total Peak flow   = 5,425,000 gallons per day
      use 5,425,000 gallons per day or 8.4 cubic feet per second

2. *Selection of Pipe Size*
In designing the sewer system, selection of pipe begins at the first manhole and proceeds downstream. The section of pipe preceding the final section is an 18-inch diameter, with slope = 0.0045 feet per foot. Therefore, for the final section the same pipe size will be checked and used unless it has inadequate capacity, excessive slope or inadequate velocity.

Enter Figure 5, from $Q = 8.4$ cubic feet per second on the vertical scale project a horizontal line to the 18-inch diameter pipe, read velocity = 4.7 feet per second.

From the intersection, project a vertical line to the horizontal scale, read slope = 0.63 feet per 100 feet.

3. *Partial Flow*
Enter Figure 20, from Proportion of Value for Full Flow = 0.33 on the horizontal scale project a line vertically to "flow" curve, from intersection project a line horizontally to "velocity" curve, from intersection project a line vertically to horizontal scale, read Proportion of Value for Full Flow = 0.83.
Velocity at minimum flow = 0.83 × 4.7 = 3.9 feet per second.

Answer: Use 18-inch diameter concrete pipe with slope of 0.0063 feet per foot.

The preceding computations are summarized in the following tabular forms, Illustrations 2.1 and 2.2.

Illustration 2.1 — Population and Flow

Manhole No.	DRAINAGE AREA			PEAK-FLOW — M G D					Cum. Flow cfs.
	Zoning	Acres	Ultimate Population	Domestic	Indus-trial	Infil-tration	Total	Cum. Total	
19	From Preceding Computations							4.53	7.0
20	Multi-family	58	1740	0.87	—	0.03	0.90	5.43	8.4
21	Trunk Sewer Interceptor Manhole								

Illustration 2.2 — Sanitary Sewer Design Data

Manhole		Flow cfs	SEWER					Manhole Flow-line Elevations	
No.	Sta.		Length ft.	Slope ft./ft.	Pipe Dia. in.	Velocity fps	Fall ft.	In	Out
19	46	7.0							389.51
20	50	8.4	400	0.0045	18	4.0	1.80	387.71	387.71
21	54		400	0.0063	18	4.7	2.52	385.19	

EXAMPLE 2 - 5
STORM SEWER DESIGN

General: A portion of the storm sewer system for the multi-family development is to serve a drainage area of about 30 acres. The state Department of Health specifies a 10-inch diameter minimum pipe size.

Circular concrete pipe will be used, "*n*" = 0.011, with a minimum velocity of 3 feet per second when flowing full. Minimum time of concentration is 10 minutes with a maximum spacing between manholes of 400 feet.

Given: Drainage Area $A = 30$ acres (total)
Runoff Coefficient $C = 0.40$
Rainfall Intensity i as shown in Figure 26
Roughness Coefficient $n = 0.011$ *(See discussion of Manning's "n" Value)*

Velocity $V = 3.0$ feet per second (minimum at full flow)

Find: Design of the storm system as shown in Illustration 2.3, "Plan for Storm Sewer Example," adapted from "Design and Construction of Concrete Sewers," published by the Portland Cement Association.

Solution: The hydraulic properties of the storm sewer will be entered as they are determined on the example form Illustration 2.4, "Computation Sheet for Hydraulic Properties of Storm Sewer." The design of the system begins at the upper manhole and proceeds downstream.

Illustration 2.3 — Plan for Storm Sewer Example

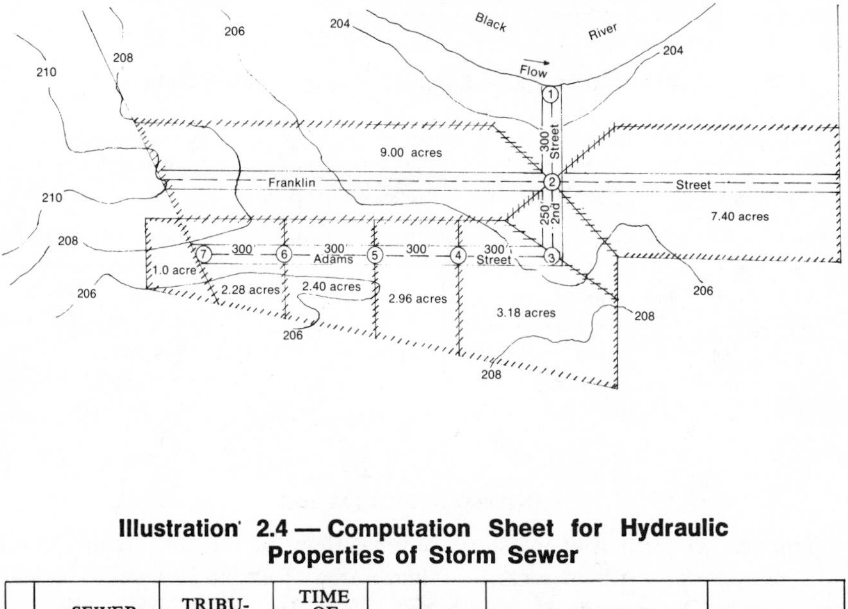

Illustration 2.4 — Computation Sheet for Hydraulic Properties of Storm Sewer

Line number	SEWER LOCATION		TRIBUTARY AREA		TIME OF FLOW (minutes)				SEWER DESIGN					PROFILE	
														Elevation of invert	
	Street	From M.H. / To M.H.	Increment acres	Total acres A	To upper end	In section	Rate of rainfall (in. per hour) i	Runoff (cfs) Q	Slope (ft. per 100 ft.)	Diameter (in.)	Capacity (cfs.)	Velocity (fps.)	Length (ft.)	Upper end	Lower end
1	2 3		4	5	6	7	8	9	10	11	12	13	14	15	16
1	Adams	7 6	1.00	1.00	10.0	1.7	4.2	1.68	0.39	10	1.7	3.0	300	200.00	198.83
2	Adams	6 5	2.28	3.28	11.7	1.7	4.0	5.25	0.18	18	5.3	3.0	300	198.16	197.62
3	Adams	5 4	2.40	5.68	13.4	1.3	3.8	8.63	0.23	21	8.65	3.8	300	197.37	196.68
4	Adams	4 3	2.96	8.64	14.7	1.2	3.7	12.0	0.23	24	13.0	4.1	300	196.43	195.74
5	2nd	3 2	3.18	11.82	15.9	0.9	3.6	17.0	0.23	27	17.0	4.5	250	195.49	194.91
6	2nd	2 1	17.84	29.66	16.8	—	3.5	41.6	0.30	36	42.0	6.1	300	194.41	193.51

The areas contributing to each manhole are determined, entered incrementally in column 4, and as cumulative totals in column 5. The initial inlet time of 10 minutes minimum is entered in column 6, line 1, and from Figure 26 the intensity is found to be 4.2 inches per hour which is entered in column 8, line 1. Solving the Rational formula, $Q = 1.68$ cubic feet per second is entered in column 9, line 1. Enter Figure 3, for $V = 3$ feet per second and $Q = 1.68$ cubic feet per second, the 10-inch diameter pipe requires a slope $= 0.39$ feet per 100 feet. Columns 10, 12, 13, 14, 15 and 16, line 1, are now filled in. The flow time from manhole 7 to 6 is found by dividing the length (300 feet) between manholes by the velocity of flow (3 feet per second) and converting the answers to minutes (1.7 minutes) which is entered in column 7, line 1. This time increment is added to the 10-minute time of concentration for manhole 7 to arrive at 11.7 minutes time of concentration for manhole 6 which is entered in column 6, line 2.

From Figure 26, the intensity is found to be 4.0 inches per hour for a time of concentration of 11.7 minutes which is entered in column 8, line 2. The procedure outlined in the preceding paragraph is repeated for each section of sewer as shown in the table.

Answer: The design pipe sizes, slopes and other properties are as indicated in Illustration 2.4.

EXAMPLE 2 - 6
SANITARY SEWER DESIGN

Given: A concrete box section sanitary sewer with "n" $= 0.013$, slope of 1.0% and required full flow capacity of 250 cubic feet per second.

Find: Size of concrete box section required for full flow.

Solution: This problem can be solved using Figure 19 or Table 6.

Figure 19 Find the intersection of a horizontal line through $Q = 250$ cubic feet per second and a slope of 1.0 feet per 100 feet. The minimum size box section is either a 6 foot span by 4 foot rise or a 5 foot span by 5 foot rise.

Table 6 For $Q = 250$ cubic feet per second and $S^{1/2} = 0.100$

$$C_1 = \frac{Q}{S^{1/2}} = \frac{250}{0.100} = 2,500$$

In Table 6, under the column headed $n = 0.013$, 3,338 is the first value of C_1 equal to or larger than 2,500, therefore a box section with a 5 foot span $\times$ a 5 foot rise is adequate. Looking further in the same column, a box section with a 6 foot span and a 4 foot rise is found to have a C_1 value of 3,096, therefore a 6 × 4 box section is also adequate.

Answer: Either a 5 foot × 5 foot or a 6 foot × 4 foot box section would have a full flow capacity equal to or greater than $Q = 250$ cubic feet per second.

CHAPTER 3

HYDRAULICS OF CULVERTS

The hydraulic design procedure for culverts requires:

1. Determination of Design Flow
2. Selection of Culvert Size
3. Determination of Outlet Velocity

DETERMINATION OF DESIGN FLOW

The United States Geological Survey has developed a nationwide series of water-supply papers titled the "Magnitude and Frequency of Floods in the United States." These reports contain tables of maximum known floods and charts for estimating the probable magnitude of floods of frequencies ranging from 1.1 to 50 years. Table 11 indicates the Geological Survey regions, USGS district and principal field offices and the applicable water-supply paper numbers. Most states have adapted and consolidated those parts of the water-supply papers which pertain to specific hydrologic areas within the particular state. The hydrologic design procedures developed by the various states enable quick and accurate determination of design flow. It is recommended that the culvert design flow be determined by methods based on USGS data.

If USGS data are not available for a particular culvert location, flow quantities may be determined by the Rational Method or by statistical methods using records of flow and runoff. An example of the latter method is a nomograph developed by California and shown in Figure 27.

FACTORS AFFECTING CULVERT DISCHARGE

Factors affecting culvert discharge are depicted on the culvert cross section shown in Illustration 3.1 and are used in determining the type of discharge control.

15

Inlet Control. The control section is located at or near the culvert entrance, and, for any given shape and size of culvert, the discharge is dependent only on the inlet geometry and headwater depth. Inlet control will exist as long as water can flow through the barrel of the culvert at a greater rate than water can enter the inlet. Since the control section is at the inlet, the capacity is not affected by any hydraulic factors beyond the

Illustration 3.1 — Factors Affecting Culvert Discharge

D = Inside diameter for circular pipe
HW = Headwater depth at culvert entrance
L = Length of culvert
n = Surface roughness of the pipe wall,
    usually expressed in terms of
    Manning's n
S_o = Slope of the culvert pipe
TW = Tailwater depth at culvert outlet

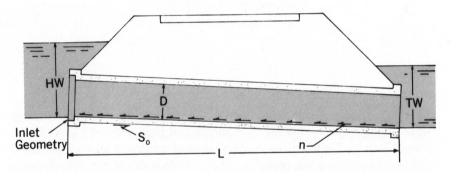

culvert entrance such as slope, length or surface roughness. Culverts operating under inlet control will always flow partially full.

Outlet Control. The control section is located at or near the culvert outlet and for any given shape and size of culvert, the discharge is dependent on all of the hydraulic factors upstream from the outlet such as shape, slope, length, surface roughness, tailwater depth, headwater depth and inlet geometry. Outlet control will exist as long as water can enter the culvert at a greater rate than water can flow through it. Culverts operating under outlet control can flow either full or partially full.

Critical Depth. Critical flow occurs when the sum of the kinetic energy (velocity head) plus the potential energy (static or depth head equal to the depth of the flow) for a given discharge is at a minimum. Conversely, the discharge through a pipe with a given total energy head will be maximum at critical flow. The depth of the flow at this point is defined as critical depth, and the slope required to produce the flow is defined as critical slope. Capacity of a culvert with an unsubmerged outlet will be established at the point where critical flow occurs. Since under inlet control, the discharge of the culvert is not reduced by as many hydraulic factors as under outlet control, for a given energy head, a culvert will have maximum possible discharge if it is operating at critical flow with inlet control. The energy head at the inlet control section is approximately equal to the head at the inlet minus entrance losses. Discharge is not limited by culvert roughness or outlet conditions but is dependent only on the shape and size of the culvert entrance. Although the discharge of a culvert operating with inlet control is not related to the pipe roughness, the roughness does determine the minimum slope (critical slope) at which inlet control will occur. Pipe with a smooth interior can be installed on a very flat slope and still have inlet control. Pipe with a rough interior must be installed on a much steeper slope to have inlet control. Charts of critical depth for various pipe and box section sizes and flows are shown in Figures 28 through 32.

SELECTION OF CULVERT SIZE

The many hydraulic design procedures available for determining the required size of a culvert vary from empirical formulas to a comprehensive mathematical analysis. Most empirical formulas, while easy to use, do not lend themselves to proper evaluation of all the factors that affect the flow of water through a culvert. The mathematical solution, while giving precise results, is time consuming. A systematic and simple design procedure for the proper selection of a culvert size is provided by Hydraulic Engineering Circular No. 5, "Hydraulic Charts for the Selection of Highway Culverts" and No. 10, "Capacity Charts for the Hydraulic Design of Highway Culverts," developed by the Bureau of Public Roads. The procedure when selecting a culvert is to determine the headwater depth from the charts for both assumed inlet and outlet controls. The solution which yields the higher headwater depth indicates the governing control. When this procedure is followed, Inlet Control Nomographs, Figures 33 through 37, and Outlet Control Nomographs, Figures 38 through 41, are used.

An alternative and simpler method is to use the Culvert Capacity Charts, Figures 42 through 145. These charts are based on the data given in Circular No. 5 and enable the hydraulic solution to be obtained directly without using the double solution for both inlet and outlet control required when the nomographs are used.

Culvert Capacity Chart Procedure. The Culvert Capacity Charts are a convenient tool for selection of pipe sizes when the culvert is installed with conditions as indicated on the charts. The nomographs must be used for other shapes, roughness coefficients, inlet conditions or submerged outlets.

List Design Data
   A. Design discharge Q, in cubic feet per second, with average return period (i.e., Q_{25} or Q_{50}, etc.).
   B. Approximate length L of culvert, in feet.
   C. Slope of culvert.

D. Allowable headwater depth, in feet, which is the vertical distance from the culvert invert (flow line) at the entrance to the water surface elevation permissible in the headwater pool or approach channel upstream from the culvert.

E. Mean and maximum flood velocities in natural stream.

F. Type of culvert for first trial selection, including barrel cross sectional shape and entrance type.

Select Culvert Size

A. Select the appropriate capacity chart, Figures 42 to 145, for the culvert size approximately equal to the allowable headwater depth divided by 2.0.

B. Project a vertical line from the design discharge Q to the inlet control curve. From this intersection project a line horizontally and read the headwater depth on the vertical scale. If this headwater depth is more than the allowable, try the next larger size pipe. If the headwater depth is less than the allowable, check the outlet control curves.

C. Extend the vertical line from the design discharge to the outlet control curve representing the length of the culvert. From this intersection project a line horizontally and read the headwater depth plus S_oL on the vertical scale. Subtract S_oL from the outlet control value to obtain the headwater depth. If the headwater depth is more than the allowable, try the next larger size pipe. If the headwater depth is less than the allowable, check the next smaller pipe size following the same procedure for both inlet control and outlet control.

D. Compare the headwater depths for inlet and outlet control. The higher headwater depth indicates the governing control.

Determine Outlet Velocity

A. If outlet control governs, the outlet velocity equals the flow quantity divided by the flow cross sectional area at the outlet. Depending upon the tailwater conditions, this flow area will be between that corresponding to critical depth and the full area of the pipe. If the outlet is not submerged, it is usually sufficiently accurate to calculate the flow area based on a depth of flow equal to the average of the critical depth and the vertical height of the pipe.

B. If inlet control governs, the outlet velocity may be approximated by Manning's formula using Figures 2 through 19 for full flow values and Figures 20 through 24 for partial flow values.

Record Selection

Record final selection of culvert with size, type, required headwater and outlet velocity.

Nomograph Procedure. The nomograph procedure is used for selection of culverts with entrance conditions other than projecting or for submerged outlets.

List Design Data

A. Design discharge Q, in cubic feet per second, with average return period (i.e., Q_{25} or Q_{50}, etc.).

B. Approximate length L of culvert, in feet.

C. Slope of culvert.

D. Allowable headwater depth, in feet, which is the vertical distance from the culvert invert (flow line) at the entrance to the water surface elevation permissible in the headwater pool or approach channel upstream from the culvert.

E. Mean and maximum flood velocities in natural stream.

F. Type of culvert for first trial selection, including barrel cross sectional shape and entrance type.

Select Trial Culvert Size

Select a trial culvert with a rise or diameter equal to the allowable headwater divided by 2.0.

Find Headwater Depth for Trial Culvert

A. *Inlet Control*

(1) Given Q, size and type of culvert, use appropriate inlet control nomograph Figures 33 through 37 to find headwater depth:

(a) Connect with a straightedge the given culvert diameter or height (D) and the discharge Q; mark intersection of straightedge on HW/D scale marked (1).

(b) HW/D scale marked (1) represents entrance type used, read HW/D on scale (1). If another of the three entrance types listed on the nomograph is used, extend the point of intersection in (a) horizontally to scale (2) or (3) and read HW/D.

(c) Compute HW by multiplying HW/D by D.

(2) If HW is greater or less than allowable, try another trial size until HW is acceptable for inlet control.

B. *Outlet Control*

(1) Given Q, size and type of culvert and estimated depth of tailwater TW, in feet, above the invert at the outlet for the design flood condition in the outlet channel:

(a) Locate appropriate outlet control nomograph (Figures 38 through 41) for type of culvert selected. Find k_e for entrance type from Table 12.

(b) Begin nomograph solution by locating starting point on length scale for proper k_e.

(c) Using a straightedge, connect point on length scale to size of culvert barrel and mark the point of crossing on the "turning line."

(d) Pivot the straightedge on this point on the turning line and connect given discharge rate. Read head in feet on the head (H) scale.

(2) For tailwater TW elevation equal to or greater than the top of the culvert at the outlet set h_o equal to TW and find HW by the following equation:

$$HW = H + h_o - S_oL \qquad (4)$$

(3) For tailwater TW elevations less than the top of the culvert at the outlet, use $h_o = \dfrac{d_c + D}{2}$ or TW, whichever is the greater, where d_c, the critical depth in feet is determined from the appropriate critical depth chart (Figures 28 through 32).

C. Compare the headwaters found in paragraphs A (*Inlet Control*) and B (*Outlet Control*). The higher headwater governs and indicates the flow control existing under the given conditions for the trial size selected.

D. If outlet control governs and the HW is higher than acceptable, select a larger trial size and find HW as instructed under paragraph B. Inlet control need not be checked, if the smaller size was satisfactory for this control as determined under paragraph A.

Try Another Culvert

Try a culvert of another size or shape and repeat the above procedure.

Determine Outlet Velocity

A. If outlet control governs, the outlet velocity equals the flow quantity divided by the flow cross sectional area at the outlet. Depending upon the tailwater conditions, this flow area will be between that corresponding to critical depth and the full area of the pipe. If the outlet is not submerged, it is sufficiently accurate to calculate flow area based on a depth of flow equal to the average of the critical depth and vertical height of the pipe.

B. If inlet control governs, the outlet velocity may be approximated by Manning's formula using Figures 2 through 19 for full flow values and Figures 20 through 24 for partial flow values.

Record Selection

Record final selection of culvert with size, type, required headwater and outlet velocity.

EXAMPLE PROBLEMS
EXAMPLE 3 - 1
CULVERT CAPACITY CHART PROCEDURE

List Design Data

A. $Q_{25} = 180$ cubic feet per second
   $Q_{50} = 225$ cubic feet per second
B. $L = 200$ feet
C. $S_o = 0.01$ feet per foot
D. Allowable $HW = 10$ feet for 25 and 50-year storms
E. $TW = 3.5$ feet for 25-year-storm
   $TW = 4.0$ feet for 50-year storm

F. Circular concrete culvert with a projecting entrance, $n = 0.012$

Select Culvert Size

A. Try $D = \dfrac{HW}{2.0} = \dfrac{10}{2.0} = 5$ feet or 60 inch diameter as first trial size.

B. In Figure 54, project a vertical line from $Q = 180$ cubic feet per second to the inlet control curve and read horizontally $HW = 6.2$.
Since $HW = 6.2$ is considerably less than the allowable try a 54 inch diameter.
In Figure 53, project a vertical line from $Q = 180$ cubic feet per second to the inlet control curve and read horizontally $HW = 7.2$ feet.
In Figure 53, project a vertical line from $Q = 225$ cubic feet per second to the inlet control curve and read horizontally $HW = 9.6$ feet.

C. In Figure 53, extend the vertical line from $Q = 180$ cubic feet per second to the $L = 200$ feet outlet control curve and read horizontally $HW + S_oL = 8.0$ feet.
In Figure 53, extend the vertical line from $Q = 225$ cubic feet per second to the $L = 200$ feet outlet control curve and read horizontally $HW + S_oL = 10.2$ feet.
$S_oL = 0.01 \times 200 = 2.0$ feet.
Therefore $HW = 8.0 - 2.0 = 6.0$ feet for 25-year storm
$\qquad\qquad HW = 10.2 - 2.0 = 8.2$ feet for 50-year storm

D. Since the calculated HW for inlet control exceeds the calculated HW for outlet control in both cases, inlet control governs for both the 25 and 50-year storm flows.

Determine Outlet Velocity

B. Enter Figure 4 on the horizontal scale at a pipe slope of 0.01 feet per foot (1.0 feet per 100 feet). Project a vertical line to the line representing 54-inch pipe diameter. Read a full flow value of 210 cubic feet per second on the vertical scale and a full flow velocity of 13.5 feet per second. Calculate $\dfrac{Q_{50}}{Q_{Full}} = \dfrac{225}{210} = 1.07$.
Enter Figure 20 at 1.07 on the horizontal scale and project a vertical line to the "flow" curve. At this intersection project a horizontal line to the "velocity" curve. Directly beneath this intersection read $\dfrac{V_{50}}{V_{Full}} = 1.12$ on the horizontal scale. Calculate $V_{50} = 1.12\ V_{Full} = 1.12 \times 13.5 = 15.1$ feet per second.

Record Selection

Use a 54-inch diameter concrete pipe with allowable $HW = 10.0$ feet and actual $HW = 7.2$ and 9.6 feet respectively for the 25 and 50-year storm flows, and a maximum outlet velocity of 15.1 feet per second.

EXAMPLE 3 - 2

NOMOGRAPH PROCEDURE

List Design Data
    A. $Q_{25} = 180$ cubic feet per second
       $Q_{50} = 225$ cubic feet per second
    B. $L = 200$ feet
    C. $S_o = 0.01$ feet per foot
    D. Allowable $HW = 10$ feet for 25 and 50-year storms
    E. $TW = 3.5$ feet for 25-year storm
       $TW = 4.0$ feet for 50-year storm
    F. Circular concrete culvert with a projecting entrance, $n = 0.012$

Select Trial Culvert Size
$$D = \frac{HW}{2.0} = \frac{10}{2.0} = 5 \text{ feet}$$

Determine Trial Culvert Headwater Depth
    A. *Inlet Control*
        (1) For $Q = 180$ cubic feet per second and $D = 60$ inches, Figure 33 indicates $HW/D = 1.25$. Therefore $HW = 1.25 \times 5 = 6.2$ feet.
        (2) Since $HW = 6.2$ feet is considerably less than allowable try a 54-inch pipe.
        For $Q = 180$ cubic feet per second and $D = 54$ inches, Figure 33 indicates $HW/D = 1.6$. Therefore $HW = 1.6 \times 4.5 = 7.2$ feet.
        For $Q = 225$ cubic feet per second and $D = 54$ inches, Figure 33 indicates $HW/D = 2.14$. Therefore $HW = 2.14 \times 4.5 = 9.6$ feet.
    B. *Outlet Control*
        (1) $TW = 3.5$ and 4.0 feet is less than $D = 4.5$ feet.
        (3) Table 12, $k_e = 0.2$.
        For $D = 54$ inches, $Q = 180$ cubic feet per second, Figure 28 indicates $d_c = 3.9$ feet which is less than $D = 4.5$ feet. Calculate $h_o = \frac{d_c + D}{2} = \frac{3.9 + 4.5}{2} = 4.2$ feet.
        For $D = 54$ inches, $Q = 180$ cubic feet per second, $k_e = 0.2$ and $L = 200$ feet.
        Figure 38 indicates $H = 3.8$ feet.
        Therefore $HW = 3.8 + 4.2 - (0.01 \times 200) = 6.0$ feet (Equation 3).
        For $D = 54$ inches, $Q = 225$ cubic feet per second, Figure 28 indicates $d_c = 4.2$ feet which is less than $D = 4.5$ feet. Calculate $h_o = \frac{d_c + D}{2} = \frac{4.2 + 4.5}{2} = 4.3$ feet.
        For $D = 54$ inches, $Q = 225$ cubic feet per second, $k_e = 0.2$ and $L = 200$ feet.
        Figure 38 indicates $H = 5.9$ feet.
        Therefore $HW = 5.9 + 4.3 - (0.01 \times 200) = 8.2$ feet (Equation 3).

C. Inlet control governs for both the 25 and 50-year design flows.

Try Another Culvert

A 48-inch culvert would be sufficient for the 25-year storm flow but for the 50-year storm flow the *HW* would be greater than the allowable.

Determine Outlet Velocity

B. Enter Figure 4 on the horizontal scale at a pipe slope of 0.01 feet per foot (1.0 feet per 100 feet). Project a vertical line to the line representing 54-inch pipe diameter. Read a full flow value of 210 cubic feet per second on the vertical scale and a full flow velocity of 13.5 feet per second. Calculate $\dfrac{Q_{50}}{Q_{Full}} = \dfrac{225}{210} = 1.07.$

Enter Figure 20 at 1.07 on the horizontal scale and project a vertical line to the "flow" curve. At this intersection project a horizontal line to the "velocity" curve. Directly beneath this intersection read $\dfrac{V_{50}}{V_{Full}} = 1.12$ on the horizontal scale. Calculate $V_{50} = 1.12\ V_{full} = 1.12 \times 13.5 = 15.1$ feet per second.

Record Selection

Use a 54-inch diameter concrete pipe with allowable *HW* = 10.0 feet and actual *HW* = 7.2 and 9.6 feet respectively for the 25 and 50-year storm flows, and a maximum outlet velocity of 15.1 feet per second.

EXAMPLE 3 - 3
CULVERT DESIGN

General: A highway is to be constructed on embankment over a creek draining 400 acres. The embankment will be 41-feet high with 2:1 side slopes and a top width of 80 feet. Hydraulic design criteria requires a circular concrete pipe, $n = 0.012$, with the inlet projecting from the fill. To prevent flooding of upstream properties, the allowable headwater is 10.0 feet, and the design storm frequency is 25 years.

Given: Drainage Area $\quad A = 400$ acres
Roughness Coefficient $n = 0.012$ (*See discussion of Manning's "n" Value*)
Headwater $\quad HW = 10$ feet (allowable)

Find: The required culvert size.

Solution: 1. *Design Flow*
The design flow for 400 acres should be obtained using USGS data. Rather than present an analysis for a specific area, the

design flow will be assumed as 250 cubic feet per second for a 25-year storm.

2. Selection of Culvert Size

The culvert will be set on the natural creek bed which has a one percent slope. A cross sectional sketch of the culvert and embankment indicates a culvert length of about 250 feet. No flooding of the outlet is expected.

$$\text{Trial diameter } HW/D = 2.0 \qquad D = \frac{10}{2} = 5 \text{ feet.}$$

Enter Figure 54, from $Q = 250$ cubic feet per second project a line vertically to the inlet control curve, read $HW = 8.8$ feet on the vertical scale. Extend the vertical line to the outlet control curve for $L = 250$ feet, read $H + S_oL = 9.6$ on the vertical scale. $S_oL = 250 \times 0.01 = 2.5$ feet. Therefore, outlet control $HW = 9.6 - 2.5 = 7.1$ feet and inlet control governs.

Enter Figure 53, from $Q = 250$ cubic feet per second project a line vertically to the inlet control curve, read $HW = 10.8$ feet which is greater than the allowable.

3. Determine Outlet Velocity

For inlet control, the outlet velocity is determined from Manning's formula. Entering Figure 4, a 60-inch diameter pipe with $S_o = 1.0$ foot per 100 feet will have a velocity = 14.1 feet per second flowing full and a capacity of 280 cubic feet per second. Enter Figure 20 with a Proportion of Value for Full Flow = $\frac{250}{280}$ or 0.9, read Depth of Flow = 0.74 and Velocity Proportion = 1.13. Therefore, outlet velocity = $1.13 \times 14.1 = 15.9$ feet per second.

Answer: A 60-inch diameter circular pipe would be required.

EXAMPLE 3 - 4
CULVERT DESIGN

General: An 800-foot long box culvert with an $n = 0.012$ is to be installed on a 0.5% slope. Because utility lines are to be installed in the embankment above the box culvert, the maximum rise is limited to 8 feet. The box section is required to carry a maximum flow of 1,000 cubic feet per second with an allowable headwater depth of 15 feet.

List Design Data
  A. $Q = 1,000$ cubic feet per second
  B. $L = 800$ feet
  C. $S_o = 0.5\% = 0.005$ feet per foot

D. Allowable $HW = 15$ feet

E. Box culvert with projecting entrance and $n = 0.012$

Select Culvert Size

Inspecting the box section culvert capacity charts for boxes with rise equal to or less than 8 feet, it is found that a 8 × 8 foot and a 9 × 7 foot box section will all discharge 1,000 cubic feet per second with a headwater depth equal to or less than 15 feet under inlet control. Therefore, each of the two sizes will be investigated.

Determine Headwater Depth

8 × 8 foot Box Section

A. *Inlet Control*

Enter Figure 124, from $Q = 1,000$ project a vertical line to the inlet control curve. Project horizontally to the vertical scale and read a headwater depth of 14.8 feet for inlet control.

B. *Outlet Control*

Continue vertical projection from $Q = 1,000$ to the outlet control curve for $L = 800$ feet. Project horizontally to vertical scale and read a value for $(HW + S_oL) = 17.5$ feet. Then $HW = 17.5 - S_oL = 17.5 - (0.005 \times 800) = 13.5$ feet for outlet control.

Therefore inlet control governs.

9 × 7 — foot Box Section

Entering Figure 127, and proceeding in a similar manner, find a headwater depth of 14.7 for inlet control and 13.6 feet for outlet control with inlet control governing.

Determine Outlet Velocity

Entering Table 6, find area and C_1 value for each size box section and Table A-1 find value of $S^{1/2}$ for $S_o = 0.005$, then $Q_{full} = C_1S^{1/2}$.

For 8 × 8 — foot Box Section

$Q_{full} = 12711 \times 0.07071 = 899$ cubic feet per second

$V_{full} = Q/A = 899 \div 63.11 = 14.2$ feet per second.

Then

$$\frac{Q_{partial}}{Q_{full}} = \frac{1000}{899} = 1.11$$

Entering Figure 24.9 on the horizontal scale at 1.11, project a vertical line to intersect the flow curve. From this point, proceed horizontally to the right and intersect the velocity curve. From this point drop vertically to the horizontal scale and read a value of 1.18 for $V_{partial}/V_{full}$ ratio.

Then

$$V_{partial} = 1.18 \times 14.2 = 16.8 \text{ feet per second}$$

Proceeding in a similar manner for the 9 × 7 foot box section, Figure 24.7, find a $V_{partial} = 16.9$ feet per second.

Record Selection

Use either a 8 × 8 foot box section with an actual HW of 14.8 feet and an outlet velocity of 16.8 feet per second or a 9 × 7 foot box section with an actual HW of 14.7 feet and an outlet velocity of 16.9 feet per second.

CHAPTER 4

LOADS AND SUPPORTING STRENGTHS

The design procedure for the selection of pipe strength requires:

1. Determination of Earth Load
2. Determination of Live Load
3. Selection of Bedding
4. Determination of Load Factor
5. Application of Factor of Safety
6. Selection of Pipe Strength

DETERMINATION OF EARTH LOAD

The earth load transmitted to a pipe is largely dependent on the type of installation, and the four common types are Trench, Positive Projecting Embankment, Negative Projecting Embankment and Induced Trench. Pipe are also installed by jacking or tunneling methods where deep installations are necessary or where conventional open excavation and backfill methods may not be feasible. The essential features of each of these installations are shown in Figure 146.

Trench. This type of installation is normally used in the construction of sewers, drains and water mains. The pipe is installed in a relatively narrow trench excavated in undisturbed soil and then covered with backfill extending to the ground surface.

The backfill load on pipe installed in a trench condition is computed by the equation:

$$W_d = C_d w B_d^2 \tag{5}$$

C_d is further defined as:

$$C_d = \frac{1 - e^{-2K\mu' \frac{H}{B_d}}}{2K\mu'} \tag{6}$$

Tables 13 through 42 are based on equation (5) and list backfill loads in pounds per linear foot for various heights of backfill and trench widths. There are four tables for each circular pipe size based on $K\mu' = 0.165$, 0.150, 0.130 and 0.110. The "Transition Width" column gives the trench width at which the backfill load on the pipe is a maximum and remains constant regardless of any increase in the width of the trench. For any given height of backfill, the maximum load at the transition width is shown by **bold type.**

Figures 147 through 162 also present backfill loads for circular, vertical elliptical, horizontal elliptical and arch pipe installed in a trench condition. The solid lines represent trench widths and the dashed lines represent pipe size for the evaluation of transition widths and maximum backfill loads. If, when entering the figures from the horizontal axis, the dashed line representing pipe size is interesected before the solid line representing trench width, the actual trench width is wider than the transition width and the maximum backfill load should be read at the intersection of the height of backfill and the dashed line representing pipe size.

Positive Projecting Embankment. This type of installation is normally used when the culvert is installed in a relatively flat stream bed or drainage path. The pipe is installed on the original ground or compacted fill and then covered by an earth fill or embankment. The fill load on a pipe installed in a positive projecting embankment condition is computed by the equation:

$$W_c = C_c w B_c^2 \qquad \qquad {}^1(7)$$

C_c is further defined as:

$$C_c = \frac{e^{2K\mu\frac{H}{B_c}} - 1}{2K\mu} \text{ when } H \le H_e \qquad (8)$$

and

$$C_c = \frac{e^{2K\mu\frac{H_e}{B_c}} - 1}{2K\mu} + \left(\frac{H}{B_c} - \frac{H_e}{B_c}\right) e^{2K\mu\frac{H_e}{B_c}} \text{ when } H > H_e \qquad (9)$$

The settlements which influence loads on positive projecting embankment installations are shown in Illustration 4.1. To evaluate the H_e term in equation (9), it is necessary to determine numerically the relationship between the pipe deflection and the relative settlement between the prism

---

[1] Pipe widths are based on a wall thickness equivalent to thicknesses indicated for Wall B in ASTM C 76 and designated thicknesses in other applicable ASTM Standards. Loads corresponding to these wall thicknesses are sufficiently accurate for the normal range of pipe widths for any particular pipe size. For extra heavy wall thicknesses, resulting in a pipe width considerably in excess of the normal range, interpolation within the Tables and Figures may be necessary.

Illustration 4.1 — Settlements Which Influence Loads
Positive Projecting Embankment Installation

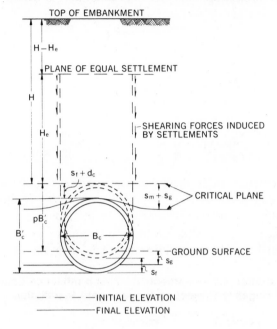

of fill directly above the pipe and the adjacent soil. This relationship is defined as a settlement ratio, expressed as:

$$r_{sd} = \frac{(s_m + s_g) - (s_f + d_c)}{s_m} \tag{10}$$

The fill load on a pipe installed in a positive projecting embankment condition is influenced by the product of the settlement ratio (r_{sd}) and the projection ratio (p). The projection ratio (p) is the vertical distance the pipe projects above the original ground divided by the outside vertical height of the pipe (B'). Recommended settlement ratio design values are listed in Table 43.

Figures 163 through 182 include fill loads in pounds per linear foot for various fill heights and pipe sizes for each pipe shape based on $r_{sd}p$ values of 0, 0.1, 0.3, 0.5 and 1.0. The dashed $H = H_e$ line represents the condition where the height of the plane of equal settlement (H_e) is equal to the height of fill (H).

Negative Projecting Embankment. This type of installation is normally used when the culvert is installed in a relatively narrow and deep stream bed or drainage path. The pipe is installed in a shallow trench of such depth that the top of the pipe is below the natural ground surface or compacted fill and then covered with an earth fill or embankment which extends above the original ground level. The fill load on a pipe installed in a negative projecting embankment condition is computed by the equation:

$$W_n = C_n w B_d^2 \qquad (11)$$

C_n is further defined as:

$$C_n = \frac{e^{-2K\mu \frac{H}{B_d}} - 1}{-2K\mu} \text{ when } H \leq H_e \qquad (12)$$

and

$$C_n = \frac{e^{-2K\mu \frac{H_e}{B_d}} - 1}{-2K\mu} + \left(\frac{H}{B_d} - \frac{H_e}{B_d}\right) e^{-2K\mu \frac{H_e}{B_d}} \text{ when } H > H_e \qquad (13)$$

When the material within the subtrench is densely compacted, equation (11) can be expressed as $W_n = C_n w B_d B'_d$ where B'_d is the average of the trench width and the outside diameter of the pipe.

The settlements which influence loads on negative projecting embankment installations are shown in Illustration 4.2. As in the case of the posi-

Illustration 4.2 — Settlements Which Influence Loads Negative Projecting Embankment Installation

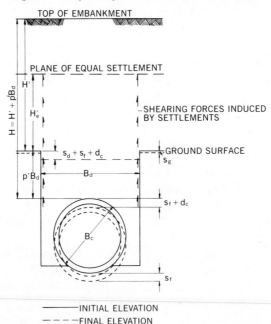

tive projecting embankment installation, it is necessary to define the settlement ratio. Equating the deflection of the pipe and the total settlement of the prism of fill above the pipe to the settlement of the adjacent soil:

$$r_{sd} = \frac{s_g - (s_d + s_f + d_c)}{s_d} \qquad (14)$$

Recommended settlement ratio design values are listed in Table 43. The projection ratio (p') for this type of installation is the distance from the top of the pipe to the surface of the natural ground or compacted fill at the time of installation divided by the width of the trench. Where the ground surface is sloping, the average vertical distance from the top of the pipe to the original ground should be used in determining the projection ratio (p'). Figures 183 through 202 present fill loads in pounds per linear foot for circular pipe based on projection ratios of 0.5, 1.0, 1.5, 2.0 and settlement ratios of 0, -0.1, -0.3, -0.5 and -1.0. The dashed $H = p' B_d$ line represents the limiting condition where the height of fill is at the same elevation as the natural ground surface. The dashed $H = H_e$ line represents the condition where the height of the plane of equal settlement (H_e) is equal to the height of fill (H).

Induced Trench. This type of installation is normally used in the construction of culverts placed under high embankments. As shown in Illustration 4.3, the pipe is initially installed in a positive projecting condition. When the embankment fill has been placed to an elevation of two to three

Illustration 4.3 — Settlements Which Influence Loads Induced Trench Installation

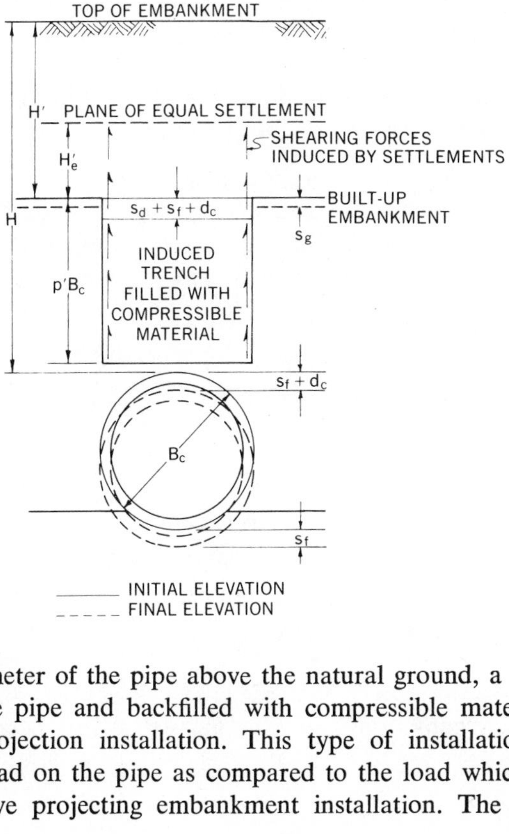

times the diameter of the pipe above the natural ground, a trench is excavated over the pipe and backfilled with compressible material simulating a negative projection installation. This type of installation significantly reduces the load on the pipe as compared to the load which would result from a positive projecting embankment installation. The fill load on a pipe installed by the induced trench method of construction is computed by the equation:

$$W_i = C_i w B_c^2 \qquad\qquad {}^1(15)$$

C_i is further defined as

$$C_i = \frac{e^{-2K\mu\frac{H}{B_e}} - 1}{-2K\mu} \text{ when } H \leq H_e \qquad\qquad (16)$$

and

$$C_i = \frac{e^{-2K\mu\frac{H_e}{B_e}} - 1}{-2K\mu} + \left(\frac{H}{B_c} - \frac{H_e}{B_c}\right) e^{-2K\mu\frac{H_e}{B_c}} \text{ when } H > H_e \qquad (17)$$

Because of the relatively compressible material placed in the induced trench, a smaller (larger negative) settlement ratio value can be used to account for the larger relative settlement. Recommended design values of settlement ratio are listed in Table 43. The projection ratio (p′) for this type of installation is the depth of the induced trench divided by the outside diameter of the pipe. Figures 203 through 218 present fill loads in pounds per linear foot for circular pipe based on projection ratios of 0.5, 1.0, 1.5, 2.0 and settlement ratios of −0.5, −0.7, −1.0 and −2.0. The dashed $H = p' B_c$ line represents the limiting condition where the compressible material within the induced trench is at the same elevation as the built-up embankment in which the induced trench is excavated. The dashed $H = H_e$ line represents the condition where the height of the plane of equal settlement (H_e) is equal to the height of fill (H).

Jacked or Tunneled. This type of installation is used where surface conditions make it difficult to install the pipe by conventional open excavation and backfill methods, or where it is necessary to install the pipe under an existing embankment. The earth load on a pipe installed by these methods is computed by the equation:

$$W_t = C_t w B_t^2 - 2c C_t B_t \qquad\qquad (18)$$

C_t is further defined as:

$$C_t = \frac{1 - e^{-2K\mu'\frac{H}{B_t}}}{2K\mu'} \qquad\qquad (19)$$

In equation (18) the $C_t\, w\, B_t{}^2$ term is similar to the trench equation (5) for trench loads and the $2\, c\, C_t B_t$ term accounts for the cohesion of undisturbed soil. Conservative design values of the coefficient of cohesion for various soils are listed in Table 44. Figures 219, 221, 223 and 225 present values of the trench load term ($C_t\, w\, B_t{}^2$) in pounds per linear foot for a soil density of 120 pounds per cubic foot and $K\mu'$ values of 0.165, 0.150, 0.130 and

---

[1] *Op. cit., p. 28*

0.110. Figures 220, 222, 224 and 226 present values of the cohesion term $(2\,c\,C_t B_t)$ divided by the design values for the coefficient of cohesion (c). To obtain the total earth load for any given height of cover, width of bore or tunnel and type of soil, the value of the cohesion term must be multiplied by the appropriate coefficient of cohesion (c) and this product subtracted from the value of the trench load term.

DETERMINATION OF LIVE LOAD

In the selection of pipe, it is necessary to evaluate the effect of live loads. Live load considerations are necessary in the design of pipe installed with shallow cover under railroads, airports and unsurfaced highways. The distribution of a live load at the surface on any horizontal plane in the subsoil is shown in Illustration 4.4. The intensity of the load on any plane

Illustration 4.4 — Live Load Distribution

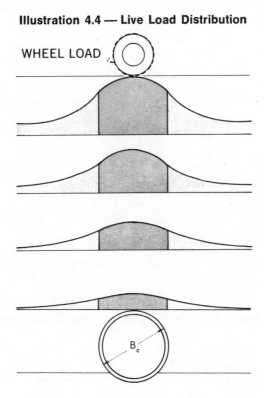

WHEEL LOAD

B_c

in the soil mass is greatest at the vertical axis directly beneath the point of application and decreases in all directions outward from the center of application. As the distance between the plane and the surface increases, the intensity of the load at any point on the plane decreases.

Highways. If a rigid or flexible pavement designed for heavy duty traffic is provided, the intensity of a truck wheel load is usually reduced sufficiently so that the live load transmitted to the pipe is negligible. In the case of flexible pavements designed for light duty traffic but subjected to heavy truck traffic; the flexible pavement should be considered as fill material over the top of the pipe.

In analyses, the most critical AASHTO loadings shown in illustration 4.5 are used in either the single mode or passing mode.

Illustration 4.5 — AASHTO Live Loads

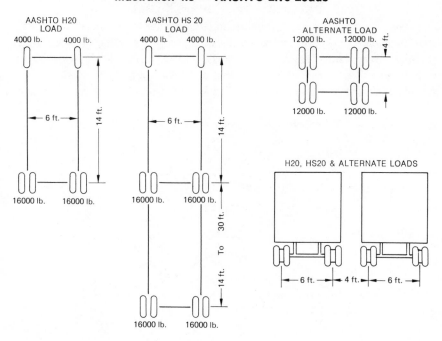

Each of these loadings is assumed to be applied through dual wheel assemblies uniformly distributed over a surface area of 10 inches by 20 inches as shown in Illustration 4.6.

Illustration 4.6 — Wheel Load Surface Contact Area

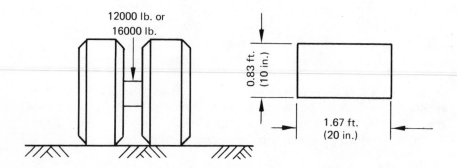

As recommended by AASHTO, the total wheel load is then assumed to be transmitted and uniformly distributed over a rectangular area on a horizontal plane at the depth, H, as shown in Illustration 4.7 for a single HS-20 dual wheel.

Illustration 4.7 — Distributed Load Area, Single Dual Wheel

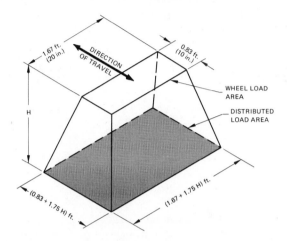

Distributed load areas for the alternate load and the passing mode for either loading are developed in a similar manner.

The average pressure intensity on the subsoil plan at the outside top of the pipe at depth, H, is determined by the equation:

$$w_L = \frac{P(I_f)}{A_{LL}} \tag{20}$$

where

   w_L = average pressure intensity, pounds per square foot
   P = total applied surface wheel loads, pounds
   A_{LL} = distributed live load area, square feet
   I_f = impact factor

Recommended impact factors, I_f, to be used in determining live loads imposed on pipe with less than 3 feet of cover when subjected to dynamic traffic loads are listed in the accompanying Table.

Impact Factors For Highway Truck Loads

H, HEIGHT OF COVER	I_f, IMPACT FACTOR
0'-0" to 1'-0"	1.3
1'-1" to 2'-0"	1.2
2'-1" to 2'-11"	1.1
3'-0" and greater	1.0

NOTE: Impact Factors recommended by the American Association of State Highway and Transportation Officials in "Standard Specifications for Highway Bridges."

As the depth, H, increases, the critical loading configuration can be either one HS-20 wheel load, two HS-20 wheel loads in the passing mode or the alternate load in the passing mode. Since the exact geometric relationship of individual or combinations of surface wheel loads cannot be anticipated, the most critical loading configurations and the outside dimensions of the distributed load areas within the indicated cover depths are summarized in the accompanying Table.

Critical Loading Configurations

H, feet	P, pounds	A_{LL}, Distributed Load Area
$H<1.33$	16,000	$(0.83 + 1.75H)\ (1.67 + 1.75H)$
$1.33 \leqq H < 4.10$	32,000	$(0.83 + 1.75H)\ (5.67 + 1.75H)$
$4.10 \leqq H$	48,000	$(4.83 + 1.75H)\ (5.67 + 1.75H)$

The total live load acting on the pipe is determined by the following formula:

$$W_T = w_L L S_L \tag{21}$$

where

$\quad W_T \quad$ = total live load, pounds
$\quad L \quad$ = Length of A_{LL} parallel to logitudinal axis of pipe, feet
$\quad S_L \quad$ = outside horizontal span of pipe or width of A_{LL} transverse to longitudinal axis of pipe, whichever is less, feet.

The live load acting on the pipe in pounds per linear foot is determined by the following equation:

$$W_L = \frac{W_T}{L_e} \tag{22}$$

where

$\quad W_L \quad$ = live load on pipe, pounds per linear foot
$\quad L_e \quad$ = effective supporting length of pipe, feet

Since the buried concrete pipe is similar to a beam on continuous supports, the effective supporting length of the pipe is assumed as in Illustration 4.8 and determined by the following equation:

$$L_e = L + 1.75 \left(\frac{3B_c}{4} \right) \tag{23}$$

Illustration 4.8 — Effective Supporting Length of Pipe

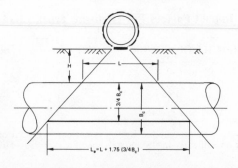

Analysis of possible pipe alignments relative to load orientation confirms the most critical loading can occur when the longitudinal pipe axis is either parallel or transverse to the direction of travel and centered under the distributed load area. Tables 45 through 48 present the maximum highway live loads in pounds per linear foot imposed on circular, horizontal elliptical, vertical elliptical and arch pipe.

Airports. The distribution of aircraft wheel loads on any horizontal plane in the soil mass is dependent on the magnitude and characteristics of the aircraft loads, the aircraft's landing gear configuration, the type of pavement structure and the subsoil conditions. Heavier gross aircraft weights have resulted in multiple wheel undercarriages consisting of dual wheel assemblies and/or dual tandem assemblies. The distribution of wheel loads through rigid and flexible pavements are shown in Illustrations 4.9 and 4.10.

If a rigid pavement is provided, an aircraft wheel load concentration is distributed over an appreciable area and is substantially reduced in intensity at the subgrade. For multi-wheeled landing gear assemblies, the total pressure intensity is dependent on the interacting pressures produced by each individual wheel. The maximum load transmitted to a pipe varies with the pipe size under consideration, the pipe's relative location with respect to the particular landing gear configuration and the height of fill between the top of the pipe and the subgrade surface.

For a flexible pavement, the area of the load distribution at any plane in the soil mass is considerably less than for a rigid pavement. The interaction of pressure intensities due to individual wheels of a multi-wheeled landing gear assembly is also less pronounced at any given depth of cover.

In present airport design practices, the aircraft's maximum takeoff weight is used since the maximum landing weight is usually considered to be about three-fourths the takeoff weight. Impact is not considered as criteria are not yet available to include dynamic effects in the design process.

Rigid Pavement. The pressure intensity is computed by the equation:

$$p_{(H,X)} = \frac{CP}{R_s^2} \qquad (24)$$

R_s is further defined as:

$$R_s = \sqrt[4]{\frac{Eh^3}{12(1 - u^2)k}} \qquad (25)$$

Tables 49 through 53 present pressure coefficients in terms of the radius of stiffness as developed by the Portland Cement Association and published in the report "Vertical Pressure on Culverts Under Wheel Loads on Concrete Pavement Slabs."[3]

Values of radius of stiffness are listed in Table 55 for pavement thickness and modulus of subgrade reaction.

Flexible Pavement. The pressure intensity is computed by the equation:

$$p_{(H,X)} = Cp_o \qquad\qquad (26)$$

Illustration 4.9 — Aircraft Pressure Distribution Rigid Pavement

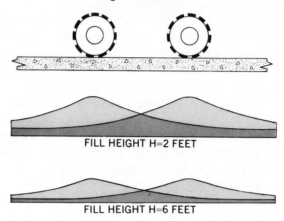

FILL HEIGHT H=2 FEET

FILL HEIGHT H=6 FEET

Illustration 4.10 — Aircraft Pressure Distribution Flexible Pavement

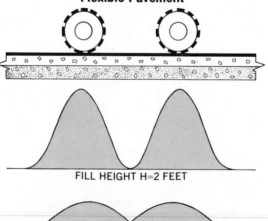

FILL HEIGHT H=2 FEET

FILL HEIGHT H=6 FEET

---

[3] The values given in Tables 49 through 53 are the pressures on planes at depth H in a semi-infinite elastic body. The presence of a pipe introduces a boundary condition which theoretically creates a problem approaching that of an elastic layer of depth H resting on a rigid base. Although pressures based on this assumption are somewhat higher than those given, uncertainties as to the exact elastic properties of the backfill over the pipe, the rigidity of the pipe and other factors are such that theoretically more accurate computations are not considered justified.

The pressure coefficient, C, is dependent on the horizontal distance (X), the vertical distance (H) between the pipe and surface load and the radius of the circle of pressure at the surface (r).

r is further defined as:

$$r = \sqrt{\frac{P}{p_o \pi}} \qquad (27)$$

Pressure coefficients in terms of the radius of the circle of pressure at the surface (r) are presented in Table 54.

For rigid and flexible pavements, Tables 56 through 58 present aircraft loads in pounds per linear foot for circular, horizontal elliptical and arch pipe. The Tables are based on equations [1](24) and [1](25) using a 180,000-pound dual tandem wheel assembly, 190 pounds per square inch tire pressure, 26-inch spacing between dual tires, 66-inch spacing between tandem axles, k value of 300 pounds per cubic inch, 12-inch thick concrete pavement and an R_s value of 37.44 inches. Subgrade and subbase support for a rigid pavement is evaluated in terms of k, the modulus of subgrade reaction. A k value of 300 pounds per cubic inch was used, since this value represents a desirable subgrade or subbase material. In addition, because of the interaction between the pavement and subgrade, a lower value of k (representing reduced subgrade support) results in less load on the pipe.

Although Tables 56 through 58 are for specific values of aircraft weights and landing gear configuration, the tables can be used with sufficient accuracy for all heavy commercial aircraft currently in operation. Investigation of the design loads of future jets indicates that although the total loads will greatly exceed present aircraft loads, the distribution of such loads over a greater number of landing gears and wheels will not impose loads on underground conduits greater than by commercial aircraft currently in operation. For lighter aircrafts and/or different rigid pavement thicknesses, it is necessary to calculate loads as illustrated in Example 4.11.

Railroads. In determining the live load transmitted to a pipe installed under railroad tracks, the weight on the locomotive driver axles plus the weight of the track structure, including ballast, is considered to be uniformly distributed over an area equal to the length occupied by the drivers multiplied by the length of ties.

The American Railway Engineering Association (AREA) recommends a Cooper E80 loading with axle loads and axle spacing as shown in Illustration 4.11. Based on a uniform load distribution at the bottom of the ties and through the soil mass, the live load transmitted to a pipe underground is computed by the equation:

$$W_L = C p_o B_c I_f \qquad [4](28)$$

---

[1] *Op. cit.*, p. 28

[4] Equation (28) is recommended by WPCF-ASCE Manual, The Design and Construction of Sanitary Storm Sewers.

Tables 59 through 61 present live loads in pounds per linear foot based on equation (28) with a Cooper E80 design loading, track structure weighing 200 pounds per linear foot and the locomotive load uniformly distributed over an area 8 feet × 20 feet yielding a uniform live load of 2025 pounds per square foot. In accordance with AREA "Manual of Recommended Practice" an impact factor of 1.4 at zero cover decreasing to 1.0 at ten feet of cover is included in the Tables.

Illustration 4.11 — Cooper E 80 Design Load

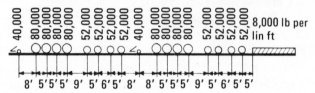

Construction Loads. During grading operations it may be necessary for heavy construction equipment to travel over an installed pipe. Unless adequate protection is provided, the pipe may be subjected to load concentrations in excess of the design loads. Before heavy construction equipment is permitted to cross over a pipe, a temporary earth fill should be constructed to an elevation at least 3 feet over the top of the pipe. The fill should be of sufficient width to prevent possible lateral displacement of the pipe.

SELECTION OF BEDDING

A bedding is provided to distribute the vertical reaction around the lower exterior surface of the pipe and reduce stress concentrations within the pipe wall. The load that a concrete pipe will support depends on the width of the bedding contact area and the quality of the contact between the pipe and bedding. An important consideration in selecting a material for bedding is to be sure that positive contact can be obtained between the bed and the pipe. Since most granular materials will shift to attain positive contact as the pipe settles an ideal load distribution can be attained through the use of clean coarse sand, well-rounded pea gravel or well-graded crushed rock.

Trench Beddings. Four general classes of bedding for the installation of circular pipe in a trench condition are illustrated in Figure 227. Trench bedding for horizontal elliptical, arch and vertical elliptical pipe are shown in Figure 228.

Embankment Beddings. Four general classes of bedding for the installation of circular pipe in an embankment condition are shown in Figure 229. Embankment beddings for horizontal elliptical, arch and vertical elliptical pipe are shown in Figure 230. Class A through D bedding classifications are presented as a guideline which should be reasonably attainable under field conditions. To assure that the in-place supporting strength of the pipe is adequate, the width of the band of contact between the pipe and the bedding material should be in accordance with the specified class of bedding. With the development of mechanical methods for subgrade preparation, pipe installation, backfilling and compaction, the flat bottom trench with granular foundation is generally the more practical method of bedding. If the pipe is installed in a flat bottom trench, it is essential that the bedding material be uniformly compacted under the haunches of the pipe.

DETERMINATION OF BEDDING FACTOR

Under installed conditions the vertical load on a pipe is distributed over its width and the reaction is distributed in accordance with the type of bedding. When the pipe strength used in design has been determined by plant testing, bedding factors must be developed to relate the in-place supporting strength to the more severe plant test strength. The bedding factor is the ratio of the strength of the pipe under the installed condition of loading and bedding to the strength of the pipe in the plant test. This same ratio was defined originally by Spangler as the load factor. This latter term, however, was subsequently defined in the ultimate strength method of reinforced concrete design with an entirely different meaning. To avoid confusion, therefore, Spangler's term was renamed the bedding factor. The three-edge bearing test as shown in Illustration 4.12 is the normally accepted plant test so that all bedding factors described below relate the in-place supporting strength to the three-edge bearing strength.

Illustration 4.12 — Three Edge Bearing Test

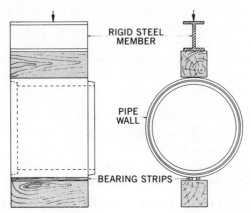

Trench Bedding Factors. Bedding factors for pipe installed in a trench condition are listed below the particular classes of beddings shown in Figures 227 and 228.

Positive Projecting Embankment Bedding Factors. For pipe installed in a positive projecting embankment condition, active lateral pressure is exerted against the sides of the pipe. Bedding factors for this type of installation are computed by the equation:

$$B_f = \frac{A}{N - xq} \tag{29}$$

For circular pipe q is further defined as:

$$q = \frac{pK}{C_c}\left(\frac{H}{B_c} + \frac{p}{2}\right) \qquad [1](30)$$

For elliptical and arch pipe q is further defined as:

$$q = \frac{pB'_c K}{C_c B_c^2}\left(H + \frac{pB'_c}{2}\right) \qquad [1](31)$$

Tables 62 through 65 list bedding factors for circular, vertical elliptical, horizontal elliptical and arch pipe.

Negative Projecting Embankment Bedding Factors. The trench bedding factors listed in Figures 227 and 228 should be used for negative projecting embankment installations.

Induced Trench Bedding Factors. Bedding factors for this type of installation are calculated in the same manner as for the positive projecting embankment installation, using larger values of q to account for the decrease in vertical load. Table 66 lists bedding factors for circular pipe installed by the induced trench method of construction.

Jacked or Tunneled Bedding Factor. Since the jacking method of construction affords positive contact around the lower exterior surface of the pipe and the surrounding earth, an ideal bedding condition is provided. This positive contact can be obtained by close control of the bore excavation to the outside dimensions and shape of the pipe or, if the bore is over-excavated, the space between the pipe and the bore can be filled with sand, grout, concrete or other suitable material. For this type of installation a bedding factor of 3 is recommended. If the bore is slightly over-excavated and the space between the pipe and the bore is not filled, a minimum bedding factor of 1.9 is recommended.

The usual procedure in tunnel construction is to complete excavation of the tunnel bore first and then install the pipe. If the pipe is designed to carry the earth load, or a portion of the load, the bedding factor should be in accordance with the particular type of bedding provided. The bedding factors listed in Figures 227 and 228 are recommended.

APPLICATION OF FACTOR OF SAFETY

The total earth and live load on a buried concrete pipe is computed and multiplied by a factor of safety to determine the pipe supporting strength required. The safety factor is defined as the relationship between the ultimate strength D-load and the 0.01-inch crack D-load. This relationship is specified in the ASTM standards on reinforced concrete pipe. Therefore, for reinforced concrete pipe a factor of safety of 1.0 should be applied if the 0.01-inch crack strength is used as the design criterion. For non-reinforced concrete pipe a factor of safety of 1.25 to 1.5 is normally used.

---

[1] *Op. cit., p. 28*

SELECTION OF PIPE STRENGTH

The American Society for Testing and Materials has developed standard specifications for precast concrete pipe. Each specification contains design, manufacturing and testing criteria.

ASTM Standard C 14 covers three strength classes for nonreinforced concrete pipe. These classes are specified to meet minimum ultimate loads, expressed in terms of three-edge bearing strength in pounds per linear foot.

ASTM Standard C 76 for reinforced concrete culvert, storm drain and sewer pipe specifies strength classes based on D-load at 0.01-inch crack and/or ultimate load. The 0.01-inch crack D-load ($D_{0.01}$) is the maximum three-edge-bearing test load supported by a concrete pipe before a crack occurs having a width of 0.01 inch measured at close intervals, throughout a length of at least 1 foot. The ultimate D-load (D_u) is the maximum three-edge-bearing test load supported by a pipe. D-loads are expressed in pounds per linear foot per foot of inside diameter or horizontal span.

ASTM Standard C 506 for reinforced concrete arch culvert, storm drain, and sewer pipe specifies strengths based on D-load at 0.01-inch crack and/or ultimate load in pounds per linear foot per foot of inside span.

ASTM Standard C 507 for reinforced concrete elliptical culvert, storm drain and sewer pipe specifies strength classes for both horizontal elliptical and vertical elliptical pipe based on D-load at 0.01-inch crack and/or ultimate load in pounds per linear foot per foot of inside span.

ASTM Standard C 655 for reinforced concrete D-load culvert, storm drain and sewer pipe covers acceptance of pipe design to meet specific D-load requirements.

ASTM Standard C 789 for precast reinforced concrete box culvert, storm drain and sewer sections provides standard designs for two or more feet of earth cover when subjected to highway live loads, and zero cover or greater when subjected to only dead loads under three loading conditions.

ASTM Standard C 850 for precast reinforced concrete box culvert, storm drain and sewer sections provides standard designs for less than two feet of earth cover under two highway loading conditions.

Since numerous reinforced concrete pipe sizes are available, three-edge bearing test strengths are classified by D-loads. The D-load concept provides strength classification of pipe independent of pipe diameter. For reinforced circular pipe the three-edge bearing test load in pounds per linear foot equals D-load $\times$ inside diameter in feet. For arch, horizontal elliptical and vertical elliptical pipe the three-edge bearing test load in pounds per linear foot equals D-load $\times$ nominal inside span in feet.

The required three-edge bearing strength of non-reinforced concrete pipe is expressed in pounds per linear foot, not as a D-load, and is computed by the equation:

$$T.E.B. = \frac{W_L + W_E}{B_f} \times F.S. \tag{32}$$

The required three-edge bearing strength of circular reinforced concrete pipe is expressed as D-load and is computed by the equation:

$$D\text{-}load = \frac{W_L + W_E}{B_f \times D} \times F.S. \tag{33}$$

The determination of required strength of elliptical and arch concrete pipe is computed by the equation:

$$D\text{-}load = \frac{W_L + W_E}{B_f \times S} \times F.S. \tag{34}$$

PRECAST CONCRETE BOX SECTIONS

Precast reinforced concrete box sections are designed for installed conditions rather than for test conditions. Standard designs are presented in ASTM C 789, Precast Reinforced Concrete Box Sections for Culverts, Storm Drains and Sewers, and C 850, Precast Reinforced Concrete Box Sections for Culverts, Storm Drains and Sewers with Less Than 2 Feet of Cover Subjected to Highway Loadings, for various loading conditions and heights of earth cover. ASTM C 850 covers box sections with less than 2 feet of earth cover for both the AASHTO H20 and HS20 truck plus dead load conditions and the AASHTO alternate load plus dead load conditions. ASTM C 789 covers box sections with 2 or more feet of earth cover for the preceding loading conditions and also for anly the dead load condition with zero or greater feet of earth cover. Special designs for sizes and conditions other than as presented in the ASTM Standards are also available. Both C 789 and C 850 have been accepted and published as AASHTO standards M 259 and M 273 respectively.

EXAMPLE PROBLEMS

EXAMPLE 4 - 1
TRENCH INSTALLATION

Given: A 48-inch circular pipe is to be installed in a 7-foot wide trench with 35 feet of cover over the top of the pipe. The pipe will be backfilled with sand and gravel weighing 110 pounds per cubic foot.

Example 4 - 1

Find: The required pipe strength in terms of 0.01-inch crack D-load.

Solution: 1. *Determination of Earth Load (WE)*
From Table 26A, Sand and Gravel, the backfill load based on 100 pounds per cubic foot backfill is 12,000 pounds per linear foot. Increase the load 10 percent for 110 pound backfill material.

$$W_d = 1.10 \times 12,000$$

$$W_d = 13,200 \text{ pounds per linear foot}$$

2. *Determination of Live Load (WL)*
From Table 45, live load is negligible at a depth of 35 feet.

3. *Selection of Bedding*
A Class B bedding will be assumed for this example. In actual design, it may be desirable to consider other types of bedding in order to arrive at the most economical overall installation.

4. *Determination of Bedding Factor (B_f)*
From Figure 227, for circular pipe installed on a Class B bedding, a bedding factor of 1.9 is obtained.

5. *Application of Factor of Safety (F.S.)*
A factor of safety of 1.0 based on the 0.01-inch crack will be applied.

6. *Selection of Pipe Strength*

The *D*-load is given by Equation 33:

$$D_{0.01} = \frac{W_L + W_E}{B_f \times D} \times F.S.$$

$$W_L + W_E = W_d = 13{,}200 \text{ pounds per linear foot}$$

$$D_{0.01} = \frac{13{,}200}{1.9 \times 4.0} \times 1.0$$

$$D_{0.01} = 1737 \text{ pounds per linear foot}$$
per foot of inside diameter

Answer: A pipe which would withstand a minimum three-edge bearing test load for the 0.01-inch crack of 1737 pounds per linear foot per foot of inside diameter would be required.

EXAMPLE 4 - 2
POSITIVE PROJECTING EMBANKMENT INSTALLATION

Given: A 48-inch circular pipe is to be installed in a positive projecting embankment condition in ordinary soil. The pipe will be covered with 35 feet of 110 pounds per cubic foot overfill.

Find: The required pipe strength in terms of 0.01-inch crack *D*-load.

Example 4 - 2

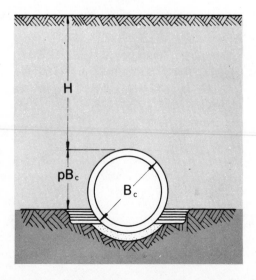

Solution: 1. *Determination of Earth Load (W_E)*

A settlement ratio must first be assumed. In Table 43 values of settlement ratio from +0.5 to +0.8 are given for positive projecting installations on a foundation of ordinary soil. A conservative value of 0.7 will be used with an assumed projection ratio of 0.7. The product of the settlement ratio and the projection ratio will be 0.49 ($r_{sd}p \approx 0.5$).

Enter Figure 166 on the horizontal scale at $H = 35$ feet. Proceed vertically until the line representing $D = 48$ inches is intersected. At this point the vertical scale shows the fill load to be 25,300 pounds per linear foot for 100 pounds per cubic foot fill material. Increase the load 10 percent for 110 pound material.

$$W_c = 1.10 \times 25,300$$

$$W_c = 27,800 \text{ pounds per linear foot}$$

2. *Determination of Live Load (W_L)*

From Table 45, live load is negligible at a depth of 35 feet.

3. *Selection of Bedding*

A Class B bedding will be assumed for this example. In actual design, it may be desirable to consider other types of bedding in order to arrive at the most economical overall installation.

4. *Determination of Bedding Factor (B_f)*

The outside diameter for a 48-inch diameter pipe is 58 inches = 4.83 feet. From Table 62.1, from an H/B_c ratio of 7.25, $r_{sd}p$ value of 0.5, p value of 0.7 and Class B bedding, a bedding factor of 2.34 is obtained.

5. *Application of Factor of Safety (F.S.)*

A factor of safety of 1.0 based on the 0.01-inch crack will be applied.

6. *Selection of Pipe Strength*

The D-load is given by equation 33:

$$D_{0.01} = \frac{W_L + W_E}{B_f \times D} \times F.S.$$

$$W_L + W_E = W_c = 27,800 \text{ pounds per linear foot}$$

$$D_{0.01} = \frac{27,800}{2.34 \times 4.0} \times 1.0$$

$$D_{0.01} = 2970 \text{ pounds per linear foot}$$
$$\text{per foot of inside diameter}$$

Answer: A pipe which would withstand a minimum three-edge bearing test load for the 0.01-inch crack of 2970 pounds per linear foot per foot of inside diameter would be required.

EXAMPLE 4 - 3
NEGATIVE PROJECTING EMBANKMENT INSTALLATION

Given: A 48-inch circular pipe is to be installed in a negative projecting embankment condition in ordinary soil. The pipe will be covered with 35 feet of 110 pounds per cubic foot overfill. A 7-foot trench width will be constructed with a 7-foot depth from the top of the pipe to the natural ground surface.

Example 4 - 3

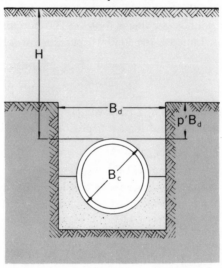

Find: The required pipe strength in terms of 0.01-inch crack *D*-load.

Solution: 1. *Determination of Earth Load (W_E)*
             A settlement ratio must first be assumed. In Table 43, for a negative projection ratio, $p' = 1.0$, the design value of the settlement ratio is -0.3.

             Enter Figure 190 on the horizontal scale at $H = 35$ feet. Proceed vertically until the line representing $B_d = 7$ feet is intersected. At this point the vertical scale shows the fill load to be 15,800 pounds per linear foot for 100 pounds per cubic foot fill material. Increase the load 10 percent for 110 pound material.

$$W_n = 1.10 \times 15,800$$

$$W_n = 17,380 \text{ pounds per linear foot}$$

2. *Determination of Live Load (W_L)*
From Table 45, live load is negligible at a depth of 35 feet.

3. *Selection of Bedding*
A Class B bedding will be assumed for this example. In actual

design, it may be desirable to consider other types of bedding in order to arrive at the most economical overall installation.

4. Determination of Bedding Factor (B_f)

In view of the relatively narrow subtrench, it is not anticipated that an appreciable amount of laterial pressure will develop against the sides of the pipe. Therefore, a constant bedding factor for a trench condition will be used.

From Figure 227 for circular pipe installed on a Class B bedding, a bedding factor of 1.9 is obtained.

5. Application of Factor of Safety (F.S.)

A factor of safety of 1.0 based on the 0.01-inch crack will be applied.

6. Selection of Pipe Strength

The D-load is given by equation 33:

$$D_{0.01} = \frac{W_L + W_E}{B_f \times D} \times F.S.$$

$$W_L + W_E = W_n = 17{,}380 \text{ pounds per linear foot}$$

$$D_{0.01} = \frac{17{,}380}{1.9 \times 4.0} \times 1.0$$

$$D_{0.01} = 2287 \text{ pounds per linear foot}$$
$$\text{per foot of inside diameter}$$

Answer: A pipe which would withstand a minimum three-edge bearing test load for the 0.01-inch crack of 2287 pounds per linear foot per foot of inside diameter would be required.

EXAMPLE 4 - 4
INDUCED TRENCH INSTALLATION

Given: A 48-inch circular pipe is to be installed by the induced trench method of construction with 35 feet of 110 pounds per cubic foot overfill. The built-up embankment will be constructed to an elevation 5 feet over the top of the pipe, and the induced trench excavated directly over the pipe to a depth and width coinciding with the outside diameter of the pipe.

Example 4 - 4

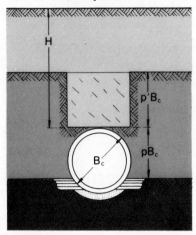

Find: The required pipe strength in terms of 0.01-inch crack D-load.

Solution: 1. *Determination of Earth Load (W_E)*
A settlement ratio must first be assumed. In Table 43, for an induced trench projection ratio, $p' = 1.0$, the design value of the settlement ratio is -0.7.

Enter Figure 208 on the horizontal scale at $H = 35$ feet. Proceed vertically until the line representing $D = 48$ inches is intersected. At this point the vertical scale shows the fill load to be 9,500 pounds per linear foot for 100 pounds per cubic foot fill material. Increase the load 10 percent for 110 pound material.

$$W_i = 1.10 \times 9{,}500$$

$$W_i = 10{,}450 \text{ pounds per linear foot}$$

2. *Determination of Live Load (W_L)*
From Table 45, live load is negligible at a depth of 35 feet.

3. *Selection of Bedding*
A Class B bedding will be assumed for this example. In actual design, it may be desirable to consider other types of bedding in order to arrive at the most economical overall installation.

4. *Determination of Bedding Factor (B_f)*
From Table 66, for an H/B_c ratio of 7.25, r_{sd} value of -0.7, p value of 0.7 and Class B bedding, a bedding factor of 3.13 is obtained by interpolation.

5. *Application of Factor of Safety (F.S.)*
A factor of safety of 1.0 based on the 0.01-inch crack will be applied.

6. *Selection of Pipe Strength*

The *D*-load is given by equation 33:

$$D_{0.01} = \frac{W_L + W_E}{B_f \times D} \times F.S.$$

$$W_L + W_E = W_i = 10,450 \text{ pounds per linear foot}$$

$$D_{0.01} = \frac{10,450}{3.13 \times 4.0} \times 1.0$$

$$D_{0.01} = 835 \text{ pounds per linear foot}$$
$$\text{per foot of inside diameter}$$

Answer: A pipe which would withstand a minimum three-edge bearing test load for the 0.01-inch crack of 835 pounds per linear foot per foot of inside diameter would be required.

EXAMPLE 4 - 5

JACKED OR TUNNELED INSTALLATION

Given: A 48-inch circular pipe is to be installed by the jacking method of construction with a height of cover over the top of the pipe of 35 feet. The pipe will be jacked through ordinary clay material weighing 110 pounds per cubic foot. The limit of excavation will be 5 feet.

Example 4 - 5

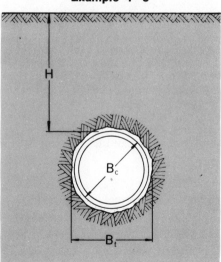

Find: The required pipe strength in terms of 0.01-inch crack *D-load*.

Solution: 1. *Determination of Earth Load (W_E)*

A coefficient of cohesion value must first be assumed. In Table 44 values of the coefficient of cohesion from 40 to 1000 are given for clay. A conservative value of 100 pounds per square foot will be used.

Enter Figure 223, Ordinary Clay, and project a horizontal line from $H = 35$ feet on the vertical scale and a vertical line from $B_t = 5$ feet on the horizontal scale. At the intersection of these two lines interpolate between the curved lines for a value of 9,500 pounds per linear foot, which accounts for earth load without cohesion. Decrease the load in proportion to $\dfrac{w_{110}}{120}$ for 110 pound material

$$W_t = \frac{110}{120} \times 9,500$$

$$W_t = 8,708 \text{ pounds per linear foot}$$

Enter Figure 224, Ordinary Clay, and project a horizontal line from $H = 35$ feet on the vertical scale and a vertical line from $B_t = 5$ feet on the horizontal scale. At the intersection of these two lines interpolate between the curved lines for a value of 32 which accounts for the cohesion of the soil. Multiply this value by the coefficient of cohesion, $c = 100$, and subtract the product from the 8,708 value obtained from Figure 223.

$$W_t = 8,708 - 100 \times 32$$

$$W_t = 5,508 \text{ pounds per linear foot}$$

2. *Determination of Live Load (W_L)*
From Table 45, live load is negligible at a depth of 35 feet.

3. *Selection of Bedding*
The annular space between the pipe and limit of excavation will be filled with grout.

4. *Determination of Bedding Factor (B_f)*
Since the space between the pipe and the bore will be filled with grout, there will be positive contact of bedding around the entire periphery of the pipe. Because of this ideal bedding condition, little or no flexural stresses should be induced in the pipe wall. A conservative bedding factor of 3.0 will be used.

5. *Application of Factor of Safety (F.S.)*
A factor of safety of 1.0 based on the 0.01-inch crack will be applied.

6. *Selection of Pipe Strength*

The *D*-load is given by equation 33:

$$D_{0.01} = \frac{W_L + W_E}{B_f \times D} \times F.S.$$

$$W_L + W_E = W_t = 5{,}508 \text{ pounds per linear foot}$$

$$D_{0.01} = \frac{5{,}508}{3.0 \times 4.0} \times 1.0$$

$$D_{0.01} = 459 \text{ pounds per linear foot}$$
$$\text{per foot of inside diameter}$$

Answer: A pipe which would withstand a minimum three-edge bearing test load for the 0.01-inch crack of 459 pounds per linear foot per foot of inside diameter would be required.

EXAMPLE 4 - 6
WIDE TRENCH INSTALLATION

Given: A 24-inch circular pipe is to be installed in a 5-foot wide trench with 9 feet of cover over the top of the pipe. The pipe will be backfilled with ordinary clay weighing 120 pounds per cubic foot.

Example 4 - 6

Find: The required three-edge bearing test strength for nonreinforced pipe and the ultimate *D*-load for reinforced pipe.

Solution: 1. *Determination of Earth Load (W_E)*
From Table 20C, the transition width for *H* = 9 feet is 4'-8".

Since the actual 5-foot trench width exceeds the transition width, the backfill load based on 100 pounds per cubic foot backfill is 3,331 pounds per linear foot as given by the bold type. Increase the load 20 percent for 120 pound backfill material.

$$W_d = 1.20 \times 3,331$$
$$W_d = 3,997 \text{ pounds per linear foot}$$

2. *Determination of Live Load* (W_L)

From Table 45, the live load is 240 pounds per linear foot.

3. *Selection of Bedding*

A Class C bedding will be assumed for this example.

4. *Determination of Bedding Factor* (B_f)

Although the trench width is relatively wide in comparison to the pipe width, it is not anticipated that an appreciable amount of lateral pressure will develop against the sides of the pipe. Therefore, a constant bedding factor for a trench condition will be used.

From Figure 227, for circular pipe installed on a Class C bedding, a bedding factor of 1.5 is obtained.

5. *Application of Factor of Safety (F.S.)*

A factor of safety of 1.5 based on the three-edge bearing strength for nonreinforced pipe and ultimate D-load for reinforced pipe will be applied.

6. *Selection of Pipe Strength*

The three-edge bearing strength for nonreinforced pipe is given by equation 32:

$$T.E.B. = \frac{W_L + W_E}{B_f} \times F.S.$$

$$W_L + W_E = W_d = 4,237 \text{ pounds per linear foot}$$

$$T.E.B. = \frac{4,237}{1.5} \times 1.5$$

$$T.E.B. = 4,237 \text{ pounds per linear foot}$$

The *D*-load for reinforced pipe is given by equation 33:

$$D_{ult.} = \frac{W_L + W_E}{B_f \times D} \times F.S.$$

$$D_{ult.} = \frac{4,237}{1.5 \times 2.0} \times 1.5$$

$$D_{ult.} = 2,119 \text{ pounds per linear foot}$$
$$\text{per foot of inside diameter}$$

Answer: A nonreinforced pipe which would withstand a minimum three-edge bearing test load of 4,237 pounds per linear foot would be required.

A reinforced pipe which would withstand a minimum three-edge bearing test load for the ultimate load of 2,119 pounds per linear foot per foot of inside diameter would be required.

EXAMPLE 4 - 7
POSITIVE PROJECTING EMBANKMENT INSTALLATION
VERTICAL ELLIPTICAL PIPE

Given: A 76-inch × 48-inch vertical elliptical pipe is to be installed in a positive projecting embankment condition in ordinary soil. The pipe will be covered with 50 feet of 120 pounds per cubic foot overfill.

Example 4 - 7

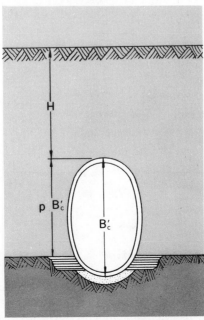

Find: The required pipe strength in terms of 0.01-inch crack *D*-load.

Solution: 1. *Determination of Earth Load (W$_E$)*

A settlement ratio must first be assumed. In Table 43 values of settlement ratio from $+0.5$ to $+0.8$ are given for positive projecting installations on a foundation of ordinary soil. A value of 0.5 will be used. The product of the settlement ratio and the projection ratio will be 0.35 ($r_{sd}\, p \approx 0.3$).

Enter Figure 170 on the horizontal scale at $H = 50$ feet. Proceed vertically until the line representing $R \times S = 76'' \times 48''$ is intersected. At this point the vertical scale shows the fill load to be 37,100 pounds per linear foot for 100 pounds per cubic foot fill material. Increase the load 20 percent for 120 pound material.

$$W_c = 1.20 \times 37,100$$

$$W_c = 44,520 \text{ pounds per linear foot}$$

2. *Determination of Live Load (W$_L$)*

From Table 47, live load is negligible at a depth of 50 feet.

3. *Selection of Bedding*

A Class B bedding will be assumed for this example.

4. *Determination of Bedding Factor (B$_f$)*

From Table 63, for an H/B_c ratio of 9.84 $r_{sd}p$ value of 0.3, p value of 0.7 and a Class B bedding, a bedding factor of 2.80 is obtained.

5. *Application of Factor of Safety (F.S.)*

A factor of safety of 1.0 based on the 0.01-inch crack will be applied.

6. *Selection of Pipe Strength*

The *D*-load is given by equation 34:

$$D_{0.01} = \frac{W_L + W_E}{B_f \times S} \times F.S.$$

$$W_L + W_E = W_c = 44,520 \text{ pounds per linear foot}$$

$$D_{0.01} = \frac{44,520}{2.80 \times 4.0} \times 1.0$$

$$D_{0.01} = 3,975 \text{ pounds per linear foot per}$$
foot of inside horizontal span

Answer: A pipe which would withstand a minimum three-edge bearing test load for the 0.01-inch crack of 3,975 pounds per linear foot per foot of inside horizontal span would be required.

EXAMPLE 4 - 8
HIGHWAY LIVE LOAD

Given: A 12-inch circular pipe is to be installed in a trench under an unsurfaced roadway and covered with 1.0 foot of 120 pounds per cubic foot backfill material.

Example 4 - 8

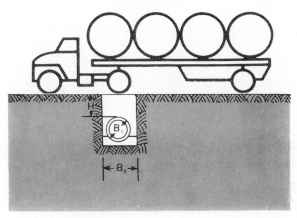

Find: The required pipe strength in terms of 0.01-inch crack D-load.

Solution: 1. *Determination of Earth Load (W_E)*
For pipe installed with less than 3 feet of cover, it is sufficiently accurate to calculate the backfill or fill load as being equal to the weight of the prism of earth on top of the pipe.

$$W_d = wHB_c$$
$$W_d = 120 \times 1.0 \times 1.33$$
$$W_d = 160 \text{ pounds per linear foot}$$

2. *Determination of Live Load (W_L)*
Since the pipe is being installed under an unsurfaced roadway with shallow cover, a truck loading based on legal load limitations should be evaluated. From Table 45, for $D = 12$ inches, $H = 1.0$ foot and AASHTO loading a live load of 2,080 pounds per linear foot is obtained. This live load value includes impact.

3. *Selection of Bedding*
A Class C bedding will be assumed for this example.

4. *Determination of Bedding Factor (B_f)*
From Figure 227, for circular pipe installed on a Class C bedding, a bedding factor of 1.5 is obtained.

5. *Application of Factor of Safety (F.S.)*
A factor of safety of 1.0 based on the 0.01-inch crack will be applied.

6. *Selection of Pipe Strength*
The *D*-load is given by equation 33:

$$D_{0.01} = \frac{W_L + W_E}{B_f \times D} \times F.S.$$

$$D_{0.01} = \frac{2,080 + 160}{1.5 \times 1.0} \times 1.0$$

$$D_{0.01} = 1,443 \text{ pounds per linear foot}$$
$$\text{per foot of inside diameter}$$

Answer: A pipe which would withstand a minimum three-edge bearing test load for the 0.01-inch crack of 1,443 pounds per linear foot per foot of inside diameter would be required.

Given: All data will remain the same as above except that the pipe size will be increased from 12-inch circular pipe to 48-inch circular pipe.

Find: The required pipe strength in terms of the 0.01-inch crack *D*-load.

Solution: 1. *Determination of Earth Load (W_E)*

$$W_d = wHB_c$$

$$W_d = 120 \times 1.0 \times 4.83$$

$$W_d = 580 \text{ pounds per linear foot}$$

2. *Determination of Live Load (W_L)*
From Table 45, for $D = 48$ inches, $H = 1.0$ foot and AASHTO loading a live load of 2,330 pounds per linear foot is obtained. This live load value includes impact.

3. *Selection of Bedding*
A Class C bedding will be assumed for this example.

4. *Determination of Bedding Factor (B_f)*
From Figure 227, for circular pipe installed on a Class C bedding, a bedding factor of 1.5 is obtained.

5. *Application of Factor of Safety (F.S.)*

A factor of safety of 1.0 based on the 0.01-inch crack will be applied.

6. *Selection of Pipe Strength*

The *D*-load is given by equation 33:

$$D_{0.01} = \frac{W_L + W_E}{B_f \times D} \times F.S.$$

$$D_{0.01} = \frac{2,330 + 580}{1.5 \times 4} \times 1.0$$

$$D_{0.01} = 485 \text{ pounds per linear foot}$$
$$\text{per foot of inside diameter}$$

Answer: A pipe which would withstand a minimum three-edge bearing test load for the 0.01-inch crack of 485 pounds per linear foot per foot of inside diameter would be required.

EXAMPLE 4 - 9
AIRCRAFT LIVE LOAD — RIGID PAVEMENT

Given: A 12-inch circular pipe is to be installed in a trench condition under a 12-inch thick concrete airfield pavement and subjected to heavy commercial aircraft loadings. The pipe will be covered with 1.0 foot (measured from top of pipe to bottom of pavement slab) of sand and gravel material weighing 120 pounds per cubic foot.

Example 4 - 9

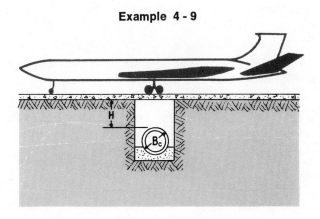

Find: The required pipe strength in terms of 0.01-inch crack *D*-load.

Solution: 1. *Determination of Earth Load (W_E)*

The earth load is equal to the weight of the backfill and the concrete pavement. For pipe installed with less than 3 feet of cover, it is sufficiently accurate to calculate the backfill load as being equal to the weight of the prism of backfill over the pipe.

$$W_d = wHB_c$$

$$W_d = 120 \times 1.0 \times 1.33$$

$$W_d = 160 \text{ pounds per linear foot}$$

Assuming 150 pounds per cubic foot concrete, the weight of the pavement is:

$$W_p = whB_c$$

$$W_p = 150 \times 1.0 \times 1.33$$

$$W_p = 200 \text{ pounds per linear foot}$$

$$W_E = W_d + W_p$$

$$W_E = 160 + 200$$

$$W_E = 360 \text{ pounds per linear foot}$$

2. *Determination of Live Load (W_L)*

It would first be necessary to determine the bearing value of the backfill and/or subgrade. A modulus of subgrade reaction, $k = 300$ pounds per cubic inch, will be assumed for this example. Based on the number of undercarriages, landing gear configurations and gross weights of existing and proposed future aircrafts, the Concorde is a reasonable commercial aircraft design loading for pipe placed under airfields. From Table 56A, for $D = 12$ inches and $H = 1.0$ foot, a live load of 1,892 pounds per linear foot is obtained.

3. *Selection of Bedding*

A Class B bedding will be assumed for this example.

4. *Determination of Bedding Factor (B_f)*

From Figure 227, for circular pipe installed in a trench condition on a Class B bedding, a bedding factor of 1.9 is obtained.

5. *Application of Factor of Safety (F.S.)*

A factor of safety of 1.0 based on the 0.01-inch crack will be applied.

6. *Selection of Pipe Strength*

The *D*-load is given by equation 33:

$$D_{0.01} = \frac{W_L + W_E}{B_f \times D} \times F.S.$$

$$D_{0.01} = \frac{1,892 + 360}{1.9 \times 1.0} \times 1.0$$

$D_{0.01} = 1185$ pounds per linear foot
per foot of inside diameter

Answer: A pipe which would withstand a minimum three-edge bearing test load for the 0.01-inch crack of 1185 pounds per linear foot per foot of inside diameter would be required.

EXAMPLE 4 - 10

AIRCRAFT LIVE LOAD — FLEXIBLE PAVEMENT

Given: A 27-inch circular pipe is to be installed in a trench condition under an airfield and subjected to Concorde aircraft loadings. A flexible pavement will be provided with 3 feet of cover between the top of the pipe and the surface of the pavement.

Example 4 - 10

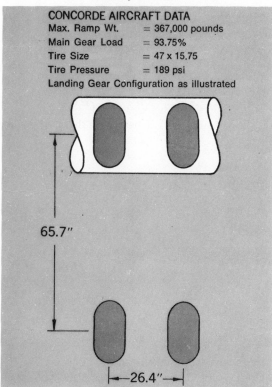

CONCORDE AIRCRAFT DATA

Max. Ramp Wt.	= 367,000 pounds
Main Gear Load	= 93.75%
Tire Size	= 47 x 15.75
Tire Pressure	= 189 psi

Landing Gear Configuration as illustrated

65.7"

|—26.4"—|

Find: The required pipe strength in terms of 0.01-inch crack D-load.

Solution: 1. *Determination of Earth Load (W_E)*

The earth load is equal to the weight of the surface course, base course, subbase and fill material. Assuming 120 pounds per cubic foot, the weight of the prism of material on top of the pipe is:

$$W_E = wHB_c$$

$$W_E = 120 \times 3.0 \times 2.79$$

$$W_E = 1{,}004 \text{ pounds per linear foot}$$

2. *Determination of Live Load (W_L)*

P 174

From Table 56B, for $D = 27$ inches and $H = 3$ feet, a live load of 8,988 pounds per linear foot is obtained.

3. *Selection of Bedding*

A Class C bedding will be assumed for this example.

4. *Determination of Bedding Factor (B_f)*

From Figure 227, for circular pipe installed in a trench condition on a Class C bedding, a bedding factor of 1.5 is obtained.

5. *Application of Factor of Safety (F.S.)*

A factor of safety of 1.0 based on the 0.01-inch crack will be applied.

6. *Selection of Pipe Strength*

The D-load is given by equation 33:

$$D_{0.01} = \frac{W_L + W_E}{B_f \times D} \times F.S.$$

$$D_{0.01} = \frac{8{,}988 + 1{,}004}{1.5 \times 2.25} \times 1.0$$

$$D_{0.01} = 3000 \text{ pounds per linear foot}$$
$$\text{per foot of inside diameter}$$

Answer: A pipe which would withstand a minimum three-edge bearing test load for the 0.01-inch crack of 3000 pounds per linear foot per foot of inside diameter would be required.

Example 4 - 11
Aircraft Live Load

Given: A 68-inch x 106-inch horizontal elliptical pipe is to be installed under a 7-inch thick concrete airfield pavement and subjected to two 60,000 pound wheel loads spaced 20 feet, center to center. The pipe will be covered with 3 feet (measured from top of pipe to bottom of pavement slab) of sand and gravel weighing 120 pounds per cubic foot.

Example 4 - 11

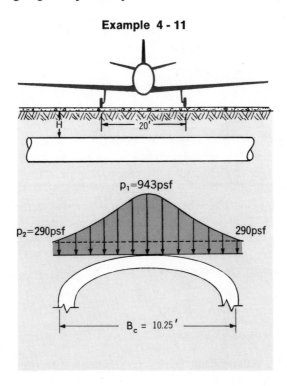

Find: The required pipe strength in terms of 0.01-inch crack D-load.

Solution: 1. *Determination of Earth Load (W_E)*

The earth load is equal to the weight of the backfill and the concrete pavement. For pipe installed with less than 3 feet of cover, it is sufficiently accurate to calculate the backfill load as being equal to the weight of the prism of backfill over the pipe.

$$W_d = wHB_c$$
$$W_d = 120 \times 3.0 \times 10.25$$
$$W_d = 3,690 \text{ pounds per linear foot}$$

Assuming 150 pounds per cubic foot concrete, the weight of the pavement is:

$$W_p = whB_c$$

$$W_p = 150 \times \frac{7}{12} \times 10.25$$

$$W_p = 896 \text{ pounds per linear foot}$$

$$W_E = W_d + W_p$$

$$W_E = 3{,}690 + 896$$

$$W_E = 4{,}586 \text{ pounds per linear foot}$$

2. Determination of Live Load (W_L)

Assuming a modulus of subgrade reaction of $k = 300$ pounds per cubic inch and a pavement thickness of $h = 7$ inches, a radius of stiffness of 24.99 inches (2.08 feet) is obtained from Table 55. The wheel spacing in terms of the radius of stiffness is $20/2.08 = 9.6\ R_s$, therefore the maximum live load on the pipe will occur when one wheel is directly over the centerline of the pipe and the second wheel disregarded. The pressure intensity on the pipe is given by equation 24:

$$p_{(H,X)} = \frac{CP}{R_s^2}$$

The pressure coefficient (C) is obtained from Table 49 at $X = O$ and $H = 3$ feet.

For $X/R_s = 0$ and $H/R_s = 3/2.08 = 1.44$, $C = 0.068$ by interpolation between $H/R_s = 1.2$ and $H/R_s = 1.6$ in Table 49.

$$p_{(3,0)} = \frac{0.068 \times 60{,}000}{(2.08)^2}$$

$$p_{(3,0)} = 943 \text{ pounds per square foot}$$

In a similar manner pressure intensities are calculated at convenient increments across the width of the pipe. The pressure coefficients and corresponding pressures in pounds per square foot are listed in the accompanying table.

Point	X/R_s								
	0.0	0.4	0.8	1.2	1.6	2.0	2.4	2.8	3.2
Pressure Coefficient C	0.068	0.064	0.058	0.050	0.041	0.031	0.022	0.015	0.010
Pressure psf	943	887	804	693	568	430	305	208	139

For convenience of computing the load in pounds per linear foot, the pressure distribution can be broken down into two components; a uniform load of 290 pounds per square foot and a parabolic load with a maximum pressure of 653 pounds per square foot.

$$W_L = p_2 \times B_c + \frac{2}{3}(p_1 - p_2) \times B_c$$

$$W_L = 290 \times 10.25 + \frac{2}{3}(943 - 290) \times 10.25$$

$$W_L = 2{,}972 + 4{,}462$$

$$W_L = 7{,}434 \text{ pounds per linear foot}$$

3. Selection of Bedding
A Class B bedding will be assumed for this example.

4. Determination of Bedding Factor (B_f)
From Figure 227, for circular pipe installed on a Class B bedding, a bedding factor of 1.9 is obtained.

5. Application of Factor of Safety (F.S.)
A factor of safety of 1.0 based on the 0.01-inch crack will be applied.

6. Selection of Pipe Strength
The D-load is given by equation 34:

$$D_{0.01} = \frac{W_L + W_E}{B_f \times S} \times F.S.$$

$$D_{0.01} = \frac{7{,}434 \times 4{,}586}{1.9 \times 8.83} \times 1.0$$

$$D_{0.01} = 716 \text{ pounds per linear foot per} \\ \text{foot of inside horizontal span}$$

Answer: A pipe which would withstand a minimum three-edge bearing test load for the 0.01-inch crack of 716 pounds per linear foot per foot of inside horizontal span would be required.

Example 4 - 12
Railroad Live Load

Given: An 11-inch x 18-inch arch pipe is to be installed under a railroad in a zero projecting condition. The pipe will be covered with 1.0 foot of 120 pounds per cubic foot overfill (measured from top of pipe to bottom of ties).

Example 4 - 12

Find: The required pipe strength in terms of 0.01-inch crack *D*-load.

Solution: 1. *Determination of Earth Load (W_E)*

For pipe installed with less than 3 feet of cover, it is sufficiently accurate to calculate the fill load as being equal to the weight of the prism of fill on top of the pipe.

$$W_c = wHB_c$$

$$W_c = 120 \times 1.0 \times 1.875$$

$$W_c = 225 \text{ pounds per linear foot}$$

2. *Determination of Live Load (W_L)*

From Table 61, for $R \times S = 11 \times 18$ inches, $H = 1.0$ foot and a Cooper E80 design load, a live load of 5,110 pounds per linear foot is obtained. This live load value includes impact.

3. Selection of Bedding

A Class C bedding will be assumed for this example.

4. Determination of Bedding Factor (B_f)

From Table 65, for arch pipe installed on a Class C bedding in a zero projecting condition, a bedding factor of 1.75 is obtained.

5. Application of Factor of Safety (F.S.)

A factor of safety of 1.0 based on the 0.01-inch crack will be applied.

6. Selection of Pipe Strength

The D-load is given by equation 34:

$$D_{0.01} = \frac{W_L + W_E}{B_f \times S} \times F.S.$$

$$D_{0.01} = \frac{5,110 + 225}{1.75 \times 1.5} \times 1.0$$

$$D_{0.01} = 2,032 \text{ pounds per liner foot per foot of inside horizontal span}$$

Answer: A pipe which would withstand a minimum three-edge bearing test load for the 0.01-inch crack of 2,032 pounds per linear foot per foot of inside horizontal span would be required.

CHAPTER 5

SUPPLEMENTAL DATA

CIRCULAR CONCRETE PIPE

Illustration 5.2 includes tables of dimensions and approximate weights of most frequently used types of circular concrete pipe. Weights are based on concrete weighing 150 pounds per cubic foot. Concrete pipe may be produced which conforms to the requirements of the respective specifications but with increased wall thickness and different concrete density.

ELLIPTICAL CONCRETE PIPE

Elliptical pipe, shown in Illustration 5.1, installed with the major axis horizontal or vertical, represents two different products from the stand-

Illustration 5.1 — Typical Cross Sections of Horizontal Elliptical and Vertical Elliptical Pipe

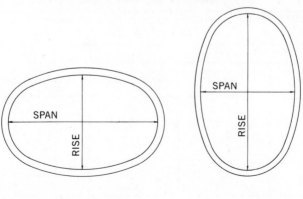

HORIZONTAL ELLIPTICAL   VERTICAL ELLIPTICAL

point of structural strength, hydraulic characteristics and type of application. Illustration 5.3 includes the dimensions and approximate weights of elliptical concrete pipe.

Horizontal Elliptical (HE) Pipe. Horizontal elliptical concrete pipe is installed with the major axis horizontal and is extensively used for minimum cover conditions or where vertical clearance is limited by existing structures. It offers the hydraulic advantage of greater capacity for the same depth of flow than most other structures of equivalent water-way area. Under most embankment conditions, its wide span results in greater earth loadings for the same height of cover than for the equivalent size circular pipe and, at the same time, there is a reduction in effective lateral support due to the smaller vertical dimension of the section. Earth loadings are normally greater than for the equivalent circular pipe in the trench

Illustration 5.2 — Dimensions and Approximate Weights of Concrete Pipe

ASTM C 14 — Nonreinforced Sewer and Culvert Pipe, Bell and Spigot Joint.						
	CLASS 1			CLASS 2		CLASS 3	
Internal Diameter, inches	Minimum Wall Thickness, inches	Approx. Weight, pounds per foot	Minimum Wall Thickness, inches	Approx. Weight, pounds per foot	Minimum Wall Thickness, inches	Approx. Weight, pounds per foot
4	⅝	9.5	¾	13	⅞	15
6	⅝	17	¾	20	1	24
8	¾	27	⅞	31	1⅛	36
10	⅞	37	1	42	1¼	50
12	1	50	1⅜	68	1¾	90
15	1¼	80	1⅝	100	1⅞	120
18	1½	110	2	160	2¼	170
21	1¾	160	2¼	210	2¾	260
24	2⅛	200	3	320	3¾	350
27	3¼	390	4	450	4⅞	450
30	3½	450	4¼	540	4¼	540
33	3¾	520	4½	620	4½	620
36	4	580	4¾	700	4¾	700

ASTM C 76 — Reinforced Concrete Culvert, Storm Drain and Sewer Pipe, Bell and Spigot Joint.				
	WALL A		WALL B	
Internal Diameter, inches	Minimum Wall Thickness inches	Approximate Weight, pounds per foot	Minimum Wall Thickness, inches	Approximate Weight, pounds per foot
12	1¾	90	2	110
15	1⅞	120	2¼	150
18	2	160	2½	200
21	2¼	210	2¾	260
24	2½	270	3	330
27	2⅝	310	3¼	390
30	2¾	360	3½	450

These tables are based on concrete weighing 150 pounds per cubic foot and will vary with heavier or lighter weight concrete.

Illustration 5.2 (Continued) — Dimensions and Approximate Weights of Concrete Pipe

ASTM C 76						
Reinforced Concrete Culvert, Storm Drain and Sewer Pipe, Tongue and Groove Joints						
	WALL A			WALL B		WALL C
Internal Diameter, inches	Minimum Wall Thickness, inches	Approximate Weight, pounds per foot	Minimum Wall Thickness, inches	Approximate Weight, pounds per foot	Minimum Wall Thickness, inches	Approximate Weight, pounds per foot
12	1¾	79	2	93	–	–
15	1⅞	103	2¼	127	–	–
18	2	131	2½	168	–	–
21	2¼	171	2¾	214	–	–
24	2½	217	3	264	3¾	366
27	2⅝	255	3¼	322	4	420
30	2¾	295	3½	384	4¼	476
33	2⅞	336	3¾	451	4½	552
36	3	383	4	524	4¾	654
42	3½	520	4½	686	5¼	811
48	4	683	5	867	5¾	1011
54	4½	864	5½	1068	6¼	1208
60	5	1064	6	1295	6¾	1473
66	5½	1287	6½	1542	7¼	1735
72	6	1532	7	1811	7¾	2015
78	6½	1797	7½	2100	8¼	2410
84	7	2085	8	2409	8¾	2660
90	7½	2395	8½	2740	9¼	3020
96	8	2710	9	3090	9¾	3355
102	8½	3078	9½	3480	10¼	3760
108	9	3446	10	3865	10¾	4160

Large Sizes of Pipe Tongue and Groove Joint			
Internal Diameter Inches	Internal Diameter Feet	Wall Thickness Inches	Approximate Weight, pounds per foot
114	9½	9½	3840
120	10	10	4263
126	10½	10½	4690
132	11	11	5148
138	11½	11½	5627
144	12	12	6126
150	12½	12½	6647
156	13	13	7190
162	13½	13½	7754
168	14	14	8339
174	14½	14½	8945
180	15	15	9572

These tables are based on concrete weighing 150 pounds per cubic foot and will vary with heavier or lighter weight concrete.

condition, since a greater trench width is usually required for HE pipe. For shallow cover, where live load requirements control the design, loading is almost identical to that for an equivalent size circular pipe with the same invert elevation.

Vertical Elliptical (VE) Pipe. Vertical elliptical concrete pipe is installed with the major axis vertical and is useful where minimum hori-

CONCRETE PIPE DESIGN MANUAL

Illustration 5.3 — Dimensions and Approximate Weights of Elliptical Concrete Pipe

ASTM C 507 — Reinforced Concrete Elliptical Culvert, Storm Drain and Sewer Pipe					
Equivalent Round Size, inches	Minor Axis, inches	Major Axis, inches	Minimum Wall Thickness, inches	Water-Way Area, square feet	Approximate Weight, pounds per foot
18	14	23	2¾	1.8	195
24	19	30	3¼	3.3	300
27	22	34	3½	4.1	365
30	24	38	3¾	5.1	430
33	27	42	3¾	6.3	475
36	29	45	4½	7.4	625
39	32	49	4¾	8.8	720
42	34	53	5	10.2	815
48	38	60	5½	12.9	1000
54	43	68	6	16.6	1235
60	48	76	6½	20.5	1475
66	53	83	7	24.8	1745
72	58	91	7½	29.5	2040
78	63	98	8	34.6	2350
84	68	106	8½	40.1	2680
90	72	113	9	46.1	3050
96	77	121	9½	52.4	3420
102	82	128	9¾	59.2	3725
108	87	136	10	66.4	4050
114	92	143	10½	74.0	4470
120	97	151	11	82.0	4930
132	106	166	12	99.2	5900
144	116	180	13	118.6	7000

zontal clearances are encountered or where unusual strength characteristics are desired. Hydraulically, it provides higher flushing velocities under minimum flow conditions and carries equal flow at a greater depth than equivalent HE or circular pipe. For trench conditions the smaller span requires less excavation than an equivalent size circular pipe and the pipe is subjected to less vertical earth load due to the narrower trench. The structural advantages of VE pipe are particularly applicable in the embankment condition where the greater height of the section increases the effective lateral support while the vertical load is reduced due to the smaller span.

CONCRETE ARCH PIPE

Arch pipe, as shown in Illustration 5.4, is useful in minimum cover situations or other conditions where vertical clearance problems are encountered. It offers the hydraulic advantage of greater capacity for the same depth of flow than most other structures of equivalent water-way area. Structural characteristics are similar to those of horizontal elliptical pipe in that under similar cover conditions it is subject to the same field load as a round pipe with the same span. For minimum cover conditions where live load requirements control the design, the loading to which arch pipe is subjected is almost identical to that for an equivalent size circular pipe with the same invert elevation. Illustration 5.5 includes the dimensions and approximate weights of concrete arch pipe.

Illustration 5.4 — Typical Cross Section of Arch Pipe

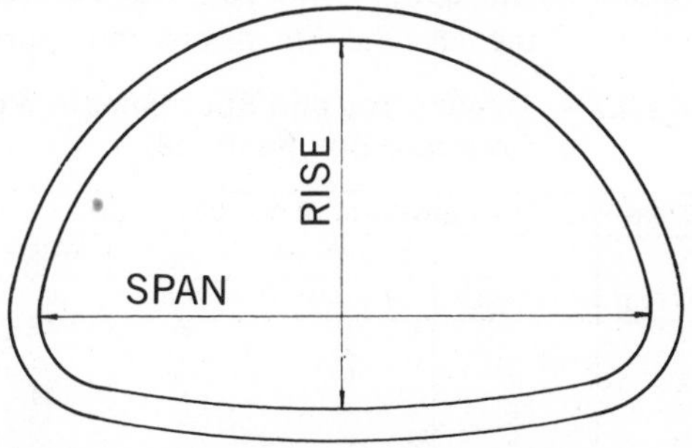

Illustration 5.5 — Dimensions and Approximate Weights of Concrete Arch Pipe

ASTM C 506—Reinforced Concrete Arch Culvert, Storm Drain and Sewer Pipe					
Equivalent Round Size, inches	Minimum Rise, inches	Minimum Span, inches	Minimum Wall Thickness, inches	Water-Way Area, square feet	Approximate Weight, pounds per foot
15	11	18	2¼	1.1	—
18	13½	22	2½	1.65	170
21	15½	26	2¾	2.2	225
24	18	28½	3	2.8	320
30	22½	36¼	3½	4.4	450
36	26⅝	43¾	4	6.4	595
42	31 5/16	51⅛	4½	8.8	740
48	36	58½	5	11.4	880
54	40	65	5½	14.3	1090
60	45	73	6	17.7	1320
72	54	88	7	25.6	1840
84	62	102	8	34.6	2520
90	72	115	8½	44.5	2750
96	77¼	122	9	51.7	3110
108	87⅛	138	10	66.0	3850
120	96⅞	154	11	81.8	5040
132	106½	168¾	10	99.1	5220

Illustration 5.6 — Typical Cross Section of Precast Concrete Box Sections

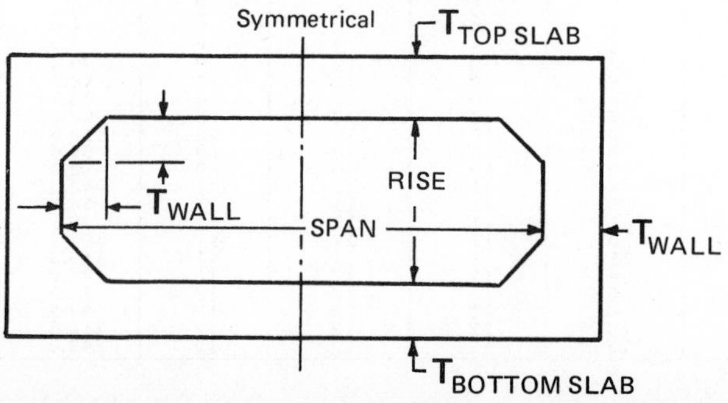

CONCRETE BOX SECTIONS

Precast concrete box sections, as shown in Illustration 5.6, are useful in minimum cover and width situations or other conditions where clearance problems are encountered, for special waterway requirements, or designer preference. Illustration 5.7 includes the dimensions and approximate weights

Illustration 5.7 — Dimensions and Approximate Weights of Concrete Box Sections

ASTM C789—PRECAST REINFORCED CONCRETE BOX SECTIONS						
		Thickness (in.)			Waterway Area (Sq. Feet)	Approx. Weight (lbs/ft)
Span (Ft.)	Rise (Ft.)	Top Slab	Bot. Slab	Wall		
3	2	4	4	4	5.8	600
3	3	4	4	4	8.8	700
4	2	5	5	5	7.7	910
4	3	5	5	5	11.7	1030
4	4	5	5	5	15.7	1160
5	3	6	6	6	14.5	1430
5	4	6	6	6	19.5	1580
5	5	6	6	6	24.5	1730
6	3	7	7	7	17.3	1880
6	4	7	7	7	23.3	2060
6	5	7	7	7	29.3	2230
6	6	7	7	7	35.3	2410
7	4	8	8	8	27.1	2600
7	5	8	8	8	34.1	2800
7	6	8	8	8	41.1	3000
7	7	8	8	8	48.1	3200
8	4	8	8	8	31.1	2800
8	5	8	8	8	39.1	3000
8	6	8	8	8	47.1	3200
8	7	8	8	8	55.1	3400
8	8	8	8	8	63.1	3600
9	5	9	9	9	43.9	3660
9	6	9	9	9	52.9	3880
9	7	9	9	9	61.9	4110
9	8	9	9	9	70.9	4330
9	9	9	9	9	79.9	4560
10	5	10	10	10	48.6	4380
10	6	10	10	10	58.6	4630
10	7	10	10	10	68.6	4880
10	8	10	10	10	78.6	5130
10	9	10	10	10	88.6	5380
10	10	10	10	10	98.6	5630
ASTM C850—PRECAST REINFORCED CONCRETE BOX SECTIONS						
		Thickness (in.)			Waterway Area (Sq. Feet)	Approx. Weight (lbs/ft)
Span (Ft.)	Rise (Ft.)	Top Slab	Bot. Slab	Wall		
3	2	7	6	4	5.8	830
3	3	7	6	4	8.8	930
4	2	7½	6	5	7.7	1120
4	3	7½	6	5	11.7	1240
4	4	7½	6	5	15.7	1370
5	3	8	7	6	14.5	1650
5	4	8	7	6	19.5	1800
5	5	8	7	6	24.5	1950
6	3	8	7	7	17.3	1970
6	4	8	7	7	23.3	2150
6	5	8	7	7	29.3	2320
6	6	8	7	7	35.3	2500
7	4	8	8	8	27.1	2600
7	5	8	8	8	34.1	2800
7	6	8	8	8	41.1	3000
7	7	8	8	8	48.1	3200
8	4	8	8	8	31.1	2800
8	5	8	8	8	39.1	3000
8	6	8	8	8	47.1	3200
8	7	8	8	8	55.1	3400
8	8	8	8	8	63.1	3600
9	5	9	9	9	43.9	3660
9	6	9	9	9	52.9	3880
9	7	9	9	9	61.9	4110
9	8	9	9	9	70.9	4330
9	9	9	9	9	79.9	4560
10	5	10	10	10	48.6	4380
10	6	10	10	10	58.6	4630
10	7	10	10	10	68.6	4880
10	8	10	10	10	78.6	5130
10	9	10	10	10	88.6	5380
10	10	10	10	10	98.6	5630
11	4	11	11	11	42.3	4880
11	6	11	11	11	64.3	5430
11	8	11	11	11	86.3	5980
11	10	11	11	11	108.3	6530
11	11	11	11	11	119.3	6810
12	4	12	12	12	46.0	5700
12	6	12	12	12	70.0	6300
12	8	12	12	12	94.5	6900
12	10	12	12	12	118.0	7500
12	12	12	12	12	142.0	8100

of standard precast concrete box sections. Special design precast concrete box sections may be produced which conform to the requirements of the respective specifications but in different size and cover conditions.

SPECIAL SECTIONS

Precast Concrete Manhole Sections. Precast manholes offer significant savings in installed cost over cast-in-place concrete, masonry or brick manholes and are universally accepted for use in sanitary or storm sewers. Precast, reinforced concrete manhole sections are available throughout the United States and Canada, and are generally manufactured in accordance with the provisions of American Society for Testing and Materials Standard C 478.

The typical precast concrete manhole as shown in Illustration 5.8 consists of riser sections, a top section and grade rings and, in many cases, precast base sections or tee sections. The riser sections are usually 48 inches in diameter, but are available from 36 inches up to 72 inches and larger. They are of circular cross section, and a number of sections may be joined vertically on top of the base or junction chamber. Most precast manholes employ an eccentric or a concentric cone section instead of a slab top. These reinforced cone sections affect the transition from the inside diameter of the riser sections to the specified size of the top opening. Flat slab tops are normally used for very shallow manholes and consist of a reinforced circular slab at least 6-inches thick for risers up to 48 inches in diameter and 8-inches thick for larger riser sizes. The slab which rests on top of the riser sections is cast with an access opening.

Precast grade rings, which are placed on top of either the cone or flat slab top section, are used for close adjustment of top elevation. Cast iron manhole cover assemblies are normally placed on top of the grade rings.

The manhole assembly may be furnished with or without steps inserted into the walls of the sections. Reinforcement required by ASTM Standard C 478 is primarily designed to resist handling stresses incurred before and during installation, and is more than adequate for that purpose. Such stresses are more severe than those encountered in the vertically installed manhole. In normal installations, the intensity of the earth loads transmitted to the manhole risers is only a fraction of the intensity of the vertical pressure.

The maximum allowable depth of a typical precast concrete manhole with regard to lateral earth pressures is in excess of 300 feet or, for all practical purposes, unlimited. Because of this, the critical or limiting factor for manhole depth is the supporting strength of the base structure or the resistance to crushing of the ends of the riser section. This phenomena, being largely dependent on the relative settlement of the adjacent soil mass, does not lend itself to precise analysis. Even with extremely conservative values for soil weights, lateral pressure and friction coefficients, it may be concluded several hundred feet can be safely supported by the riser sections without end crushing, based on the assumption that provision is made for uniform bearing at the ends of the riser sections

Illustration 5.8 — Typical Configuration of Precast Manhole Sections

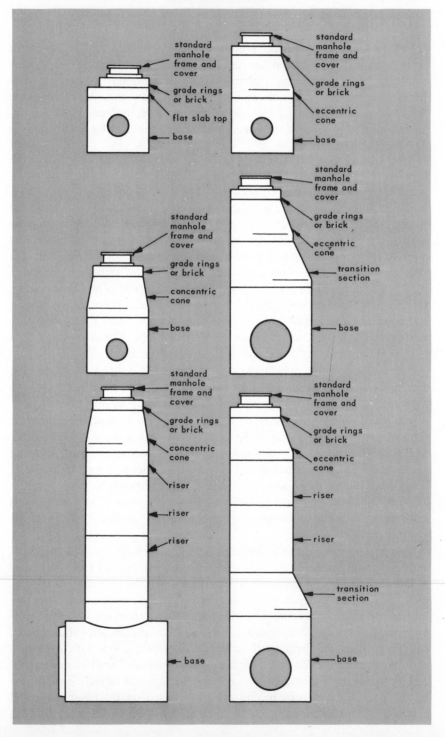

and the elimination of localized stress concentrations.

When confronted with manhole depths greater than those commonly encountered, there may be a tendency to specify additional circumferential reinforcement in the manhole riser sections. Such requirements are completely unnecessary and only result in increasing the cost of the manhole structure.

A number of joint types may be used for manhole risers and tops, including mortar, mastic, rubber gaskets or combinations of these three basic types for sealing purposes. Consideration should be given to manhole depth, the presence of groundwater and the minimum allowable leakage rates in the selection of specific joint requirements.

Flat Base Pipe. Flat base pipe as shown in Illustration 5.9 has been used as cattle passes, pedestrian underpasses and utility tunnels. It is normally furnished with joints designed for use with mortar or mastic fillers and may be installed by the conventional open trenching method or by jacking. Although not covered by any existing national specification, standard designs have been developed by various manufacturers which are appropriate for a wide range of loading conditions.

Illustration 5.9 — Typical Cross Sections of Flat Base Pipe

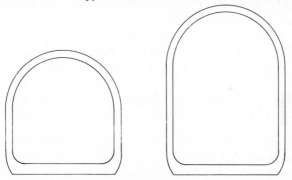

STANDARD SPECIFICATIONS FOR CONCRETE PIPE

Nationally accepted specifications covering concrete pipe along with the applicable size ranges and scopes of the individual specifications are included in the following list.

AMERICAN SOCIETY FOR TESTING AND MATERIALS (ASTM)

ASTM C 14   Concrete Sewer, Storm Drain and Culvert Pipe: Covers nonreinforced concrete pipe intended to be used for the conveyance of sewage, industrial wastes, storm water, and for the construction of culverts in sizes from 4 inches through 36 inches in diameter.

ASTM C 76   Reinforced Concrete Culvert, Storm Drain, and Sewer Pipe: Covers reinforced concrete pipe intended to be used for the conveyance of sewage, industrial wastes, and storm waters, and for the construction of culverts. Class I — 60 inches through 144 inches in diameter; Class II, III, IV and V — 12 inches through 144 inches in diameter. Larger sizes and higher classes are available as special designs.

ASTM C 118 Concrete Pipe for Irrigation or Drainage: Covers concrete pipe intended to be used for the conveyance of irrigation water under low hydrostatic heads, generally not exceeding 25 feet, and for use in drainage in sizes from 4 inches through 24 inches in diameter.

ASTM C 361 Reinforced Concrete Low-Head Pressure Pipe: Covers reinforced concrete pipe intended to be used for the construction of pressure conduits with low internal hydrostatic heads generally not exceeding 125 feet in sizes from 12 inches through 108 inches in diameter.

ASTM C 412 Concrete Drain Tile: Covers nonreinforced concrete drain tile with internal diameters from 4 inches to 24 inches for Standard Quality, and 4 inches to 36 inches for Extra-Quality, Heavy-Duty Extra-Quality and Special Quality Concrete Drain Tile.

ASTM C 443 Joints for Circular Concrete Sewer and Culvert Pipe, with Rubber Gaskets: Covers joints where infiltration or exfiltration is a factor in the design, including the design of joints and the requirements for rubber gaskets to be used therewith for pipe conforming in all other respects to ASTM C 14 or ASTM C 76.

ASTM C 444 Perforated Concrete Pipe: Covers perforated concrete pipe intended to be used for underdrainage in sizes 4 inches and larger.

ASTM C 478 Precast Reinforced Concrete Manhole Sections: Covers precast reinforced concrete manhole risers, grade rings and tops to be used to construct manholes for storm and sanitary sewers.

ASTM C 497 Determining Physical Properties of Concrete Pipe or Tile: Covers procedures for testing concrete pipe and tile.

ASTM C 505 Nonreinforced Concrete Irrigation Pipe With Rubber Gasket Joints: Covers pipe to be used for the conveyance of irrigation water with working pressures, including hydraulic transients, of up to 30 feet of head. Higher pressures may be used up to a maximum of 50 feet for 6-inch through 12-inch diameters, and 40 feet for 15-inch through 18-inch diameters by increasing the strength of the pipe.

ASTM C 506 Reinforced Concrete Arch Culvert, Storm Drain, and Sewer Pipe: Covers pipe to be used for the conveyance of sewage, industrial waste, and storm water and for the construction of culverts in sizes from 15-inch through 132-inch equivalent circular diameter. Larger sizes are available as special designs.

ASTM C 507 Reinforced Concrete Elliptical Culvert, Storm Drain, and Sewer Pipe: Covers reinforced elliptically shaped concrete pipe to be used for the conveyance of sewage, industrial waste and storm water, and for the construction of culverts. Five standard classes of horizontal elliptical, 18 inches through 144 inches in equivalent circular diameter and five standard classes of vertical elliptical, 36 inches through 144 inches in equivalent circular diameter are included. Larger sizes are available as special designs.

ASTM C 655 Reinforced Concrete D-load Culvert, Storm Drain and Sewer Pipe: Covers acceptance of pipe design and production pipe based upon the D-load concept and statistical sampling techniques for concrete pipe to be used for the conveyance of sewage, industrial waste and storm water and construction of culverts.

ASTM C 789 Precast Reinforced Concrete Box Sections for Culverts, Storm Drains and Sewers: Covers box sections with 2 or more feet of earth cover when subjected to highway live loads, and zero cover or greater when subjected to only dead load, to be used for the conveyance of sewage, industrial waste, and storm water, and for the construction of culverts in sizes from 3-foot span by 2-foot rise to 10-foot span by 10-foot rise.

ASTM C 822 Standard Definitions and Terms Relating to Concrete Pipe and Related Products: Covers words and terms used in concrete pipe standards.

ASTM C 850 Precast Reinforced Concrete Box Sections for Culverts, Storm Drains and Sewers with less than 2 feet of Cover Subjected to Highway Loadings: Covers box sections with less than 2 feet of earth cover for the conveyance of sewage, industrial waste, and storm water, and for the construction of culverts in sizes from 3-foot span by 2-foot rise to 12-foot span by 12-foot rise.

ASTM C 877 External Sealing Bands for Non-Circular Concrete Sewer, Storm Drain and Culvert Pipe: Covers external sealing bands to be used for noncircular pipe conforming to ASTM C 506, C 507, C 789 and C 850.

ASTM C 923 Resilient Connectors Between Reinforced Concrete Manhole Structures and Pipes: Covers the minimum performance and material requirements for resilient connections between pipe and reinforced concrete manholes conforming to ASTM C 478.

ASTM C 924 Testing Concrete Pipe Sewer Lines by Low-Pressure Air Test Method: Covers procedures for testing concrete pipe sewer lines when using the low-pressure air test method to demonstrate the integrity of the installed material and construction procedures.

AMERICAN ASSOCIATION OF STATE HIGHWAY AND TRANSPORTATION
   OFFICIALS (AASHTO)
AASHTO M 86   Concrete Sewer, Storm Drain, and Culvert Pipe: Similar
   to ASTM C 14.
AASHTO M 170   Reinforced Concrete Culvert, Storm Drain, and Sewer
   Pipe: Similar to ASTM C 76.
AASHTO M 175   Perforated Concrete Pipe: Similar to ASTM C 444.
AASHTO M 178   Concrete Drain Tile: Similar to ASTM C 412.
AASHTO M 198   Joints for Circular Concrete Sewer and Culvert Pipe,
   Using Flexible, Watertight Gaskets: Similar to ASTM C 443 except
   includes a section on flexible plastic mastic gaskets.
AASHTO M 199   Precast Reinforced Concrete Manhole Sections: Similar
   to ASTM C 478.
AASHTO M 206   Reinforced Concrete Arch Culvert, Storm Drain, and
   Sewer Pipe: Similar to ASTM C 506.
AASHTO M 207   Reinforced Concrete Elliptical Culvert, Storm Drain,
   and Sewer Pipe: Similar to ASTM C 507.
AASHTO M 242   Reinforced Concrete D-Load Culvert, Storm Drain, and
   Sewer Pipe: Similar to ASTM C 655.
AASHTO M 259   Precast Reinforced Concrete Box Sections for Culverts,
   Storm Drains and Sewers: Similar to ASTM C 789.
AASHTO M 273   Precast Reinforced Box Section for Culverts, Storm
   Drains, and Sewers with less than 2 feet of Cover Subjected to High-
   way Loadings: Similar to ASTM C 850.
FEDERAL SPECIFICATIONS
Federal SS-P-371   Pipe; Concrete, (Nonreinforced, Sewer, Storm Drain,
   and Culvert): Similar to ASTM C 14.

PIPE JOINTS

Pipe joints perform a variety of functions depending upon the type of
pipe and its application. To select a proper joint, determine which of
the following characteristics are pertinent and what degree of performance
is acceptable.

Joints are designed to provide:
1. Resistance to infiltration of ground water and/or backfill material.
2. Resistance to exfiltration of sewage or storm water.
3. Control of leakage from internal or external heads.
4. Flexibility to accommodate lateral deflection or longitudinal move-
    ment without creating leakage problems.
5. Resistance to shear stresses between adjacent pipe sections without
    creating leakage problems.
6. Hydraulic continuity and a smooth flow line.
7. Controlled infiltration of ground water for subsurface drainage.
8. Ease of installation.

The actual field performance of any pipe joint depends primarily upon
the inherent performance characteristics of the joint itself, the severity of
the conditions of service, and the care with which it is installed.

Since economy is important, it is usually necessary to compare the installed cost of several types of joints against pumping and treatment costs resulting from increased or decreased amounts of infiltration.

The concrete pipe industry utilizes a number of different joints, listed below, to satisfy a broad range of performance requirements. These joints vary in cost, as well as in inherent performance characteristics. The field performance of all is dependent upon proper installation procedures.

- Concrete surfaces, either bell and spigot or tongue and groove, with some packing such as cement mortar, a preformed mastic compound, or a trowel applied mastic compound, as shown in Illustration 5.10. These joints have no inherent watertightness but depend exclusively upon the workmanship of the contractor. Field poured concrete diapers or collars are sometimes used with these joints to improve performance. Joints employing mortar joint fillers are rigid, and any deflection or movement after installation will cause cracks permitting leakage. If properly applied, mastic joint fillers provide a degree of flexibility without impairing watertightness. These joints are not generally recommended for any internal or external head conditions if leakage is an important consideration. Another jointing system used with this type joint is the external sealing band type rubber gasket conforming to ASTM C 877. Generally limited to straight wall and modified tongue and groove configurations, this jointing system has given good results in resisting external heads of the magnitude normally encountered in sewer construction.

Illustration 5.10 — Typical Cross Sections of Joints With Mortar or Mastic Packing

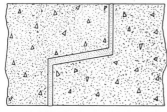 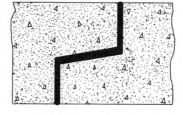

MORTAR PACKING   MASTIC PACKING

- Concrete surfaces, with or without shoulders on the tongue or the groove, with a compression type rubber gasket as shown in Illustration 5.11. Although there is wide variation in joint dimensions and gasket cross section for this type joint, most are manufactured in conformity with ASTM C 443. This type joint is primarily intended for use with pipe manufactured to meet the requirements of ASTM C 14 or ASTM C 76 and may be used with either bell and spigot or tongue and groove pipe.

Illustration 5.11 — Typical Cross Sections of Basic Compression Type Rubber Gasket Joints

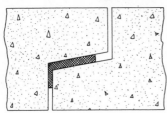
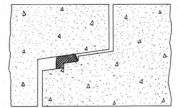

- Concrete surfaces with opposing shoulders on both the bell and spigot for use with an O-ring, or circular cross section, rubber gasket as shown in Illustration 5.12. Basically designed for low pressure capability, these joints are frequently used for irrigation lines, waterlines, sewer force mains, and gravity or low head sewer lines where infiltration or exfiltration is a factor in the design. Meeting all of the requirements of ASTM C 443, these type joints are also employed with pipe meeting the requirements of ASTM C 361. They provide good inherent watertightness in both the straight and deflected positions, which can be demonstrated by plant tests.

Illustration 5.12— Typical Cross Sections of Opposing Shoulder Type Joint With O-ring Gasket

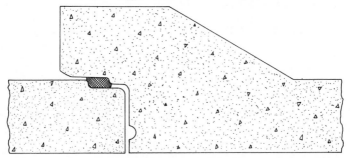

- Concrete surfaces with a groove on the spigot for an O-ring rubber gasket, as shown in Illustration 5.13. Also referred to as a confined O-ring type joint, these are designed for low pressure capabilities and are used for irrigation lines, water lines, sewer force mains, and sewers where infiltration or exfiltration is a factor in the design. This type joint, which provides excellent inherent watertightness in both the straight and deflected positions, may be employed to meet the joint requirements of ASTM C 443 and ASTM C 361.

Illustration 5.13 — Typical Cross Section of Spigot Groove Type Joint With O-ring Gasket

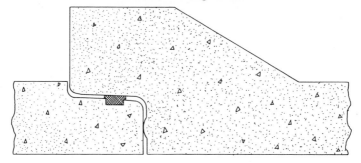

- Steel bell and spigot rings with a groove on the spigot for an O-ring rubber gasket, as shown in Illustration 5.14. Basically a high pressure joint designed for use in water transmission and distribution lines, these are also used for irrigation lines, sewer force mains, and sewers where infiltration or exfiltration is a factor in the design. This type of joint will meet the joint requirements of ASTM C 443 and ASTM C 361. Combining great shear strength, and excellent inherent watertightness and flexibility, this type joint is the least subject to damage during installation.

Illustration 5.14 — Typical Cross Section of Steel End Ring Joint With Spigot Groove and O-ring Gasket

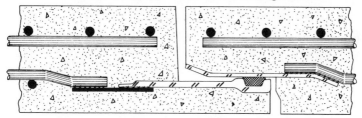

Since both field construction practices and conditions of service are subject to variation, it is impossible to precisely define the field performance characteristics of each of the joint types. Consultation with local concrete pipe manufacturers will provide information on the availability and cost of the various joints. Based on this information and an evaluation of groundwater conditions, the specifications should define allowable infiltration or exfiltration rates and/or the joint types which are acceptable.

JACKING CONCRETE PIPE

Concrete pipelines were first jacked in place by the Northern Pacific Railroad between 1896 and 1900. In more recent years, this technique has been applied to sewer construction where intermediate shafts along the line of the sewer are used as jacking stations.

Reinforced concrete pipe as small as 18-inch inside diameter and as large as 132-inch inside diameter have been installed by jacking. Since conventional jacking procedures require access by workmen through the pipe to the heading, a 36-inch diameter pipe is the smallest practical size used for most jacking operations.

Required Characteristics of Concrete Jacking Pipe. Two types of loading conditions are imposed on concrete pipe installed by the jacking method; the axial load due to the jacking pressures applied during installation, and the earth loading due to the overburden, with some possible influence from live loadings, which will generally become effective only after installation is completed.

It is necessary to provide for relatively uniform distribution of the axial load around the periphery of the pipe to prevent localized stress concentrations. This is accomplished by keeping the pipe ends parallel within the tolerances prescribed by ASTM C 76, by using a cushion material, such as plywood or hardboard, between the pipe sections, and by care on the part of the contractor to insure that the jacking force is properly distributed through the jacking frame to the pipe and parallel with the axis of the pipe. The cross sectional area of the concrete pipe wall is more than adequate to resist pressures encountered in any normal jacking operation. For projects where extreme jacking pressures are anticipated due to long jacking distances or excessive unit frictional forces, higher concrete compressive strength may be required, along with greater care to avoid bearing stress concentrations. Little or no gain in axial crushing resistance is provided by specifying a higher class of pipe.

For a comprehensive treatment of earth loads on jacked pipe see Chapter 4. The earth loads on jacked pipe are similar to loads on a pipe installed in a trench with the same width as the bore with one significant difference. In a jacked pipe installation the cohesive forces within the soil mass in most instances are appreciable and tend to reduce the total vertical load on the pipe. Thus the vertical load on a jacked pipe will always be less than on a pipe in a trench installation with the same cover and, unless noncohesive materials are encountered, can be substantially less.

With the proper analysis of loadings and selection of the appropriate strength class of pipe, few additional characteristics of standard concrete pipe need be considered. Pipe with a straight wall, without any increase in outside diameter at the bell or groove, obviously offers fewer problems and minimizes the required excavation. Considerable quantities of modified tongue and groove pipe have been jacked, however, and presented no unusual problems.

The Jacking Method. The usual procedure in jacking concrete pipe is to equip the leading edge with a cutter, or shoe, to protect the pipe. As succeeding lengths of pipe are added between the lead pipe and the jacks, and the pipe jacked forward, soil is excavated and removed through the pipe. Material is trimmed with care and excavation does not precede the

Illustration 5.15 — Steps in Jacking Concrete Pipe

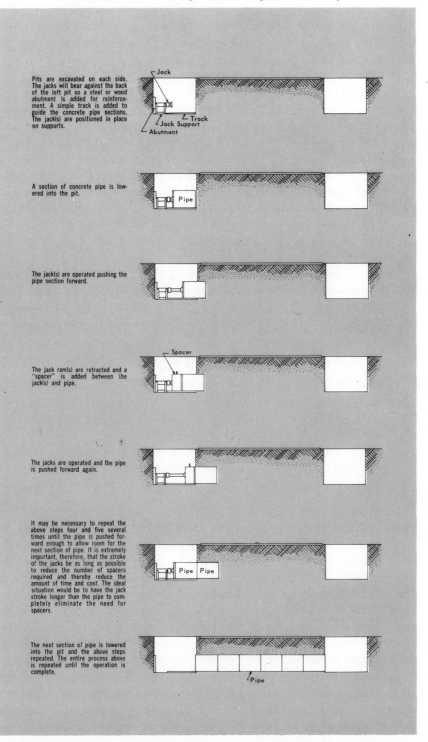

Pits are excavated on each side. The jacks will bear against the back of the left pit so a steel or wood abutment is added for reinforcement. A simple track is added to guide the concrete pipe sections. The jack(s) are positioned in place on supports.

A section of concrete pipe is lowered into the pit.

The jack(s) are operated pushing the pipe section forward.

The jack ram(s) are retracted and a "spacer" is added between the jack(s) and pipe.

The jacks are operated and the pipe is pushed forward again.

It may be necessary to repeat the above steps four and five several times until the pipe is pushed forward enough to allow room for the next section of pipe. It is extremely important, therefore, that the stroke of the jacks be as long as possible to reduce the number of spacers required and thereby reduce the amount of time and cost. The ideal situation would be to have the jack stroke longer than the pipe to completely eliminate the need for spacers.

The next section of pipe is lowered into the pit and the above steps repeated. The entire process above is repeated until the operation is complete.

jacking operation more than necessary. Such a procedure usually results in minimum disturbance of the natural soils adjacent to the pipe.

Contractors occasionally find it desirable to coat the outside of the pipe with a lubricant, such as bentonite, to reduce the frictional resistance. In some instances, this lubricant has been pumped through special fittings installed in the wall of the lead pipe.

Because of the tendency of jacked pipe to "set" when forward movement is interrupted for as long as a few hours, resulting in significantly increased frictional resistance, it is desirable to continue jacking operations until completed.

In all jacking operations it is important that the direction of jacking be carefully established prior to beginning the operation. This requires the erection of guide rails in the bottom of the jacking pit or shaft. In the case of large pipe, it is desirable to have such rails carefully set in a concrete slab. The number and capacity of the jacks required depend primarily upon the size and length of the pipe to be jacked and the type of soil encountered.

Backstops for the jacks must be strong enough and large enough to distribute the maximum capacity of the jacks against the soil behind the backstops. A typical installation for jacking concrete pipe is shown in Illustration 5.15.

BENDS AND CURVES

Changes in direction of concrete pipe sewers are most commonly effected at manhole structures. This is accomplished by proper location of the inlet and outlet openings and finishing of the invert in the structure to reflect the desired angular change of direction.

In engineering both grade and alignment changes in concrete pipelines it is not always practical or feasible to restrict such changes to manhole structures. Fortunately there are a number of economical alternatives.

Deflected Straight Pipe. With concrete pipe installed in straight alignment and the joints in a home (or normal) position, the joint space, or distance between the ends of adjacent pipe sections, will be essentially uniform around the periphery of the pipe. Starting from this home position any joint may be opened up to a maximum permissible joint opening on one side while the other side remains in the home position. The difference between the home and opened joint space is generally designated as the *pull*. This maximum permissible opening retains some margin between it and the limit for satisfactory function of the joint. It varies for different joint configurations and is best obtained from the pipe manufacturer.

Opening a joint in this manner effects an angular deflection of the axis of the pipe, which, for any given pull is a function of the pipe diameter. Thus, given the values of any two of the three factors; pull, pipe diameter, and deflection angle, the remaining factor may be readily calculated.

The radius of curvature which may be obtained by this method is a function of the deflection angle per joint and the length of the pipe sections. Thus, longer lengths of pipe will provide a longer radius for the same pull than would be obtained with shorter lengths.

The radius of curvature is computed by the equation:

$$R = \frac{L}{2 \left(tan\ \frac{1}{2}\ \frac{\Delta}{N} \right)}$$

where:

R = Radius of curvature, feet

L = Average laid length of pipe sections measured along the centerline, feet

Δ = Total deflection angle of curve, degrees

N = Number of pipe with pulled joints

$\dfrac{\Delta}{N}$ = Total deflection of each pipe, degrees

Using the deflected straight pipe method, Illustration 5.16 shows that the P.C. (point of curve) will occur at the midpoint of the last undeflected pipe and the P.T. (point of tangent) will occur at the midpoint of the last pulled pipe.

Illustration 5.16 — Curved Alignment Using Deflected Straight Pipe

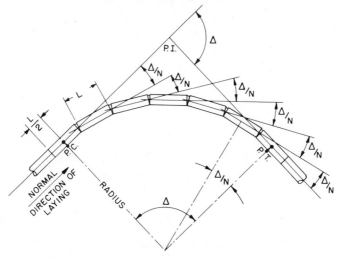

Radius Pipe. Sharper curvature with correspondingly shorter radii can be accommodated with radius pipe than with deflected straight pipe. This is due to the greater deflection angle per joint which may be used. In this

case the pipe is manufactured longer on one side than the other and the deflection angle is built in at the joint. Also referred to as bevelled or mitered pipe, it is similar in several respects to deflected straight pipe. Thus, shorter radii may be obtained with shorter pipe lengths; the maximum angular deflection which can be obtained at each joint is a function of both the pipe diameter and a combination of the geometric configuration of the joint and the method of manufacture.

These last two factors relate to how much shortening or *drop* can be applied to one side of the pipe. The maximum drop for any given pipe is best obtained from the manufacturer of the pipe since it is based on manufacturing feasibility.

The typical alignment problem is one in which the total Δ angle of the curve and the required radius of curvature have been determined. The diameter and direction of laying of the pipe are known. To be determined is whether the curve can be negotiated with radius pipe and, if so, what combination of pipe lengths and drop are required. Information required from the pipe manufacturer is the maximum permissible drop, the wall thicknesses of the pipe and the standard lengths in which the pipe is available. Any drop up to the maximum may be used as required to fit the curve.

Values obtained by the following method are approximate, but are within a range of accuracy that will permit the pipe to be readily installed to fit the required alignment.

The tangent of the deflection angle, $\dfrac{\Delta}{N}$, required at each joint is computed by the equation:

$$tan \frac{\Delta}{N} = \frac{L}{R + D/2 + t}$$

where:

$\Delta =$ Total deflection angle of curve, degrees

$N =$ Number of radius pipe

$L =$ The standard pipe length being used, feet

$R =$ Radius of curvature, feet

$D =$ Inside diameter of the pipe, feet

$t =$ Wall thickness of the pipe, feet

The required drop in inches to provide the deflection angle, $\dfrac{\Delta}{N}$, is computed by the equation:

$$\text{Drop} = 12\,(D + 2\,t)\ tan\ \frac{\Delta}{N}$$

The number of pieces of radius pipe required is equal to the length of the circular curve in feet divided by the centerline length of the radius pipe $(L - 1/2\ \text{Drop})$. Minor modifications in the radius are normally made so this quotient will be a whole number.

If the calculated drop exceeds the maximum permissible drop, it will be necessary to either increase the radius of curvature or to use shorter pipe lengths. Otherwise special fittings must be used as covered in the next section.

It is essential that radius pipe be oriented such that the plane of the dropped joint is at right angles to the theoretical circular curve. For this reason lifting holes in the pipe must be accurately located, or, if lifting holes are not provided, the top of the pipe should be clearly and accurately marked by the manufacturer so that the deflection angle is properly oriented.

It should also be noted that a reasonable amount of field adjustment is possible by pulling the radius pipe joints in the same manner as with deflected straight pipe.

Illustration 5.17 — Curved Alignment Using Radius Pipe

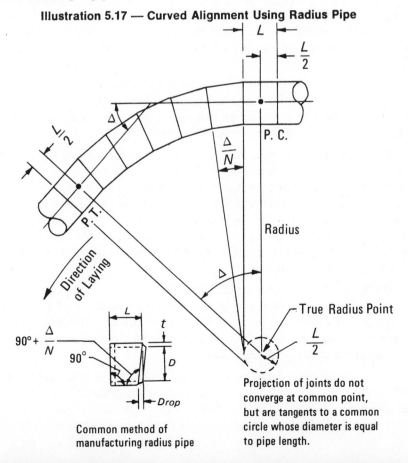

Common method of manufacturing radius pipe

Projection of joints do not converge at common point, but are tangents to a common circle whose diameter is equal to pipe length.

As indicated in Illustration 5.17, the P.C. (point of curve) falls at the midpoint of the last straight pipe and the P.T. (point of tangent) falls one half of the standard pipe length back from the straight end of the last radius pipe. To assure that the P.C. will fall at the proper station it is generally necessary that a special short length of pipe be installed in the line ahead of the P.C.

Bends and Special Sections. Extremely short radius curves cannot be negotiated with either deflected straight pipe or with conventional radius pipe. Several alternatives are available through the use of special precast sections to solve such alignment problems.

Sharper curves can be handled by using special short lengths of radius pipe rather than standard lengths. These may be computed in accordance with the methods discussed for radius pipe.

Certain types of manufacturing processes permit the use of a dropped joint on both ends of the pipe, which effectively doubles the deflection. Special bends, or elbows can be manufactured to meet any required deflection angle and some manufacturers produce standard bends which provide given angular deflection per section.

One or more of these methods may be employed to meet the most severe alignment problems. Since manufacturing processes and local standards vary, local concrete pipe manufacturers should be consulted to determine the availability and geometric configuration of special sections.

SIGNIFICANCE OF CRACKING

The occurrence, function and significance of cracks have probably been the subject of more misunderstanding and unnecessary concern by engineers than any other phenomena related to reinforced concrete pipe.

Reinforced concrete pipe, like reinforced concrete structures in general, are made of concrete reinforced with steel in such a manner that the high compressive strength of the concrete is balanced by the high tensile strength of the steel. In reinforced concrete pipe design, no value is given to the tensile strength of the concrete. The tensile strength of the concrete, however, is important since all parts of the pipe are subject to tensile forces at some time subsequent to manufacture. When concrete is subjected to tensile forces in excess of its tensile strength, it cracks.

Unlike most reinforced concrete structures, reinforced concrete sewer and culvert pipe is designed to meet a specified cracking load rather than a specified stress level in the reinforcing steel. This is both reasonable and conservative since reinforced concrete pipe may be *pretested* in accordance with detailed national specifications.

In the early days of the concrete pipe industry, the first visible crack observed in a three-edge bearing test was the accepted criterion for pipe performance. However, the observation of such cracks was subject to variations depending upon the zeal and eyesight of the observer. The need soon became obvious for a criterion based on a measurable crack of a specified width. Eventually the 0.01-inch crack, as measured by a feeler gage of a specified shape, became the accepted criterion for pipe performance.

The most valid basis for selection of a maximum allowable crack width is the consideration of exposure and potential corrosion of the reinforcing steel. If a crack is sufficiently wide to provide access to the steel by both moisture and oxygen, corrosion will be initiated. Oxygen is consumed by the oxidation process and in order for corrosion to be progressive there must be a constant replenishment.

Bending cracks are widest at the surface and get rapidly smaller as they approach the reinforcing steel. Unless the crack is wide enough to allow circulation of the moisture and replenishment of oxygen, corrosion is unlikely. Corrosion is even further inhibited by the alkaline environment resulting from the cement.

While cracks considerably in excess of 0.01-inch have been observed after a period of years with absolutely no evidence of corrosion, 0.01-inch is a conservative and universally accepted maximum crack width for design of reinforced concrete pipe.

- Reinforced concrete pipe is designed to crack. Cracking under load indicates that the tensile stresses have been transferred to the reinforcing steel.
- A crack 0.01-inch wide does not indicate structural distress and is not harmful.
- Cracks much wider than 0.01-inch should probably be sealed to insure protection of the reinforcing steel.
- An exception to the above occurs with pipe manufactured with greater than 1 inch cover over the reinforcing steel. In these cases acceptable crack width should be increased in proportion to the additional concrete cover.

TABLES

TABLE 1

SEWAGE FLOWS USED FOR DESIGN

City	Year of Data	Average rate of water consumption in gpcd[1]	Population served in thousands	Per capita sewage flow average[2] in gpcd[1]	Sewer design basis in gpcd[1]	Remarks
Baltimore, Md.	–	160	1,300	100	135 x factor	Factor 4 to 2
Berkeley, Calif.	–	76	113	60	92	–
Boston, Mass.	–	145	801	140	150	Flowing half full
Cleveland, Ohio[3]	1946	–	–	100	–	–
Cranston, R.I.[3]	1943	–	–	119	167	–
Des Moines, Iowa[3]	1949	–	–	100	200	–
Grand Rapids, Mich.	–	178	200	189.5	200	–
Great Peoria, Illinois	1960	90	150	75	800, 8.500	Based on 12 persons per acre for lateral and trunk sewers respectively
Greenville County, South Carolina	1959	110	200	150	300	Service area includes city of Greenville.[3] Sewers 24" and less designed to flow 1/2 full at 300 gpcd,[1] sewers larger than 24" designed to have 1' freeboard
Hagerstown, Md.	–	100	38	100	250	–
Jefferson County, Ala.	–	102	500	100	300	–
Johnson County, Kans. Indian Creek Main Sewer Dist.	1958	70	30	60	675	Most houses have basements with interior foundation drains
Mission Township Main Sewer Dist.	–	70	70	60	1.350	Most houses have basements with exterior foundation drains
Kansas City, Mo.	1958	–	500	60	675, 1.350	For trunks and interceptors. For laterals and submains. Many houses have basements and exterior foundation drains
Lancaster County, Neb.	1962	167	148	92	400	Serves City of Lincoln
Las Vegas, Nev.	–	410	45	209	250	–
Lincoln, Neb. (Lateral Dists.)	1964	–	–	60	See remarks	For lateral sewers max. flow by formula: peak flow= $5 \times \text{avg. flow} \div (\text{Pop in 1000's})^{0.2}$ [2]
Little Rock, Ark.	–	50	100	50	100	–
Los Angeles, Calif.	1965	185	2.710	85	*	*85 gpcd[1] residential multiplied by peak factor.
Los Angeles County Sanitation District	1964	200	3.500	70*	–	Domestic flow only, ranges from 50 to 90 gpcd[1] depending on cost of water, type of residence, etc. Domestic plus industrial averages 90 gpcd[1]
Madison, Wisc.[3]	1937	–	–	100	300	Maximum hourly rate
Memphis, Tenn.	–	125	450	100	100	All in 12 hr-250-gpcd[1] rate
Milwaukee, Wisc.[3]	1945	–	–	125	–	–
Orlando, Fla.	–	150	75	70	190	Includes infiltration and roof water
Painesville, Ohio[3]	1947	–	–	125	600	–
Rapid City, S. Dak.	–	122	40	121	125	New York State Board of Health standard
Rochester, N.Y.[3]	1946	–	–	–	250	–
Santa Monica, Calif.	–	137	75	92	92	Sewer design is 150 gpcd[1] plus 600 gp acre per day infiltration. Sewers 24" in diameter and less designed to flow 1/2 full, sewers larger than 24" designed to have 1' freeboard
Shreveport, La.	1961	125	165	–	–	–
Springfield, Mass.[3]	1949	–	–	–	200	150 gpcd[1] was used on a special project
St. Joseph, Mo.	1960	–	85	125	450, 350	Main Sewers / Interceptors
Toledo, Ohio[3]	1946	–	–	–	160	–
Washington, D. C. Suburban Sanitary District[3]	1946	–	–	100	2 to 3.3 x average	–
Wyoming, Mich.	1960	150	50	82*	400	*Calculated actual domestic sewage flow, not including infiltration or industrial flow

[1] Gallons per capita per day. To convert to liters per capita per day multiply by 3.8.

[2] Measure or estimated domestic sewage.

[3] "Sewer Capacity Design Practice" by William E. Stanley and Warren J. Kaufman, Journal, Boston Soc. of Civil Engrs., October, 1953, p. 317, Table 2.

TABLE 2   **SEWER CAPACITY ALLOWANCES FOR COMMERCIAL AND INDUSTRIAL AREAS**

City	Year data	Commercial	Industrial
Baltimore, Md.[1]	1949	135 gpcd[2] (range 6,750 to 13,500 gpd per acre), resident population	7,500 gpd per acre minimum
Berkeley, Calif	—	—	50,000 gpd per acre
Buffalo, N.Y.[3]	—	60,000 gpd per acre	—
Cincinnati, Ohio[3]	—	40,000 gpd per acre	—
Columbus, Ohio[1]	1946	40,000 gpd per acre; excess added to residential amount	
Cranston, R.I.[1]	1943	25,000 gpd per acre	—
Dallas, Texas	1960	30,000 gpd per acre added to domestic rate for down town: 60,000 gpd per acre for tunnel relief sewers	—
Detroit, Mich.	—	50,000 gpd per acre	—
Grand Rapids, Mich.	—	40-50 gpcd,[2] office buildings 400-500 gpd per room, hotels 200 gpd per bed, hospitals 200-300 gpd per room, schools	250,000 gpd per acre
Hagerstown, Md.	—	180-250 gpd per room, hotels 150, gpd per bed, hospitals 120-150 gpd per room, schools	—
Houston, Texas	1960	Office Bldgs. — 0.36 gal per sq ft per day (peak) Retail Space — 0.20 gp sq ft pd (peak) Hotels — 0.93 gp sq ft pd (peak)	—
Las Vegas, Nev.	—	310-525 gpd per room, resort hotels 15 gpcd,[2] schools	—
Lincoln, Neb.	1962	7,000 gpd per acre	
Los Angeles, Calif.	1965	Commercial, 11,700 gpd per acre Industrial, 0.024 cfs per acre Hospital, 0.75 mgd per hospital School, 0.12 mgd per school University, 0.73 mgd per university	
Los Angeles County Sanitation District	1964	10,000 gpd per acre, avg. 25,000 gpd per acre, peak	—
Kansas City, Mo.	1958	5,000 gpd per acre	10,000 gpd per acre
Memphis, Tenn.	—	2,000 gpd per acre	2,000 gpd per acre
Milwaukee, Wis.[1]	1945	60,500 gpd per acre	—
Santa Monica, Calif.	—	9,700 gpd per acre, commercial 7,750 gpd per acre, hotels	13,600 gpd per acre
Shreveport, La.	—	3,000 gpd per acre	—
St. Joseph, Mo.	1962	6,000 gpd per acre	—
St. Louis, Mo.	1960	90,000 gpd per acre avg. 165,000 gpd per acre peak	—
Toledo, Ohio[1]	1946	15,000 to 30,000 gpd per acre, average to peak allowances	—
Toronto	1960	63,500 gpd per acre downtown sewers	—

[1] *"Sewer Capacity Design Practice," by William E. Stanley and Warren J. Kaufman, Journal, Boston Soc. of Civ., Engrs., October, 1953. p. 320. Table 3.*

[2] *Gallons per capita per day.*

[3] *Sludge & Sewage Treatment, Harold Bobbitt, 6-Edition, John Wiley & Sons.*

TABLE 3

FULL FLOW COEFFICIENT VALUES
CIRCULAR CONCRETE PIPE

D Pipe Diameter (inches)	A Area (Square Feet)	R Hydraulic Radius (Feet)	Value of $C_1 = \dfrac{1.486}{n} \times A \times R^{2/3}$			
			n=0.010	n=0.011	n=0.012	n=0.013
8	0.349	0.167	15.8	14.3	13.1	12.1
10	0.545	0.208	28.4	25.8	23.6	21.8
12	0.785	0.250	46.4	42.1	38.6	35.7
15	1.227	0.312	84.1	76.5	70.1	64.7
18	1.767	0.375	137	124	114	105
21	2.405	0.437	206	187	172	158
24	3.142	0.500	294	267	245	226
27	3.976	0.562	402	366	335	310
30	4.909	0.625	533	485	444	410
33	5.940	0.688	686	624	574	530
36	7.069	0.750	867	788	722	666
42	9.621	0.875	1308	1189	1090	1006
48	12.566	1.000	1867	1698	1556	1436
54	15.904	1.125	2557	2325	2131	1967
60	19.635	1.250	3385	3077	2821	2604
66	23.758	1.375	4364	3967	3636	3357
72	28.274	1.500	5504	5004	4587	4234
78	33.183	1.625	6815	6195	5679	5242
84	38.485	1.750	8304	7549	6920	6388
90	44.170	1.875	9985	9078	8321	7681
96	50.266	2.000	11850	10780	9878	9119
102	56.745	2.125	13940	12670	11620	10720
108	63.617	2.250	16230	14760	13530	12490
114	70.882	2.375	18750	17040	15620	14420
120	78.540	2.500	21500	19540	17920	16540
126	86.590	2.625	24480	22260	20400	18830
132	95.033	2.750	27720	25200	23100	21330
138	103.870	2.875	31210	28370	26010	24010
144	113.100	3.000	34960	31780	29130	26890

TABLE 4

FULL FLOW COEFFICIENT VALUES
ELLIPTICAL CONCRETE PIPE

Pipe Size R x S (HE) S x R (VE) (Inches)	Approximate Equivalent Circular Diameter (Inches)	A Area (Square Feet)	R Hydraulic Radius (Feet)	Value of $C_1 = \dfrac{1.486}{n} \times A \times R^{2/3}$			
				n = 0.010	n = 0.011	n = 0.012	n = 0.013
14 x 23	18	1.8	0.367	138	125	116	108
19 x 30	24	3.3	0.490	301	274	252	232
22 x 34	27	4.1	0.546	405	368	339	313
24 x 38	30	5.1	0.613	547	497	456	421
27 x 42	33	6.3	0.686	728	662	607	560
29 x 45	36	7.4	0.736	891	810	746	686
32 x 49	39	8.8	0.812	1140	1036	948	875
34 x 53	42	10.2	0.875	1386	1260	1156	1067
38 x 60	48	12.9	0.969	1878	1707	1565	1445
43 x 68	54	16.6	1.106	2635	2395	2196	2027
48 x 76	60	20.5	1.229	3491	3174	2910	2686
53 x 83	66	24.8	1.352	4503	4094	3753	3464
58 x 91	72	29.5	1.475	5680	5164	4734	4370
63 x 98	78	34.6	1.598	7027	6388	5856	5406
68 x 106	84	40.1	1.721	8560	7790	7140	6590
72 x 113	90	46.1	1.845	10300	9365	8584	7925
77 x 121	96	52.4	1.967	12220	11110	10190	9403
82 x 128	102	59.2	2.091	14380	13070	11980	11060
87 x 136	108	66.4	2.215	16770	15240	13970	12900
92 x 143	114	74.0	2.340	19380	17620	16150	14910
97 x 151	120	82.0	2.461	22190	20180	18490	17070
106 x 166	132	99.2	2.707	28630	26020	23860	22020
116 x 180	144	118.6	2.968	36400	33100	30340	28000

TABLE 5

FULL FLOW COEFFICIENT VALUES
CONCRETE ARCH PIPE

Pipe Size R x S (Inches)	Approximate Equivalent Circular Diameter (Inches)	A Area (Square Feet)	R Hydraulic Radius (Feet)	Value of $C_1 = \dfrac{1.486}{n} \times A \times R^{2/3}$			
				n = 0.010	n = 0.011	n = 0.012	n = 0.013
11 x 18	15	1.1	0.25	65	59	54	50
13½ x 22	18	1.6	0.30	110	100	91	84
15½ x 26	21	2.2	0.36	165	150	137	127
18 x 28½	24	2.8	0.45	243	221	203	187
22½ x 36¼	30	4.4	0.56	441	401	368	339
26⅝ x 43¾	36	6.4	0.68	736	669	613	566
31⁵⁄₁₆x 51⅛	42	8.8	0.80	1125	1023	938	866
36 x 58½	48	11.4	0.90	1579	1435	1315	1214
40 x 65	54	14.3	1.01	2140	1945	1783	1646
45 x 73	60	17.7	1.13	2851	2592	2376	2193
54 x 88	72	25.6	1.35	4641	4219	3867	3569
62 x 102	84	34.6	1.57	6941	6310	5784	5339
72 x 115	90	44.5	1.77	9668	8789	8056	7436
77¼ x 122	96	51.7	1.92	11850	10770	9872	9112
87⅛ x 138	108	66.0	2.17	16430	14940	13690	12640
96⅞ x 154	120	81.8	2.42	21975	19977	18312	16904
106½ x 168¾	132	99.1	2.65	28292	25720	23577	21763

TABLE 6

FULL FLOW COEFFICIENT VALUES
PRECAST CONCRETE BOX SECTIONS

Box Size Span x Rise (Feet)	A Area (Square Feet)	R Hydraulic Radius (Feet)	$C = 1.486/n(A \times R^{2/3})$ n = 0.012	n = 0.013
3 X 2	5.78	0.63	524	484
3 X 3	8.78	0.78	923	852
4 X 2	7.65	0.69	743	686
4 X 3	11.65	0.90	1340	1240
4 X 4	15.65	1.04	1990	1840
5 X 3	14.50	0.98	1770	1630
5 X 4	19.50	1.16	2660	2460
5 X 5	24.50	1.30	3620	3340
6 X 3	17.32	1.04	2200	2030
6 X 4	23.32	1.25	3350	3100
6 X 5	29.32	1.42	4590	4240
6 X 6	35.32	1.56	5880	5430
7 X 4	27.11	1.33	4050	3740
7 X 5	34.11	1.52	5590	5160
7 X 6	41.11	1.68	7200	6650
7 X 7	48.11	1.82	8880	8200
8 X 4	31.11	1.39	4790	4420
8 X 5	39.11	1.60	6630	6120
8 X 6	47.11	1.78	8760	7920
8 X 7	55.11	1.94	10600	9790
8 X 8	63.11	2.07	12700	11700

Box Size Span x Rise (Feet)	A Area (Square Feet)	R Hydraulic Radius (Feet)	$C = 1.486/n(A \times R^{2/3})$ n = 0.012	n = 0.013
9 X 5	43.88	1.67	7060	7070
9 X 6	52.88	1.87	9950	9180
9 X 7	61.88	2.05	12400	11400
9 X 8	70.88	2.20	14800	13700
9 X 9	79.88	2.33	17400	16100
10 X 5	48.61	1.73	8690	8020
10 X 6	58.61	1.95	11300	10462
10 X 7	68.61	2.14	14100	13000
10 X 8	78.61	2.31	17000	15700
10 X 9	88.61	2.46	20000	18500
10 X 10	98.61	2.59	23000	21300
11 X 4	42.32	1.52	6930	6390
11 X 6	64.32	2.02	12730	11700
11 X 8	86.32	2.41	19200	17700
11 X 10	108.32	2.72	26100	24100
11 X 11	119.32	2.85	29700	27400
12 X 4	46.00	1.55	7630	7050
12 X 6	70.00	2.08	14100	13000
12 X 8	94.00	2.50	21400	19800
12 X 10	118.00	2.83	29300	27000
12 X 12	142.00	3.11	37500	34600

TABLE 7

SLOPES REQUIRED FOR V = 2fps
AT FULL AND HALF FULL FLOW

Pipe Diameter (Inches)	Slope in %			
	n = 0.010	n = 0.011	n = 0.012	n = 0.013
8	0.197	0.238	0.284	0.332
10	0.147	0.178	0.213	0.248
12	0.115	0.139	0.166	0.194
15	0.086	0.104	0.123	0.145
18	0.067	0.081	0.097	0.114
21	0.055	0.066	0.079	0.092
24	0.046	0.055	0.066	0.077
27	0.039	0.047	0.056	0.065
30	0.034	0.041	0.049	0.057
33	0.030	0.036	0.043	0.051
36	0.027	0.032	0.038	0.045
42	0.022	0.026	0.031	0.036
48	0.018	0.022	0.026	0.031
54	0.015	0.019	0.022	0.027
60	0.013	0.016	0.019	0.023
66	0.012	0.014	0.017	0.020
72	0.011	0.013	0.015	0.018
78	0.010	0.011	0.014	0.016
84	0.009	0.010	0.012	0.015
90	0.008	0.010	0.011	0.013
96	0.007	0.009	0.010	0.012
102	0.007	0.008	0.010	0.011
108	0.006	0.007	0.009	0.010
114	0.006	0.007	0.008	0.010
120	0.005	0.006	0.008	0.009
126	0.005	0.006	0.007	0.008
132	0.004	0.006	0.007	0.008
138	0.004	0.005	0.006	0.007
144	0.004	0.005	0.006	0.007

Note: For a velocity V other than 2fps, multiple the above by $\frac{V^2}{4}$.

TABLE 8

RUNOFF COEFFICIENTS FOR VARIOUS AREAS

DESCRIPTION OF AREA	RUNOFF COEFFICIENTS
Business:	
Downtown areas	0.70 to 0.95
Neighborhood areas	0.50 to 0.70
Residential:	
Single-family areas	0.30 to 0.50
Multi units, detached	0.40 to 0.60
Multi units, attached	0.60 to 0.75
Residential (suburban)	0.25 to 0.40
Apartment dwelling areas	0.50 to 0.70
Industrial:	
Light areas	0.50 to 0.80
Heavy areas	0.60 to 0.90
Parks, cemeteries	0.10 to 0.25
Playgrounds	0.20 to 0.35
Railroad yard areas	0.20 to 0.40
Unimproved areas	0.10 to 0.30

TABLE 9

RAINFALL INTENSITY CONVERSION FACTORS

Duration in Minutes	Factor	Duration in Minutes	Factor
5	2.22	40	0.8
10	1.71	50	0.7
15	1.44	60	0.6
20	1.25	90	0.5
30	1.00	120	0.4

TABLE 10

RECURRENCE INTERVAL FACTORS

Recurrence Interval in Years	Factor
2	1.0
5	1.3
10	1.6
25	1.9
50	2.2

TABLE 11

NATIONWIDE FLOOD-FREQUENCY PROJECTS

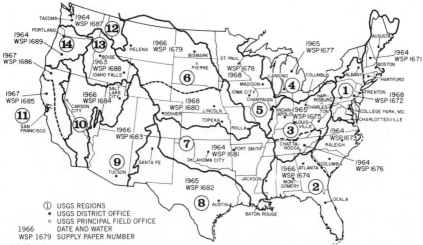

① USGS REGIONS
● USGS DISTRICT OFFICE
○ USGS PRINCIPAL FIELD OFFICE
1966 DATE AND WATER
WSP 1679 SUPPLY PAPER NUMBER

TABLE 12

ENTRANCE LOSS COEFFICIENTS

Coefficient k_e to apply to velocity head $\dfrac{V^2}{2g}$ for determination of head loss at entrance to a structure, such as a culvert or conduit, operating full or partly full with *control at the outlet.*

$$\text{Entrance head loss } H_e = k_e \frac{V^2}{2g}$$

TYPE OF ENTRANCE	COEFFICIENT k_e
Projecting from fill, socket end (groove-end)	0.2
Projecting from fill, sq. cut end	0.5
Headwall or headwall and wingwalls	
Socket end of pipe (groove-end)	0.2
Square-edge	0.5
Rounded (radius = 1/12D)	0.2
End-Section conforming to fill slope	0.5

Note: "End Section conforming to fill slope" are the sections commonly available from manufacturers. From limited hydraulic tests they are equivalent in operation to a headwall in both inlet and outlet control. Some end sections, incorporating a closed taper in their design have a superior hydraulic performance.

TYPE OF STRUCTURE AND DESIGN OF ENTRANCE BOX, REINFORCED CONCRETE	COEFFICIENT k_e
Headwall parallel to embankment (no wing walls)	
Square-edged on 3 edges	0.5
Rounded on 3 edges to radius of 1/12 barrel dimension	0.2
Wing walls at 30° to 75° to barrel	
Square-edged at crown	0.4
Crown edge rounded to radius of 1/12 barrel dimension	0.2
Wing walls at 10° to 25° to barrel	
Square-edged at crown	0.5
Wing walls parallel (extension of sides)	
Square-edged at crown	0.7

TABLE 13

BACKFILL LOADS ON CIRCULAR PIPE IN TRENCH INSTALLATION

LOADS IN POUNDS PER LINEAR FOOT
* 100 POUNDS PER CUBIC FOOT BACKFILL MATERIAL

Pipe size: **6"**

A — SAND AND GRAVEL, Kμ' = 0.165

HEIGHT OF BACKFILL H ABOVE TOP OF PIPE, FEET	\multicolumn{10}{c}{TRENCH WIDTH AT TOP OF PIPE}	TRANSITION WIDTH
H	1'-3"	1'-6"	1'-9"	2'-0"	2'-3"	2'-6"	2'-9"	3'-0"	3'-3"	3'-6"	
5	347	470									1'-6"
6	376	499	564								1'-8"
7	398	535	658								1'-9"
8	416	564	722	753							1'-10"
9	429	587	758	848							1'-11"
10	439	606	787	942							1'-11"
11	447	621	811	1037							2'-0"
12	453	633	831	1044	1132						2'-1"
13	458	642	848	1070	1227						2'-2"
14	461	650	861	1091	1320						2'-3"
15	464	656	873	1110	1364	1416					2'-4"
16	466	661	882	1125	1387	1512					2'-4"
17	468	665	890	1138	1407	1602					2'-5"
18	469	668	896	1149	1424	1701					2'-6"
19	470	671	902	1159	1439	1797					2'-6"
20	471	673	906	1167	1452	1758	1887				2'-7"
21	472	675	910	1174	1463	1775	1983				2'-8"
22	472	676	913	1179	1473	1790	2074				2'-8"
23	472	677	915	1184	1481	1802	2173				2'-9"
24	472	678	917	1189	1488	1814	2163	2269			2'-10"
25	473	679	919	1192	1494	1824	2177	2362			2'-11"
26	473	679	921	1195	1500	1832	2190	2451			2'-11"
27	473	680	922	1198	1504	1840	2201	2553			3'-0"
28	473	680	923	1200	1508	1846	2212	2652			3'-0"
29	473	680	924	1201	1512	1852	2221	2614	2749		3'-1"
30	473	680	924	1203	1515	1857	2229	2626	2843		3'-2"
31	473	681	925	1204	1517	1862	2236	2637	2935		3'-2"
32	473	681	925	1205	1520	1866	2242	2646	3024		3'-3"
33	473	681	926	1206	1521	1869	2247	2654	3109		3'-3"
34	473	681	926	1207	1523	1872	2252	2662	3099	3217	3'-4"
35	473	681	926	1208	1525	1875	2257	2669	3109	3296	3'-5"
36	473	681	926	1208	1526	1877	2261	2675	3118	3400	3'-5"
37	473	681	927	1209	1527	1879	2264	2680	3126	3503	3'-6"
38	473	681	927	1209	1528	1881	2267	2685	3133	3605	3'-6"
39	473	681	927	1210	1529	1882	2270	2689	3139	3671	3'-6"
40	473	681	927	1210	1529	1884	2272	2693	3145	3768	3'-7"

B — SATURATED TOP SOIL, Kμ' = 0.150

HEIGHT OF BACKFILL H ABOVE TOP OF PIPE, FEET	\multicolumn{10}{c}{TRENCH WIDTH AT TOP OF PIPE}	TRANSITION WIDTH
H	1'-3"	1'-6"	1'-9"	2'-0"	2'-3"	2'-6"	2'-9"	3'-0"	3'-3"	3'-6"	
5	363	470									1'-6"
6	397	524	564								1'-7"
7	423	565	658								1'-8"
8	444	598	753								1'-9"
9	460	626	802	848							1'-10"
10	473	648	836	942							1'-11"
11	483	666	865	1037							1'-11"
12	491	681	890	1132							2'-0"
13	497	694	910	1143	1227						2'-1"
14	502	704	928	1170	1320						2'-2"
15	506	712	942	1192	1416						2'-2"
16	509	719	955	1212	1512						2'-3"
17	512	724	965	1229	1534	1602					2'-4"
18	513	729	974	1243	1553	1701					2'-5"
19	515	733	981	1256	1570	1797					2'-6"
20	516	736	987	1266	1584	1887					2'-6"
21	517	738	992	1276	1597	1915	1983				2'-7"
22	518	740	997	1284	1608	1934	2074				2'-7"
23	518	742	1001	1291	1618	1951	2173				2'-8"
24	519	743	1004	1296	1627	1966	2269				2'-9"
25	519	744	1006	1301	1634	1979	2362				2'-9"
26	519	745	1008	1306	1641	1991	2373	2451			2'-10"
27	520	746	1010	1310	1647	2001	2388	2553			2'-11"
28	520	747	1012	1313	1652	2010	2401	2652			2'-11"
29	520	747	1013	1316	1656	2019	2414	2749			3'-0"
30	520	748	1014	1318	1660	2026	2425	2843			3'-0"
31	520	748	1015	1320	1663	2032	2435	2935			3'-0"
32	520	748	1016	1322	1666	2038	2444	2877	3024		3'-1"
33	520	749	1017	1323	1669	2043	2451	2889	3109		3'-1"
34	520	749	1017	1325	1671	2048	2465	2899	3217		3'-2"
35	520	749	1018	1326	1673	2052	2471	2909	3296		3'-2"
36	520	749	1018	1327	1675	2055	2476	2918	3400		3'-3"
37	520	749	1019	1328	1676	2058	2480	2925	3405	3503	3'-4"
38	520	749	1019	1328	1678	2061	2485	2932	3415	3605	3'-4"
39	520	749	1019	1329	1679	2064	2488	2939	3424	3671	3'-4"
40	520	749	1019	1330	1679	2066	2490	2945	3433	3768	3'-5"

HEIGHT OF BACKFILL H ABOVE TOP OF PIPE, FEET

D — SATURATED CLAY Kμ'—0.110

Trench width at top of pipe (transition loads in **bold**):

H (ft)	1'-3"	1'-6"	1'-9"	2'-0"	2'-3"	2'-6"	2'-9"	3'-0"	Transition Width
5	415	**470**							1'-4"
6	463	**564**							1'-5"
7	503	**658**							1'-6"
8	536	706	**753**						1'-7"
9	564	749	**848**						1'-7"
10	588	786	**942**						1'-8"
11	607	818	**1037**						1'-9"
12	624	846	1084	**1132**					1'-10"
13	638	870	1120	**1227**					1'-10"
14	649	891	1152	**1320**					1'-11"
15	659	909	1180	**1416**					1'-11"
16	667	924	1205	**1512**					2'-0"
17	674	938	1227	1537	**1602**				2'-1"
18	680	949	1247	1567	**1701**				2'-1"
19	685	959	1264	1593	**1797**				2'-2"
20	689	968	1279	1616	**1887**				2'-2"
21	692	975	1292	1637	**1983**				2'-3"
22	695	982	1304	1656	**2074**				2'-3"
23	697	987	1314	1673	2058	**2173**			2'-4"
24	699	992	1323	1688	2080	**2269**			2'-4"
25	701	996	1331	1701	2101	**2362**			2'-5"
26	702	1000	1339	1714	2120	**2451**			2'-5"
27	704	1003	1345	1724	2136	**2553**			2'-6"
28	705	1005	1350	1734	2152	**2652**			2'-6"
29	705	1008	1355	1743	2166	2619	**2749**		2'-7"
30	706	1010	1360	1751	2178	2638	**2843**		2'-7"
31	707	1011	1363	1758	2190	2655	**2935**		2'-8"
32	707	1013	1367	1764	2200	2670	**3024**		2'-8"
33	708	1014	1370	1769	2209	2685	**3109**		2'-8"
34	708	1015	1372	1774	2218	2698	**3217**		2'-9"
35	708	1016	1374	1779	2226	2710	**3296**		2'-9"
36	708	1017	1376	1783	2233	2721	3244	**3400**	2'-10"
37	709	1018	1378	1787	2239	2731	3259	**3503**	2'-10"
38	709	1018	1380	1790	2245	2740	3273	**3605**	2'-11"
39	709	1019	1381	1793	2250	2749	3285	**3671**	2'-11"
40	709	1019	1382	1795	2255	2756	3297	**3768**	3'-0"

C — ORDINARY CLAY Kμ'—0.130

Trench width at top of pipe (transition loads in **bold**):

H (ft)	1'-3"	1'-6"	1'-9"	2'-0"	2'-3"	2'-6"	2'-9"	3'-0"	3'-3"	Transition Width
5	388	**470**								1'-5"
6	428	**564**								1'-6"
7	460	608	**658**							1'-7"
8	487	649	**753**							1'-8"
9	508	683	**848**							1'-9"
10	525	712	**942**							1'-10"
11	539	736	948	**1037**						1'-11"
12	551	757	979	**1132**						2'-0"
13	560	774	1007	**1227**						2'-1"
14	568	788	1030	**1320**						2'-2"
15	574	801	1051	1319	**1416**					2'-2"
16	579	811	1068	1346	**1512**					2'-3"
17	583	819	1083	1369	**1602**					2'-4"
18	586	827	1096	1390	**1701**					2'-5"
19	589	833	1107	1408	1730	**1797**				2'-5"
20	591	838	1117	1424	1754	**1887**				2'-6"
21	593	842	1125	1438	1775	**1983**				2'-6"
22	594	846	1133	1450	1793	**2074**				2'-7"
23	595	849	1139	1461	1810	**2173**				2'-8"
24	596	851	1144	1470	1825	**2269**				2'-8"
25	597	854	1149	1478	1838	2225	**2362**			2'-9"
26	598	855	1153	1486	1850	2242	**2451**			2'-9"
27	598	857	1156	1492	1861	2258	**2553**			2'-10"
28	599	858	1159	1498	1870	2273	**2652**			2'-10"
29	599	859	1162	1502	1878	2286	**2749**			2'-11"
30	599	860	1164	1507	1886	2297	2738	**2843**		3'-0"
31	600	861	1166	1511	1892	2308	2753	**2935**		3'-0"
32	600	862	1167	1514	1898	2317	2767	**3024**		3'-1"
33	600	862	1169	1517	1904	2326	2780	**3109**		3'-1"
34	600	862	1170	1519	1908	2333	2791	**3217**		3'-2"
35	600	863	1171	1522	1913	2340	2802	**3296**		3'-2"
36	600	863	1172	1524	1916	2346	2811	3308	**3400**	
37	600	863	1173	1525	1920	2352	2820	3321	**3503**	
38	600	863	1173	1527	1922	2357	2828	3333	**3605**	
39	600	864	1174	1528	1925	2362	2835	3343	**3671**	
40	600	864	1174	1529	1927	2366	2842	3353	**3768**	

* For backfill weighing 110 pounds per cubic foot; increase loads 10%; for 120 pounds per cubic foot, increase 20%; etc.
▲ Transition loads (bold type) and widths based on Kμ'—0.19, rsdp—0.5 in the embankment equation
Interpolate for intermediate heights of backfill and/or trench widths

TABLE 14   8″   8″   8″

BACKFILL LOADS ON CIRCULAR PIPE IN TRENCH INSTALLATION

*100 POUNDS PER CUBIC FOOT BACKFILL MATERIAL   LOADS IN POUNDS PER LINEAR FOOT

HEIGHT OF BACKFILL H ABOVE TOP OF PIPE, FEET

A — SAND AND GRAVEL Kμ′–0.165

H	1′-6″	1′-9″	2′-0″	2′-3″	2′-6″	2′-9″	3′-0″	3′-3″	3′-6″	4′-0″	TRANSITION WIDTH
5	454	566	**603**								1′-10″
6	499	628	**724**								1′-11″
7	535	680	**847**								2′-0″
8	564	722	888	**969**							2′-1″
9	587	758	937	**1088**							2′-2″
10	606	787	979	**1213**							2′-3″
11	621	811	1014	1228	**1332**						2′-4″
12	633	831	1044	1270	**1458**						2′-5″
13	642	848	1070	1306	**1575**						2′-6″
14	650	861	1091	1337	1595	**1698**					2′-7″
15	656	873	1110	1364	1632	**1818**					2′-8″
16	661	882	1125	1387	1664	**1942**					2′-9″
17	665	890	1138	1407	1693	1993	**2065**				2′-10″
18	668	896	1149	1424	1717	2027	**2182**				2′-10″
19	671	902	1159	1439	1739	2057	**2308**				2′-11″
20	673	906	1167	1452	1758	2083	2456	**2429**			3′-0″
21	675	910	1174	1463	1775	2107	2484	**2553**			3′-1″
22	676	913	1179	1473	1790	2128	2510	**2673**			3′-2″
23	677	915	1184	1481	1802	2146	2532	2947	**2788**		3′-3″
24	678	917	1189	1488	1814	2163	2552	2972	**2910**		3′-4″
25	679	919	1192	1494	1824	2177	2571	2994	**3041**		3′-5″
26	679	921	1195	1500	1832	2190	2587	3014	**3154**		3′-6″
27	680	922	1198	1504	1840	2201	2601	3032	3512	**3278**	3′-6″
28	680	923	1200	1508	1846	2212	2614	3048	3530	**3398**	3′-7″
29	680	924	1201	1512	1852	2221	2626	3063	3546	**3514**	3′-8″
30	680	924	1203	1515	1857	2236	2637	3076	3561	**3646**	3′-8″
31	681	925	1204	1517	1862	2247	2646	3088	3575	**3776**	3′-9″
32	681	925	1205	1520	1866	2252	2654	3099	3587	**3880**	3′-9″
33	681	926	1206	1521	1869	2257	2662	3109	3598	**4004**	3′-10″
34	681	926	1207	1523	1872	2261	2669	3118	3608	**4124**	3′-11″
35	681	926	1208	1525	1875	2264	2675	3126	3618	**4241**	3′-11″
36	681	927	1208	1526	1877	2267	2680	3133	3626	**4384**	4′-0″
37	681	927	1209	1527	1879	2270	2685	3139		**4495**	4′-0″
38	681	927	1209	1528	1881	2272	2689	3142		**4603**	4′-0″
39	681	927	1210	1529	1882		2693			**4740**	4′-0″
40	681	927	1210	1529	1884					**4877**	4′-1″

B — SATURATED TOP SOIL Kμ′–0.150

H	1′-6″	1′-9″	2′-0″	2′-3″	2′-6″	2′-9″	3′-0″	3′-3″	3′-6″	4′-0″	TRANSITION WIDTH
5	474	**603**									1′-9″
6	524	655	**724**								1′-11″
7	565	713	**847**								2′-0″
8	598	761	931	**969**							2′-1″
9	626	802	987	**1088**							2′-2″
10	648	836	1035	**1213**							2′-3″
11	666	865	1077	**1332**							2′-3″
12	681	890	1112	1346	**1458**						2′-4″
13	694	910	1143	1389	**1575**						2′-5″
14	704	928	1170	1426	**1698**						2′-6″
15	712	942	1192	1459	1738	**1818**					2′-7″
16	719	955	1212	1487	1777	**1942**					2′-8″
17	724	965	1229	1512	1812	**2065**					2′-8″
18	729	974	1243	1534	1843	**2182**					2′-9″
19	733	981	1256	1553	1870	2203	**2308**				2′-10″
20	736	987	1266	1570	1894	2236	**2429**				2′-11″
21	738	992	1276	1584	1915	2265	**2553**				2′-11″
22	740	997	1284	1597	1934	2292	**2673**				3′-0″
23	742	1001	1291	1608	1951	2315	2699	**2788**			3′-1″
24	743	1004	1296	1618	1966	2336	2727	**2910**			3′-2″
25	744	1006	1301	1627	1979	2355	2753	**3041**			3′-3″
26	745	1008	1306	1634	1991	2373	2777	**3154**			3′-3″
27	746	1010	1310	1641	2001	2388	2798	**3278**			3′-4″
28	747	1012	1313	1647	2010	2401	2817	3255	**3398**		3′-5″
29	747	1013	1316	1652	2019	2414	2834	3278	**3514**		3′-5″
30	748	1014	1318	1656	2026	2425	2850	3300	**3646**		3′-6″
31	748	1015	1320	1660	2032	2435	2864	3319	**3776**		3′-6″
32	748	1016	1322	1663	2038	2444	2877	3337	**3880**		3′-7″
33	748	1017	1323	1666	2043	2451	2889	3353	3842	**4004**	3′-7″
34	749	1017	1325	1669	2048	2459	2899	3368	3861	**4124**	3′-8″
35	749	1018	1326	1671	2052	2465	2909	3381	3880	**4241**	3′-8″
36	749	1018	1327	1673	2055	2471	2918	3393	3896	**4384**	3′-9″
37	749	1019	1328	1675	2058	2476	2925	3405	3912	**4495**	3′-9″
38	749	1019	1328	1676	2061	2480	2932	3415	3926	**4603**	3′-10″
39	749	1019	1329	1678	2064	2485	2939	3424	3939	**4740**	3′-10″
40	749	1019	1330	1679	2066	2488	2945	3433	3950	**4877**	3′-11″

HEIGHT OF BACKFILL H ABOVE TOP OF PIPE, FEET

C — ORDINARY CLAY Kμ'—0.130

TRENCH WIDTH AT TOP OF PIPE

H	▲TRANSITION WIDTH	1'-6"	1'-9"	2'-0"	2'-3"	2'-6"	2'-9"	3'-0"	3'-3"	3'-6"	4'-0"
5	1'-9"	501	**603**								
6	1'-10"	559	694	**724**							
7	1'-11"	608	761	**847**							
8	2'-0"	649	819	**969**							
9	2'-0"	683	868	**1088**							
10	2'-1"	712	911	1119	**1213**						
11	2'-2"	736	948	1170	**1332**						
12	2'-3"	757	979	1215	**1458**						
13	2'-4"	774	1007	1254	1513	**1575**					
14	2'-4"	788	1030	1289	1560	**1698**					
15	2'-5"	801	1051	1319	1603	**1818**					
16	2'-6"	811	1068	1346	1640	**1942**					
17	2'-7"	819	1083	1369	1674	1993	**2065**				
18	2'-7"	827	1096	1390	1703	2034	**2182**				
19	2'-8"	833	1107	1408	1730	2070	**2308**				
20	2'-9"	838	1117	1424	1754	2103	**2429**				
21	2'-9"	842	1125	1438	1775	2133	**2553**				
22	2'-10"	846	1133	1450	1793	2159	2545	**2673**			
23	2'-11"	849	1139	1461	1810	2184	2578	**2788**			
24	2'-11"	851	1144	1470	1825	2205	2607	**2910**			
25	3'-0"	854	1149	1478	1838	2225	2635	**3041**			
26	3'-0"	855	1153	1486	1850	2242	2659	**3154**			
27	3'-1"	857	1156	1492	1861	2258	2682	3128	**3278**		
28	3'-2"	858	1159	1498	1870	2273	2702	3155	**3398**		
29	3'-2"	859	1162	1502	1878	2286	2721	3181	**3514**		
30	3'-3"	860	1164	1507	1886	2297	2738	3204	**3646**		
31	3'-3"	861	1166	1511	1892	2308	2753	3225	**3776**		
32	3'-4"	862	1167	1514	1898	2317	2767	3245	3748	**3880**	
33	3'-4"	862	1169	1517	1904	2326	2780	3263	3772	**4004**	
34	3'-5"	862	1170	1519	1908	2333	2791	3279	3794	**4124**	
35	3'-5"	863	1171	1522	1913	2340	2802	3294	3815	**4241**	
36	3'-6"	863	1172	1524	1916	2346	2811	3308	3834	**4384**	
37	3'-6"	863	1173	1525	1920	2352	2820	3321	3851	**4495**	
38	3'-7"	864	1173	1527	1922	2357	2828	3333	3868	4431	**4603**
39	3'-7"	864	1174	1528	1925	2362	2835	3343	3883	4451	**4740**
40	3'-8"	864	1174	1529	1927	2366	2842	3353	3896	4470	**4877**

D — SATURATED CLAY Kμ'—0.110

TRENCH WIDTH AT TOP OF PIPE

H	▲TRANSITION WIDTH	1'-6"	1'-9"	2'-0"	2'-3"	2'-6"	2'-9"	3'-0"	3'-3"	3'-6"	4'-0"
5	1'-8"	531	**603**								
6	1'-9"	598	**724**								
7	1'-10"	656	814	**847**							
8	1'-10"	706	882	**969**							
9	1'-11"	749	943	**1088**							
10	2'-0"	786	996	**1213**							
11	2'-1"	818	1042	1276	**1332**						
12	2'-1"	846	1084	1332	**1458**						
13	2'-2"	870	1120	1383	**1575**						
14	2'-2"	891	1152	1428	**1698**						
15	2'-3"	909	1180	1469	**1818**						
16	2'-4"	924	1205	1505	1819	**1942**					
17	2'-5"	938	1227	1537	1864	**2065**					
18	2'-5"	949	1247	1567	1905	**2182**					
19	2'-6"	959	1264	1593	1942	**2308**					
20	2'-7"	968	1279	1616	1975	2352	**2429**				
21	2'-7"	975	1292	1637	2005	2393	**2553**				
22	2'-8"	982	1304	1656	2033	2431	**2673**				
23	2'-8"	987	1314	1673	2058	2465	**2788**				
24	2'-9"	992	1323	1688	2080	2497	**2910**				
25	2'-9"	996	1331	1701	2101	2526	**3041**				
26	2'-10"	1000	1339	1714	2120	2552	3008	**3154**			
27	2'-10"	1003	1345	1724	2136	2576	3041	**3278**			
28	2'-11"	1005	1350	1734	2152	2599	3071	**3398**			
29	3'-0"	1008	1355	1743	2166	2619	3099	**3514**			
30	3'-0"	1010	1360	1751	2178	2638	3125	**3646**			
31	3'-1"	1011	1363	1758	2190	2655	3149	3669	**3776**		
32	3'-1"	1013	1367	1764	2200	2670	3171	3699	**3880**		
33	3'-2"	1014	1370	1769	2209	2685	3192	3727	**4004**		
34	3'-2"	1015	1372	1774	2218	2698	3211	3752	**4124**		
35	3'-3"	1016	1374	1779	2226	2710	3228	3776	**4241**		
36	3'-3"	1017	1376	1783	2233	2721	3244	3798	**4384**		
37	3'-3"	1018	1378	1787	2239	2731	3259	3819	**4495**		
38	3'-4"	1018	1380	1790	2245	2740	3273	3838	4434	**4603**	
39	3'-4"	1019	1381	1793	2250	2749	3285	3856	4458	**4740**	
40	3'-5"	1019	1382	1795	2255	2756	3297	3873	4480	**4877**	

* For backfill weighing 110 pounds per cubic foot, increase loads 10%; for 120 pounds per cubic foot, increase 20%, etc.

Transition loads (**bold type**) and widths based on Kμ—0.19, $r_{sd}p$—0.5 in the embankment equation

▲Transition width

Interpolate for intermediate heights of backfill and/or trench widths

TABLE 15   10″

BACKFILL LOADS ON CIRCULAR PIPE IN TRENCH INSTALLATION
*100 POUNDS PER CUBIC FOOT BACKFILL MATERIAL — LOADS IN POUNDS PER LINEAR FOOT

A — SAND AND GRAVEL Kµ′ − 0.165

10″ — HEIGHT OF BACKFILL **H** ABOVE TOP OF PIPE, FEET

TRENCH WIDTH AT TOP OF PIPE

H	1′-9″	2′-0″	2′-3″	2′-6″	2′-9″	3′-0″	3′-3″	3′-6″	4′-0″	4′-6″	Transition Width
5	566	680	**743**								2′-2″
6	628	761	**893**								2′-3″
7	680	830	984	**1043**							2′-4″
8	722	888	1059	**1193**							2′-5″
9	758	937	1124	**1344**							2′-6″
10	787	979	1180	1388	**1495**						2′-8″
11	811	1014	1228	1450	**1645**						2′-8″
12	831	1044	1270	1505	1748	**1795**					2′-10″
13	848	1070	1306	1553	1810	**1946**					2′-11″
14	861	1091	1337	1595	1864	**2094**					3′-0″
15	873	1110	1364	1632	1912	**2241**					3′-0″
16	882	1125	1387	1664	1955	2258	**2395**				3′-1″
17	890	1138	1407	1693	1993	2306	**2547**				3′-2″
18	896	1149	1424	1717	2027	2350	**2698**				3′-3″
19	902	1159	1439	1739	2057	2389	2735	**2842**			3′-4″
20	906	1167	1452	1758	2083	2425	2780	**2994**			3′-5″
21	910	1174	1463	1775	2107	2456	2821	**3150**			3′-6″
22	913	1179	1473	1790	2128	2484	2857	**3301**			3′-6″
23	915	1184	1481	1802	2146	2510	2891	3287	**3445**		3′-7″
24	917	1189	1488	1814	2163	2532	2920	3325	**3595**		3′-8″
25	919	1192	1494	1824	2177	2552	2947	3360	**3739**		3′-9″
26	921	1195	1500	1832	2190	2571	2972	3392	**3892**		3′-9″
27	922	1198	1504	1840	2201	2587	2994	3421	**4041**		3′-10″
28	923	1200	1508	1846	2212	2601	3014	3447	**4201**		3′-11″
29	924	1201	1512	1852	2221	2614	3032	3471	**4340**		4′-0″
30	924	1203	1515	1857	2229	2626	3048	3492	**4493**		4′-0″
31	925	1204	1517	1862	2236	2637	3063	3512	4472	**4642**	4′-1″
32	925	1205	1520	1866	2242	2646	3076	3530	4502	**4786**	4′-2″
33	926	1206	1521	1869	2247	2654	3088	3546	4529	**4950**	4′-3″
34	926	1207	1523	1872	2252	2662	3099	3561	4555	**5085**	4′-3″
35	926	1208	1525	1875	2257	2669	3109	3575	4578	**5243**	4′-4″
36	926	1208	1526	1877	2261	2675	3118	3587	4599	**5397**	4′-4″
37	927	1209	1527	1879	2264	2680	3126	3598	4619	**5549**	4′-5″
38	927	1209	1528	1881	2267	2685	3133	3608	4637	**5697**	4′-6″
39	927	1210	1529	1882	2270	2689	3139	3618	4654	**5842**	4′-6″
40	927	1210	1529	1884	2272	2693	3145	3626	4669	**5983**	4′-7″

B — SATURATED TOP SOIL Kµ′ − 0.150

10″ — HEIGHT OF BACKFILL **H** ABOVE TOP OF PIPE, FEET

TRENCH WIDTH AT TOP OF PIPE

H	1′-9″	2′-0″	2′-3″	2′-6″	2′-9″	3′-0″	3′-3″	3′-6″	4′-0″	4′-6″	Transition Width
5	587	703	**743**								2′-1″
6	655	791	**893**								2′-2″
7	713	866	**1043**								2′-3″
8	761	931	1106	**1193**							2′-4″
9	802	987	1179	**1344**							2′-5″
10	836	1035	1242	1455	**1495**						2′-7″
11	865	1077	1298	1526	**1645**						2′-8″
12	890	1112	1346	1589	**1795**						2′-9″
13	910	1143	1389	1645	**1946**						2′-9″
14	928	1170	1426	1695	1973	**2094**					2′-10″
15	942	1192	1459	1738	2030	**2241**					2′-11″
16	955	1212	1487	1777	2080	**2395**					3′-0″
17	965	1229	1512	1812	2126	2451	**2547**				3′-1″
18	974	1243	1534	1843	2167	2504	**2698**				3′-2″
19	981	1256	1553	1870	2203	2551	**2842**				3′-3″
20	987	1266	1570	1894	2236	2593	**2994**				3′-3″
21	992	1276	1584	1915	2265	2632	3014	**3150**			3′-4″
22	997	1284	1597	1934	2292	2667	3058	**3301**			3′-5″
23	1001	1291	1608	1951	2315	2699	3099	**3445**			3′-6″
24	1004	1296	1618	1966	2336	2727	3136	**3595**			3′-6″
25	1006	1301	1627	1979	2355	2753	3170	3604	**3739**		3′-7″
26	1008	1306	1634	1991	2373	2777	3201	3643	**3892**		3′-8″
27	1010	1310	1641	2001	2388	2798	3229	3679	**4041**		3′-9″
28	1012	1313	1647	2010	2401	2817	3255	3712	**4201**		3′-10″
29	1013	1316	1652	2019	2414	2834	3278	3743	**4340**		3′-11″
30	1014	1318	1656	2026	2425	2850	3300	3771	**4493**		4′-0″
31	1015	1320	1660	2032	2435	2864	3319	3796	**4642**		4′-0″
32	1016	1322	1663	2038	2444	2877	3337	3820	**4786**		4′-1″
33	1017	1323	1666	2043	2451	2889	3353	3842	**4950**		4′-2″
34	1017	1325	1669	2048	2459	2899	3368	3861	4916	**5085**	4′-3″
35	1018	1326	1671	2052	2465	2909	3381	3880	4946	**5243**	4′-3″
36	1018	1327	1673	2055	2471	2918	3393	3896	4974	**5397**	4′-4″
37	1019	1328	1675	2058	2476	2925	3405	3912	5000	**5549**	4′-5″
38	1019	1328	1676	2061	2480	2932	3415	3926	5024	**5697**	4′-5″
39	1019	1329	1678	2064	2485	2939	3424	3939	5047	**5842**	4′-6″
40	1019	1330	1679	2066	2488	2945	3433	3950	5067	**5983**	4′-7″

HEIGHT OF BACKFILL H ABOVE TOP OF PIPE, FEET

C — ORDINARY CLAY Kμ'—0.130

TRENCH WIDTH AT TOP OF PIPE

H	1'-9"	2'-0"	2'-3"	2'-6"	2'-9"	3'-0"	3'-3"	3'-6"	4'-0"	4'-6"	▲TRANSITION WIDTH
5	617	**743**									2'-0"
6	694	833	**893**								2'-1"
7	761	919	**1043**								2'-2"
8	819	994	**1193**								2'-3"
9	868	1060	1258	**1344**							2'-4"
10	911	1119	1334	**1495**							2'-5"
11	948	1170	1400	**1645**							2'-6"
12	979	1215	1460	1713	**1795**						2'-7"
13	1007	1254	1513	1781	**1946**						2'-8"
14	1030	1289	1560	1843	**2094**						2'-9"
15	1051	1319	1603	1898	2267	**2241**					2'-10"
16	1068	1346	1640	1948	2325	**2395**					2'-11"
17	1083	1369	1674	1993	2378	**2547**					3'-0"
18	1096	1390	1703	2034	2426	2849	**2698**				3'-1"
19	1107	1408	1730	2070	2469	2900	**2842**				3'-2"
20	1117	1424	1754	2103	2509	2947	**2994**				3'-3"
21	1125	1438	1775	2133	2545	2989	3466	**3150**			3'-4"
22	1133	1450	1793	2159	2578	3029	3512	**3301**			3'-5"
23	1139	1461	1810	2184	2607	3064	3554	**3445**			3'-6"
24	1144	1470	1825	2205	2635	3097	3593	4165	**3595**		3'-7"
25	1149	1478	1838	2225	2659	3128	3630	4204	**3739**		3'-8"
26	1153	1486	1850	2242	2682	3155	3663	4240	**3892**		3'-9"
27	1156	1492	1861	2258	2702	3181	3693	4274	**4041**		3'-9"
28	1159	1498	1870	2273	2721	3204	3722	4305	**4201**		3'-10"
29	1162	1502	1878	2286	2738	3225	3748	4334	**4340**		3'-11"
30	1164	1507	1886	2297	2753	3245	3772	4361	**4493**		3'-11"
31	1166	1511	1892	2308	2767	3263	3794	4386	**4642**		4'-0"
32	1167	1514	1898	2317	2780	3279	3815	4409	**4786**		4'-0"
33	1169	1517	1904	2326	2791	3294	3834	4431	4911	**4950**	4'-1"
34	1171	1519	1908	2333	2802	3308	3851	4451	4951	**5085**	4'-1"
35	1171	1522	1913	2340	2811	3321	3868	4470	4988	**5243**	
36	1172	1524	1916	2346	2820	3333	3883		5024	**5397**	
37	1173	1525	1920	2352	2828	3343	3896		5549	**5549**	
38	1173	1527	1922	2357	2835	3353			5666	**5697**	
39	1174	1528	1925	2362	2842				5666	**5842**	
40	1174	1529	1927	2366					5696	**5983**	

D — SATURATED CLAY Kμ'—0.110

TRENCH WIDTH AT TOP OF PIPE

H	1'-9"	2'-0"	2'-3"	2'-6"	2'-9"	3'-0"	3'-3"	3'-6"	4'-0"	4'-6"	▲TRANSITION WIDTH
5	649	**743**									1'-11"
6	737	**893**									2'-0"
7	814	976	**1043**								2'-1"
8	882	1064	**1193**								2'-2"
9	943	1142	**1344**								2'-3"
10	996	1212	1435	**1495**							2'-4"
11	1042	1276	1516	**1645**							2'-5"
12	1084	1332	1589	**1795**							2'-5"
13	1120	1383	1655	**1946**							2'-6"
14	1152	1428	1715	2012	**2094**						2'-7"
15	1180	1469	1770	2082	**2241**						2'-8"
16	1205	1505	1819	2145	**2395**						2'-8"
17	1227	1537	1864	2204	**2547**						2'-9"
18	1247	1567	1905	2258	2685	**2698**					2'-10"
19	1264	1593	1942	2307	2743	**2842**					2'-10"
20	1279	1616	1975	2352	2796	**2994**					2'-11"
21	1292	1637	2005	2431	2846	**3150**					3'-0"
22	1304	1656	2033	2465	2891	**3301**					3'-0"
23	1314	1673	2058	2497	2933	3333	**3445**				3'-1"
24	1323	1688	2080	2526	2972	3387	**3595**				3'-1"
25	1331	1701	2101	2552	3008	3436	**3739**				3'-2"
26	1339	1714	2120	2576	3041	3483	**3892**				3'-2"
27	1345	1724	2136	2599	3071	3526	**4041**				3'-3"
28	1350	1734	2152	2619	3099	3566	4079	**4201**			3'-3"
29	1355	1743	2166	2638	3125	3603	4126	**4340**			3'-4"
30	1360	1751	2178	2655	3149	3637	4171	**4493**			3'-5"
31	1363	1758	2190	2670	3171	3669	4212	**4642**			3'-5"
32	1367	1764	2200	2685	3192	3699	4250	**4786**			3'-6"
33	1370	1769	2209	2698	3211	3727	4286	**4950**			3'-6"
34	1372	1774	2218	2710	3226	3752	4320	4911	**5085**		3'-7"
35	1374	1779	2226	2721	3244	3776	4351	4951	**5243**		3'-7"
36	1376	1783	2233	2731	3259	3798	4381	4988	**5397**		3'-8"
37	1378	1787	2239	2740	3273	3819	4408	5024	**5549**		3'-8"
38	1380	1790	2245	2749	3285	3856	4434	5057	**5697**		3'-9"
39	1381	1793	2250	2756	3297	3873	4458	5088	**5842**		3'-9"
40	1382	1795	2255				4480	5117	**5983**		3'-10"

* For backfill weighing 110 pounds per cubic foot; for 120 pounds per cubic foot, increase loads 10%; for … , increase 20%; etc.

▲Transition loads (**bold type**) and widths based on Kμ—0.19, rsdp—0.5 in the embankment equation

Interpolate for intermediate heights of backfill and/or trench widths

TABLE 16

BACKFILL LOADS ON CIRCULAR PIPE IN TRENCH INSTALLATION

*100 POUNDS PER LINEAR FOOT

B — SATURATED TOP SOIL Kμ'—0.150 — 12"

HEIGHT OF BACKFILL H ABOVE TOP OF PIPE, FEET

H	TRENCH WIDTH AT TOP OF PIPE										TRANSITION WIDTH
	2'-0"	2'-3"	2'-6"	2'-9"	3'-0"	3'-3"	3'-6"	4'-0"	4'-6"	5'-0"	
5	703	821	939	**985**							2'-7"
6	791	929	1069	**1185**							2'-8"
7	866	1023	1183	1346	**1385**						2'-10"
8	931	1106	1285	1467	**1585**						2'-11"
9	987	1179	1375	1576	**1786**						3'-0"
10	1035	1242	1455	1674	1896	**1982**					3'-1"
11	1077	1298	1526	1761	2001	**2182**					3'-2"
12	1112	1346	1589	1840	2096	**2385**					3'-3"
13	1143	1389	1645	1910	2182	2460	**2581**				3'-4"
14	1170	1426	1695	1973	2260	2553	**2785**				3'-5"
15	1192	1457	1738	2030	2330	2639	**2986**				3'-6"
16	1212	1487	1777	2080	2394	2716	3047	**3186**			3'-7"
17	1229	1512	1812	2126	2451	2787	3132	**3385**			3'-8"
18	1243	1534	1843	2167	2504	2852	3210	**3588**			3'-9"
19	1256	1553	1870	2203	2551	2911	3282	**3780**			3'-10"
20	1266	1570	1894	2236	2593	2965	3347	**3979**			3'-11"
21	1276	1584	1915	2265	2632	3014	3408	**4177**			4'-0"
22	1284	1597	1934	2292	2667	3058	3463	4383	**4377**		4'-1"
23	1291	1608	1951	2315	2699	3099	3514	4451	**4581**		4'-2"
24	1296	1618	1966	2336	2727	3136	3561	4515	**4777**		4'-3"
25	1301	1627	1979	2355	2753	3170	3604	4574	**4979**		4'-4"
26	1306	1634	1991	2373	2777	3201	3643	4629	**5174**		4'-5"
27	1310	1641	2001	2388	2798	3229	3679	4680	**5377**		4'-6"
28	1313	1647	2010	2401	2817	3255	3712	4727	**5575**		4'-7"
29	1316	1652	2019	2414	2834	3278	3743	4771	**5784**		4'-8"
30	1318	1656	2026	2425	2850	3300	3771	4811	5836	**5969**	4'-9"
31	1320	1660	2032	2435	2864	3319	3796	4849	5895	**6188**	4'-10"
32	1322	1663	2038	2444	2877	3337	3820	4884	5950	**6381**	4'-11"
33	1323	1666	2043	2451	2889	3353	3842	4916	6002	**6569**	5'-0"
34	1325	1669	2048	2459	2899	3368	3861	4946	6050	**6774**	5'-1"
35	1326	1671	2052	2465	2909	3381	3880	4974	6095	**6976**	5'-2"
36	1327	1673	2055	2471	2918	3393	3896	5000	6137	**7173**	
37	1328	1675	2058	2476	2925	3405	3912	5024	6177	**7365**	
38	1328	1676	2061	2480	2932	3415	3926	5047	6214	**7583**	
39	1329	1678	2064	2485	2939	3424	3939	5067	6248	**7765**	
40	1330	1679	2066	2488	2945	3433	3950		6280	**7976**	

*100 POUNDS PER CUBIC FOOT BACKFILL MATERIAL

A — SAND AND GRAVEL Kμ'—0.165 — 12"

HEIGHT OF BACKFILL H ABOVE TOP OF PIPE, FEET

H	TRENCH WIDTH AT TOP OF PIPE										TRANSITION WIDTH
	2'-0"	2'-3"	2'-6"	2'-9"	3'-0"	3'-3"	3'-6"	4'-0"	4'-6"	5'-0"	
5	680	797	915	**985**							2'-8"
6	761	897	1036	**1185**							2'-9"
7	830	984	1142	1302	**1385**						2'-11"
8	888	1059	1235	1414	**1585**						3'-0"
9	937	1124	1316	1513	1713	**1786**					3'-1"
10	979	1180	1388	1601	1819	**1982**					3'-2"
11	1014	1228	1450	1679	1914	**2182**					3'-3"
12	1044	1270	1505	1748	1998	2254	**2385**				3'-5"
13	1070	1306	1553	1810	2074	2345	**2581**				3'-7"
14	1091	1337	1595	1864	2142	2428	2720	**2785**			3'-8"
15	1110	1364	1632	1912	2203	2502	2809	**2986**			3'-10"
16	1125	1387	1664	1955	2258	2570	2890	**3186**			3'-11"
17	1138	1407	1693	1993	2306	2631	2964	**3385**			4'-0"
18	1149	1424	1717	2027	2350	2686	3032	**3588**			4'-1"
19	1159	1439	1739	2057	2389	2735	3093	**3780**			4'-2"
20	1167	1452	1758	2083	2425	2780	3148	**3979**			4'-3"
21	1174	1463	1775	2107	2456	2821	3199	3991	**4177**		4'-4"
22	1179	1473	1790	2128	2484	2857	3245	4058	**4377**		4'-5"
23	1184	1481	1802	2146	2510	2891	3287	4121	**4581**		4'-6"
24	1189	1488	1814	2163	2532	2920	3325	4179	**4777**		4'-7"
25	1192	1494	1824	2177	2552	2947	3360	4232	**4979**		4'-8"
26	1195	1500	1832	2190	2571	2972	3392	4280	**5174**		4'-10"
27	1198	1504	1840	2201	2587	2994	3425	4325	5289	**5377**	4'-10"
28	1200	1508	1846	2212	2601	3014	3447	4367	5349	**5575**	4'-11"
29	1201	1512	1852	2221	2614	3032	3471	4405	5404	**5784**	5'-1"
30	1203	1515	1857	2229	2626	3048	3492	4440	5456	**5969**	5'-2"
31	1204	1517	1862	2236	2637	3063	3512	4472	5504	**6188**	5'-3"
32	1205	1520	1866	2242	2646	3076	3530	4502	5549	**6381**	5'-4"
33	1206	1521	1869	2252	2654	3088	3546	4529	5589	**6569**	
34	1207	1523	1872	2257	2662	3099	3562	4555	5629	**6774**	
35	1208	1525	1875	2261	2669	3109	3575	4578	5665	**6976**	
36	1208	1526	1877	2264	2675	3118	3587	4599	5698	**7173**	
37	1209	1527	1879	2267	2680	3126	3598	4619	5729	**7365**	
38	1209	1528	1881	2270	2685	3133	3608	4637	5758	**7583**	
39	1210	1529	1882	2272	2689	3139	3618	4654	5784	**7765**	
40	1210	1529	1884	2272	2693	3145	3626	4669	5809	**7976**	

C — ORDINARY CLAY Kμ'—0.130

HEIGHT OF BACKFILL H ABOVE TOP OF PIPE, FEET — TRENCH WIDTH AT TOP OF PIPE

(Bold = transition load. ▲ = transition width.)

H	2'-0"	2'-3"	2'-6"	2'-9"	3'-0"	3'-3"	3'-6"	4'-0"	4'-6"	5'-0"	▲TRANSITION WIDTH
5	735	854	**985**								2'-6"
6	833	973	1115	**1185**							2'-7"
7	919	1079	1243	**1385**							2'-9"
8	994	1174	1357	1543	**1585**						2'-10"
9	1060	1258	1461	1666	**1786**						2'-11"
10	1119	1334	1554	1778	**1982**						3'-0"
11	1170	1400	1638	1880	2127	**2182**					3'-1"
12	1215	1460	1713	1973	2238	**2385**					3'-2"
13	1254	1513	1781	2057	2339	**2581**					3'-2"
14	1289	1560	1843	2134	2432	**2785**					3'-3"
15	1319	1603	1898	2204	2518	2838	**2986**				3'-4"
16	1346	1640	1948	2267	2596	2932	**3186**				3'-5"
17	1369	1674	1993	2325	2668	3019	**3385**				3'-6"
18	1390	1703	2034	2378	2734	3099	**3588**				3'-6"
19	1408	1730	2070	2426	2794	3173	3562	**3780**			3'-8"
20	1424	1754	2103	2469	2849	3242	3645	**3979**			3'-8"
21	1438	1775	2133	2509	2900	3305	3721	**4177**			3'-9"
22	1450	1793	2159	2545	2947	3363	3792	**4377**			3'-10"
23	1461	1810	2184	2578	2989	3417	3858	**4581**			3'-11"
24	1470	1825	2205	2607	3029	3466	3919	**4777**			3'-11"
25	1478	1838	2225	2635	3064	3512	3975	**4979**			4'-0"
26	1486	1850	2242	2659	3097	3554	4028	5018	**5174**		4'-1"
27	1492	1861	2258	2682	3128	3593	4077	5089	**5377**		4'-2"
28	1498	1870	2273	2702	3155	3630	4122	5156	**5575**		4'-2"
29	1502	1878	2286	2721	3181	3663	4165	5219	**5784**		4'-3"
30	1507	1886	2297	2738	3204	3693	4204	5278	**5969**		4'-4"
31	1511	1892	2308	2753	3225	3722	4240	5333	**6188**		4'-5"
32	1514	1898	2317	2767	3245	3748	4274	5385	**6381**		4'-5"
33	1517	1904	2326	2780	3263	3772	4305	5433	**6569**		4'-6"
34	1519	1908	2333	2791	3279	3794	4334	5478	**6774**		4'-6"
35	1522	1913	2340	2802	3294	3815	4361	5521	6757	**6976**	4'-7"
36	1524	1916	2346	2811	3308	3834	4386	5561	6815	**7173**	4'-8"
37	1525	1920	2352	2821	3321	3851	4409	5598	6870	**7365**	4'-8"
38	1527	1922	2357	2828	3333	3868	4431	5633	6921	**7583**	4'-9"
39	1528	1925	2362	2835	3343	3883	4451	5666	6970	**7765**	4'-9"
40	1529	1927	2366	2842	3353	3896	4470	5696	7016	**7976**	4'-10"

D — SATURATED CLAY Kμ'—0.110

HEIGHT OF BACKFILL H ABOVE TOP OF PIPE, FEET — TRENCH WIDTH AT TOP OF PIPE

(Bold = transition load. ▲ = transition width.)

H	2'-0"	2'-3"	2'-6"	2'-9"	3'-0"	3'-3"	3'-6"	4'-0"	4'-6"	5'-0"	▲TRANSITION WIDTH
5	769	889	**985**								2'-5"
6	878	1021	**1185**								2'-6"
7	976	1140	1306	**1385**							2'-7"
8	1064	1248	1435	**1585**							2'-8"
9	1142	1346	1554	**1786**							2'-9"
10	1212	1435	1662	1892	**1982**						2'-10"
11	1276	1516	1761	2011	**2182**						2'-11"
12	1332	1589	1852	2121	**2385**						3'-0"
13	1383	1655	1935	2222	2514	**2581**					3'-1"
14	1428	1715	2012	2315	2625	**2785**					3'-2"
15	1469	1770	2082	2402	2729	**2986**					3'-2"
16	1505	1819	2145	2481	2825	**3186**					3'-3"
17	1537	1864	2203	2555	2914	3282	**3385**				3'-4"
18	1567	1905	2258	2623	2998	3381	**3588**				3'-5"
19	1593	1942	2307	2685	3075	3474	**3780**				3'-5"
20	1616	1975	2352	2743	3147	3561	**3979**				3'-6"
21	1637	2005	2393	2796	3213	3642	4080	**4177**			3'-7"
22	1656	2033	2431	2846	3275	3718	4171	**4377**			3'-7"
23	1673	2058	2465	2891	3333	3789	4256	**4581**			3'-8"
24	1688	2080	2497	2933	3387	3855	4336	**4777**			3'-9"
25	1701	2101	2526	2972	3436	3917	4411	**4979**			3'-9"
26	1714	2120	2552	3008	3483	3975	4481	**5174**			3'-10"
27	1724	2136	2576	3041	3526	4029	4548	**5377**			3'-11"
28	1734	2152	2599	3071	3566	4079	4610	**5575**			3'-11"
29	1743	2166	2619	3099	3603	4126	4668	**5784**			4'-0"
30	1751	2178	2638	3125	3637	4171	4723	**5969**			4'-0"
31	1758	2190	2655	3146	3669	4212	4774	5950	**6188**		4'-1"
32	1764	2200	2670	3171	3699	4250	4823	6021	**6381**		4'-2"
33	1769	2209	2685	3192	3727	4286	4868	6088	**6569**		4'-2"
34	1774	2218	2698	3211	3752	4320	4911	6151	**6774**		4'-3"
35	1779	2226	2710	3228	3776	4351	4951	6211	**6976**		4'-4"
36	1783	2233	2721	3244	3798	4381	4988	6268	**7173**		4'-4"
37	1787	2239	2731	3259	3819	4408	5024	6322	**7365**		4'-5"
38	1790	2245	2740	3273	3838	4434	5057	6373	**7583**		4'-6"
39	1793	2250	2749	3285	3856	4458	5088	6421	**7765**		4'-6"
40	1795	2255	2756	3297	3873	4480	5117	6466	**7976**		4'-6"

For backfill weighing 110 pounds per cubic foot, increase loads 10%; for 120 pounds per cubic foot, increase 20%; etc.

▲ *Transition loads (**bold type**) and widths based on Kμ—0.19, $r_{sd}p$—0.5 in the embankment equation*

Interpolate for intermediate heights of backfill and/or trench widths

TABLE 17

BACKFILL LOADS ON CIRCULAR PIPE IN TRENCH INSTALLATION

15″

A — 15″ — SAND AND GRAVEL Kμ'—0.165
*100 POUNDS PER CUBIC FOOT BACKFILL MATERIAL

HEIGHT OF BACKFILL H (FEET)	2'-3"	2'-6"	2'-9"	3'-0"	3'-3"	3'-6"	4'-0"	4'-6"	5'-0"	6'-0"	TRANSITION WIDTH
5	797	915	1033	1153	**1203**						3'-1"
6	897	1036	1176	1317	**1448**						3'-3"
7	984	1142	1302	1464	1628	**1692**					3'-4"
8	1059	1235	1414	1596	1780	**1938**					3'-5"
9	1124	1316	1513	1713	1917	2123	**2183**				3'-7"
10	1180	1388	1601	1819	2041	2266	**2429**				3'-8"
11	1228	1450	1679	1914	2153	2396	**2672**				3'-9"
12	1270	1505	1748	1998	2254	2514	**2920**				3'-11"
13	1306	1553	1810	2074	2345	2622	**3162**				4'-0"
14	1337	1595	1864	2142	2428	2720	3320	**3408**			4'-1"
15	1364	1632	1912	2203	2502	2809	3441	**3647**			4'-2"
16	1387	1664	1955	2258	2570	2890	3553	**3900**			4'-3"
17	1407	1693	1993	2306	2631	2964	3655	**4142**			4'-4"
18	1424	1717	2027	2350	2686	3032	3750	**4382**			4'-5"
19	1439	1739	2057	2389	2735	3093	3837	**4624**			4'-6"
20	1452	1758	2083	2425	2780	3148	3917	4720	**4870**		4'-7"
21	1463	1775	2107	2456	2821	3199	3991	4820	**5123**		4'-8"
22	1473	1790	2128	2484	2857	3245	4058	4913	**5368**		4'-9"
23	1481	1802	2146	2510	2891	3291	4121	5000	**5603**		4'-10"
24	1488	1814	2163	2532	2920	3325	4179	5080	**5851**		4'-11"
25	1494	1824	2177	2552	2947	3360	4232	5155	**6091**		5'-0"
26	1500	1832	2190	2571	2972	3392	4280	5224	6213	**6350**	5'-1"
27	1504	1840	2201	2587	2994	3421	4325	5289	6300	**6588**	5'-2"
28	1508	1846	2212	2601	3014	3447	4367	5349	6382	**6833**	5'-3"
29	1512	1852	2221	2614	3032	3471	4405	5404	6458	**7070**	5'-3"
30	1515	1857	2229	2626	3048	3492	4440	5456	6529	**7319**	5'-4"
31	1517	1862	2236	2637	3063	3512	4472	5504	6596	**7561**	5'-5"
32	1520	1866	2242	2646	3076	3530	4502	5549	6659	**7818**	5'-6"
33	1521	1869	2247	2654	3088	3546	4529	5590	6717	**8046**	5'-7"
34	1523	1872	2252	2662	3099	3561	4555	5629	6772	**8290**	5'-8"
35	1525	1875	2257	2669	3109	3575	4578	5665	6823	**8556**	5'-8"
36	1526	1877	2261	2675	3118	3587	4599	5698	6871	**8789**	5'-9"
37	1527	1879	2264	2680	3126	3598	4619	5729	6916	**9045**	5'-10"
38	1528	1881	2267	2685	3133	3608	4637	5758	6958	**9265**	5'-11"
39	1529	1882	2270	2689	3139	3618	4654	5784	6998	**9510**	6'-0"
40	1529	1884	2272	2693	3145	3626	4669	5809	7035	**9785**	6'-0"

B — 15″ — SATURATED TOP SOIL Kμ'—0.150
LOADS IN POUNDS PER LINEAR FOOT

HEIGHT OF BACKFILL H ABOVE TOP OF PIPE (FEET)	2'-3"	2'-6"	2'-9"	3'-0"	3'-3"	3'-6"	4'-0"	4'-6"	5'-0"	6'-0"	TRANSITION WIDTH
5	821	939	1059	1180	**1203**						3'-1"
6	929	1069	1210	1353	**1448**						3'-2"
7	1023	1183	1346	1510	**1692**						3'-3"
8	1106	1285	1467	1652	1838	**1938**					3'-5"
9	1179	1375	1576	1780	1986	**2183**					3'-6"
10	1242	1455	1674	1896	2122	2350	**2429**				3'-7"
11	1298	1526	1761	2001	2245	2492	**2672**				3'-8"
12	1346	1589	1840	2096	2357	2623	**2920**				3'-9"
13	1389	1645	1910	2182	2460	2743	**3162**				3'-10"
14	1426	1695	1973	2260	2553	2853	**3408**				3'-11"
15	1459	1738	2030	2330	2639	2954	**3647**				4'-0"
16	1487	1777	2080	2394	2716	3047	3726	**3900**			4'-2"
17	1512	1812	2126	2451	2787	3132	3843	**4142**			4'-3"
18	1534	1843	2167	2504	2852	3210	3950	**4382**			4'-4"
19	1553	1870	2203	2551	2911	3282	4050	**4624**			4'-5"
20	1570	1894	2236	2593	2965	3347	4143	**4870**			4'-6"
21	1584	1915	2265	2632	3014	3408	4229	**5123**			4'-7"
22	1597	1934	2292	2667	3058	3463	4309	5192	**5368**		4'-8"
23	1608	1951	2315	2699	3099	3514	4383	5293	**5603**		4'-9"
24	1618	1966	2336	2727	3136	3561	4451	5387	**5851**		4'-10"
25	1627	1979	2355	2753	3170	3604	4515	5475	**6091**		4'-11"
26	1634	1991	2373	2777	3201	3643	4574	5557	**6350**		5'-0"
27	1641	2001	2388	2798	3229	3679	4629	5634	**6588**		5'-2"
28	1647	2010	2401	2817	3255	3712	4680	5706	**6833**		5'-3"
29	1652	2019	2414	2834	3278	3743	4727	5773	6870	**7070**	5'-4"
30	1656	2026	2425	2850	3300	3771	4771	5836	6955	**7319**	5'-5"
31	1660	2032	2435	2864	3319	3796	4811	5895	7036	**7561**	5'-6"
32	1663	2038	2444	2877	3337	3820	4849	5950	7111	**7818**	5'-7"
33	1666	2043	2451	2889	3353	3842	4884	6002	7182	**8046**	5'-8"
34	1669	2048	2459	2899	3368	3861	4916	6050	7249	**8290**	5'-9"
35	1671	2052	2465	2909	3381	3880	4946	6095	7312	**8556**	5'-10"
36	1673	2055	2471	2918	3393	3896	4974	6137	7372	**8789**	5'-11"
37	1675	2058	2476	2925	3405	3912	5000	6177	7428	**9045**	6'-0"
38	1676	2061	2480	2932	3415	3926	5024	6214	7480	**9265**	6'-0"
39	1678	2064	2485	2939	3424	3939	5047	6248	7530	**9510**	6'-0"
40	1679	2066	2488	2945	3433	3950	5067	6280	7577	**9785**	6'-0"

TRENCH WIDTH AT TOP OF PIPE

HEIGHT OF BACKFILL H ABOVE TOP OF PIPE, FEET

D — SATURATED CLAY Kμ'—0.110

TRENCH WIDTH AT TOP OF PIPE (bold = transition loads/widths)

H	2'-3"	2'-6"	2'-9"	3'-0"	3'-3"	3'-6"	4'-0"	4'-6"	5'-0"	6'-0"	TRANSITION WIDTH
5	889	1011	1133	**1203**							2'-11"
6	1021	1165	1310	**1448**							3'-0"
7	1140	1306	1473	1642	**1692**						3'-1"
8	1248	1435	1624	1815	**1938**						3'-2"
9	1346	1554	1764	1976	**2183**						3'-3"
10	1435	1662	1892	2126	2361	**2429**					3'-4"
11	1516	1761	2011	2264	2520	**2672**					3'-5"
12	1589	1852	2121	2394	2670	**2920**					3'-6"
13	1655	1935	2222	2514	2809	**3162**					3'-7"
14	1715	2012	2315	2625	2940	3258	**3408**				3'-8"
15	1770	2082	2402	2729	3061	3399	**3647**				3'-9"
16	1819	2145	2481	2825	3175	3531	**3900**				3'-10"
17	1864	2204	2555	2914	3282	3655	**4142**				3'-11"
18	1905	2258	2623	2998	3381	3772	**4382**				3'-11"
19	1942	2307	2685	3075	3474	3881	**4624**				4'-0"
20	1975	2352	2743	3147	3561	3984	**4870**				4'-1"
21	2005	2393	2796	3213	3642	4080	4981	**5123**			4'-2"
22	2033	2431	2846	3275	3718	4171	5104	**5368**			4'-3"
23	2058	2465	2891	3333	3789	4256	5220	**5603**			4'-4"
24	2080	2497	2933	3387	3855	4336	5329	**5851**			4'-5"
25	2101	2526	2972	3436	3917	4411	5433	**6091**			4'-6"
26	2120	2552	3008	3483	3975	4481	5532	**6350**			4'-7"
27	2136	2576	3041	3526	4029	4548	5625	**6588**			4'-8"
28	2152	2599	3071	3566	4079	4610	5713	**6833**			4'-8"
29	2166	2619	3099	3603	4126	4668	5797	**7070**			4'-9"
30	2178	2638	3125	3637	4171	4723	5876	7081	**7319**		4'-10"
31	2190	2655	3149	3669	4212	4774	5950	7182	**7561**		4'-10"
32	2200	2670	3171	3699	4250	4823	6021	7278	**7818**		4'-11"
33	2209	2685	3192	3727	4286	4868	6088	7370	**8046**		5'-0"
34	2218	2698	3211	3752	4320	4911	6151	7458	**8290**		5'-1"
35	2226	2710	3228	3776	4351	4951	6211	7541	**8556**		5'-2"
36	2233	2721	3244	3798	4381	4988	6268	7620	**8789**		
37	2239	2731	3259	3819	4408	5024	6322	7696	**9045**		
38	2245	2740	3273	3838	4434	5057	6373	7768	**9265**		
39	2250	2749	3285	3856	4458	5088	6421	7836	9320	**9510**	
40	2255	2756	3297	3873	4480	5117	6466	7902	9408	**9785**	

C — ORDINARY CLAY Kμ'—0.130

TRENCH WIDTH AT TOP OF PIPE (bold = transition loads/widths)

H	2'-3"	2'-6"	2'-9"	3'-0"	3'-3"	3'-6"	4'-0"	4'-6"	5'-0"	6'-0"	TRANSITION WIDTH
5	854	974	1095	**1203**							3'-0"
6	973	1115	1259	1403	**1448**						3'-1"
7	1079	1243	1408	1574	**1692**						3'-2"
8	1174	1357	1543	1731	**1938**						3'-3"
9	1258	1461	1666	1874	2085	**2183**					3'-4"
10	1334	1554	1778	2006	2237	**2429**					3'-5"
11	1400	1638	1880	2127	2377	2672	**2920**				3'-6"
12	1460	1713	1973	2238	2506	2779	**3162**				3'-8"
13	1513	1781	2057	2339	2626	2917	**3408**				3'-8"
14	1560	1843	2134	2432	2736	3046	**3647**				3'-9"
15	1603	1898	2204	2518	2838	3165	**3900**				3'-10"
16	1640	1948	2267	2596	2932	3276	**3900**				3'-11"
17	1674	1993	2325	2668	3019	3378	**4142**				4'-0"
18	1703	2034	2378	2734	3099	3474	4243	**4382**			4'-1"
19	1730	2070	2426	2794	3173	3562	4364	**4624**			4'-2"
20	1754	2103	2469	2849	3242	3645	4476	**4870**			4'-3"
21	1775	2133	2509	2900	3305	3721	4582	**5123**			4'-4"
22	1793	2159	2545	2947	3363	3792	4681	**5368**			4'-5"
23	1810	2184	2578	2989	3417	3858	4773	**5603**			4'-5"
24	1825	2205	2607	3029	3466	3919	4860	**5851**			4'-6"
25	1838	2225	2635	3064	3512	3975	4942	5951	**6091**		4'-7"
26	1850	2242	2659	3097	3554	4028	5018	6054	**6350**		4'-8"
27	1861	2258	2682	3128	3593	4077	5089	6151	**6588**		4'-8"
28	1870	2273	2702	3155	3630	4122	5156	6243	**6833**		4'-9"
29	1878	2286	2721	3181	3663	4165	5219	6330	**7070**		4'-10"
30	1886	2297	2738	3204	3693	4204	5278	6412	**7319**		4'-11"
31	1892	2308	2753	3225	3722	4240	5333	6489	7561		4'-11"
32	1898	2317	2767	3245	3748	4274	5385	6562	**7818**		5'-0"
33	1904	2326	2780	3263	3772	4305	5433	6631	7886	**8046**	5'-1"
34	1908	2333	2791	3279	3794	4334	5478	6696	7974	**8290**	5'-2"
35	1913	2340	2802	3294	3815	4361	5521	6757	8057	**8556**	5'-2"
36	1916	2346	2811	3308	3834	4386	5561	6815	8136	**8789**	5'-3"
37	1920	2352	2820	3321	3851	4409	5598	6870	8211	**9045**	5'-4"
38	1922	2357	2828	3333	3868	4431	5633	6921	8282	**9265**	5'-4"
39	1925	2362	2835	3343	3883	4451	5666	6970	8350	**9510**	5'-5"
40	1927	2366	2842	3353	3896	4470	5696	7016	8414	**9785**	5'-6"

HEIGHT OF BACKFILL H ABOVE TOP OF PIPE, FEET

* For backfill weighing 110 pounds per cubic foot. For backfill weighing 120 pounds per cubic foot, increase loads 10%; for 120 pounds per cubic foot, increase 20%; etc.

▲Transition loads (**bold type**) and widths based on Kμ—0.19, rsdp—0.5 in the embankment equation

Interpolate for intermediate heights of backfill and/or trench widths

TABLE 18   **18"**

BACKFILL LOADS ON CIRCULAR PIPE IN TRENCH INSTALLATION

*100 POUNDS PER CUBIC FOOT BACKFILL MATERIAL   LOADS IN POUNDS PER LINEAR FOOT

HEIGHT OF BACKFILL **H** ABOVE TOP OF PIPE, FEET

A. SAND AND GRAVEL Kμ'—0.165

18" — TRENCH WIDTH AT TOP OF PIPE

H	2'-6"	2'-9"	3'-0"	3'-3"	3'-6"	4'-0"	4'-6"	5'-0"	6'-0"	7'-0"	TRANSITION WIDTH
5	915	1033	1153	1274	**1411**						3'- 6"
6	1036	1176	1317	1460	1603	**1700**					3'- 8"
7	1142	1302	1464	1628	1793	**1989**					3'-10"
8	1235	1414	1596	1780	1966	**2277**					3'-11"
9	1316	1513	1713	1917	2123	**2566**					4'- 0"
10	1388	1601	1819	2041	2266	2723	**2855**				4'- 2"
11	1450	1679	1914	2153	2396	2891	**3145**				4'- 3"
12	1505	1748	1998	2254	2514	3046	**3431**				4'- 4"
13	1553	1810	2074	2345	2622	3189	**3718**				4'- 5"
14	1595	1864	2142	2428	2720	3320	3938	**4012**			4'- 7"
15	1632	1912	2203	2502	2809	3441	4093	**4298**			4'- 8"
16	1664	1955	2258	2570	2890	3553	4238	**4584**			4'- 9"
17	1693	1993	2306	2631	2964	3655	4372	**4877**			4'-10"
18	1717	2027	2350	2686	3032	3750	4497	**5168**			4'-11"
19	1739	2057	2389	2735	3093	3837	4613	**5444**			5'- 0"
20	1758	2083	2425	2780	3148	3917	4720	5552	**5737**		5'- 1"
21	1775	2107	2456	2821	3199	3991	4820	5681	**6035**		5'- 2"
22	1790	2128	2484	2857	3245	4058	4913	5802	**6324**		5'- 3"
23	1802	2146	2510	2891	3287	4121	5000	5915	**6600**		5'- 4"
24	1814	2163	2532	2920	3325	4179	5080	6021	**6887**		5'- 5"
25	1824	2177	2552	2947	3360	4232	5155	6120	**7189**		5'- 6"
26	1832	2190	2571	2972	3392	4280	5224	6213	**7455**		5'- 7"
27	1840	2201	2587	2994	3421	4325	5289	6300	**7768**		5'- 8"
28	1846	2212	2601	3014	3447	4367	5349	6382	**8044**		5'- 9"
29	1852	2221	2614	3032	3471	4405	5404	6458	**8344**		5'-10"
30	1857	2229	2626	3048	3492	4440	5456	6530	**8636**		5'-11"
31	1862	2236	2637	3063	3512	4472	5504	6596	**8901**		6'- 0"
32	1866	2242	2646	3076	3530	4502	5549	6659	9032	**9198**	6'- 1"
33	1869	2247	2654	3088	3546	4529	5590	6717	9132	**9488**	6'- 2"
34	1872	2252	2662	3099	3561	4555	5629	6772	9227	**9771**	6'- 3"
35	1875	2257	2669	3109	3575	4578	5665	6823	9317	**10070**	6'- 4"
36	1877	2261	2675	3118	3587	4599	5698	6871	9402	**10340**	6'- 5"
37	1879	2264	2680	3126	3598	4619	5729	6916	9483	**10630**	6'- 6"
38	1881	2267	2685	3133	3608	4637	5758	6958	9559	**10940**	6'- 7"
39	1882	2270	2689	3139	3618	4654	5784	6998	9631	**11220**	6'- 8"
40	1884	2272	2693	3145	3626	4669	5809	7035	9700	**11520**	6'- 9"

B. SATURATED TOP SOIL Kμ'—0.150

18" — TRENCH WIDTH AT TOP OF PIPE

H	2'-6"	2'-9"	3'-0"	3'-3"	3'-6"	4'-0"	4'-6"	5'-0"	6'-0"	7'-0"	TRANSITION WIDTH
5	939	1059	1180	1301	**1411**						3'- 6"
6	1069	1210	1353	1497	1641	**1700**					3'- 7"
7	1183	1346	1510	1675	1842	**1989**					3'- 9"
8	1285	1467	1652	1838	2026	**2277**					3'-10"
9	1375	1576	1780	1986	2195	**2566**					3'-11"
10	1455	1674	1896	2122	2350	2814	**2855**				4'- 1"
11	1526	1761	2001	2245	2492	2996	**3145**				4'- 2"
12	1589	1840	2096	2357	2623	3164	**3431**				4'- 3"
13	1645	1910	2182	2460	2743	3321	**3718**				4'- 4"
14	1695	1973	2260	2553	2853	3466	**4012**				4'- 5"
15	1738	2030	2330	2639	2954	3601	**4298**				4'- 6"
16	1777	2080	2394	2716	3047	3726	4426	**4584**			4'- 7"
17	1812	2126	2451	2787	3132	3843	4576	**4877**			4'- 8"
18	1843	2167	2504	2852	3210	3950	4716	**5168**			4'- 9"
19	1870	2203	2551	2911	3282	4050	4848	**5444**			4'-10"
20	1894	2236	2593	2965	3347	4143	4970	**5737**			4'-11"
21	1915	2265	2632	3014	3408	4229	5085	**6035**			5'- 0"
22	1934	2292	2667	3058	3463	4309	5192	6107	**6324**		5'- 1"
23	1951	2315	2699	3099	3514	4383	5293	6236	**6600**		5'- 2"
24	1966	2336	2727	3136	3561	4451	5387	6358	**6887**		5'- 3"
25	1979	2355	2753	3170	3604	4515	5475	6473	**7189**		5'- 4"
26	1991	2373	2777	3201	3643	4574	5557	6582	**7455**		5'- 5"
27	2001	2388	2798	3229	3679	4629	5634	6684	**7768**		5'- 6"
28	2010	2401	2817	3255	3712	4680	5706	6780	**8044**		5'- 7"
29	2019	2414	2834	3278	3743	4727	5773	6870	**8344**		5'- 8"
30	2026	2425	2850	3300	3771	4771	5836	6955	**8636**		5'- 9"
31	2032	2435	2864	3319	3796	4811	5895	7036	**8901**		5'-10"
32	2038	2444	2877	3337	3820	4849	5950	7111	**9198**		5'-11"
33	2043	2451	2889	3353	3842	4884	6002	7182	**9488**		6'- 0"
34	2048	2459	2899	3368	3861	4916	6050	7249	**9771**		6'- 1"
35	2052	2465	2909	3381	3880	4946	6095	7312	9914	**10070**	6'- 2"
36	2055	2471	2918	3393	3896	4974	6137	7372	10020	**10340**	6'- 3"
37	2058	2476	2925	3405	3912	5000	6177	7428	10110	**10630**	6'- 4"
38	2061	2480	2932	3415	3926	5024	6214	7480	10200	**10940**	6'- 5"
39	2064	2485	2939	3424	3939	5047	6248	7530	10290	**11220**	6'- 6"
40	2066	2488	2945	3433	3950	5067	6280	7577	10380	**11520**	6'- 7"

C — ORDINARY CLAY Kμ'=0.130

HEIGHT OF BACKFILL H ABOVE TOP OF PIPE, FEET

H	2'-6"	2'-9"	3'-0"	3'-3"	3'-6"	4'-0"	4'-6"	5'-0"	6'-0"	7'-0"	▲TRANSITION WIDTH
5	974	1095	1217	1339	**1411**						3'-5"
6	1115	1259	1403	1548	**1700**						3'-6"
7	1243	1408	1574	1741	1910	**1989**					3'-7"
8	1357	1543	1731	1920	2110	**2277**					3'-9"
9	1461	1666	1874	2085	2297	**2566**					3'-10"
10	1554	1778	2006	2237	2470	**2855**					3'-11"
11	1638	1880	2127	2377	2630	**3145**					4'-1"
12	1713	1973	2238	2506	2779	3332	**3431**				4'-2"
13	1781	2057	2339	2626	2917	3510	**3718**				4'-3"
14	1843	2134	2432	2736	3046	3676	**4012**				4'-4"
15	1898	2204	2518	2838	3165	3832	**4298**				4'-5"
16	1948	2267	2596	2932	3276	3978	**4584**				4'-6"
17	1993	2325	2668	3019	3378	4115	**4877**				4'-7"
18	2034	2378	2734	3099	3474	4243	5035	**5168**			4'-8"
19	2070	2426	2794	3173	3562	4364	5190	**5444**			4'-9"
20	2103	2469	2849	3242	3645	4476	5336	**5737**			4'-10"
21	2133	2509	2900	3305	3721	4582	5473	**6035**			4'-11"
22	2159	2545	2947	3363	3792	4681	5603	**6324**			4'-11"
23	2184	2578	2989	3417	3858	4773	5726	**6600**			5'-1"
24	2205	2607	3029	3466	3919	4860	5842	**6887**			5'-2"
25	2225	2635	3064	3512	3975	4942	5951	6994	**7189**		5'-3"
26	2242	2659	3097	3554	4028	5018	6054	7127	**7455**		5'-4"
27	2258	2682	3128	3593	4077	5089	6151	7253	**7768**		5'-5"
28	2273	2702	3155	3630	4122	5156	6243	7373	**8044**		5'-6"
29	2286	2721	3181	3663	4165	5219	6330	7486	**8344**		5'-7"
30	2297	2738	3204	3693	4204	5278	6412	7594	**8636**		5'-7"
31	2308	2753	3225	3722	4240	5333	6489	7697	**8901**		5'-8"
32	2317	2767	3245	3748	4274	5385	6562	7794	**9198**		5'-9"
33	2326	2780	3263	3772	4305	5433	6631	7886	**9488**		5'-10"
34	2333	2791	3279	3794	4334	5478	6696	7974	**9771**		5'-11"
35	2340	2802	3294	3815	4361	5521	6757	8057	**10070**		5'-11"
36	2346	2811	3308	3834	4386	5561	6815	8136	**10340**		6'-0"
37	2352	2820	3321	3851	4409	5598	6870	8211	**10630**		6'-0"
38	2357	2828	3333	3868	4431	5633	6921	8282	**10940**		6'-0"
39	2362	2835	3343	3883	4451	5666	6970	8350	**11220**		6'-0"
40	2366	2842	3353	3896	4470	5696	7016	8414	**11520**		6'-0"

D — SATURATED CLAY Kμ'=0.110

TRENCH WIDTH AT TOP OF PIPE

H	2'-6"	2'-9"	3'-0"	3'-3"	3'-6"	4'-0"	4'-6"	5'-0"	6'-0"	7'-0"	▲TRANSITION WIDTH
5	1011	1133	1255	1378	**1411**						3'-4"
6	1165	1310	1456	1602	**1700**						3'-5"
7	1306	1473	1642	1811	**1989**						3'-6"
8	1435	1624	1815	2007	2200	**2277**					3'-7"
9	1554	1764	1976	2190	2405	**2566**					3'-8"
10	1662	1892	2126	2361	2598	**2855**					3'-9"
11	1761	2011	2264	2520	2779	**3145**					3'-10"
12	1852	2121	2394	2670	2949	**3431**					3'-11"
13	1935	2222	2514	2809	3108	**3718**					4'-1"
14	2012	2315	2625	2940	3258	3905	**4012**				4'-2"
15	2082	2402	2729	3061	3399	4085	**4298**				4'-3"
16	2145	2481	2825	3175	3531	4256	**4584**				4'-3"
17	2204	2555	2914	3282	3655	4417	**4877**				4'-4"
18	2258	2623	2998	3381	3772	4570	**5168**				4'-4"
19	2307	2685	3075	3474	3881	4714	**5444**				4'-6"
20	2352	2743	3147	3561	3984	4851	**5737**				4'-6"
21	2393	2796	3213	3642	4080	4981	5907	**6035**			4'-7"
22	2431	2846	3275	3718	4171	5104	6064	**6324**			4'-8"
23	2465	2891	3333	3789	4256	5220	6214	**6600**			4'-8"
24	2497	2933	3387	3855	4336	5329	6357	**6887**			4'-9"
25	2526	2972	3436	3917	4411	5433	6493	**7189**			4'-10"
26	2552	3008	3483	3975	4481	5532	6622	**7455**			4'-11"
27	2576	3041	3526	4029	4548	5625	6745	**7768**			4'-11"
28	2599	3071	3566	4079	4610	5713	6863	**8044**			5'-0"
29	2619	3099	3603	4126	4668	5797	6974	**8191**			5'-1"
30	2638	3125	3637	4171	4723	5876	7081	**8328**			5'-2"
31	2655	3149	3669	4212	4774	5950	7182	**8458**			5'-3"
32	2670	3171	3699	4250	4823	6021	7278	**8583**			5'-3"
33	2685	3192	3727	4286	4868	6088	7370	**8703**			5'-4"
34	2698	3211	3752	4320	4911	6151	7458	**8817**			5'-4"
35	2710	3228	3776	4351	4951	6211	7541	**8927**			5'-5"
36	2721	3244	3798	4381	4988	6268	7620	9032	**10340**		5'-5"
37	2731	3259	3819	4408	5024	6322	7696	9132	**10630**		5'-6"
38	2740	3273	3838	4434	5057	6373	7768	9228	**10940**		5'-7"
39	2749	3285	3856	4458	5088	6421	7836	9320	**11220**		5'-7"
40	2756	3297	3873	4480	5117	6466	7902	9408	**11520**		5'-8"

* For backfill weighing 110 pounds per cubic foot, increase loads 10%; for 120 pounds per cubic foot, increase 20%; etc.
▲Transition loads (bold type) and widths based on Kμ—0.19, rsdp—0.5 in the embankment equation
Interpolate for intermediate heights of backfill and/or trench widths

TABLE 19 — 21"

BACKFILL LOADS ON CIRCULAR PIPE IN TRENCH INSTALLATION

*100 POUNDS PER CUBIC FOOT BACKFILL MATERIAL — LOADS IN POUNDS PER LINEAR FOOT

HEIGHT OF BACKFILL **H** ABOVE TOP OF PIPE, FEET

A — SAND AND GRAVEL $K\mu'$ − 0.165

H	_____ TRENCH WIDTH AT TOP OF PIPE _____										TRANSITION WIDTH
	3'-0"	3'-3"	3'-6"	3'-9"	4'-0"	4'-6"	5'-0"	5'-6"	6'-0"	7'-0"	
5	1153	1274	1395	1516							4'- 0"
6	1317	1460	1603	1748	1617	1951					4'- 1"
7	1464	1628	1793	1959	1892	2284					4'- 3"
8	1596	1780	1966	2153	2127	2617					4'- 4"
9	1713	1917	2123	2331	2342	2950					4'- 6"
10	1819	2041	2266	2493	2540	3189	3282				4'- 7"
11	1914	2153	2396	2642	2723	3397	3612				4'- 8"
12	1998	2254	2514	2779	2891	3591	3947				4'-10"
13	2074	2345	2622	2903	3046	3771	4280				4'-11"
14	2142	2428	2720	3018	3189	3938	4610				5'- 0"
15	2203	2502	2809	3123	3320	4093	4760	4942			5'- 3"
16	2258	2570	2890	3218	3441	4238	4940	5273			5'- 4"
17	2306	2631	2964	3306	3553	4372	5108	5606			5'- 5"
18	2350	2686	3032	3387	3655	4497	5266	5934			5'- 5"
19	2389	2735	3093	3460	3750	4613	5413	6274			5'- 6"
20	2425	2780	3148	3528	3837	4720	5552	6405	6598		5'- 7"
21	2456	2821	3199	3589	3917	4820	5681	6566	6942		5'- 8"
22	2484	2857	3245	3646	3991	4913	5802	6717	7273		5'- 9"
23	2510	2891	3287	3698	4058	5000	5915	6860	7591		5'-10"
24	2532	2920	3325	3745	4121	5080	6021	6994	7916		6'- 0"
25	2552	2947	3360	3789	4179	5155	6120	7121	8255		6'- 0"
26	2571	2972	3392	3828	4232	5224	6213	7240	8298	8582	6'- 1"
27	2587	2994	3421	3865	4280	5289	6300	7352	8438	8928	6'- 3"
28	2601	3014	3447	3898	4325	5349	6382	7458	8570	9266	6'- 4"
29	2614	3032	3471	3929	4367	5404	6458	7557	8695	9593	6'- 5"
30	2626	3048	3492	3957	4405	5456	6529	7651	8814	9910	6'- 5"
31	2637	3063	3512	3982	4440	5504	6596	7739	8926	10260	6'- 6"
32	2646	3076	3530	4006	4472	5549	6659	7822	9032	10590	6'- 7"
33	2654	3088	3546	4027	4502	5590	6717	7901	9132	10920	6'- 8"
34	2662	3099	3561	4047	4529	5629	6772	7974	9227	11250	6'- 9"
35	2669	3109	3575	4065	4555	5665	6823	8044	9317	11580	6'-11"
36	2675	3118	3587	4082	4578	5698	6871	8109	9402	11910	6'-11"
37	2680	3126	3598	4097	4599	5729	6916	8171	9483	12230	7'- 0"
38	2685	3133	3608	4110	4619	5758	6958	8229	9551	12580	7'- 1"
39	2689	3139	3618	4123	4637	5784	6998	8283	9631	12920	7'- 2"
40	2693	3145	3626	4135	4654	5809	7035	8335	9700	13250	7'- 3"

B — SATURATED TOP SOIL $K\mu'$ − 0.150

H	_____ TRENCH WIDTH AT TOP OF PIPE _____										TRANSITION WIDTH
	3'-0"	3'-3"	3'-6"	3'-9"	4'-0"	4'-6"	5'-0"	5'-6"	6'-0"	7'-0"	
5	1180	1301	1423	1545	1617						3'-11"
6	1353	1497	1641	1786	1951						4'- 0"
7	1510	1675	1842	2009	2178	2284					4'- 2"
8	1652	1838	2026	2215	2406	2617					4'- 3"
9	1780	1986	2195	2405	2617	2950					4'- 5"
10	1896	2122	2350	2581	2814	3282					4'- 6"
11	2001	2245	2492	2743	2996	3507	3612				4'- 7"
12	2096	2357	2623	2892	3164	3717	3947				4'- 8"
13	2182	2460	2743	3030	3321	3912	4280				4'-10"
14	2260	2553	2853	3158	3466	4095	4610				4'-11"
15	2330	2639	2954	3275	3601	4266	4942				5'- 0"
16	2394	2716	3047	3384	3726	4426	5142	5273			5'- 1"
17	2451	2787	3132	3484	3843	4576	5328	5606			5'- 2"
18	2504	2852	3210	3576	3950	4716	5503	5934			5'- 3"
19	2551	2911	3282	3662	4050	4848	5668	6274			5'- 4"
20	2593	2965	3347	3741	4143	4970	5823	6598			5'- 5"
21	2632	3014	3408	3813	4229	5085	5969	6942			5'- 6"
22	2667	3058	3463	3881	4309	5192	6107	7046	7273		5'- 7"
23	2699	3099	3514	3943	4383	5293	6236	7207	7591		5'- 8"
24	2727	3136	3561	4000	4451	5387	6358	7360	7916		5'- 9"
25	2753	3170	3604	4053	4515	5475	6473	7504	8255		5'-10"
26	2777	3201	3643	4101	4574	5557	6582	7641	8582		5'-11"
27	2798	3229	3679	4146	4629	5634	6684	7771	8928		6'- 0"
28	2817	3255	3712	4188	4680	5706	6780	7893	9040	9266	6'- 1"
29	2834	3278	3743	4226	4727	5773	6870	8010	9185	9593	6'- 2"
30	2850	3300	3771	4262	4771	5836	6955	8120	9322	9910	6'- 3"
31	2864	3319	3796	4294	4811	5895	7036	8224	9453	10260	6'- 4"
32	2887	3337	3820	4325	4849	5950	7111	8323	9577	10590	6'- 5"
33	2889	3353	3842	4352	4884	6002	7182	8416	9695	10920	6'- 6"
34	2899	3368	3861	4378	4916	6050	7249	8505	9807	11250	6'- 6"
35	2909	3381	3880	4402	4946	6095	7312	8588	9914	11580	6'- 7"
36	2918	3393	3896	4424	4974	6137	7372	8668	10020	11910	6'- 8"
37	2925	3405	3912	4444	5000	6177	7428	8743	10110	12230	6'- 9"
38	2932	3415	3926	4463	5024	6214	7480	8814	10200	12580	6'-10"
39	2939	3424	3939	4480	5047	6248	7530	8881	10290	12920	6'-11"
40	2945	3433	3950	4496	5067	6280	7577	8945	10380	13250	6'-11"

D — SATURATED CLAY $K\mu' - 0.110$

HEIGHT OF BACKFILL **H** ABOVE TOP OF PIPE, FEET — TRENCH WIDTH AT TOP OF PIPE

H	3'-0"	3'-3"	3'-6"	3'-9"	4'-0"	4'-6"	5'-0"	5'-6"	6'-0"	7'-0"	▲Trans. Width
5	1255	1378	1501	**1617**	**1951**						3'-9"
6	1456	1602	1749	1896	**2284**						3'-10"
7	1642	1811	1982	2152	2394	**2617**					3'-11"
8	1815	2007	2200	2394	2622	**2839**					4'-0"
9	1976	2190	2405	2622	2839	**2950**					4'-1"
10	2126	2361	2598	2836	3076	**3282**					4'-3"
11	2264	2520	2779	3039	3301	**3612**					4'-4"
12	2394	2670	2949	3230	3513	**3947**					4'-5"
13	2514	2809	3108	3410	3714	**4280**					4'-6"
14	2625	2940	3258	3580	3905	**4610**					4'-7"
15	2729	3061	3399	3740	4085	4783	**4942**				4'-8"
16	2825	3175	3531	3891	4256	4994	**5273**				4'-10"
17	2914	3282	3655	4034	4417	5195	**5606**				4'-11"
18	2998	3381	3772	4168	4570	5386	**5934**				5'-0"
19	3075	3474	3881	4295	4714	5568	**6274**				5'-1"
20	3147	3561	3984	4414	4851	5742	**6598**				5'-2"
21	3213	3642	4080	4527	4981	5907	**6942**				5'-4"
22	3275	3718	4171	4633	5104	6064	7047	**7273**			5'-5"
23	3333	3789	4256	4733	5220	6214	7233	**7591**			5'-7"
24	3387	3855	4336	4828	5329	6357	7410	**7916**			5'-7"
25	3436	3917	4411	4917	5433	6493	7581	**8255**			5'-8"
26	3483	3975	4481	5001	5532	6622	7743	**8582**			5'-10"
27	3526	4029	4548	5080	5625	6745	7899	**8928**			5'-10"
28	3566	4079	4610	5155	5713	6863	8048	**9266**			5'-11"
29	3603	4126	4668	5225	5797	6974	8191	9439	**9593**		6'-0"
30	3637	4171	4723	5292	5876	7081	8328	9608	**9910**		6'-0"
31	3669	4212	4774	5354	5950	7182	8458	9770	**10260**		6'-1"
32	3699	4250	4823	5414	6021	7278	8583	9926	**10590**		6'-2"
33	3727	4286	4868	5469	6088	7370	8703	10080	**10920**		
34	3752	4320	4911	5522	6151	7458	8817	10220	**11250**		
35	3776	4351	4951	5571	6211	7541	8927	10360	**11580**		
36	3798	4381	4988	5618	6268	7620	9032	10490	**11910**		
37	3819	4408	5024	5662	6322	7696	9132	10620	**12230**		
38	3838	4434	5057	5704	6373	7768	9228	10740	12300	**12580**	
39	3856	4458	5088	5743	6421	7836	9320	10860	12590	**12920**	
40	3873	4480	5117	5780	6466	7902	9408	10970		**13250**	

C — ORDINARY CLAY $K\mu' - 0.130$

HEIGHT OF BACKFILL **H** ABOVE TOP OF PIPE, FEET — TRENCH WIDTH AT TOP OF PIPE

H	3'-0"	3'-3"	3'-6"	3'-9"	4'-0"	4'-6"	5'-0"	5'-6"	6'-0"	7'-0"	▲Trans. Width
5	1217	1339	1461	**1584**	**1617**						3'-9"
6	1403	1548	1694	1840	**1951**						3'-11"
7	1574	1741	1910	2079	2249	**2284**					4'-1"
8	1731	1920	2110	2302	2495	**2617**					4'-2"
9	1874	2085	2297	2510	2725	**2950**					4'-3"
10	2006	2237	2470	2704	2941	**3282**					4'-4"
11	2127	2377	2630	2885	3143	3612	**3947**				4'-5"
12	2238	2506	2779	3054	3332	3894	**4280**				4'-7"
13	2339	2626	2917	3212	3510	4113	**4610**				4'-8"
14	2432	2736	3046	3359	3676	4319	**4942**				4'-9"
15	2518	2838	3165	3496	3832	4514	**5273**				4'-10"
16	2596	2932	3276	3624	3978	4698	**5606**				4'-11"
17	2668	3019	3378	3744	4115	4871	5844	**5934**			5'-0"
18	2734	3099	3474	3855	4243	5035	6035	**6274**			5'-1"
19	2794	3173	3562	3959	4364	5190	6216	**6598**			5'-2"
20	2849	3242	3645	4056	4476	5336	6388	**6942**			5'-3"
21	2900	3305	3721	4147	4582	5473	6552	**7273**			5'-4"
22	2947	3363	3792	4232	4681	5603	6707	**7591**			5'-5"
23	2989	3417	3858	4310	4773	5726	6855	**7916**			5'-6"
24	3029	3466	3919	4384	4860	5842	6994	8066	**8255**		5'-7"
25	3064	3512	3975	4452	4942	5951	7127	8230	**8582**		5'-7"
26	3097	3554	4028	4516	5018	6054	7253	8387	**8928**		5'-9"
27	3128	3593	4077	4576	5089	6151	7373	8537	**9266**		5'-10"
28	3155	3630	4122	4632	5156	6243	7486	8680	**9593**		5'-11"
29	3181	3663	4165	4684	5219	6330	7594	8817	**9910**		6'-0"
30	3204	3693	4204	4732	5278	6412	7697	8947	**10260**		6'-1"
31	3225	3722	4240	4778	5333	6489	7794	9071	10380	**10590**	6'-2"
32	3245	3748	4274	4820	5385	6562	7886	9189	10530	**10920**	6'-3"
33	3263	3772	4305	4859	5433	6631	7974	9302	10670	**11250**	6'-4"
34	3279	3794	4334	4896	5478	6696	8057	9410	10810	**11580**	6'-5"
35	3294	3815	4361	4930	5521	6757	8136	9513	10940	**11910**	6'-5"
36	3308	3834	4386	4962	5561	6815	8211	9610	11060	**12230**	6'-6"
37	3321	3851	4409	4992	5598	6870	8282	9704	11180	**12580**	6'-7"
38	3333	3868	4431	5020	5633	6921	8350	9793	11290	**12920**	
39	3343	3883	4451	5046	5666	6970	8414	9878	11400	**13250**	
40	3353	3896	4470	5070	5696	7016					

* For backfill weighing 110 pounds per cubic foot; increase loads 10%; for 120 pounds per cubic foot, increase 20%; etc.
Transition loads (**bold type**) and widths based on $K\mu - 0.19$, $r_{sd}p - 0.5$ in the embankment equation
▲Interpolate for intermediate heights of backfill and/or trench widths

TABLE 20

BACKFILL LOADS ON CIRCULAR PIPE IN TRENCH INSTALLATION

*100 POUNDS PER CUBIC FOOT BACKFILL MATERIAL — LOADS IN POUNDS PER LINEAR FOOT

24″ — A — SAND AND GRAVEL Kμ′ – 0.165

HEIGHT OF BACKFILL **H** ABOVE TOP OF PIPE, FEET — TRENCH WIDTH AT TOP OF PIPE

H	3'-6"	4'-0"	4'-6"	5'-0"	5'-6"	6'-0"	6'-6"	7'-0"	7'-6"	8'-0"	Transition Width
5	1395	1638	**1819**								4'-4"
6	1603	1892	**2199**								4'-6"
7	1793	2127	2463	**2576**							4'-8"
8	1966	2342	2723	**2954**							4'-10"
9	2123	2540	2964	**3331**							4'-11"
10	2266	2723	3189	**3705**							5'-0"
11	2396	2891	3397	3910	**4081**						5'-2"
12	2514	3046	3591	4144	**4456**						5'-3"
13	2622	3189	3771	4363	**4836**						5'-5"
14	2720	3320	3938	4568	**5209**						5'-6"
15	2809	3441	4093	4760	5439	**5580**					5'-7"
16	2890	3553	4238	4940	5656	**5955**					5'-8"
17	2964	3655	4372	5108	5861	**6330**					5'-10"
18	3032	3750	4497	5266	6053	**6708**					5'-11"
19	3093	3837	4613	5413	6234	**7082**					6'-0"
20	3148	3917	4720	5552	6405	7277	**7454**				6'-1"
21	3199	3991	4820	5681	6566	7472	**7842**				6'-2"
22	3245	4058	4913	5802	6717	7656	**8217**				6'-4"
23	3287	4121	5000	5915	6860	7830	**8598**				6'-5"
24	3325	4179	5080	6021	6994	7994	**8965**				6'-6"
25	3360	4232	5155	6120	7121	8150	9204	**9341**			6'-7"
26	3392	4280	5224	6213	7240	8298	9382	**9704**			6'-8"
27	3421	4325	5289	6300	7352	8438	9552	**10080**			6'-9"
28	3447	4367	5349	6382	7458	8570	9713	**10450**			6'-10"
29	3471	4405	5404	6458	7557	8695	9866	**10840**			6'-11"
30	3492	4440	5456	6529	7651	8814	10010	**11220**			7'-0"
31	3512	4472	5504	6596	7739	8926	10150	11400	**11580**		7'-1"
32	3530	4502	5549	6659	7822	9032	10280	11560	**11990**		7'-2"
33	3546	4529	5590	6717	7901	9132	10400	11710	**12330**		7'-3"
34	3561	4555	5629	6772	7974	9227	10520	11860	**12720**		7'-4"
35	3575	4578	5665	6823	8044	9317	10640	12000	**13090**		7'-5"
36	3587	4599	5698	6871	8109	9402	10740	12130	**13450**		7'-6"
37	3598	4619	5729	6916	8181	9483	10850	12250	13700	**13860**	7'-7"
38	3608	4637	5758	6958	8229	9559	10940	12370	13840	**14210**	7'-8"
39	3618	4654	5784	6998	8283	9631	11040	12490	13980	**14610**	7'-9"
40	3626	4669	5809	7035	8335	9700	11120	12600	14110	**14970**	7'-10"

24″ — B — SATURATED TOP SOIL Kμ′ – 0.150

HEIGHT OF BACKFILL **H** ABOVE TOP OF PIPE, FEET — TRENCH WIDTH AT TOP OF PIPE

H	3'-6"	4'-0"	4'-6"	5'-0"	5'-6"	6'-0"	6'-6"	7'-0"	7'-6"	8'-0"	Transition Width
5	1423	1667	**1819**								4'-4"
6	1641	1932	**2199**								4'-5"
7	1842	2178	2517	**2576**							4'-7"
8	2026	2406	2790	**2954**							4'-8"
9	2195	2617	3045	**3331**							4'-10"
10	2350	2814	3284	**3705**							4'-11"
11	2492	2996	3507	4026	**4081**						5'-1"
12	2623	3164	3717	4277	**4456**						5'-2"
13	2743	3321	3912	4513	**4836**						5'-3"
14	2853	3466	4095	4735	**5209**						5'-4"
15	2954	3601	4266	4945	**5580**						5'-6"
16	3047	3726	4426	5142	5870	**5955**					5'-7"
17	3132	3843	4576	5328	6094	**6330**					5'-8"
18	3210	3950	4716	5503	6305	**6708**					5'-9"
19	3282	4050	4848	5668	6506	**7082**					5'-10"
20	3347	4143	4970	5823	6696	**7454**					5'-11"
21	3408	4229	5085	5969	6876	**7842**					6'-0"
22	3463	4309	5192	6107	7046	8005	**8217**				6'-1"
23	3514	4383	5293	6236	7207	8200	**8598**				6'-2"
24	3561	4451	5387	6358	7360	8385	**8965**				6'-3"
25	3604	4515	5475	6473	7504	8561	**9341**				6'-4"
26	3643	4574	5557	6582	7641	8729	**9704**				6'-5"
27	3679	4629	5634	6684	7771	8889	**10080**				6'-6"
28	3712	4680	5706	6780	7893	9040	10220	**10450**			6'-7"
29	3743	4727	5773	6870	8010	9185	10390	**10840**			6'-8"
30	3771	4771	5836	6955	8120	9322	10560	**11220**			6'-9"
31	3796	4811	5895	7036	8224	9453	10720	**11580**			6'-10"
32	3820	4849	5950	7111	8323	9577	10870	**11990**			6'-11"
33	3842	4884	6002	7182	8416	9695	11010	**12330**			7'-0"
34	3861	4916	6050	7249	8505	9807	11150	12530	**12720**		7'-1"
35	3880	4946	6095	7312	8588	9914	11280	12690	**13090**		7'-2"
36	3896	4974	6137	7372	8668	10020	11410	12840	**13450**		7'-3"
37	3912	5000	6177	7428	8743	10110	11530	12990	**13860**		7'-4"
38	3926	5024	6214	7480	8814	10200	11640	13130	**14210**		7'-5"
39	3939	5047	6248	7530	8881	10290	11760	13260	**14610**		7'-6"
40	3950	5067	6280	7577	8945	10380	11860	13390	**14970**		7'-6"

D — SATURATED CLAY Kµ'—0.110

HEIGHT OF BACKFILL H ABOVE TOP OF PIPE, FEET

H	— TRENCH WIDTH AT TOP OF PIPE										TRANSITION WIDTH
	3'-6"	4'-0"	4'-6"	5'-0"	5'-6"	6'-0"	6'-6"	7'-0"	7'-6"	8'-0"	
5	1501	1748	**1819**								4'-2"
6	1749	2044	**2199**								4'-3"
7	1982	2323	**2576**								4'-4"
8	2200	2588	**2954**								4'-5"
9	2405	2839	**3331**								4'-7"
10	2598	3076	3559	**3705**							4'-8"
11	2779	3301	3828	**4081**							4'-9"
12	2949	3513	4085	**4456**							4'-10"
13	3108	3714	4329	**4836**							4'-11"
14	3258	3905	4562	**5209**							5'-0"
15	3399	4085	4783	5490	**5580**						5'-1"
16	3531	4256	4994	5743	**5955**						5'-2"
17	3655	4417	5195	5985	**6330**						5'-3"
18	3772	4570	5386	6216	**6708**						5'-3"
19	3881	4714	5568	6438	**7082**						5'-4"
20	3984	4851	5742	6650	**7454**						5'-5"
21	4080	4981	5907	6853	**7842**						5'-6"
22	4171	5104	6064	7047	8046	**8217**					5'-7"
23	4256	5220	6214	7233	8270	**8598**					5'-8"
24	4336	5329	6357	7410	8485	**8965**					5'-9"
25	4411	5433	6493	7581	8691	**9341**					5'-9"
26	4481	5532	6622	7743	8889	9704					5'-10"
27	4548	5625	6745	7899	9080	10080					5'-11"
28	4610	5713	6863	8048	9263	10450					6'-0"
29	4668	5797	6974	8191	9439	10710	**10840**				6'-1"
30	4723	5876	7081	8328	9608	10920	**11220**				6'-1"
31	4774	5950	7182	8458	9770	11110	11580				6'-2"
32	4823	6021	7278	8583	9926	11300	11990				6'-3"
33	4868	6088	7370	8703	10080	11480	12330				6'-4"
34	4911	6151	7458	8817	10220	11660	12720				6'-4"
35	4951	6211	7541	8927	10360	11830	13090				6'-5"
36	4988	6268	7620	9032	10490	11990	13450				6'-6"
37	5024	6322	7696	9132	10620	12150	13720	**13860**			6'-7"
38	5057	6373	7768	9228	10740	12300	13900	**14210**			6'-7"
39	5088	6421	7836	9320	10860	12450	14070	**14610**			6'-8"
40	5117	6466	7902	9408	10970	12590	14240	**14970**			6'-8"

C — ORDINARY CLAY Kµ'—0.130

HEIGHT OF BACKFILL H ABOVE TOP OF PIPE, FEET

H	— TRENCH WIDTH AT TOP OF PIPE										TRANSITION WIDTH
	3'-6"	4'-0"	4'-6"	5'-0"	5'-6"	6'-0"	6'-6"	7'-0"	7'-6"	8'-0"	
5	1461	1707	**1819**								4'-3"
6	1694	1987	**2199**								4'-4"
7	1910	2249	**2576**								4'-6"
8	2110	2495	2882	**2954**							4'-7"
9	2297	2725	3158	**3331**							4'-8"
10	2470	2941	3418	**3705**							4'-10"
11	2630	3143	3663	**4081**							4'-11"
12	2779	3332	3894	**4456**							5'-0"
13	2917	3510	4113	4724	**4836**						5'-1"
14	3046	3676	4319	4972	**5209**						5'-2"
15	3165	3832	4514	5207	**5580**						5'-3"
16	3276	3978	4698	5430	**5955**						5'-4"
17	3378	4115	4871	5643	**6330**						5'-5"
18	3474	4243	5035	5844	**6708**						5'-6"
19	3562	4364	5190	6035	6855	**7842**					5'-7"
20	3645	4476	5336	6216	7114	**8217**					5'-8"
21	3721	4582	5473	6388	7323	**8537**					5'-9"
22	3792	4681	5603	6552	7522	**8750**					5'-10"
23	3858	4773	5726	6707	7712	**8860**					5'-11"
24	3919	4860	5842	6855	7893	**8965**					6'-0"
25	3975	4942	5951	6994	8066	9341	**9548**				6'-2"
26	4028	5018	6054	7127	8230	9358	**9905**				6'-2"
27	4077	5089	6151	7253	8387	9548	**10230**				6'-3"
28	4122	5156	6243	7373	8537	9731	**10530**				6'-4"
29	4165	5219	6330	7486	8680	9905	**10820**				6'-5"
30	4204	5278	6412	7594	8817	10070	**11060**				6'-6"
31	4240	5333	6489	7697	8947	10230	11250	**11580**			6'-7"
32	4274	5385	6562	7794	9071	10380	11480	**11990**			6'-8"
33	4305	5433	6631	7886	9189	10530	11730	**12330**			6'-9"
34	4334	5478	6696	7974	9302	10670	11910	**12720**			6'-9"
35	4361	5521	6757	8057	9410	10800	12080	**13090**			6'-10"
36	4386	5561	6815	8211	9513	10940	12240	**13450**			6'-11"
37	4409	5598	6870	8282	9610	11060	12550	**13860**			7'-0"
38	4431	5633	6921	8282	9704	11180	12700	**14210**			7'-0"
39	4451	5666	6970	8350	9793	11290	12840	14420	**14610**		7'-1"
40	4470	5696	7016	8414	9878	11400	12970	14580	**14970**		7'-2"

* For backfill weighing 100 pounds per cubic foot. For backfill weighing 110 pounds per cubic foot, increase loads 10%; for 120 pounds per cubic foot, increase 20%; etc.

▲ Transition loads (**bold type**) and widths based on Kµ—0.19, $r_{sd}P$—0.5 in the embankment equation

Interpolate for intermediate heights of backfill and/or trench widths

TABLE 21

BACKFILL LOADS ON CIRCULAR PIPE IN TRENCH INSTALLATION
LOADS IN POUNDS PER LINEAR FOOT

27" — SAND AND GRAVEL BACKFILL MATERIAL
*100 POUNDS PER CUBIC FOOT Ku'—0.165

HEIGHT OF BACKFILL **H** ABOVE TOP OF PIPE, FEET — TRENCH WIDTH AT TOP OF PIPE

H	3'-6"	4'-0"	4'-6"	5'-0"	5'-6"	6'-0"	6'-6"	7'-0"	7'-6"	8'-0"	Trans. Width
5	1395	1638	1883	1988							4'-9"
6	1603	1892	2184	2444							4'-11"
7	1793	2127	2463	2802	2868						5'-1"
8	1966	2342	2723	3107	3288						5'-3"
9	2123	2540	2964	3393	3708						5'-4"
10	2266	2723	3189	3660	4129						5'-6"
11	2396	2891	3397	3910	4428	4550					5'-7"
12	2514	3046	3591	4144	4704	4968					5'-9"
13	2622	3189	3771	4363	4964	5385					5'-10"
14	2720	3320	3938	4568	5209	5809					6'-0"
15	2809	3441	4093	4760	5439	6128	6229				6'-1"
16	2890	3553	4238	4940	5656	6384	6641				6'-2"
17	2964	3655	4372	5108	5861	6626	7069				6'-3"
18	3032	3750	4497	5266	6053	6855	7489				6'-5"
19	3093	3837	4613	5413	6234	7072	7900				6'-6"
20	3148	3917	4720	5552	6405	7277	8164	8319			6'-7"
21	3199	3991	4820	5681	6566	7472	8394	8737			6'-8"
22	3245	4058	4913	5802	6717	7656	8612	9155			6'-9"
23	3287	4122	5000	5915	6860	7830	8820	9577			6'-10"
24	3325	4179	5080	6021	6994	7994	9017	10010			7'-0"
25	3360	4232	5155	6120	7121	8150	9204	10280	10420		7'-1"
26	3392	4280	5224	6213	7240	8298	9382	10490	10850		7'-2"
27	3421	4325	5289	6300	7352	8438	9552	10690	11260		7'-3"
28	3447	4367	5349	6382	7458	8570	9713	10880	11660		7'-4"
29	3471	4405	5404	6458	7557	8695	9866	11060	12080		7'-6"
30	3492	4440	5456	6529	7651	8814	10010	11240	12520		7'-7"
31	3512	4472	5504	6596	7739	8926	10150	11400	12690	12910	7'-8"
32	3530	4502	5549	6659	7822	9032	10280	11560	12880	13330	7'-9"
33	3546	4529	5590	6717	7901	9132	10410	11710	13060	13780	7'-10"
34	3561	4555	5629	6772	7974	9227	10520	11810	13230	14180	7'-11"
35	3575	4578	5665	6823	8044	9317	10640	12000	13390	14620	8'-0"
36	3587	4599	5698	6871	8109	9402	10740	12130	13550	15040	8'-1"
37	3598	4619	5729	6916	8171	9483	10850	12260	13700	15460	8'-2"
38	3608	4637	5758	6958	8229	9559	10940	12370	13840	15870	8'-3"
39	3618	4654	5784	6998	8283	9631	11040	12490	13980	16270	8'-4"
40	3626	4669	5809	7035	8335	9700	11120	12600	14110	16720	8'-4"

27" — SATURATED TOP SOIL Ku'—0.150

HEIGHT OF BACKFILL **H** ABOVE TOP OF PIPE, FEET — TRENCH WIDTH AT TOP OF PIPE

H	3'-6"	4'-0"	4'-6"	5'-0"	5'-6"	6'-0"	6'-6"	7'-0"	7'-6"	8'-0"	Trans. Width
5	1423	1667	1913	1988							4'-8"
6	1641	1932	2225	2444							4'-11"
7	1842	2178	2517	2868							5'-0"
8	2026	2406	2790	3176	3288						5'-2"
9	2195	2617	3045	3477	3708						5'-3"
10	2350	2814	3284	3759	4129						5'-5"
11	2492	2966	3507	4026	4550						5'-6"
12	2623	3164	3717	4277	4843	4968					5'-7"
13	2743	3321	3912	4513	5121	5385					5'-9"
14	2853	3466	4095	4735	5384	5809					5'-10"
15	2954	3601	4266	4945	5634	6229					5'-11"
16	3047	3726	4426	5142	5870	6641					6'-1"
17	3132	3843	4576	5328	6094	6871	7069				6'-1"
18	3210	3950	4716	5503	6305	7121	7489				6'-3"
19	3282	4050	4848	5668	6506	7359	7900				6'-4"
20	3347	4143	4970	5823	6696	7585	8319				6'-5"
21	3408	4229	5085	5969	6876	7800	8737				6'-6"
22	3463	4309	5192	6107	7046	8005	8981	9155			6'-8"
23	3514	4383	5293	6236	7207	8189	9211	9577			6'-9"
24	3561	4451	5387	6358	7360	8385	9431	10010			6'-10"
25	3604	4515	5475	6473	7504	8561	9641	10420			6'-10"
26	3643	4574	5557	6582	7641	8729	9841	10850			7'-1"
27	3679	4629	5634	6684	7771	8889	10030	11260			7'-1"
28	3712	4680	5706	6780	7893	9040	10220	11410	11660		7'-2"
29	3743	4727	5773	6870	8010	9185	10390	11620	12080		7'-3"
30	3771	4771	5836	6955	8120	9322	10560	11820	12520		7'-4"
31	3796	4811	5895	7036	8224	9453	10720	12010	12910		7'-6"
32	3820	4849	5950	7111	8323	9577	10870	12190	13330		7'-8"
33	3842	4884	6002	7182	8416	9695	11010	12360	13780		7'-9"
34	3861	4916	6050	7249	8505	9807	11150	12530	13940	14180	7'-10"
35	3880	4946	6095	7312	8588	9914	11280	12690	14130	14620	7'-11"
36	3896	4974	6137	7372	8668	10020	11410	12840	14310	15040	7'-11"
37	3912	5000	6177	7428	8743	10110	11530	12990	14480	15460	8'-1"
38	3926	5024	6214	7480	8814	10200	11640	13130	14650	15870	8'-2"
39	3939	5047	6248	7530	8881	10290	11760	13260	14810	16270	8'-3"
40	3950	5067	6280	7577	8945	10380	11860	13390	14960	16720	8'-4"

HEIGHT OF BACKFILL H ABOVE TOP OF PIPE, FEET

C — ORDINARY CLAY Kμ'=0.130

TRENCH WIDTH AT TOP OF PIPE

H (ft)	3'-6"	4'-0"	4'-6"	5'-0"	5'-6"	6'-0"	6'-6"	7'-0"	7'-6"	8'-0"	Transition Width
5	1461	1707	1954	**1988**							4'-7"
6	1694	1987	2281	**2444**							4'-9"
7	1910	2249	2590	**2868**							4'-11"
8	2110	2495	2882	**3288**							5'-0"
9	2297	2725	3158	3593	**3708**						5'-2"
10	2470	2941	3418	3898	**4129**						5'-3"
11	2630	3143	3663	4188	**4550**						5'-4"
12	2779	3332	3894	4463	**4968**						5'-5"
13	2917	3510	4113	4724	**5385**						5'-6"
14	3046	3676	4319	4972	5632	**5809**					5'-8"
15	3165	3832	4514	5207	5909	**6229**					5'-9"
16	3276	3978	4698	5430	6173	**6641**					5'-10"
17	3378	4115	4871	5643	6425	**7069**					5'-11"
18	3474	4243	5035	5844	6666	**7489**					6'-0"
19	3562	4364	5190	6035	6895	7768	**7900**				6'-1"
20	3645	4478	5336	6216	7114	8025	**8319**				6'-2"
21	3721	4582	5473	6388	7323	8272	**8737**				6'-3"
22	3792	4681	5603	6552	7522	8509	**9155**				6'-4"
23	3858	4773	5726	6707	7712	8735	**9577**				6'-5"
24	3919	4860	5842	6855	7893	8952	**10010**				6'-6"
25	3975	4942	5951	6994	8066	9159	10270	**10420**			6'-7"
26	4028	5018	6054	7127	8230	9358	10510	**10850**			6'-8"
27	4077	5089	6151	7253	8387	9548	10730	**11260**			6'-9"
28	4122	5156	6243	7373	8537	9731	10950	**11660**			6'-10"
29	4165	5219	6330	7486	8680	9905	11160	**12080**			6'-11"
30	4204	5279	6412	7594	8817	10070	11360	**12520**			7'-0"
31	4240	5333	6489	7697	8947	10230	11550	12910	**13330**		7'-1"
32	4274	5385	6562	7794	9071	10380	11730	13100	**13780**		7'-2"
33	4305	5433	6631	7886	9189	10530	11910	13310	**14180**		7'-3"
34	4334	5478	6696	7974	9302	10670	12090	13510	**14620**		7'-4"
35	4361	5521	6757	8057	9410	10810	12240	13710	**15040**		7'-5"
36	4386	5561	6815	8136	9513	10940	12400	13900	**15460**		7'-6"
37	4409	5598	6870	8211	9613	11060	12550	14080	**15870**		7'-7"
38	4431	5633	6921	8282	9704	11180	12700	14250	**16040**		7'-7"
39	4451	5666	6970	8350	9793	11290	12840	14420	16230	**16270**	7'-8"
40	4470	5696	7016	8414	9878	11400	12970	14580		**16720**	7'-8"

D — SATURATED CLAY Kμ'=0.110

TRENCH WIDTH AT TOP OF PIPE

H (ft)	3'-6"	4'-0"	4'-6"	5'-0"	5'-6"	6'-0"	6'-6"	7'-0"	7'-6"	8'-0"	Transition Width
5	1501	1748	**1988**								4'-6"
6	1694	2044	2340	**2444**							4'-8"
7	1982	2323	2667	**2868**							4'-10"
8	2200	2588	2979	**3288**							4'-11"
9	2405	2839	3276	**3708**							5'-0"
10	2598	3076	3559	4045	**4129**						5'-1"
11	2779	3301	3828	4360	**4550**						5'-2"
12	2949	3513	4085	4661	**4968**						5'-3"
13	3108	3714	4329	4950	**5385**						5'-4"
14	3258	3905	4562	5226	**5809**						5'-5"
15	3399	4085	4783	5490	**6229**						5'-6"
16	3531	4256	4994	5743	6499	**6641**					5'-6"
17	3655	4417	5195	5985	6784	**7069**					5'-7"
18	3772	4570	5386	6216	7057	**7489**					5'-8"
19	3881	4714	5568	6438	7319	**7900**					5'-9"
20	3984	4851	5742	6650	7571	**8319**					5'-10"
21	4080	4981	5907	6853	7813	**8737**					5'-11"
22	4171	5104	6064	7047	8046	**9155**					6'-0"
23	4256	5220	6214	7233	8270	9322	**9577**				6'-0"
24	4336	5329	6357	7410	8485	9576	**10010**				6'-1"
25	4411	5433	6493	7581	8691	9820	**10420**				6'-2"
26	4481	5532	6622	7743	8889	10060	**10850**				6'-3"
27	4548	5625	6745	7899	9080	10280	**11260**				6'-4"
28	4610	5713	6863	8048	9263	10500	**11660**				6'-5"
29	4668	5797	6974	8191	9439	10710	**12080**				6'-6"
30	4723	5876	7081	8328	9608	10920	12250	**12520**			6'-6"
31	4774	5950	7182	8458	9770	11110	12480	**12910**			6'-7"
32	4823	6021	7278	8583	9926	11300	12700	**13330**			6'-8"
33	4868	6088	7370	8703	10080	11480	12920	**13780**			6'-9"
34	4911	6151	7458	8817	10220	11660	13130	**14180**			6'-10"
35	4951	6211	7541	8927	10360	11830	13330	**14620**			6'-11"
36	4988	6268	7620	9032	10490	11990	13530	**15040**			7'-0"
37	5024	6322	7696	9132	10620	12150	13720	15310	**15460**		7'-0"
38	5077	6373	7768	9228	10740	12300	13900	15520	**15870**		7'-1"
39	5088	6421	7836	9320	10860	12450	14070	15730	**16270**		7'-2"
40	5117	6466	7902	9408	10970	12590	14240	15940	**16720**		7'-3"

* For backfill weighing 110 pounds per cubic foot; for 120 pounds per cubic foot, increase loads 10%; for 130 pounds per cubic foot, increase 20%; etc.

▲Transition loads (**bold type**) and widths based on Kμ'=0.19, $r_s d P$=0.5 in the embankment equation

Interpolate for intermediate heights of backfill and/or trench widths

TABLE 22

BACKFILL LOADS ON CIRCULAR PIPE IN TRENCH INSTALLATION
LOADS IN POUNDS PER LINEAR FOOT

30″

A — SAND AND GRAVEL Kμ′—0.165 (*100 POUNDS PER CUBIC FOOT BACKFILL MATERIAL)

H (ft)	*TRENCH WIDTH AT TOP OF PIPE 4'-0"	4'-6"	5'-0"	5'-6"	6'-0"	6'-6"	7'-0"	7'-6"	8'-0"	9'-0"	▲TRANSITION WIDTH
5	1638	1883	2119								5'-0"
6	1892	2184	2477	2686							5'-4"
7	2127	2463	2802	3155							5'-6"
8	2342	2723	3107	3494	3620						5'-8"
9	2540	2964	3393	3824	4085						5'-10"
10	2723	3189	3660	4135	4551						5'-11"
11	2891	3397	3910	4428	4951	5015					6'-2"
12	3046	3591	4144	4704	5270	5478					6'-4"
13	3189	3771	4363	4964	5572	5938					6'-5"
14	3320	3938	4568	5209	5858	6401					6'-6"
15	3441	4093	4760	5439	6128	6862					6'-8"
16	3553	4238	4940	5656	6384	7120	7330				6'-10"
17	3655	4372	5108	5861	6626	7401	7791				7'-0"
18	3750	4497	5266	6053	6855	7669	8250				7'-1"
19	3837	4613	5413	6234	7072	7923	8711				7'-2"
20	3917	4720	5552	6405	7277	8164	9064	9179			7'-3"
21	3991	4820	5681	6566	7472	8394	9331	9643			7'-4"
22	4058	4913	5802	6717	7656	8612	9585	10110			7'-5"
23	4121	5000	5915	6860	7830	8820	9827	10570			7'-7"
24	4179	5080	6021	6994	7994	9017	10060	11020			7'-8"
25	4232	5155	6120	7121	8150	9204	10280	11370	11500		7'-9"
26	4280	5224	6213	7240	8298	9382	10490	11620	11960		7'-10"
27	4325	5289	6300	7352	8438	9552	10690	11850	12400		7'-11"
28	4367	5349	6382	7458	8570	9717	10880	12070	12860		8'-0"
29	4405	5404	6458	7557	8695	9866	11060	12290	13340		8'-1"
30	4440	5456	6529	7651	8814	10010	11240	12490	13810		8'-2"
31	4472	5504	6596	7739	8926	10150	11420	12690	13990	14270	8'-3"
32	4502	5549	6659	7822	9032	10280	11560	12880	14210	14710	8'-5"
33	4529	5590	6717	7901	9132	10400	11710	13060	14420	15180	8'-6"
34	4555	5629	6772	7974	9227	10520	11860	13230	14620	15640	8'-7"
35	4578	5665	6823	8044	9317	10640	12000	13390	14820	16140	8'-8"
36	4599	5698	6871	8109	9402	10740	12130	13550	15000	16570	8'-9"
37	4619	5729	6916	8171	9483	10850	12250	13700	15180	17050	8'-10"
38	4637	5758	6958	8229	9559	10940	12370	13840	15350	17520	
39	4654	5784	6998	8283	9631	11040	12490	13980	15510	17980	
40	4669	5809	7035	8335	9700	11120	12600	14110	15670	18430	

B — SATURATED TOP SOIL Kμ′—0.150

H (ft)	TRENCH WIDTH AT TOP OF PIPE 4'-0"	4'-6"	5'-0"	5'-6"	6'-0"	6'-6"	7'-0"	7'-6"	8'-0"	9'-0"	▲TRANSITION WIDTH
5	1667	1913	2119								4'-11"
6	1932	2225	2519	2686							5'-3"
7	2178	2517	2857	3155							5'-5"
8	2406	2790	3176	3565	3620						5'-7"
9	2617	3045	3477	3911	4085						5'-8"
10	2814	3284	3759	4239	4551						5'-10"
11	2996	3507	4026	4549	5015						5'-11"
12	3164	3717	4277	4843	5414	5478					6'-1"
13	3321	3912	4513	5121	5735	5938					6'-2"
14	3466	4095	4735	5384	6040	6401					6'-4"
15	3601	4266	4945	5634	6331	6862					6'-5"
16	3726	4426	5142	5870	6608	7330					6'-6"
17	3843	4576	5328	6094	6871	7657	7791				6'-8"
18	3950	4716	5503	6305	7121	7947	8250				6'-8"
19	4050	4848	5668	6506	7359	8223	8711				6'-9"
20	4143	4970	5823	6696	7585	8488	9179				6'-10"
21	4229	5085	5969	6876	7800	8740	9643				7'-0"
22	4309	5192	6107	7046	8005	8981	9971	10110			7'-1"
23	4383	5293	6236	7207	8200	9211	10240	10570			7'-2"
24	4451	5387	6358	7360	8385	9431	10490	11020			7'-3"
25	4515	5475	6473	7504	8561	9641	10740	11500			7'-4"
26	4574	5557	6582	7641	8729	9841	10970	11960			7'-5"
27	4629	5634	6684	7771	8889	10030	11200	12400			7'-6"
28	4680	5706	6780	7893	9040	10220	11410	12630	12860		7'-8"
29	4727	5773	6870	8010	9185	10390	11620	12870	13340		7'-9"
30	4771	5836	6955	8120	9322	10560	11820	13100	13810		7'-10"
31	4811	5895	7036	8224	9453	10720	12010	13320	14270		7'-10"
32	4849	5950	7111	8323	9577	10870	12190	13540	14710		7'-11"
33	4884	6002	7182	8416	9695	11010	12360	13740	15180		8'-0"
34	4916	6050	7249	8505	9807	11150	12530	13940	15370	15640	8'-1"
35	4946	6095	7312	8588	9914	11280	12690	14130	15590	16140	8'-3"
36	4974	6137	7372	8668	10020	11410	12840	14310	15800	16570	8'-4"
37	5000	6177	7428	8743	10110	11530	12990	14480	16010	17050	8'-5"
38	5024	6214	7480	8814	10200	11640	13130	14650	16200	17520	8'-6"
39	5047	6248	7530	8881	10290	11760	13260	14810	16390	17980	8'-7"
40	5067	6280	7577	8945	10380	11860	13390	14960	16570	18430	8'-7"

HEIGHT OF BACKFILL **H** ABOVE TOP OF PIPE, FEET

HEIGHT OF BACKFILL H ABOVE TOP OF PIPE, FEET

D — SATURATED CLAY Kμ'–0.110

H	— TRENCH WIDTH AT TOP OF PIPE										TRANSITION WIDTH
	4'-0"	4'-6"	5'-0"	5'-6"	6'-0"	6'-6"	7'-0"	7'-6"	8'-0"	9'-0"	
5	1748	1996	**2119**								4'-9"
6	2044	2340	2636	**2686**							5'-1"
7	2323	2667	3012	**3155**							5'-2"
8	2588	2979	3371	**3620**							5'-4"
9	2839	3276	3715	**4085**							5'-5"
10	3076	3559	4045	**4551**							5'-6"
11	3301	3828	4360	4894	**5015**						5'-7"
12	3513	4085	4661	5241	**5478**						5'-8"
13	3714	4329	4950	5575	**5938**						5'-9"
14	3905	4562	5226	5895	**6401**						5'-10"
15	4085	4783	5490	6203	**6862**						6'-0"
16	4256	4994	5743	6499	7262	**7330**					6'-1"
17	4417	5195	5985	6784	7590	**7791**					6'-1"
18	4570	5386	6216	7057	7906	**8250**					6'-2"
19	4714	5568	6438	7319	8210	**8711**					6'-3"
20	4851	5742	6650	7571	8504	**9179**					6'-4"
21	4981	5907	6853	7813	8787	**9643**					6'-5"
22	5104	6064	7047	8046	9059	**10110**					6'-6"
23	5220	6214	7233	8270	9322	10390	**10570**				6'-6"
24	5329	6357	7410	8485	9576	10680	**11020**				6'-8"
25	5433	6493	7581	8691	9820	10960	**11500**				6'-9"
26	5532	6622	7743	8889	10060	11240	**11960**				6'-10"
27	5625	6745	7899	9080	10280	11500	**12400**				6'-10"
28	5713	6863	8048	9263	10500	11760	**12860**				6'-11"
29	5797	6974	8191	9439	10710	12010	**13340**				7'-1"
30	5876	7081	8328	9608	10920	12250	13600	**13810**			7'-1"
31	5950	7182	8458	9770	11110	12480	13860	**14270**			7'-2"
32	6021	7278	8583	9926	11300	12700	14120	**14710**			7'-3"
33	6088	7370	8703	10080	11480	12920	14380	**15180**			7'-3"
34	6151	7458	8817	10220	11660	13130	14620	**15640**			7'-4"
35	6211	7541	8927	10360	11830	13330	14860	**16140**			7'-5"
36	6268	7620	9032	10490	11990	13530	15090	**16570**			7'-6"
37	6322	7696	9132	10620	12150	13720	15310	**17050**			7'-6"
38	6373	7768	9228	10740	12300	13900	15520	17180	**17520**		7'-7"
39	6421	7836	9320	10860	12450	14070	15730	17420	**17980**		7'-8"
40	6466	7902	9408	10970	12590	14240	15940	17660	**18430**		7'-8"

C — ORDINARY CLAY Kμ'–0.130

H	— TRENCH WIDTH AT TOP OF PIPE										TRANSITION WIDTH
	4'-0"	4'-6"	5'-0"	5'-6"	6'-0"	6'-6"	7'-0"	7'-6"	8'-0"	9'-0"	
5	1707	1954	**2119**								4'-10"
6	1987	2281	2577	**2686**							5'-1"
7	2249	2590	2933	**3155**							5'-2"
8	2495	2882	3272	**3620**							5'-4"
9	2725	3158	3593	4031	**4085**						5'-5"
10	2941	3418	3898	4382	**4551**						5'-7"
11	3143	3663	4188	4717	**5015**						5'-8"
12	3332	3894	4463	5036	**5478**						5'-10"
13	3510	4113	4724	5341	**5938**						6'-0"
14	3676	4319	4972	5632	6297	**6401**					6'-1"
15	3832	4514	5207	5909	6617	**6862**					6'-2"
16	3978	4698	5430	6173	6924	**7330**					6'-3"
17	4115	4871	5643	6425	7217	**7791**					6'-4"
18	4243	5035	5844	6666	7498	**8250**					6'-5"
19	4364	5190	6035	6895	7768	**8711**					6'-6"
20	4476	5336	6216	7114	8025	8948	**9179**				6'-6"
21	4582	5473	6388	7323	8272	9234	**9643**				6'-9"
22	4681	5603	6552	7522	8509	9509	**10110**				6'-10"
23	4773	5726	6707	7712	8735	9774	**10570**				6'-10"
24	4860	5842	6855	7893	8952	10030	**11020**				7'-0"
25	4942	5951	6994	8066	9159	10270	11400	**11500**			7'-1"
26	5018	6054	7127	8230	9358	10510	11670	**11960**			7'-1"
27	5089	6151	7253	8387	9548	10730	11930	**12400**			7'-2"
28	5156	6243	7373	8537	9731	10950	12180	**12860**			7'-3"
29	5219	6330	7486	8680	9905	11160	12430	**13340**			7'-4"
30	5278	6412	7594	8817	10070	11360	12660	**13810**			7'-5"
31	5333	6489	7697	8947	10230	11550	12890	**14270**			7'-6"
32	5385	6562	7794	9071	10380	11730	13100	14500	**14710**		7'-7"
33	5433	6631	7886	9189	10530	11910	13310	14740	**15180**		7'-8"
34	5478	6696	7974	9302	10670	12080	13520	14980	**15640**		7'-8"
35	5521	6757	8057	9410	10810	12240	13710	15200	**16140**		7'-10"
36	5561	6815	8136	9513	10940	12400	13900	15420	**16570**		7'-10"
37	5598	6870	8211	9610	11060	12550	14080	15640	**17050**		7'-11"
38	5633	6921	8282	9704	11180	12700	14250	15840	**17520**		8'-0"
39	5666	6970	8350	9793	11290	12840	14420	16040	17680	**17980**	8'-1"
40	5696	7016	8414	9878	11400	12970	14580	16230	17910	**18430**	8'-1"

* For backfill weighing 110 pounds per cubic foot, increase loads 10%; for 120 pounds per cubic foot, increase 20%; etc.

▲ Transition loads (**bold type**) and widths based on Kμ–0.19, for saturated clay based on Kμ—0.19. $r_{sd}p$—0.5 in the embankment equation

Interpolate for intermediate heights of backfill and/or trench widths

TABLE 23

BACKFILL LOADS ON CIRCULAR PIPE IN TRENCH INSTALLATION

*100 POUNDS PER CUBIC FOOT BACKFILL MATERIAL — LOADS IN POUNDS PER LINEAR FOOT

33″ — SAND AND GRAVEL Ku'−0.165

HEIGHT OF BACKFILL H ABOVE TOP OF PIPE, FEET	TRENCH WIDTH AT TOP OF PIPE										TRANSITION WIDTH
	4'-6"	5'-0"	5'-6"	6'-0"	6'-6"	7'-0"	7'-6"	8'-0"	9'-0"	10'-0"	
5	1883	2129	2258								5'- 3"
6	2184	2477	2771	2880							5'- 8"
7	2463	2802	3143	3450							5'-11"
8	2723	3107	3494	3883	3963						6'- 1"
9	2964	3393	3824	4259	4474						6'- 4"
10	3189	3660	4135	4615	4983						6'- 6"
11	3397	3910	4428	4951	5492						6'- 6"
12	3591	4144	4704	5270	5841	6003					6'- 8"
13	3771	4363	4964	5572	6185	6512					6'- 9"
14	3938	4568	5209	5858	6513	7019					6'-11"
15	4093	4760	5439	6128	6824	7526					7'- 0"
16	4238	4940	5656	6384	7120	7864	8034				7'- 1"
17	4372	5108	5861	6626	7401	8186	8542				7'- 3"
18	4497	5266	6053	6855	7669	8492	9045				7'- 4"
19	4613	5413	6234	7072	7923	8785	9559				7'- 5"
20	4720	5552	6405	7277	8164	9064	10060				7'- 6"
21	4820	5681	6566	7472	8394	9331	10280	10580			7'- 8"
22	4913	5802	6717	7656	8612	9585	10570	11070			7'- 9"
23	5000	5915	6860	7830	8820	9827	10850	11580			7'-10"
24	5080	6021	6994	7994	9017	10060	11120	12090			8'- 0"
25	5155	6120	7121	8150	9204	10280	11370	12480	12610		8'- 1"
26	5224	6213	7240	8298	9382	10490	11620	12760	13110		8'- 2"
27	5289	6300	7352	8438	9552	10690	11850	13030	13630		8'- 3"
28	5349	6382	7458	8570	9713	10880	12070	13280	14120		8'- 4"
29	5404	6458	7557	8695	9866	11060	12290	13530	14630		8'- 5"
30	5456	6529	7651	8814	10010	11240	12490	13770	15130		8'- 6"
31	5504	6596	7739	8926	10150	11420	12690	13990	15650		8'- 7"
32	5549	6659	7822	9032	10280	11560	12880	14210	16150		8'- 9"
33	5590	6717	7901	9132	10400	11710	13060	14420	16640		8'-10"
34	5629	6772	7974	9227	10520	11860	13230	14620	17170		8'-11"
35	5665	6823	8044	9317	10640	12010	13390	14820	17680		9'- 0"
36	5698	6871	8109	9402	10740	12130	13550	15000	17990	18180	9'- 1"
37	5729	6916	8171	9483	10850	12250	13700	15180	18220	18670	9'- 2"
38	5758	6958	8229	9559	10940	12370	13840	15350	18450	19200	9'- 3"
39	5784	6998	8283	9631	11040	12490	13980	15510	18670	19730	9'- 4"
40	5809	7035	8335	9700	11120	12600	14110	15670	18880	20240	9'- 5"

33″ — SATURATED TOP SOIL Ku'−0.150

HEIGHT OF BACKFILL H ABOVE TOP OF PIPE, FEET	TRENCH WIDTH AT TOP OF PIPE										TRANSITION WIDTH
	4'-6"	5'-0"	5'-6"	6'-0"	6'-6"	7'-0"	7'-6"	8'-0"	9'-0"	10'-0"	
5	1913	2159	2258								5'- 3"
6	2225	2519	2814	2880							5'- 7"
7	2517	2857	3200	3450							5'-10"
8	2790	3176	3565	3963							6'- 0"
9	3045	3477	3911	4348	4474						6'- 2"
10	3284	3759	4239	4721	4983						6'- 3"
11	3507	4026	4549	5076	5492						6'- 5"
12	3717	4277	4843	5414	6003						6'- 6"
13	3912	4513	5121	5735	6354	6512					6'- 7"
14	4095	4735	5384	6040	6702	7019					6'- 9"
15	4266	4945	5634	6331	7035	7526					6'-10"
16	4426	5142	5870	6608	7353	8034					7'- 0"
17	4576	5328	6094	6871	7657	8450	8542				7'- 1"
18	4716	5503	6305	7121	7947	8781	9045				7'- 2"
19	4848	5668	6506	7359	8223	9098	9559				7'- 3"
20	4970	5823	6696	7585	8488	9401	10060				7'- 4"
21	5085	5969	6876	7800	8740	9692	10580				7'- 6"
22	5192	6107	7046	8005	8981	9971	10970				7'- 6"
23	5293	6236	7207	8200	9211	10240	11280	11580			7'- 8"
24	5387	6358	7360	8385	9431	10490	11570	12090			7'- 9"
25	5475	6473	7504	8561	9641	10740	11850	12610			7'-10"
26	5557	6582	7641	8729	9841	10970	12120	13110			7'-11"
27	5634	6684	7771	8889	10030	11200	12380	13630			8'- 0"
28	5706	6780	7893	9040	10220	11410	12630	13870	14120		8'- 1"
29	5773	6870	8010	9185	10360	11620	12870	14140	14630		8'- 2"
30	5836	6955	8120	9322	10560	11820	13100	14410	15130		8'- 3"
31	5895	7036	8224	9453	10720	12010	13320	14660	15650		8'- 4"
32	5950	7111	8323	9577	10870	12190	13540	14910	16150		8'- 5"
33	6002	7182	8416	9695	11010	12360	13740	15140	16640		8'- 6"
34	6050	7249	8505	9807	11150	12530	13940	15370	17170		8'- 7"
35	6095	7312	8588	9914	11280	12690	14130	15590	17680		8'- 8"
36	6137	7372	8668	10010	11410	12840	14310	15800	18180		8'- 9"
37	6177	7428	8743	10110	11530	12990	14480	16010	18670		8'-10"
38	6214	7480	8814	10200	11640	13130	14650	16200	19200		8'-11"
39	6248	7530	8881	10290	11760	13260	14810	16390	19730		9'- 0"
40	6280	7577	8945	10380	11860	13390	14960	16570	19880	20240	9'- 1"

HEIGHT OF BACKFILL H ABOVE TOP OF PIPE, FEET

C — ORDINARY CLAY $K\mu'$-0.130

TRENCH WIDTH AT TOP OF PIPE

H	4'-6"	5'-0"	5'-6"	6'-0"	6'-6"	7'-0"	7'-6"	8'-0"	9'-0"	10'-0"	Transition Width
5	1954	2201	**2258**								5'-1"
6	2281	2577	**2880**								5'-6"
7	2590	2933	3277	**3450**							5'-9"
8	2882	3272	3663	**3963**							5'-11"
9	3158	3593	4031	**4474**							6'-0"
10	3418	3898	4382	4869	**4983**						6'-1"
11	3663	4188	4717	5249	**5492**						6'-3"
12	3894	4463	5036	5614	**6003**						6'-4"
13	4113	4724	5341	5963	**6512**						6'-5"
14	4319	4972	5632	6297	**7019**						6'-6"
15	4514	5207	5909	6617	7331	**7526**					6'-8"
16	4698	5430	6173	6924	7681	**8034**					6'-9"
17	4871	5643	6425	7217	8017	**8542**					6'-10"
18	5035	5844	6666	7498	8340	**9045**					6'-11"
19	5190	6035	6895	7768	8650	**9559**					7'-0"
20	5336	6216	7114	8025	8948	9880	**10060**				7'-1"
21	5473	6388	7323	8272	9234	10210	**10580**				7'-2"
22	5603	6552	7522	8509	9509	10520	**11070**				7'-3"
23	5726	6707	7712	8735	9774	10820	**11580**				7'-4"
24	5842	6855	7893	8952	10030	11120	**12090**				7'-5"
25	5951	6994	8066	9159	10270	11400	**12610**				7'-6"
26	6054	7127	8230	9358	10510	11670	12850	**13110**			7'-7"
27	6151	7253	8387	9548	10730	11930	13150	**13630**			7'-8"
28	6243	7373	8537	9731	10950	12180	13440	**14120**			7'-10"
29	6330	7486	8680	9905	11160	12430	13720	**14630**			7'-11"
30	6412	7594	8817	10070	11360	12660	13990	**15130**			8'-0"
31	6489	7697	8947	10230	11550	12890	14250	**15650**			8'-2"
32	6562	7794	9071	10380	11730	13100	14500	15910	**16150**		8'-3"
33	6631	7886	9189	10530	11910	13310	14740	16190	**16640**		8'-4"
34	6696	7974	9302	10670	12080	13520	14980	16460	**17170**		8'-5"
35	6757	8057	9410	10810	12240	13710	15200	16690	**17680**		8'-5"
36	6815	8136	9513	10940	12400	13900	15420	16980	**18180**		8'-6"
37	6870	8211	9610	11060	12550	14080	15640	17220	**18670**		8'-8"
38	6921	8282	9704	11180	12700	14250	15840	17460	**19200**		
39	6970	8350	9793	11290	12840	14420	16040	17680	**19730**		
40	7016	8414	9878	11400	12970	14580	16230	17910	**20240**		

* For backfill weighing 110 pounds per cubic foot; increase loads 10%; for 120 pounds per cubic foot, increase 20%; etc.
▲ Transition loads (**bold type**) and widths based on Kμ–0.19, $r_{sd}p$–0.5 in the embankment equation
Interpolate for intermediate heights of backfill and/or trench widths

D — SATURATED CLAY $K\mu'$-0.110

TRENCH WIDTH AT TOP OF PIPE

H	4'-6"	5'-0"	5'-6"	6'-0"	6'-6"	7'-0"	7'-6"	8'-0"	9'-0"	10'-0"	Transition Width
5	1996	2244	**2258**								5'-0"
6	2340	2636	**2880**								5'-5"
7	2667	3012	3357	**3450**							5'-8"
8	2979	3371	3765	**3963**							5'-9"
9	3276	3715	4156	**4474**							5'-10"
10	3559	4045	4533	**4983**							6'-0"
11	3828	4360	4894	5431	**5492**						6'-1"
12	4085	4661	5241	5824	**6003**						6'-2"
13	4329	4950	5575	6204	**6512**						6'-3"
14	4562	5226	5895	6570	**7019**						6'-4"
15	4783	5490	6203	6922	**7526**						6'-5"
16	4994	5743	6499	7262	**8034**						6'-6"
17	5195	5985	6784	7590	8402	**8542**					6'-7"
18	5386	6216	7057	7906	8761	**9045**					6'-8"
19	5568	6438	7319	8210	9109	**9559**					6'-9"
20	5742	6650	7571	8504	9445	**10060**					6'-10"
21	5907	6853	7813	8787	9770	**10580**					6'-11"
22	6064	7047	8046	9059	10080	**11070**					7'-0"
23	6214	7233	8270	9322	10390	11460	**11580**				7'-1"
24	6357	7410	8485	9576	10680	11800	**12090**				7'-2"
25	6493	7581	8691	9820	10960	12120	**12610**				7'-3"
26	6622	7743	8889	10060	11240	12440	**13110**				7'-4"
27	6745	7899	9080	10280	11500	12740	**13630**				7'-5"
28	6863	8048	9263	10500	11760	13030	**14120**				7'-6"
29	6974	8191	9439	10710	12010	13320	**14630**				7'-7"
30	7081	8328	9608	10920	12250	13600	14960	**15130**			7'-8"
31	7182	8458	9770	11110	12480	13860	15270	**15650**			7'-9"
32	7278	8583	9926	11300	12700	14120	15570	**16150**			7'-10"
33	7370	8703	10080	11480	12920	14380	15860	**16640**			7'-11"
34	7458	8817	10220	11660	13130	14620	16140	**17170**			8'-0"
35	7541	8927	10360	11830	13330	14860	16410	**17680**			8'-0"
36	7620	9032	10490	11990	13530	15090	16670	**18180**			8'-1"
37	7696	9132	10620	12150	13720	15310	16930	**18670**			8'-3"
38	7768	9228	10740	12300	13900	15520	17180	18860	**19200**		
39	7836	9320	10860	12450	14070	15730	17420	19140	**19730**		
40	7902	9408	10970	12590	14240	15940	17660	19410	**20240**		

* For backfill weighing 110 pounds per cubic foot, increase loads 10%; for 120 pounds per cubic foot, increase 20%; etc.
▲ Transition loads (**bold type**) and widths based on Kμ–0.19, $r_{sd}p$–0.5 in the embankment equation
Interpolate for intermediate heights of backfill and/or trench widths

TABLE 24

36″

BACKFILL LOADS ON CIRCULAR PIPE IN TRENCH INSTALLATION
*100 POUNDS PER CUBIC FOOT BACKFILL MATERIAL — LOADS IN POUNDS PER LINEAR FOOT

HEIGHT OF BACKFILL **H** ABOVE TOP OF PIPE, FEET

A — SAND AND GRAVEL Kμ—0.165

H	5'-0"	5'-6"	6'-0"	6'-6"	7'-0"	7'-6"	8'-0"	8'-6"	9'-0"	10'-0"	▲TRANSITION WIDTH
5	2129	2375	**2394**								5'- 7"
6	2477	2771	**3038**								5'-11"
7	2802	3143	3485	**3730**							6'- 4"
8	3107	3494	3883	**4289**							6'- 6"
9	3393	3824	4259	4695	**4846**						6'- 8"
10	3660	4135	4615	5097	**5401**						6'-10"
11	3910	4428	4951	5478	**5952**						6'-11"
12	4144	4704	5270	5841	6415	**6508**					7'- 1"
13	4363	4964	5572	6185	6803	**7060**					7'- 3"
14	4568	5209	5858	6513	7174	**7609**					7'- 4"
15	4760	5439	6128	6824	7527	**8160**					7'- 5"
16	4940	5656	6384	7120	7864	8614	**8717**				7'- 7"
17	5108	5861	6626	7401	8186	8977	**9261**				7'- 8"
18	5266	6053	6855	7669	8492	9324	**9817**				7'- 9"
19	5413	6234	7072	7923	8785	9657	**10370**				7'-11"
20	5552	6405	7277	8164	9064	9975	**10930**				8'- 0"
21	5681	6566	7472	8394	9331	10280	11240	**11470**			8'- 1"
22	5802	6717	7656	8612	9585	10570	11570	**12030**			8'- 3"
23	5915	6860	7830	8820	9827	10850	11880	**12580**			8'- 4"
24	6021	6994	7994	9017	10060	11120	12190	**13120**			8'- 5"
25	6121	7121	8150	9204	10280	11370	12480	**13670**			8'- 6"
26	6213	7240	8298	9382	10490	11620	12760	13920	**14240**		8'- 8"
27	6300	7352	8438	9552	10690	11850	13030	14220	**14790**		8'- 9"
28	6382	7458	8570	9713	10880	12070	13280	14510	**15350**		8'-10"
29	6458	7557	8695	9866	11060	12290	13530	14790	**15890**		8'-11"
30	6529	7651	8814	10010	11240	12490	13770	15060	**16450**		9'- 0"
31	6596	7739	8926	10150	11400	12690	13990	15320	16670	**16990**	9'- 1"
32	6659	7822	9032	10280	11560	12880	14210	15570	16950	**17520**	9'- 2"
33	6717	7901	9132	10400	11710	13060	14420	15810	17230	**18080**	9'- 4"
34	6772	7974	9227	10520	11860	13230	14620	16040	17490	**18620**	9'- 5"
35	6823	8044	9317	10640	12000	13390	14820	16270	17740	**19190**	9'- 6"
36	6871	8109	9402	10740	12130	13550	15000	16480	17990	**19750**	9'- 8"
37	6916	8171	9483	10850	12250	13700	15180	16690	18220	**20300**	9'- 9"
38	6958	8229	9559	10940	12370	13840	15350	16890	18450	**20840**	9'-10"
39	6998	8283	9631	11040	12490	13980	15510	17080	18670	**21370**	9'-11"
40	7035	8335	9700	11120	12600	14110	15670	17260	18880	**21940**	

B — SATURATED TOP SOIL Kμ—0.150

H	5'-0"	5'-6"	6'-0"	6'-6"	7'-0"	7'-6"	8'-0"	8'-6"	9'-0"	10'-0"	▲TRANSITION WIDTH
5	2159	**2394**									5'- 6"
6	2519	2814	**3038**								5'-11"
7	2857	3200	3543	**3730**							6'- 3"
8	3176	3565	3956	**4289**							6'- 5"
9	3477	3911	4348	4787	**4846**						6'- 7"
10	3759	4239	4721	5206	**5401**						6'- 8"
11	4026	4549	5076	5606	**5952**						6'-10"
12	4277	4843	5414	5989	**6508**						6'-11"
13	4513	5121	5735	6354	6976	**7060**					7'- 1"
14	4735	5384	6040	6702	7369	**7609**					7'- 2"
15	4945	5634	6331	7035	7745	**8160**					7'- 3"
16	5142	5870	6608	7353	8105	**8717**					7'- 5"
17	5328	6094	6871	7657	8450	**9261**					7'- 6"
18	5503	6305	7121	7947	8781	9623	**9817**				7'- 7"
19	5668	6506	7359	8223	9098	9981	**10370**				7'- 8"
20	5823	6696	7585	8488	9401	10320	**10930**				7'-10"
21	5969	6876	7800	8740	9692	10660	**11470**				7'-11"
22	6107	7046	8005	8981	9971	10970	**12030**				8'- 0"
23	6236	7207	8200	9211	10240	11280	**12580**				8'- 0"
24	6358	7360	8385	9431	10490	11570	12880	**13120**			8'- 1"
25	6473	7504	8561	9641	10740	11850	13080	**13670**			8'- 3"
26	6582	7641	8729	9841	10970	12120	13290	**14240**			8'- 5"
27	6684	7771	8889	10030	11200	12380	13580	**14790**			8'- 6"
28	6780	7893	9040	10220	11410	12630	13870	15120	**15350**		8'- 7"
29	6870	8010	9185	10390	11620	12870	14140	15430	**15890**		8'- 8"
30	6955	8120	9322	10560	11820	13100	14410	15730	**16450**		8'- 9"
31	7036	8224	9453	10720	12010	13320	14660	16020	**16990**		8'-10"
32	7111	8323	9577	10870	12190	13540	14910	16300	**17520**		8'-11"
33	7182	8416	9695	11010	12360	13740	15140	16570	**18080**		9'- 0"
34	7249	8505	9807	11150	12530	13940	15370	16830	18310	**18620**	9'- 1"
35	7312	8588	9914	11280	12690	14130	15590	17080	18590	**19190**	9'- 2"
36	7372	8668	10020	11410	12840	14310	15800	17320	18870	**19750**	9'- 3"
37	7428	8743	10110	11530	12990	14480	16010	17560	19130	**20300**	9'- 5"
38	7480	8814	10200	11640	13130	14650	16210	17780	19390	**20840**	9'- 5"
39	7530	8881	10290	11760	13260	14810	16390	18000	19640	**21370**	9'- 6"
40	7577	8945	10380	11860	13390	14960	16570	18210	19880	**21940**	9'- 7"

TRENCH WIDTH AT TOP OF PIPE

HEIGHT OF BACKFILL **H** ABOVE TOP OF PIPE, FEET

HEIGHT OF BACKFILL H ABOVE TOP OF PIPE, FEET

D — SATURATED CLAY $K\mu'$—0.110

TRENCH WIDTH AT TOP OF PIPE

H	5'-0"	5'-6"	6'-0"	6'-6"	7'-0"	7'-6"	8'-0"	8'-6"	9'-0"	10'-0"	TRANSITION WIDTH
5	2244	**2394**									5'- 4"
6	2636	2933	**3038**								5'- 8"
7	3012	3357	3704	**3730**							6'- 1"
8	3371	3765	4160	**4289**							6'- 2"
9	3715	4156	4599	**4846**							6'- 3"
10	4045	4533	5022	**5401**							6'- 5"
11	4360	4894	5431	**5952**							6'- 6"
12	4661	5241	5824	6410	**6508**						6'- 7"
13	4950	5575	6204	6836	**7060**						6'- 8"
14	5226	5895	6570	7247	**7609**						6'- 9"
15	5490	6203	6922	7645	**8160**						6'-10"
16	5743	6499	7262	8030	**8717**						6'-11"
17	5985	6784	7590	8402	**9261**						7'- 0"
18	6216	7057	7906	8761	9622	**9817**					7'- 1"
19	6438	7319	8210	9109	10010	**10370**					7'- 2"
20	6650	7571	8504	9445	10390	**10930**					7'- 3"
21	6853	7813	8787	9770	10760	**11470**					7'- 4"
22	7047	8046	9059	10080	11120	**12030**					7'- 5"
23	7233	8270	9322	10390	11460	**12580**					7'- 6"
24	7410	8485	9576	10680	11800	12920	**13120**				7'- 7"
25	7581	8691	9820	10960	12120	13290	**13670**				7'- 7"
26	7743	8889	10060	11240	12440	13640	**14240**				7'- 9"
27	7899	9080	10280	11500	12740	13990	**14790**				7'-10"
28	8048	9263	10500	11760	13030	14320	**15350**				7'-11"
29	8191	9439	10710	12010	13320	14650	**15890**				7'-11"
30	8328	9608	10920	12250	13600	14960	**16450**				8'- 0"
31	8458	9770	11110	12480	13860	15270	16690	**16990**			8'- 1"
32	8583	9926	11300	12700	14120	15570	17020	**17520**			8'- 2"
33	8703	10080	11480	12920	14380	15860	17350	**18080**			8'- 3"
34	8817	10220	11660	13130	14620	16140	17670	**18620**			8'- 3"
35	8927	10360	11830	13330	14860	16410	17980	**19190**			8'- 4"
36	9032	10490	11990	13530	15090	16670	18280	**19750**			8'- 5"
37	9132	10620	12150	13720	15310	16930	18570	**20300**			8'- 6"
38	9228	10740	12300	13900	15520	17180	18860	20560	**20840**		8'- 7"
39	9320	10860	12450	14070	15730	17420	19140	20870	**21370**		8'- 8"
40	9408	10970	12590	14240	15940	17660	19410	21180	**21940**		8'- 9"

C — ORDINARY CLAY $K\mu'$—0.130

TRENCH WIDTH AT TOP OF PIPE

H	5'-0"	5'-6"	6'-0"	6'-6"	7'-0"	7'-6"	8'-0"	8'-6"	9'-0"	10'-0"	TRANSITION WIDTH
5	2201	**2394**									5'- 5"
6	2577	2873	**3038**								5'- 9"
7	2933	3277	3622	**3730**							6'- 2"
8	3272	3663	4056	**4289**							6'- 3"
9	3593	4031	4471	**4846**							6'- 5"
10	3898	4382	4869	5357	**5401**						6'- 7"
11	4188	4717	5249	5784	**5952**						6'- 8"
12	4463	5036	5614	6194	**6508**						6'- 9"
13	4724	5341	5963	6589	**7060**						6'-10"
14	4972	5632	6297	6967	**7609**						7'- 0"
15	5207	5909	6617	7331	8050	**8160**					7'- 1"
16	5430	6173	6924	7681	8443	**8717**					7'- 2"
17	5643	6425	7217	8017	8823	**9261**					7'- 3"
18	5844	6666	7498	8340	9188	**9817**					7'- 4"
19	6035	6895	7768	8650	9540	**10370**					7'- 6"
20	6216	7114	8025	8948	9880	10820	**10930**				7'- 7"
21	6388	7323	8272	9234	10210	11190	**11470**				7'- 8"
22	6552	7522	8509	9509	10520	11540	**12030**				7'- 9"
23	6707	7712	8735	9774	10820	11890	**12580**				7'-10"
24	6855	7893	8952	10030	11120	12220	**13120**				7'-11"
25	6994	8066	9159	10270	11400	12540	**13670**				8'- 0"
26	7127	8230	9358	10510	11670	12850	14040	**14240**			8'- 1"
27	7253	8387	9548	10730	11930	13150	14380	**14790**			8'- 2"
28	7373	8537	9731	10950	12180	13440	14710	**15350**			8'- 3"
29	7486	8680	9905	11160	12430	13720	15020	**15890**			8'- 4"
30	7594	8817	10070	11360	12660	13990	15330	**16450**			8'- 5"
31	7697	8947	10230	11550	12890	14250	15630	**16990**			8'- 6"
32	7794	9071	10380	11730	13110	14500	15910	17350	**17520**		8'- 7"
33	7886	9189	10530	11910	13310	14740	16190	17660	**18080**		8'- 8"
34	7974	9302	10670	12080	13520	14980	16460	17970	**18620**		8'- 9"
35	8057	9410	10810	12240	13710	15200	16720	18260	**19190**		8'-10"
36	8136	9513	10940	12400	13900	15420	16980	18550	**19750**		8'-11"
37	8211	9610	11060	12550	14080	15640	17220	18830	**20300**		9'- 0"
38	8282	9704	11180	12700	14250	15840	17460	19100	20560	**20840**	9'- 1"
39	8350	9793	11290	12840	14420	16040	17680	19360	20870	**21370**	9'- 2"
40	8414	9878	11400	12970	14580	16230	17910	19610	21180	**21940**	9'- 2"

* For backfill weighing 110 pounds per cubic foot. For backfill weighing 100 pounds per cubic foot, decrease loads 10%; for 120 pounds per cubic foot, increase 20%; etc.

▲ Transition loads (**bold type**) and widths based on $K\mu$—0.19, $r_{sd}p$—0.5 in the embankment equation

Interpolate for intermediate heights of backfill and/or trench widths

TABLE 25

BACKFILL LOADS ON CIRCULAR PIPE IN TRENCH INSTALLATION
*100 POUNDS PER CUBIC FOOT BACKFILL MATERIAL
LOADS IN POUNDS PER LINEAR FOOT

HEIGHT OF BACKFILL H ABOVE TOP OF PIPE, FEET

A — 42″ — SAND AND GRAVEL Kµ′—0.165

TRENCH WIDTH AT TOP OF PIPE

H	6′-0″	6′-6″	7′-0″	7′-6″	8′-0″	8′-6″	9′-0″	9′-6″	10′-0″	11′-0″	Transition Width
5	2622	2671									6′-1″
6	3066	3361									6′-6″
7	3485	3829	4114								6′-11″
8	3883	4273	4665	4932							7′-4″
9	4259	4695	5134	5582							7′-6″
10	4615	5097	5581	6067	6227						7′-8″
11	4951	5478	6008	6540	6869						7′-10″
12	5270	5841	6415	6992	7510						7′-11″
13	5572	6185	6803	7425	7994	8150					8′-2″
14	5858	6513	7174	7839	8428	8789					8′-4″
15	6128	6824	7527	8235	8850	9434					8′-6″
16	6384	7120	7864	8614	9260	9775	10070				8′-7″
17	6626	7401	8186	8977	9658	10160	10710				8′-8″
18	6855	7669	8492	9324	10040	10540	11350				8′-10″
19	7072	7923	8785	9657	10410	10890	11980				8′-11″
20	7277	8164	9064	9975	10770	11220	12190	12630			9′-1″
21	7472	8394	9331	10280	11110	11540	12610	13270			9′-3″
22	7656	8612	9585	10580	11440	11840	13000	13900			9′-4″
23	7830	8820	9827	10850	11750	12120	13360	14550			9′-6″
24	7994	9017	10060	11120	12050	12390	13690	14730	15190		9′-8″
25	8150	9204	10280	11370	12340	12650	14010	15060	15830		9′-9″
26	8298	9382	10490	11620	12610	12900	14220	15420	16470		9′-11″
27	8438	9552	10690	11850	12870	13140	14510	15750	17090		10′-0″
28	8570	9713	10880	12070	13120	13370	14790	16070	17360	17740	10′-1″
29	8695	9866	11060	12290	13360	13600	15060	16370	17360	18380	10′-2″
30	8814	10010	11240	12490	13590	13820	15320	16670	17990	19000	10′-3″
31	8926	10150	11400	12690	13810	14030	15570	16950	18220	19670	10′-4″
32	9032	10280	11560	12880	14020	14230	15810	17230	18450	20280	10′-5″
33	9132	10400	11710	13060	14220	14420	16040	17500	18670	20920	10′-7″
34	9227	10520	11860	13230	14410	14620	16270	17740	18950	21540	10′-8″
35	9317	10640	12000	13390	14590	14820	16480	17990	19240	22190	10′-9″
36	9402	10740	12130	13550	14760	15000	16670	18220	19520	22830	10′-10″
37	9483	10850	12250	13700	14920	15180	16850	18450	19780	23500	10′-11″
38	9559	10940	12370	13840	15070	15350	17030	18670	20040	24110	
39	9631	11040	12490	13980	15210	15510	17200	18880	20290	24760	
40	9700	11120	12600	14110	15340	15670	17360	19080	20530	25400	

B — 42″ — SATURATED TOP SOIL Kµ′—0.150

TRENCH WIDTH AT TOP OF PIPE

H	6′-0″	6′-6″	7′-0″	7′-6″	8′-0″	8′-6″	9′-0″	9′-6″	10′-0″	11′-0″	Transition Width
5	2671										6′-0″
6	3110	3361									6′-5″
7	3543	3888	4114								6′-10″
8	3956	4348	4740	4932							7′-3″
9	4348	4787	5227	5582							7′-7″
10	4721	5206	5693	6181	6227						7′-8″
11	5076	5606	6139	6674	6869						7′-10″
12	5414	5989	6567	7147	7510						7′-11″
13	5735	6354	6976	7602	8150						8′-0″
14	6040	6702	7369	8039	8508	8789					8′-2″
15	6331	7035	7745	8459	8948	9434					8′-3″
16	6608	7353	8105	8863	9370	10070					8′-5″
17	6871	7657	8450	9250	9775	10710					8′-6″
18	7121	7947	8781	9623	10160	11160	11350				8′-8″
19	7359	8223	9098	9981	10540	11570	11980				8′-10″
20	7585	8488	9401	10320	10890	11960	12630				8′-11″
21	7800	8740	9692	10660	11220	12340	13000	13270			9′-1″
22	8005	8981	9971	10970	11540	12690	13390	13900			9′-2″
23	8200	9211	10240	11280	11840	13020	13760	14550			9′-4″
24	8385	9431	10490	11570	12120	13330	14120	15190			9′-5″
25	8561	9641	10740	11850	12390	13630	14460	15830			9′-6″
26	8729	9841	10970	12120	12650	13910	14800	16470			9′-8″
27	8889	10030	11200	12380	12900	14180	15120	17090			9′-10″
28	9040	10220	11410	12630	13140	14430	15430	17740			9′-11″
29	9185	10390	11620	12870	13370	14680	15730	18040	18380		10′-0″
30	9322	10560	11820	13100	13580	14910	16020	18420	19000		10′-1″
31	9453	10720	12010	13320	13790	15130	16300	18780	19670		10′-2″
32	9577	10870	12190	13540	13990	15340	16570	19130	20280		10′-3″
33	9695	11010	12360	13740	14180	15540	16830	19470	20920		10′-4″
34	9807	11150	12530	13940	14360	15730	17080	19800	21310	21540	10′-5″
35	9914	11280	12690	14130	14530	15920	17320	20120	21670	22190	10′-6″
36	10020	11410	12840	14310	14700	16090	17560	20430	22010	22830	10′-7″
37	10110	11530	12990	14480	14860	16260	17780	20730	22350	23500	
38	10200	11640	13130	14650	15010	16420	18000	21020	22670	24110	
39	10290	11760	13260	14810	15150	16580	18210	21300	22990	24760	
40	10380	11860	13390	14960	15290	16730	18420	21580	23290	25400	

HEIGHT OF BACKFILL H ABOVE TOP OF PIPE, FEET

D — SATURATED CLAY Kμ'-0.110

H	6'-0"	6'-6"	7'-0"	7'-6"	8'-0"	8'-6"	9'-0"	9'-6"	10'-0"	11'-0"	▲TRANSITION WIDTH
5	**2671**										5'-10"
6	3231	**3361**									6'-3"
7	3704	4051	**4114**								6'-7"
8	4160	4555	**4932**								7'-0"
9	4599	5042	5487	**5582**							7'-1"
10	5022	5514	6006	**6227**							7'-3"
11	5431	5969	6509	**6869**							7'-4"
12	5824	6410	6997	**7510**							7'-5"
13	6204	6836	7470	**8150**							7'-6"
14	6570	7247	7928	8611	**8789**						7'-7"
15	6922	7645	8372	9101	**9434**						7'-9"
16	7262	8030	8802	9577	**10070**						7'-10"
17	7590	8402	9218	10040	**10710**						7'-11"
18	7906	8761	9622	10490	**11350**						8'-0"
19	8210	9109	10010	10920	11840	**11980**					8'-1"
20	8504	9445	10390	11350	12310	**12630**					8'-2"
21	8787	9770	10760	11760	12760	**13270**					8'-3"
22	9059	10080	11120	12160	13200	**13900**					8'-4"
23	9322	10390	11460	12540	13640	**14550**					8'-5"
24	9576	10680	11800	12920	14060	**15190**					8'-6"
25	9820	10960	12120	13290	14460	15640	**15830**				8'-7"
26	10060	11240	12440	13640	14860	16080	**16470**				8'-8"
27	10280	11500	12740	13990	15240	16510	**17090**				8'-9"
28	10500	11760	13030	14320	15620	16930	**17740**				8'-10"
29	10710	12010	13320	14650	15990	17340	**18380**				8'-10"
30	10920	12250	13600	14960	16340	17730	**19000**				9'-0"
31	11110	12480	13860	15270	16690	18120	**19670**				9'-0"
32	11300	12700	14120	15570	17020	18500	19980	**20280**			9'-1"
33	11480	12920	14380	15860	17350	18860	20380	**20920**			9'-2"
34	11660	13130	14620	16140	17670	19220	20780	**21540**			9'-3"
35	11830	13330	14860	16410	17980	19570	21170	**22190**			9'-4"
36	11990	13530	15090	16670	18280	19910	21550	**22830**			9'-5"
37	12150	13720	15310	16930	18570	20240	21920	**23500**			9'-6"
38	12300	13900	15520	17180	18860	20560	22280	**24110**			9'-6"
39	12450	14070	15730	17420	19140	20870	22630	24400	**24760**		9'-7"
40	12590	14240	15940	17660	19410	21180	22970	24780	**25400**		9'-8"

C — ORDINARY CLAY Kμ'-0.130

H	6'-0"	6'-6"	7'-0"	7'-6"	8'-0"	8'-6"	9'-0"	9'-6"	10'-0"	11'-0"	▲TRANSITION WIDTH
5	**2671**										5'-11"
6	3170	**3361**									6'-4"
7	3622	3968	**4114**								6'-8"
8	4056	4450	4844	**4932**							7'-1"
9	4471	4912	5355	**5582**							7'-3"
10	4869	5357	5847	**6227**							7'-5"
11	5249	5784	6321	**6869**							7'-6"
12	5614	6194	6777	7362	**7510**						7'-7"
13	5963	6589	7217	7848	**8150**						7'-9"
14	6297	6967	7641	8318	**8789**						7'-10"
15	6617	7331	8050	8772	**9434**						7'-11"
16	6924	7681	8443	9210	**10070**						8'-0"
17	7217	8017	8823	9633	10450	**10710**					8'-2"
18	7498	8340	9188	10040	10900	**11350**					8'-3"
19	7768	8650	9540	10440	11340	**11980**					8'-4"
20	8025	8948	9880	10820	11760	**12630**					8'-5"
21	8272	9234	10210	11190	12180	13170	**13270**				8'-7"
22	8509	9509	10520	11540	12570	13610	**13900**				8'-8"
23	8735	9774	10820	11890	12960	14040	**14550**				8'-9"
24	8952	10030	11120	12220	13330	14450	**15190**				8'-10"
25	9159	10270	11400	12540	13690	14850	**15830**				8'-11"
26	9358	10510	11670	12850	14040	15240	**16470**				9'-0"
27	9548	10730	11930	13150	14380	15620	16870	**17090**			9'-1"
28	9731	10950	12180	13440	14710	15990	17280	**17740**			9'-2"
29	9905	11160	12430	13720	15020	16340	17670	**18380**			9'-3"
30	10070	11360	12660	13990	15330	16690	18060	**19000**			9'-4"
31	10230	11550	12890	14250	15630	17020	18430	**19670**			9'-5"
32	10380	11730	13100	14500	15910	17350	18790	**20280**			9'-6"
33	10530	11910	13310	14740	16190	17660	19140	20640	**20920**		9'-7"
34	10670	12080	13520	14980	16460	17960	19490	21020	**21540**		9'-8"
35	10810	12240	13710	15200	16720	18260	19820	21390	**22190**		9'-9"
36	10940	12400	13900	15420	16980	18550	20140	21750	**22830**		9'-10"
37	11060	12550	14080	15640	17230	18830	20460	22100	**23500**		9'-11"
38	11180	12700	14250	15840	17460	19100	20760	22440	**24110**		10'-0"
39	11290	12840	14420	16040	17680	19360	21060	22770	24510	**24760**	10'-1"
40	11400	12970	14580	16230	17910	19610	21340	23100	24870	**25400**	10'-2"

Column headings for both tables: TRENCH WIDTH AT TOP OF PIPE — 6'-0", 6'-6", 7'-0", 7'-6", 8'-0", 8'-6", 9'-0", 9'-6", 10'-0", 11'-0"

* For backfill weighing 110 pounds per cubic foot, increase loads 10%; for 120 pounds per cubic foot, increase 20%; etc.

▲ Transition loads (**bold type**) and widths based on Kμ—0.19, rsdP—0.5 in the embankment equation

Interpolate for intermediate heights of backfill and/or trench widths

TABLE 26

BACKFILL LOADS ON CIRCULAR PIPE IN TRENCH INSTALLATION

LOADS IN POUNDS PER LINEAR FOOT
*100 POUNDS PER CUBIC FOOT BACKFILL MATERIAL

48" — SAND AND GRAVEL Ku'=0.165

HEIGHT OF BACKFILL **H** ABOVE TOP OF PIPE, FEET — TRENCH WIDTH AT TOP OF PIPE

H	6'-6"	7'-0"	7'-6"	8'-0"	8'-6"	9'-0"	9'-6"	10'-0"	11'-0"	12'-0"	Transition Width
5	2870	2950									6'- 8"
6	3361	3658	3691								7'- 1"
7	3829	4173	4490								7'- 6"
8	4273	4665	5057	5354							7'-11"
9	4695	5134	5573	6014	6287						8'- 4"
10	5097	5581	6067	6555	7041						8'- 6"
11	5478	6008	6540	7074	7609	7776					8'- 9"
12	5841	6415	6992	7571	8153	8508					8'-11"
13	6185	6803	7425	8049	8676	9235					9'- 1"
14	6513	7174	7839	8508	9180	9855	9966				9'- 2"
15	6824	7527	8235	8948	9664	10380	10690				9'- 4"
16	7120	7864	8614	9370	10130	10890	11420				9'- 5"
17	7401	8186	8977	9775	10580	11380	12150				9'- 7"
18	7669	8492	9324	10160	11010	11860	12870	13600			9'- 9"
19	7923	8785	9657	10540	11420	12320	13210	14330			9'-10"
20	8164	9064	9975	10890	11820	12760	13700	15060			10'- 0"
21	8394	9331	10280	11240	12200	13180	14160	15640			10'- 1"
22	8612	9585	10570	11570	12570	13590	14610	16120	15770		10'- 2"
23	8820	9827	10850	11880	12930	13980	15050	16580	16510		10'- 3"
24	9017	10060	11120	12190	13270	14360	15470	17010	17230		10'- 5"
25	9204	10280	11370	12480	13590	14730	15870	17450	17960		10'- 6"
26	9382	10490	11620	12760	13920	15080	16260	17870	18680		10'- 7"
27	9552	10690	11850	13030	14220	15420	16640	18270	19400		10'- 8"
28	9713	10880	12070	13280	14510	15750	17010	18660	20120		10'-10"
29	9866	11060	12290	13530	14790	16070	17360	19040	20850		10'-11"
30	10010	11240	12490	13770	15060	16370	17700	19410	21590		11'- 1"
31	10150	11400	12690	13990	15320	16670	18030	19760	22200	22320	11'- 1"
32	10280	11560	12880	14210	15570	16950	18350	20100	22630	23020	11'- 3"
33	10400	11710	13060	14420	15810	17230	18660	20440	23040	23740	11'- 4"
34	10520	11860	13230	14620	16040	17490	18950	20760	23440	24490	11'- 5"
35	10640	12000	13390	14820	16260	17740	19240	21060	23840	25220	11'- 6"
36	10740	12130	13550	15000	16480	17990	19520	21360	24210	25930	11'- 8"
37	10850	12250	13700	15180	16690	18220	19780	21660	24580	26680	11'- 9"
38	10940	12370	13840	15350	16900	18450	20040	21940	24940	27410	11'-10"
39	11040	12490	13980	15510	17080	18670	20290	22210	25290	28130	11'-11"
40	11120	12600	14110	15670	17260	18880	20530	22450	25620	28820	

48" — SATURATED TOP SOIL Ku'=0.150

HEIGHT OF BACKFILL **H** ABOVE TOP OF PIPE, FEET — TRENCH WIDTH AT TOP OF PIPE

H	6'-6"	7'-0"	7'-6"	8'-0"	8'-6"	9'-0"	9'-6"	10'-0"	11'-0"	12'-0"	Transition Width
5	2902	2950									6'- 7"
6	3406	3691									7'- 0"
7	3888	4233	4490								7'- 4"
8	4348	4740	5134	5354							7'- 9"
9	4787	5227	5668	6110	6287						8'- 2"
10	5206	5693	6181	6671	7041						8'- 5"
11	5606	6139	6674	7210	7776						8'- 6"
12	5989	6567	7147	7730	8315	8508					8'- 8"
13	6354	6976	7602	8231	8862	9235					8'- 9"
14	6702	7369	8039	8713	9389	9966					8'-11"
15	7035	7745	8459	9177	9899	10690					9'- 0"
16	7353	8105	8863	9625	10390	11160	11420				9'- 2"
17	7657	8450	9250	10060	10870	11680	12150				9'- 3"
18	7947	8781	9623	10470	11320	12180	12870				9'- 5"
19	8223	9098	9981	10870	11770	12670	13600				9'- 6"
20	8488	9401	10320	11260	12190	13140	14090	14330			9'- 8"
21	8740	9692	10660	11630	12610	13590	14580	15060			9'- 9"
22	8981	9971	10970	11980	13000	14030	15060	15770			9'-10"
23	9211	10240	11280	12330	13390	14460	15530	16510			9'-11"
24	9431	10490	11570	12660	13760	14870	15980	17110	17230		10'- 1"
25	9641	10740	11850	12980	14120	15260	16420	17590	17960		10'- 2"
26	9841	10970	12120	13290	14460	15650	16850	18050	18680		10'- 3"
27	10030	11200	12380	13580	14800	16020	17260	18500	19400		10'- 4"
28	10220	11410	12630	13870	15120	16380	17660	18940	20120		10'- 5"
29	10390	11620	12870	14140	15430	16730	18040	19370	20850		10'- 7"
30	10560	11820	13100	14410	15730	17070	18420	19780	21590		10'- 8"
31	10720	12010	13320	14660	16020	17390	18780	20180	22320		10'-10"
32	10870	12190	13540	14910	16300	17710	19130	20570	23020		10'-11"
33	11010	12360	13740	15140	16570	18010	19470	20950	23740		11'- 1"
34	11150	12530	13940	15370	16830	18310	19800	21310	24490		11'- 1"
35	11280	12690	14130	15590	17080	18590	20120	21670	24800	25220	11'- 3"
36	11410	12840	14310	15800	17320	18870	20430	22010	25220	25930	11'- 4"
37	11530	12990	14480	16010	17560	19130	20730	22350	25630	26680	11'- 5"
38	11640	13130	14650	16200	17780	19390	21020	22670	26020	27410	11'- 6"
39	11760	13260	14810	16390	18000	19640	21300	22990	26410	28130	11'- 7"
40	11860	13390	14960	16570	18210	19880	21580	23290	26780	28820	

HEIGHT OF BACKFILL H ABOVE TOP OF PIPE, FEET

D — SATURATED CLAY Kμ'—0.110

TRENCH WIDTH AT TOP OF PIPE

H	6'-6"	7'-0"	7'-6"	8'-0"	8'-6"	9'-0"	9'-6"	10'-0"	11'-0"	12'-0"	TRANSITION WIDTH
5	2950										6'-5"
6	3529	3691									6'-9"
7	4051	4398	4490								7'-2"
8	4555	4951	5354								7'-6"
9	5042	5487	5932	6287							7'-11"
10	5514	6006	6500	6994	7041						8'-1"
11	5969	6509	7051	7593	7776						8'-2"
12	6410	6997	7586	8176	8508						8'-3"
13	6836	7470	8106	8744	9235						8'-5"
14	7247	7928	8611	9295	9966						8'-6"
15	7645	8372	9101	9832	10570	10690					8'-7"
16	8030	8802	9577	10360	11140	11420					8'-8"
17	8402	9218	10040	10860	11690	12150					8'-9"
18	8761	9622	10490	11360	12230	12870					8'-10"
19	9109	10010	10920	11840	12760	13600					9'-0"
20	9445	10390	11350	12310	13270	14330					9'-1"
21	9770	10760	11760	12760	13770	14780	15060				9'-2"
22	10080	11120	12160	13200	14260	15310	15770				9'-3"
23	10390	11460	12540	13640	14730	15830	16510				9'-4"
24	10680	11800	12920	14060	15200	16340	17230				9'-5"
25	10960	12120	13290	14460	15640	16840	17960				9'-6"
26	11240	12440	13640	14860	16080	17320	18560	18680			9'-7"
27	11500	12740	13990	15240	16510	17790	19070	19400			9'-8"
28	11760	13030	14320	15620	16930	18250	19570	20120			9'-8"
29	12010	13320	14650	15990	17340	18700	20060	20850			9'-10"
30	12250	13600	14960	16340	17730	19130	20540	21590			9'-10"
31	12480	13860	15270	16690	18120	19560	21010	22320			9'-11"
32	12700	14120	15570	17020	18500	19980	21470	23020			10'-0"
33	12920	14380	15860	17350	18860	20380	21920	23460	23740		10'-1"
34	13130	14620	16140	17670	19220	20780	22360	23940	24490		10'-2"
35	13330	14860	16410	17980	19570	21150	22780	24410	25220		10'-3"
36	13530	15090	16670	18280	19910	21550	23200	24870	25930		10'-4"
37	13720	15310	16930	18570	20240	21920	23610	25310	26680		10'-5"
38	13900	15520	17180	18860	20560	22280	24010	25750	27410		10'-6"
39	14070	15730	17420	19140	20870	22630	24400	26180	28130		10'-6"
40	14240	15940	17660	19410	21180	22970	24780	26600	28820		10'-7"

C — ORDINARY CLAY Kμ'—0.130

TRENCH WIDTH AT TOP OF PIPE

HEIGHT OF BACKFILL H ABOVE TOP OF PIPE, FEET

H	6'-6"	7'-0"	7'-6"	8'-0"	8'-6"	9'-0"	9'-6"	10'-0"	11'-0"	12'-0"	TRANSITION WIDTH
5	2950										6'-6"
6	3467	3691									6'-11"
7	3968	4314	4490								7'-3"
8	4450	4844	5239	5354							7'-8"
9	4912	5355	5798	6242	6287						8'-1"
10	5357	5847	6338	6830	7041						8'-2"
11	5784	6321	6859	7398	7776						8'-4"
12	6194	6777	7362	7949	8508						8'-6"
13	6589	7217	7848	8482	9117	9235					8'-7"
14	6967	7641	8318	8998	9679	9966					8'-9"
15	7331	8050	8772	9497	10220	10690					8'-10"
16	7681	8443	9210	9981	10750	11420					8'-11"
17	8017	8823	9633	10450	11270	12150					9'-0"
18	8340	9188	10040	10900	11760	12630	12870				9'-2"
19	8650	9540	10440	11340	12250	13160	13600				9'-3"
20	8948	9880	10820	11760	12720	13670	14330				9'-4"
21	9234	10210	11190	12180	13170	14170	15060				9'-5"
22	9509	10520	11540	12570	13610	14650	15770				9'-6"
23	9774	10820	11890	12960	14040	15120	16210	16510			9'-8"
24	10030	11120	12220	13330	14450	15580	16710	17230			9'-9"
25	10270	11400	12540	13690	14850	16020	17200	17960			9'-10"
26	10510	11670	12850	14040	15240	16450	17670	18680			9'-11"
27	10730	11930	13150	14380	15620	16870	18130	19400			10'-0"
28	10950	12180	13440	14710	15990	17280	18580	19890	20120		10'-1"
29	11160	12430	13720	15020	16340	17670	19020	20370	20850		10'-2"
30	11360	12660	13990	15330	16690	18060	19440	20830	21590		10'-3"
31	11550	12890	14250	15630	17020	18430	19850	21280	22320		10'-4"
32	11730	13100	14500	15910	17350	18790	20250	21720	23020		10'-5"
33	11910	13310	14740	16190	17660	19140	20640	22150	23740		10'-6"
34	12080	13520	14980	16460	17970	19490	21020	22570	24490		10'-7"
35	12240	13710	15200	16720	18260	19820	21390	22980	25220		10'-8"
36	12400	13900	15420	16980	18550	20140	21750	23380	25930		10'-9"
37	12550	14080	15640	17220	18830	20460	22100	23760	26680		10'-10"
38	12700	14250	15840	17460	19100	20760	22440	24140	27410		10'-11"
39	12830	14420	16040	17680	19360	21060	22770	24510	28130		10'-11"
40	12970	14580	16230	17910	19610	21340	23100	24870	28460	28820	11'-1"

* For backfill weighing 110 pounds per cubic foot; for 120 pounds per cubic foot, increase loads 10%; for 130 pounds per cubic foot, increase 20%; etc.

▲ Transition loads (**bold type**) and widths based on Kμ'—0.19, $f_s dP$—0.5 in the embankment equation

Interpolate for intermediate heights of backfill and/or trench widths

CONCRETE PIPE DESIGN MANUAL

TABLE 27

BACKFILL LOADS ON CIRCULAR PIPE IN TRENCH INSTALLATION

54″

LOADS IN POUNDS PER LINEAR FOOT

*100 POUNDS PER CUBIC FOOT BACKFILL MATERIAL

A — SAND AND GRAVEL Ku′—0.165

TRENCH WIDTH AT TOP OF PIPE (bold values = transition load)

H (ft)	7′-0″	7′-6″	8′-0″	8′-6″	9′-0″	9′-6″	10′-0″	11′-0″	12′-0″	13′-0″	Transition Width
5	3118	**3238**									7′-3″
6	3658	3954	**4030**								7′-7″
7	4173	4518	**4880**								8′-0″
8	4665	5057	5451	**5790**							8′-5″
9	5134	5573	6014	6456	**6765**						8′-10″
10	5581	6067	6555	7044	7534	**7809**					9′-3″
11	6008	6540	7074	7609	8146	**8683**					9′-6″
12	6415	6992	7571	8153	8737	9322	**9507**				9′-8″
13	6803	7425	8049	8676	9306	9937	**10330**				9′-9″
14	7114	7839	8508	9180	9855	10530	**11150**				9′-11″
15	7527	8235	8948	9664	10380	11110	11830	**11970**			10′-1″
16	7864	8614	9370	10130	10890	11660	12430	**12780**			10′-3″
17	8186	8977	9775	10580	11380	12200	13010	**13600**			10′-5″
18	8492	9324	10160	11010	11860	12710	13570	**14420**			10′-6″
19	8785	9657	10540	11420	12320	13210	14120	**15230**			10′-7″
20	9064	9975	10890	11820	12760	13700	14640	**16050**			10′-9″
21	9331	10280	11240	12200	13180	14160	15150	**16860**			10′-10″
22	9585	10570	11570	12570	13590	14610	15640	**17680**			11′-0″
23	9827	10850	11880	12930	13980	15050	16120	18280	**18490**		11′-1″
24	10060	11120	12190	13270	14360	15470	16580	18820	**19310**		11′-3″
25	10280	11370	12480	13600	14730	15870	17020	19350	**20120**		11′-4″
26	10490	11620	12760	13920	15080	16260	17450	19860	**20930**		11′-5″
27	10690	11850	13030	14220	15420	16640	17870	20360	**21750**		11′-7″
28	10880	12070	13280	14510	15750	17010	18270	20840	**22580**		11′-7″
29	11060	12290	13530	14790	16070	17360	18660	21300	**23380**		11′-9″
30	11240	12490	13770	15060	16370	17700	19040	21760	**24190**		11′-11″
31	11400	12690	13990	15320	16670	18030	19410	22200	**25010**		12′-0″
32	11560	12880	14210	15570	16950	18350	19760	22630	25540	**25840**	12′-1″
33	11710	13060	14420	15810	17230	18660	20100	23040	26030	**26650**	12′-3″
34	11860	13230	14620	16040	17490	18950	20440	23440	26500	**27440**	12′-3″
35	12000	13390	14820	16270	17740	19240	20760	23840	26900	**28250**	12′-6″
36	12130	13550	15000	16480	17990	19520	21060	24210	27420	**29090**	12′-7″
37	12250	13700	15180	16690	18220	19780	21360	24580	27860	**29910**	12′-7″
38	12370	13840	15350	16890	18450	20040	21660	24940	28290	**30720**	12′-9″
39	12490	13980	15510	17080	18670	20290	21940	25290	28710	**31500**	12′-10″
40	12600	14110	15670	17260	18880	20530	22210	25620	29110	**32330**	12′-11″

B — SATURATED TOP SOIL Ku′—0.150

TRENCH WIDTH AT TOP OF PIPE (bold values = transition load)

H (ft)	7′-0″	7′-6″	8′-0″	8′-6″	9′-0″	9′-6″	10′-0″	11′-0″	12′-0″	13′-0″	Transition Width
5	3150	**3238**									7′-2″
6	3703	4000	**4030**								7′-7″
7	4233	4579	**4880**								7′-11″
8	4740	5134	5529	**5790**							8′-4″
9	5227	5668	6110	6554	**6765**						8′-9″
10	5693	6181	6671	7161	7653	**7809**					9′-2″
11	6139	6674	7210	7748	8287	**8683**					9′-4″
12	6567	7147	7730	8315	8901	**9507**					9′-6″
13	6976	7602	8231	8862	9494	10130	**10330**				9′-8″
14	7369	8039	8713	9389	10070	10750	**11150**				9′-9″
15	7745	8459	9177	9899	10620	11350	**11970**				9′-11″
16	8105	8863	9625	10390	11160	11930	12710	**12780**			10′-1″
17	8450	9250	10060	10870	11680	12500	13320	**13600**			10′-2″
18	8781	9623	10470	11320	12180	13040	13910	**14420**			10′-4″
19	9098	9981	10870	11770	12670	13570	14480	**15230**			10′-5″
20	9401	10330	11260	12190	13140	14090	15040	**16050**			10′-6″
21	9692	10660	11630	12610	13590	14580	15580	**16860**			10′-8″
22	9971	10970	11980	13000	14030	15060	16100	**17680**			10′-9″
23	10240	11280	12330	13390	14460	15530	16610	**18490**			10′-10″
24	10490	11570	12660	13760	14870	15980	17110	**19310**			11′-0″
25	10740	11850	12980	14120	15260	16420	17590	19940	**20120**		11′-1″
26	10970	12120	13290	14460	15650	16850	18050	20480	**20930**		11′-2″
27	11200	12380	13580	14800	16020	17260	18500	21020	**21750**		11′-5″
28	11410	12630	13870	15120	16380	17660	18940	21540	**22580**		11′-6″
29	11620	12870	14140	15430	16730	18040	19370	22040	**23380**		11′-7″
30	11820	13100	14410	15730	17070	18420	19780	22540	**24190**		11′-8″
31	12010	13320	14660	16020	17390	18780	20180	23020	**25010**		11′-9″
32	12190	13540	14910	16300	17710	19130	20570	23480	**25840**		11′-11″
33	12360	13740	15140	16570	18010	19470	20950	23940	**26650**		12′-0″
34	12530	13940	15370	16830	18310	19800	21310	24380	**27440**		12′-1″
35	12690	14130	15590	17080	18590	20120	21670	24800	27990	**28250**	12′-2″
36	12840	14310	15800	17320	18870		22010	25220	28480	**29090**	12′-3″
37	12990	14490	16020	17560	19130		22350	25630	28970	**29910**	12′-4″
38	13130	14650	16200	17780	19390		22670	26020	29440	**30720**	12′-5″
39	13260	14810	16390	18000	19640		22990	26410	29890	**31500**	12′-7″
40	13390	14960	16570	18210	19880		23290	26780	30340	**32330**	12′-7″

HEIGHT OF BACKFILL H ABOVE TOP OF PIPE, FEET

C — ORDINARY CLAY Kμ'—0.130

HEIGHT OF BACKFILL H ABOVE TOP OF PIPE, FEET

TRENCH WIDTH AT TOP OF PIPE

H	7'-0"	7'-6"	8'-0"	8'-6"	9'-0"	9'-6"	10'-0"	11'-0"	12'-0"	13'-0"	▲TRANSITION WIDTH
5	3194	**3238**									7'- 1"
6	3764	**4030**									7'- 5"
7	4314	4661	**4880**								7'-10"
8	4844	5239	5635	**5790**							8'- 2"
9	5355	5798	6242	6687	**6765**						8'- 7"
10	5847	6338	6830	7323	**7809**						9'- 0"
11	6321	6859	7398	7939	8481	**8683**					9'- 4"
12	6777	7362	7949	8537	9126	**9507**					9'- 5"
13	7217	7848	8482	9117	9754	10360	**10330**				9'- 7"
14	7641	8318	8998	9679	10360	11050	**11150**				9'- 8"
15	8050	8772	9497	10220	10960	11690	**11970**				9'-11"
16	8443	9210	9981	10750	11530	12310	**12780**				10'- 0"
17	8823	9633	10450	11270	12090	12910		**13600**			10'- 2"
18	9188	10040	10900	11760	12630	13500		**14420**			10'- 4"
19	9540	10440	11340	12250	13160	14070		**15230**			10'- 5"
20	9880	10820	11760	12720	13670	14630		**16050**			10'- 6"
21	10210	11190	12180	13170	14170	15170		**16860**			10'- 8"
22	10520	11540	12570	13610	14650	15700		**17680**			10'- 9"
23	10820	11890	12950	14040	15120	16210		**18490**			10'-10"
24	11120	12220	13330	14450	15580	16710		**19310**			10'-11"
25	11400	12540	13690	14850	16020	17200		**20120**			11'- 0"
26	11670	12850	14040	15240	16450	17670			**20930**		11'- 1"
27	11930	13150	14380	15620	16870	18130			**21750**		11'- 2"
28	12180	13440	14710	15990	17280	18580			**22580**		11'- 3"
29	12430	13720	15020	16340	17670	19020		23000	**23380**		11'- 5"
30	12660	13990	15330	16690	18060	19440		23640	**24190**		11'- 6"
31	12890	14250	15630	17020	18430	19850		24170	**25010**		11'- 7"
32	13100	14500	15910	17350	18790	20250		24690	**25840**		11'- 8"
33	13310	14740	16190	17660	19140	20640		25200	**26650**		11'- 9"
34	13520	14980	16460	17970	19490	21020		25700	**27440**		11'-10"
35	13710	15200	16720	18260	19820	21390		26190	**28250**		11'-11"
36	13900	15420	16980	18550	20140	21750		26660	**29090**		12'- 0"
37	14080	15640	17220	18830	20460	22100		27130	**29910**		12'- 0"
38	14250	15840	17460	19100	20760	22440		27580	**30720**		12'- 0"
39	14420	16040	17680	19360	21060	22770		28020	**31500**		12'- 0"
40	14580	16230	17910	19610	21340	23100		28460	32100	**32330**	12'- 1"

D — SATURATED CLAY Kμ'—0.110

HEIGHT OF BACKFILL H ABOVE TOP OF PIPE, FEET

TRENCH WIDTH AT TOP OF PIPE

H	7'-0"	7'-6"	8'-0"	8'-6"	9'-0"	9'-6"	10'-0"	11'-0"	12'-0"	13'-0"	▲TRANSITION WIDTH
5	**3238**										7'- 0"
6	3827	**4030**									7'- 4"
7	4398	4746	**4880**								7'- 8"
8	4951	5347	5744	**5790**							8'- 1"
9	5487	5932	6378	**6765**							8'- 5"
10	6006	6500	6994	7489	**7809**						8'-10"
11	6509	7051	7593	8136	**8683**						9'- 0"
12	6997	7586	8176	8768	9360	**9507**					9'- 2"
13	7470	8106	8744	9382	10020	**10330**					9'- 3"
14	7928	8611	9295	9982	10670	**11150**					9'- 4"
15	8372	9101	9832	10570	11300	**11970**					9'- 5"
16	8802	9577	10360	11140	11920	12700	**12780**				9'- 7"
17	9218	10040	10860	11690	12520	13350	**13600**				9'- 8"
18	9622	10490	11360	12230	13100	13980	**14420**				9'- 9"
19	10010	10920	11840	12760	13680	14600	**15230**				9'-10"
20	10390	11350	12310	13270	14240	15210	**16050**				9'-11"
21	10760	11760	12760	13770	14780	15800	**16860**				10'- 0"
22	11120	12160	13200	14260	15310	16380	17440	**17680**			10'- 1"
23	11460	12540	13640	14730	15830	16940	18050	**18490**			10'- 2"
24	11800	12920	14060	15200	16340	17490	18650	**19310**			10'- 4"
25	12120	13290	14460	15640	16840	18030	19230	**20120**			10'- 5"
26	12440	13640	14860	16080	17320	18560	19800	**20930**			10'- 5"
27	12740	13990	15240	16510	17790	19070	20360	**21750**			10'- 6"
28	13030	14320	15620	16930	18250	19570	20900	**22580**			10'- 7"
29	13320	14650	15990	17340	18700	20060	21440	**23380**			10'- 9"
30	13600	14960	16340	17730	19130	20540	21960	**24190**			10'-10"
31	13860	15270	16690	18120	19560	21010	22470	**25010**			11'- 0"
32	14120	15570	17020	18500	19980	21470	22970		**25840**		11'- 1"
33	14380	15860	17350	18860	20380	21920	23460		**26650**		11'- 1"
34	14620	16140	17670	19220	20780	22360	23940	27140	**27440**		11'- 2"
35	14860	16410	17980	19570	21170	22780	24410	27690	**28250**		11'- 3"
36	15090	16670	18280	19910	21550	23200	24870	28230	**29090**		11'- 4"
37	15310	16930	18570	20240	21920	23610	25310	28760	**29910**		11'- 5"
38	15520	17180	18860	20560	22280	24010	25750	29280	**30720**		11'- 6"
39	15730	17420	19140	20870	22630	24400	26180	29790	**31500**		11'- 7"
40	15940	17660	19410	21180	22970	24780	26600	30290	**32330**		11'- 7"

* For backfill weighing 110 pounds per cubic foot. For 120 pounds per cubic foot, increase loads 10%; for 130 pounds per cubic foot, increase 20%; etc.

▲ Transition loads (**bold type**) and widths based on $K\mu—0.19$, $r_{sd}p—0.5$ in the embankment equation

Interpolate for intermediate heights of backfill and/or trench widths

TABLE 28

60″

BACKFILL LOADS ON CIRCULAR PIPE IN TRENCH INSTALLATION

A — SAND AND GRAVEL Kμ'—0.165
*100 POUNDS PER CUBIC FOOT BACKFILL MATERIAL

TRENCH WIDTH AT TOP OF PIPE

H (ft)	8'-0"	8'-6"	9'-0"	9'-6"	10'-0"	10'-6"	11'-0"	12'-0"	13'-0"	14'-0"	Transition Width
5	3522										7'-10"
6	4252	4368									8'-2"
7	4864	5210	5268								8'-8"
8	5451	5845	6226								9'-0"
9	6014	6456	6899	7246							9'-5"
10	6555	7044	7534	8025	8331						9'-10"
11	7074	7609	8146	8685	9224	9486					10'-3"
12	7571	8153	8737	9322	9908	10480					10'-6"
13	8049	8676	9306	9937	10570	11200	11390				10'-8"
14	8508	9180	9855	10530	11210	11890	12300				10'-10"
15	8948	9664	10380	11110	11830	12560	13210				11'-0"
16	9370	10130	10890	11660	12430	13200	13980	14120			11'-1"
17	9775	10570	11380	12200	13010	13830	14650	15020			11'-3"
18	10160	11010	11860	12710	13570	14430	15300	15930			11'-4"
19	10540	11420	12320	13210	14120	15020	15930	16830			11'-6"
20	10890	11820	12760	13680	14640	15590	16540	17740			11'-7"
21	11240	12200	13180	14160	15150	16140	17140	18640			11'-9"
22	11570	12570	13590	14610	15640	16680	17720	19540			11'-11"
23	11880	12930	13980	15050	16140	17190	18280	20440			12'-0"
24	12190	13260	14360	15470	16580	17700	18820	21080	21340		12'-1"
25	12480	13580	14730	15870	17020	18180	19350	21690	22240		12'-3"
26	12760	13890	15080	16260	17450	18650	19860	22290	23150		12'-4"
27	13030	14190	15420	16640	17870	19110	20360	22870	24060		12'-6"
28	13290	14480	15750	17010	18270	19550	20840	23430	24960		12'-7"
29	13530	14760	16070	17360	18660	19980	21300	23980	25860		12'-8"
30	13770	15030	16370	17700	19040	20400	21760	24510	26760		12'-11"
31	13990	15290	16670	18030	19410	20800	22200	25030	27680		12'-11"
32	14210	15540	16950	18350	19760	21190	22630	25540	28560		13'-0"
33	14420	15780	17230	18660	20100	21570	23040	26030	29050	29460	13'-2"
34	14620	16010	17490	18950	20430	21930	23440	26500	29610	30380	13'-3"
35	14820	16240	17740	19240	20760	22290	23840	26970	30150	31270	13'-4"
36	15000	16460	17990	19520	21060	22630	24210	27420	30680	32140	13'-5"
37	15180	16670	18230	19780	21360	22960	24580	27860	31190	33090	13'-7"
38	15350	16870	18450	20040	21660	23290	24940	28290	31690	33970	13'-8"
39	15510	17070	18670	20290	21940	23600	25290	28710	32180	34880	13'-9"
40	15670	17260	18880	20530	22210	23900	25620	29110	32660	35770	13'-10"

B — SATURATED TOP SOIL Kμ'—0.150
LOADS IN POUNDS PER LINEAR FOOT

TRENCH WIDTH AT TOP OF PIPE

H (ft)	8'-0"	8'-6"	9'-0"	9'-6"	10'-0"	10'-6"	11'-0"	12'-0"	13'-0"	14'-0"	Transition Width
5	3522										7'-9"
6	4298	4368									8'-1"
7	4925	5268									8'-6"
8	5529	5924	6226								8'-11"
9	6110	6554	6997	7246							9'-3"
10	6671	7161	7653	8146	8331						9'-8"
11	7210	7748	8287	8828	9369	9486					10'-1"
12	7730	8315	8901	9488	10080	10480					10'-4"
13	8231	8862	9494	10130	10760	11390					10'-6"
14	8713	9389	10070	10750	11430	12120	12300				10'-7"
15	9177	9899	10620	11350	12080	12810	13210				10'-10"
16	9625	10390	11160	11930	12710	13480	14120				10'-11"
17	10060	10870	11680	12490	13290	14140	14960	15020			11'-2"
18	10470	11320	12180	13040	13910	14780	15650	15930			11'-3"
19	10870	11770	12670	13570	14480	15400	16310	16830			11'-5"
20	11260	12190	13140	14090	15040	16000	16960	17740			11'-6"
21	11630	12610	13590	14580	15580	16580	17580	18640			11'-8"
22	11980	13000	14030	15060	16100	17150	18200	19540			11'-11"
23	12330	13390	14460	15530	16610	17700	18790	20440			12'-0"
24	12660	13760	14870	15980	17110	18240	19370	21300	21340		12'-1"
25	12980	14120	15260	16420	17590	18760	19940	22100	22240		12'-2"
26	13290	14460	15650	16850	18050	19270	20480	22940	23150		12'-4"
27	13580	14800	16020	17260	18500	19760	21010	23560	24060		12'-5"
28	13870	15120	16380	17660	18940	20240	21530	24160	24960		12'-7"
29	14140	15430	16730	18040	19370	20700	22030	24750	25860		12'-8"
30	14410	15730	17070	18420	19780	21150	22520	25330	26760		12'-10"
31	14660	16020	17390	18780	20180	21590	22990	25890	27680		12'-11"
32	14910	16300	17710	19130	20570	22020	23450	26430	28560		13'-0"
33	15140	16570	18010	19470	20950	22440	23900	26960	29080	29460	13'-1"
34	15370	16830	18310	19800	21310	22840	24340	27480	29640	30380	13'-2"
35	15590	17080	18590	20120	21670	23230	24770	27990	30180	31270	13'-3"
36	15800	17320	18870	20430	22010	23610	25190	28480	30710	32140	13'-4"
37	16010	17560	19130	20730	22350	23980	25600	28970	31220	33090	13'-5"
38	16200	17780	19390	21020	22670	24340	26000	29440	31720	33970	13'-6"
39	16390	18000	19640	21300	22990	24690	26390	29890	32210	34880	13'-8"
40	16570	18210	19880	21580	23290	25030	26780	30340	32690	35770	13'-9"

HEIGHT OF BACKFILL H ABOVE TOP OF PIPE, FEET

D — SATURATED CLAY Kµ'—0.110

TRENCH WIDTH AT TOP OF PIPE

H	8'-0"	8'-6"	9'-0"	9'-6"	10'-0"	10'-6"	11'-0"	11'-6"	12'-0"	13'-0"	14'-0"	Transition Width
5	**3522**											7'-7"
6	**4368**											7'-11"
7	5093	**5268**										8'-3"
8	5744	6142	**6226**									8'-7"
9	6378	6824	**7246**									9'-0"
10	6994	7489	7984	**8331**								9'-4"
11	7593	8136	8680	9225	**9486**							9'-9"
12	8176	8768	9360	9953	**10480**							9'-11"
13	8744	9383	10020	10660	11310	**11390**						10'-2"
14	9295	9982	10670	11360	12050	**12300**						10'-3"
15	9832	10570	11300	12040	12780	**13210**						10'-5"
16	10360	11140	11920	12700	13490	**14120**						10'-6"
17	10860	11690	12520	13350	14180	**15020**						10'-7"
18	11360	12230	13100	13980	14860	15740	**15930**					10'-8"
19	11840	12760	13680	14600	15530	16460	**16830**					10'-10"
20	12310	13270	14240	15210	16180	17160	**17740**					10'-11"
21	12760	13770	14780	15800	16820	17840	**18640**					11'-0"
22	13200	14260	15310	16380	17440	18510	**19540**					11'-2"
23	13640	14730	15830	16940	18050	19160	20280	**20440**				11'-3"
24	14060	15200	16340	17490	18650	19800	20970	**21340**				11'-4"
25	14460	15640	16840	18030	19230	20430	21640	**22240**				11'-5"
26	14860	16080	17320	18560	19800	21050	22300	**23150**				11'-6"
27	15240	16510	17790	19070	20360	21650	22950	**24060**				11'-7"
28	15620	16930	18250	19570	20900	22240	23580	**24960**				11'-8"
29	15990	17340	18700	20060	21440	22820	24200	**25860**				11'-9"
30	16340	17730	19130	20540	21960	23380	24820		**26760**			11'-10"
31	16690	18120	19560	21010	22470	23940	25410		**27680**			11'-11"
32	17020	18500	19980	21470	22970	24480	26000		**28560**			12'-0"
33	17350	18860	20380	21920	23460	25010	26570		**29460**			12'-1"
34	17670	19220	20780	22360	23940	25530	27140		**30380**			12'-2"
35	17980	19570	21170	22780	24410	26040	27690		31000	**31270**		12'-3"
36	18280	19910	21550	23200	24870	26540	28280		31620	**32140**		12'-4"
37	18570	20240	21920	23610	25310	27030	28760		32240	**33090**		12'-5"
38	18860	20560	22280	24010	25750	27510	29280		32840	**33970**		12'-6"
39	19140	20870	22630	24400	26180	27980	29790		33430	**34880**		12'-6"
40	19410	21180	22970	24780	26600	28440	30290		34020	**35770**		12'-6"

C — ORDINARY CLAY Kµ'—0.130

TRENCH WIDTH AT TOP OF PIPE

H	8'-0"	8'-6"	9'-0"	9'-6"	10'-0"	10'-6"	11'-0"	11'-6"	12'-0"	13'-0"	14'-0"	Transition Width
5	**3522**											7'-8"
6	**4368**											8'-0"
7	5008	**5268**										8'-5"
8	5635	6031	**6226**									8'-9"
9	6242	6687	7132	**7246**								9'-1"
10	6830	7323	7816	**8331**								9'-6"
11	7398	7939	8481	9023	**9486**							9'-11"
12	7949	8537	9126	9717	10310	**10480**						10'-2"
13	8482	9117	9754	10390	11030	**11390**						10'-3"
14	8998	9679	10360	11050	11730	**12300**						10'-5"
15	9497	10220	10960	11690	12420	**13210**						10'-6"
16	9981	10750	11530	12310	13090	13870	**14120**					10'-8"
17	10450	11270	12090	12910	13740	14570	**15020**					10'-10"
18	10900	11760	12630	13500	14370	15250	**15930**					10'-11"
19	11340	12250	13160	14070	14990	15910	**16830**					11'-0"
20	11760	12720	13670	14630	15600	16560	17530	**17740**				11'-1"
21	12180	13170	14170	15170	16180	17190	18210	**18640**				11'-3"
22	12570	13610	14650	15700	16750	17810	18870	**19540**				11'-4"
23	12960	14040	15120	16210	17310	18410	19520	**20440**				11'-5"
24	13330	14450	15580	16710	17850	19000	20150	21200	**21340**			11'-6"
25	13690	14850	16020	17200	18380	19570	20760	21950	**22240**			11'-7"
26	14040	15240	16450	17670	18900	20130	21370	22530	**23150**			11'-8"
27	14380	15620	16870	18130	19400	20680	21950	23090	**24060**			11'-10"
28	14710	15990	17280	18580	19890	21200	22530		**24960**			11'-11"
29	15020	16340	17670	19020	20370	21720	23090		**25860**			12'-0"
30	15330	16690	18060	19440	20830	22230	23640		**26760**			12'-1"
31	15630	17020	18430	19850	21280	22720	24170		**27680**			12'-2"
32	15910	17350	18790	20250	21720	23200	24690		**28560**			12'-4"
33	16190	17660	19140	20640	22150	23670	25200		**29460**			12'-5"
34	16460	17970	19490	21020	22570	24130	25700		30000	**30380**		12'-7"
35	16720	18260	19820	21390	22980	24580	26190		30540	**31270**		12'-8"
36	16980	18550	20140	21750	23380	25020	26660		31070	**32140**		12'-9"
37	17220	18830	20460	22100	23760	25430	27130		31590	**33090**		12'-10"
38	17460	19100	20760	22440	24140	25860	27580		32100	**33970**		12'-11"
39	17680	19360	21060	22770	24510	26260	28020		32190	**34880**		13'-0"
40	17910	19610	21340	23100	24870	26660	28460		32100	**35770**		13'-0"

* For backfill weighing 110 pounds per cubic foot, increase loads 10%; for 120 pounds per cubic foot, increase 20%; etc.
▲ Transition loads (**bold type**) and widths based on Kµ=0.19, rsdP—0.5 in the embankment equation
Interpolate for intermediate heights of backfill and/or trench widths

TABLE 29

BACKFILL LOADS ON CIRCULAR PIPE IN TRENCH INSTALLATION

*100 POUNDS PER CUBIC FOOT BACKFILL MATERIAL
LOADS IN POUNDS PER LINEAR FOOT

66" — A — SAND AND GRAVEL Kµ'−0.165

H (ft)	9'-0"	9'-6"	10'-0"	10'-6"	11'-0"	11'-6"	12'-0"	13'-0"	14'-0"	15'-0"	TRANSITION WIDTH
5	3807										8'-5"
6	4707										8'-9"
7	5556	5660									9'-2"
8	6240	6668									9'-6"
9	6899	7342	7735								9'-11"
10	7534	8025	8517								10'-4"
11	8146	8685	9224	8865							10'-10"
12	8737	9322	9908	9764							11'-3"
13	9306	9937	10570	10500	10061						11'-6"
14	9855	10530	11210	11200	11080						11'-8"
15	10380	11110	11830	11890	11840	11330					11'-9"
16	10890	11660	12430	12560	12570	12440					11'-11"
17	11380	12200	13010	13200	13290	13260	13440				12'-1"
18	11860	12710	13570	13830	13980	14020	14450				12'-3"
19	12320	13210	14120	14430	14650	14750	15470				12'-4"
20	12760	13700	14640	15020	15300	15470	16300				12'-6"
21	13180	14160	15150	15590	15930	16170	17040	16440			12'-8"
22	13590	14610	15640	16140	16540	16840	17760	17430			12'-9"
23	13980	15050	16120	16680	17140	17500	18460	18420			12'-11"
24	14360	15470	16580	17190	17720	18140	19140	19410			13'-0"
25	14730	15870	17020	17700	18280	18760	19810	20410	24360		13'-1"
26	15080	16260	17450	18180	18820	19360	20450	21390	25360		13'-3"
27	15420	16640	17870	18650	19350	19950	21080	22370	26350		13'-4"
28	15750	17010	18270	19110	19860	20520	21690	23430	27330		13'-6"
29	16070	17360	18660	19550	20360	21070	22290	23980	28340		13'-7"
30	16370	17700	19040	19980	20840	21610	22870	24530	29310		13'-9"
31	16670	18030	19410	20400	21300	22130	23430	25030	30320		13'-10"
32	16950	18350	19760	20800	21760	22640	23980	25540	31300	32280	13'-11"
33	17230	18660	20100	21190	22200	23130	24530	26030	32110	33290	14'-1"
34	17490	18950	20440	21570	22630	23610	25030	26500	32740	34270	14'-2"
35	17740	19240	20760	21930	23040	24080	25540	26970	33360	35270	14'-4"
36	17990	19520	21060	22290	23440	24540	26030	27400	33970	36240	14'-5"
37	18220	19780	21360	22630	23840	24970	26500	27880	34560	37250	14'-6"
38	18450	20040	21660	22970	24240	25400	26990	32180	35140	38230	14'-7"
39	18670	20290	21940	23290	24580	25810	27460	32660	35710	39190	14'-9"
40	18880	20530	22210	23600	25620	27360	29110	32660	36260	39190	14'-10"

66" — B — SATURATED TOP SOIL Kµ'−0.150

H (ft)	9'-0"	9'-6"	10'-0"	10'-6"	11'-0"	11'-6"	12'-0"	13'-0"	14'-0"	15'-0"	TRANSITION WIDTH
5	3807										8'-4"
6	4707										8'-8"
7	5618	5660									9'-1"
8	6319	6668									9'-5"
9	6997	7442	7735								9'-10"
10	7653	8146	8639								10'-3"
11	8287	8828	9369	8865							10'-8"
12	8901	9488	10080	9911							11'-1"
13	9494	10130	10760	10670	10060						11'-4"
14	10070	10750	11400	11400	11260						11'-5"
15	10620	11350	12080	12120	12040	11330					11'-7"
16	11160	11930	12710	12810	12800	12440					11'-9"
17	11680	12500	13380	13480	13540	13440					11'-11"
18	12180	13040	13910	14140	14260	14280	14450				12'-0"
19	12670	13570	14480	14780	14960	15040	15440				12'-1"
20	13140	14090	15040	15400	15650	15790	16440				12'-3"
21	13590	14560	15580	16000	16310	16520	17430				12'-5"
22	14030	15060	16100	16610	16960	17230	18150	18420			12'-6"
23	14460	15530	16610	17150	17580	17920	18890	19410			12'-8"
24	14870	15980	17110	17700	18200	18590	19600	20410			12'-9"
25	15260	16420	17590	18240	18790	19250	20310	21390			12'-11"
26	15650	16850	18050	18760	19370	19890	20990	22380			13'-0"
27	16020	17260	18500	19270	19940	20510	21660	23370	26350		13'-1"
28	16380	17660	18940	19760	20540	21120	22310	24360	27330		13'-3"
29	16730	18040	19370	20240	21120	21710	22940	25360	28340		13'-5"
30	17070	18420	19780	20700	21590	22290	23560	26120	29310		13'-6"
31	17390	18780	20180	21150	22040	22850	24160	26810	30320		13'-8"
32	17710	19130	20570	21590	22540	23400	24750	27480	31300		13'-9"
33	18010	19470	20950	22020	23020	23930	25330	28140	32280		13'-10"
34	18310	19800	21310	22440	23480	24450	25890	28790	33290		13'-11"
35	18590	20120	21670	22840	23940	24950	26430	29410	34270		14'-1"
36	18870	20430	22010	23610	25220	26850	28480	31790	35130	35270	14'-2"
37	19130	20730	22350	23980	25630	27290	28970	32350	35770	36240	14'-3"
38	19390	21020	22670	24340	26020	27720	29440	32900	36390	37250	14'-4"
39	19640	21300	22990	24690	26410	28140	29890	33430	37010	38230	14'-5"
40	19880	21580	23290	25030	26780	28560	30340	33950	37610	39190	

HEIGHT OF BACKFILL H ABOVE TOP OF PIPE, FEET — TRENCH WIDTH AT TOP OF PIPE

HEIGHT OF BACKFILL H ABOVE TOP OF PIPE, FEET

D — SATURATED CLAY Kμ'–0.110

TRENCH WIDTH AT TOP OF PIPE

H (ft)	9'-0"	9'-6"	10'-0"	10'-6"	11'-0"	11'-6"	12'-0"	13'-0"	14'-0"	15'-0"	TRANSITION WIDTH
5	3807										8'-2"
6	4707										8'-6"
7	5660										8'-10"
8	6539	**6668**									9'-2"
9	7270	**7735**									9'-6"
10	7984	8480	**8865**								9'-11"
11	8680	9225	9770	**10060**							10'-3"
12	9360	9953	10550	11140	**11330**						10'-8"
13	10020	10660	11310	11950	**12440**						10'-11"
14	10670	11360	12050	12740	**13440**						11'-0"
15	11300	12040	12780	13520	14250	**14450**					11'-2"
16	11920	12700	13490	14270	15060	**15440**					11'-3"
17	12520	13350	14180	15020	15850	**16440**					11'-4"
18	13100	13980	14860	15740	16630	**17430**					11'-6"
19	13680	14600	15530	16460	17390	18320	**18420**				11'-7"
20	14240	15210	16180	17160	18130	19110	**19410**				11'-8"
21	14780	15800	16820	17840	18860	19890	**20410**				11'-9"
22	15310	16380	17440	18510	19580	20650	**21390**				11'-10"
23	15830	16940	18050	19160	20280	21400	**22380**				11'-11"
24	16340	17490	18650	19800	20970	22130	**23370**				12'-0"
25	16840	18030	19230	20430	21640	22850	24060	**24360**			12'-1"
26	17320	18560	19800	21050	22300	23560	24820	**25360**			12'-2"
27	17790	19070	20360	21650	22950	24250	25560	**26350**			12'-4"
28	18250	19570	20900	22240	23580	24930	26280	**27330**			12'-5"
29	18700	20060	21440	22820	24200	25600	26990	**28340**			12'-6"
30	19130	20540	21960	23380	24820	26250	27690	**29310**			12'-7"
31	19560	21010	22470	23940	25410	26890	28380	**30320**			12'-8"
32	19980	21470	22970	24480	26000	27520	29050	**31300**			12'-9"
33	20380	21920	23460	25010	26570	28140	29710	**32280**			12'-10"
34	20780	22360	23940	25530	27140	28740	30360	**33290**			12'-11"
35	21170	22780	24410	26040	27690	29340	31000	**34270**			13'-0"
36	21550	23200	24870	26540	28230	29920	31620	35050	**35270**		13'-1"
37	21920	23610	25310	27030	28760	30490	32240	35750	**36240**		13'-1"
38	22280	24010	25750	27510	29280	31060	32840	36440	**37250**		13'-3"
39	22630	24400	26180	27980	29790	31610	33430	37110	**38230**		13'-3"
40	22970	24780	26600	28440	30290	32150	34020	37780	**39190**		13'-4"

C — ORDINARY CLAY Kμ'–0.130

TRENCH WIDTH AT TOP OF PIPE

H (ft)	9'-0"	9'-6"	10'-0"	10'-6"	11'-0"	11'-6"	12'-0"	13'-0"	14'-0"	15'-0"	TRANSITION WIDTH
5	3807										8'-3"
6	4707										8'-7"
7	5660										8'-11"
8	6428	**6668**									9'-4"
9	7132	7578	**7735**								9'-8"
10	7816	8310	**8865**								10'-0"
11	8481	9023	9566	**10060**							10'-6"
12	9126	9717	10310	10900	**11330**						10'-10"
13	9754	10390	11030	11670	12310	**12440**					11'-1"
14	10360	11050	11730	12420	13110	**13440**					11'-3"
15	10960	11690	12420	13160	13890	**14450**					11'-4"
16	11530	12310	13090	13870	14650	**15440**					11'-6"
17	12090	12910	13740	14570	15400	16230	**16440**				11'-7"
18	12630	13500	14370	15250	16130	17000	**17430**				11'-9"
19	13160	14070	14990	15910	16840	17760	**18420**				11'-10"
20	13670	14630	15600	16560	17530	18500	**19410**				12'-0"
21	14170	15170	16180	17190	18210	19230	20240	**20410**			12'-1"
22	14650	15700	16750	17810	18870	19930	21000	**21390**			12'-2"
23	15120	16210	17310	18410	19520	20620	21740	**22380**			12'-3"
24	15580	16710	17850	19000	20150	21300	22460	**23370**			12'-5"
25	16020	17200	18380	19570	20760	21960	23160	**24360**			12'-6"
26	16450	17670	18900	20130	21370	22610	23850	**25360**			12'-7"
27	16870	18130	19400	20670	21950	23240	24530	**26350**			12'-8"
28	17280	18580	19890	21200	22530	23860	25190	**27330**			12'-9"
29	17670	19020	20370	21710	23090	24460	25840	**28340**			12'-11"
30	18060	19440	20830	22230	23640	25050	26470	**29310**			13'-0"
31	18430	19850	21280	22720	24170	25630	27090	30030	**30320**		13'-1"
32	18790	20250	21720	23200	24690	26190	27700	30720	**31300**		13'-2"
33	19140	20640	22150	23670	25200	26740	28290	31400	**32280**		13'-3"
34	19490	21020	22570	24130	25700	27280	28870	32070	**33290**		13'-5"
35	19820	21390	22980	24580	26190	27810	29440	32720	**34270**		13'-5"
36	20140	21750	23380	25020	26660	28320	30000	33360	**35270**		13'-6"
37	20460	22100	23760	25440	27130	28830	30540	33990	**36240**		13'-8"
38	20760	22440	24140	25860	27580	29320	31070	34600	**37250**		13'-9"
39	21060	22770	24510	26270	28020	29820	31590	35200	**38230**		13'-10"
40	21340	23100	24660	26660	28460	30270	32100	35790	**39190**		13'-11"

* For backfill weighing 110 pounds per cubic foot, increase loads 10%; for 120 pounds per cubic foot, increase 20%; etc.

▲Transition loads (**bold type**) and widths based on $K\mu$—0.19, $r_{sd}p$—0.5 in the embankment equation

Interpolate for intermediate heights of backfill and/or trench widths

TABLE 30

BACKFILL LOADS ON CIRCULAR PIPE IN TRENCH INSTALLATION

*100 POUNDS PER CUBIC FOOT BACKFILL MATERIAL — LOADS IN POUNDS PER LINEAR FOOT

A — 72″ SAND AND GRAVEL $K\mu'$-0.165

TRENCH WIDTH AT TOP OF PIPE

H	9′-6″	10′-0″	10′-6″	11′-0″	11′-6″	12′-0″	13′-0″	14′-0″	15′-0″	16′-0″	TRANSITION WIDTH
5	4097										9′-0″
6	5053										9′-4″
7	5903	6060									9′-9″
8	6635	7031	7121								10′-1″
9	7342	7786	**8239**								10′-6″
10	8025	8517	9010	**9417**							10′-11″
11	8685	9224	9764	10310	**10660**						11′-4″
12	9322	9908	10500	11080	11670	**11960**					11′-9″
13	9937	10570	11200	11840	12480	13120	**13340**				12′-2″
14	10530	11210	11890	12570	13260	13940	**14590**				12′-5″
15	11110	11830	12570	13290	14020	14750	**15690**				12′-8″
16	11660	12430	13200	13980	14750	15530	**16780**				12′-10″
17	12200	13010	13830	14650	15470	16300	**17860**				12′-11″
18	12710	13570	14430	15310	16170	17040	18540	**18950**			13′-1″
19	13210	14120	15020	15930	16840	17760	19280	**20030**			13′-3″
20	13700	14640	15590	16540	17500	18460	20010	**21110**			13′-4″
21	14160	15150	16140	17120	18140	19140	20720	**22200**			13′-6″
22	14610	15640	16680	17700	18760	19810	21420	**23270**			13′-7″
23	15050	16120	17190	18260	19360	20450	22100	**24360**			13′-9″
24	15470	16580	17700	18820	19950	21080	22770	**25420**			13′-11″
25	15870	17020	18180	19350	20520	21680	23420	**26520**			14′-0″
26	16260	17450	18650	19860	21070	22270	24060	27210	**27590**		14′-2″
27	16640	17870	19110	20350	21600	22870	24690	27960	**28670**		14′-3″
28	17010	18270	19550	20840	22120	23440	25310	28700	**29760**		14′-5″
29	17360	18660	19980	21300	22630	23980	25920	29410	**30840**		14′-6″
30	17700	19040	20400	21750	23130	24530	26520	30110	**31910**		14′-8″
31	18030	19410	20800	22190	23610	25030	27100	30790	**32990**		14′-9″
32	18350	19760	21190	22630	24080	25540	27680	31460	**34060**		14′-10″
33	18660	20100	21570	23040	24530	26030	28240	32110	**35150**		15′-0″
34	18950	20440	21930	23440	24970	26500	28800	32740	35910	**36200**	15′-1″
35	19240	20760	22290	23840	25400	26970	29340	33350	36610	**37310**	15′-3″
36	19520	21060	22630	24210	25810	27420	29880	33970	37300	**38350**	15′-4″
37	19780	21360	22960	24580	26220	27860	30410	34560	37970	**39450**	15′-5″
38	20040	21660	23290	24940	26620	28290	30930	35140	38630	**40540**	15′-6″
39	20290	21940	23600	25290	27010	28710	31450	35710	39270	**41590**	15′-8″
40	20530	22210	23900	25620	27360	29110	31960	36260	39900	**42680**	15′-9″

B — 72″ SATURATED TOP SOIL $K\mu'$-0.150

HEIGHT OF BACKFILL H ABOVE TOP OF PIPE, FEET — TRENCH WIDTH AT TOP OF PIPE

H	9′-6″	10′-0″	10′-6″	11′-0″	11′-6″	12′-0″	13′-0″	14′-0″	15′-0″	16′-0″	TRANSITION WIDTH
5	4097										8′-11″
6	5053										9′-3″
7	5966	6060									9′-8″
8	6715	7121									10′-0″
9	7442	7887	8239								10′-5″
10	8146	8639	9133	**9417**							10′-9″
11	8828	9369	9911	10450	**10660**						11′-1″
12	9488	10080	10670	11260	11850	**11960**					11′-7″
13	10130	10760	11400	12040	12680	**13340**					12′-0″
14	10750	11430	12120	12800	13490	14170	**14590**				12′-3″
15	11350	12080	12810	13540	14280	15010	**15690**				12′-5″
16	11930	12710	13480	14260	15040	15820	**16780**				12′-7″
17	12500	13320	14140	14960	15790	16620	**17860**				12′-9″
18	13040	13910	14780	15650	16520	17390	**18950**				12′-11″
19	13570	14480	15400	16310	17230	18150	**20030**				13′-0″
20	14090	15040	16000	16960	17920	18890	20820	**21110**			13′-2″
21	14580	15580	16580	17580	18590	19600	21640	**22200**			13′-3″
22	15060	16100	17150	18200	19250	20310	22430	**23270**			13′-5″
23	15530	16610	17700	18790	19890	20990	23200	**24360**			13′-6″
24	15980	17110	18240	19370	20510	21660	23960	**25420**			13′-7″
25	16420	17590	18760	19940	21120	22310	24700	**26520**			13′-9″
26	16850	18050	19270	20480	21710	22940	25420	**27590**			13′-11″
27	17260	18500	19760	21020	22290	23560	26120	**28670**			14′-0″
28	17660	18940	20240	21540	22850	24160	26810	29480	**29760**		14′-1″
29	18040	19370	20700	22040	23400	24750	27480	30240	**30840**		14′-2″
30	18420	19780	21150	22540	23930	25330	28140	30980	**31910**		14′-4″
31	18780	20180	21590	23020	24450	25890	28790	31710	**32990**		14′-5″
32	19130	20570	22020	23480	24950	26430	29410	32420	**34060**		14′-7″
33	19470	20950	22440	23940	25440	26960	30030	33120	**35150**		14′-8″
34	19800	21310	22840	24380	25920	27480	30630	33800	**36200**		14′-9″
35	20120	21670	23230	24800	26390	27990	31220	34470	**37310**		14′-10″
36	20430	22010	23610	25220	26850	28480	31790	35130	**38350**		15′-0″
37	20730	22350	23980	25630	27290	28970	32350	35770	39220	**39450**	15′-1″
38	21020	22670	24340	26020	27720	29440	32920	36390	39920	**40540**	15′-2″
39	21300	22990	24690	26410	28140	29890	33430	37010	40620	**41590**	15′-3″
40	21580	23290	25030	26780	28560	30340	33950	37610	41300	**42680**	15′-5″

HEIGHT OF BACKFILL **H** ABOVE TOP OF PIPE, FEET

C — ORDINARY CLAY $K\mu'$−0.130

TRENCH WIDTH AT TOP OF PIPE

H	9'-6"	10'-0"	10'-6"	11'-0"	11'-6"	12'-0"	13'-0"	14'-0"	15'-0"	16'-0"	TRANSITION WIDTH
5	4097										8'-10"
6	5053										9'-2"
7	6060										9'-6"
8	6825	7121									9'-11"
9	7578	8024	8239								10'-3"
10	8310	8805	9300	9417							10'-8"
11	9023	9566	10110	10660							11'-0"
12	9717	10310	10900	11490	11960						11'-5"
13	10390	11030	11670	12310	12950	13340					11'-10"
14	11050	11730	12420	13110	13800	14490	14590				12'-1"
15	11690	12420	13160	13890	14630	15370	15690				12'-3"
16	12310	13090	13870	14650	15440	16220	16780				12'-4"
17	12910	13740	14570	15400	16230	17060	17860				12'-6"
18	13500	14370	15250	16130	17000	17890	18950				12'-7"
19	14070	14990	15910	16840	17760	18690	20030				12'-9"
20	14630	15600	16560	17530	18500	19480	21110				12'-10"
21	15170	16180	17190	18210	19230	20240	22200				12'-11"
22	15700	16750	17810	18870	19930	21000	23140	23270			13'-1"
23	16210	17310	18400	19520	20620	21740	23970	24360			13'-2"
24	16710	17850	19000	20150	21300	22460	24780	25420			13'-3"
25	17200	18380	19570	20760	21960	23160	25580	26520			13'-4"
26	17670	18900	20130	21370	22610	23850	26360	27590			13'-6"
27	18130	19400	20670	21950	23240	24530	27120	28670			13'-7"
28	18580	19890	21200	22530	23860	25190	27870	29760			13'-8"
29	19020	20360	21720	23090	24460	25840	28610	30840			13'-9"
30	19440	20830	22230	23640	25050	26470	29330	31910			13'-11"
31	19850	21280	22720	24170	25630	27090	30040	32990			14'-0"
32	20250	21720	23190	24690	26190	27700	30720	33780	34060		14'-1"
33	20640	22150	23670	25200	26740	28290	31400	34540	35150		14'-2"
34	21020	22570	24130	25700	27280	28870	32070	35290	36200		14'-3"
35	21390	22980	24580	26190	27810	29440	32720	36030	37310		14'-5"
36	21750	23380	24990	26660	28320	30000	33360	36750	38350		14'-5"
37	22100	23760	25440	27130	28830	30540	33990	37460	39450		14'-7"
38	22440	24140	25860	27580	29320	31070	34600	38160	40540		14'-8"
39	22770	24510	26260	28020	29800	31590	35200	38850	41590		14'-9"
40	23100	24870	26660	28460	30270	32100	35790	39520	42680		14'-10"

D — SATURATED CLAY $K\mu'$−0.110

TRENCH WIDTH AT TOP OF PIPE

H	9'-6"	10'-0"	10'-6"	11'-0"	11'-6"	12'-0"	13'-0"	14'-0"	15'-0"	16'-0"	TRANSITION WIDTH
5	4097										8'-9"
6	5053										9'-1"
7	6060										9'-5"
8	6937	7121									9'-9"
9	7717	8165	8239								10'-1"
10	8480	8976	9417								10'-5"
11	9225	9770	10320	10660							10'-10"
12	9953	10550	11140	11740	11960						11'-2"
13	10660	11310	11950	12590	13240	13340					11'-7"
14	11360	12050	12740	13430	14120	14590					11'-10"
15	12040	12780	13520	14250	15000	15690					12'-0"
16	12700	13490	14270	15060	15850	16640	16780				12'-1"
17	13350	14180	15020	15850	16690	17530	17860				12'-2"
18	13980	14860	15740	16630	17510	18400	18950				12'-4"
19	14600	15530	16460	17390	18320	19250	20030				12'-5"
20	15210	16180	17160	18130	19110	20090	21110				12'-6"
21	15800	16820	17840	18860	19890	20920	22200				12'-8"
22	16380	17440	18510	19580	20650	21720	23270				12'-8"
23	16940	18050	19160	20280	21400	22520	24360				12'-10"
24	17490	18650	19800	20970	22130	23300	25420				12'-11"
25	18030	19230	20430	21640	22850	24060	26520				13'-0"
26	18560	19800	21050	22300	23560	24820	27340	27590			13'-1"
27	19070	20360	21650	22950	24250	25560	28170	28670			13'-3"
28	19570	20900	22240	23580	24930	26280	28990	29760			13'-3"
29	20060	21440	22820	24200	25600	26990	29790	30840			13'-4"
30	20540	21960	23380	24820	26250	27690	30580	31910			13'-6"
31	21010	22470	23940	25410	26890	28380	31360	32990			13'-6"
32	21470	22970	24480	26000	27520	29050	32120	34060			13'-7"
33	21920	23460	25010	26570	28140	29710	32870	35150			13'-9"
34	22360	23940	25530	27140	28740	30360	33610	36200			13'-9"
35	22780	24410	26040	27690	29340	31000	34330	37310			13'-11"
36	23200	24870	26540	28230	29920	31620	35050	38350			14'-0"
37	23610	25310	27030	28760	30490	32240	35750	39450			14'-0"
38	24010	25750	27510	29280	31060	32840	36440	40060	40540		14'-2"
39	24400	26180	27980	29790	31620	33430	37110	40820	41590		14'-2"
40	24780	26600	28440	30290	32150	34020	37780	41570	42680		14'-3"

* For backfill weighing 110 pounds per cubic foot, increase loads 10%; for 120 pounds per cubic foot, increase 20%; etc.

▲ Transition loads (**bold type**) and widths based on $K\mu'$−0.19, $r_{sd}p$−0.5 in the embankment equation

Interpolate for intermediate heights of backfill and/or trench widths

TABLE 31

BACKFILL LOADS ON CIRCULAR PIPE IN TRENCH INSTALLATION
LOADS IN POUNDS PER LINEAR FOOT

HEIGHT OF BACKFILL H ABOVE TOP OF PIPE, FEET

78" — A: SAND AND GRAVEL Kμ'—0.165
*100 POUNDS PER CUBIC FOOT BACKFILL MATERIAL

TRENCH WIDTH AT TOP OF PIPE

H	10'-0"	10'-6"	11'-0"	11'-6"	12'-0"	13'-0"	14'-0"	15'-0"	16'-0"	17'-0"	Transition Width
5	4384										9'-6"
6	5395										9'-11"
7	6250	6457									10'-3"
8	7031	7427	7570								10'-8"
9	7786	8231	8676	8739							11'-1"
10	8517	9010	9503	9966							11'-6"
11	9224	9764	10310	10850	11250						11'-11"
12	9908	10500	11080	11670	12260	12600					12'-3"
13	10570	11200	11840	12480	13120	14020					12'-9"
14	11210	11890	12570	13260	13940	15320	15510				13'-2"
15	11830	12560	13290	14020	14750	16220	16890				13'-5"
16	12430	13200	13980	14750	15530	17090	18080				13'-7"
17	13010	13830	14650	15470	16300	17950	19250				13'-9"
18	13570	14430	15300	16170	17040	18780	20430				13'-11"
19	14120	15020	15930	16840	17760	19600	21440	21600			14'-1"
20	14640	15590	16540	17500	18460	20390	22320	22780			14'-3"
21	15150	16140	17140	18140	19140	21160	23190	23940			14'-5"
22	15640	16680	17720	18760	19810	21910	24030	25110			14'-6"
23	16120	17190	18280	19360	20450	22650	24860	26280			14'-8"
24	16580	17700	18820	19950	21080	23360	25660	27450			14'-9"
25	17020	18180	19350	20520	21690	24060	26450	28610			14'-11"
26	17450	18650	19860	21070	22290	24740	27210	29780			15'-2"
27	17870	19110	20360	21610	22870	25410	27960	30540	30940		15'-3"
28	18270	19550	20840	22130	23430	26050	28700	31360	32120		15'-5"
29	18660	19980	21300	22640	23980	26680	29410	32160	33280		15'-6"
30	19040	20400	21760	23130	24510	27300	30110	32940	34460		15'-7"
31	19410	20800	22200	23610	25030	27900	30790	33710	35600		15'-9"
32	19760	21190	22630	24080	25540	28480	31460	34460	36770		15'-11"
33	20100	21570	23040	24530	26030	29050	32110	35190	37950		16'-0"
34	20440	21930	23440	24970	26500	29610	32740	35910	39100		16'-1"
35	20760	22290	23840	25400	26970	30150	33360	36610	39890	40290	16'-4"
36	21060	22630	24210	25810	27420	30680	33970	37300	40660	41460	16'-5"
37	21360	22960	24580	26220	27860	31190	34560	37970	41410	42600	16'-7"
38	21660	23290	24940	26610	28290	31690	35140	38630	42150	43760	16'-8"
39	21940	23600	25290	26990	28710	32180	35710	39270	42870	44940	
40	22210	23900	25620	27360	29110	32660	36260	39900	43580	46100	

78" — B: SATURATED TOP SOIL Kμ'—0.150

TRENCH WIDTH AT TOP OF PIPE

H	10'-0"	10'-6"	11'-0"	11'-6"	12'-0"	13'-0"	14'-0"	15'-0"	16'-0"	17'-0"	Transition Width
5	4384										9'-6"
6	5395										9'-10"
7	6313	6457									10'-3"
8	7112	7509	7570								10'-7"
9	7887	8332	8739								11'-0"
10	8639	9133	9627	9966							11'-4"
11	9369	9911	10450	11000	11250						11'-9"
12	10080	10670	11260	11850	12440	12600					12'-2"
13	10760	11400	12040	12680	13320	14020					12'-7"
14	11430	12120	12800	13490	14170	15510					13'-0"
15	12080	12810	13540	14280	15010	16480	16890				13'-3"
16	12710	13480	14260	15040	15820	17390	18080				13'-5"
17	13320	14140	14960	15790	16620	18280	19250				13'-7"
18	13910	14780	15650	16520	17390	19150	20430				13'-9"
19	14480	15400	16310	17230	18150	20000	21600				13'-11"
20	15040	16000	16960	17920	18890	20820	22780				14'-0"
21	15580	16580	17580	18590	19600	21640	23670	23940			14'-1"
22	16100	17150	18200	19250	20310	22430	24560	25110			14'-5"
23	16610	17700	18790	19890	20990	23200	25420	26260			14'-6"
24	17110	18240	19370	20510	21660	23960	26270	27450			14'-7"
25	17590	18760	19940	21120	22310	24700	27100	28610			14'-9"
26	18050	19270	20480	21710	22940	25420	27910	29780			14'-11"
27	18500	19760	21020	22290	23560	26120	28700	30940			15'-0"
28	18940	20240	21540	22850	24160	26810	29480	32120			15'-3"
29	19370	20700	22040	23400	24750	27480	30240	33010	33280		15'-4"
30	19780	21150	22540	23930	25330	28140	30980	33840	34460		15'-5"
31	20180	21590	23020	24450	25890	28790	31710	34650	35600		15'-8"
32	20570	22020	23480	24950	26430	29410	32420	35450	36770		15'-9"
33	20950	22420	23940	25440	26960	30030	33120	36240	37950		15'-11"
34	21310	22840	24380	25920	27480	30630	33800	37000	39100		15'-11"
35	21670	23230	24800	26390	27990	31220	34470	37760	40290		
36	22010	23610	25230	26850	28480	31790	35130	38490	41460		
37	22350	23980	25630	27290	28970	32350	35770	39220	42600		
38	22670	24340	26020	27720	29440	32900	36390	39920	43480	43760	16'-1"
39	22990	24690	26410	28140	29890	33430	37010	40620	44260	44940	16'-2"
40	23290	25030	26780	28560	30340	33950	37610	41300	45020	46100	16'-3"

HEIGHT OF BACKFILL H ABOVE TOP OF PIPE, FEET

D — SATURATED CLAY Kμ'—0.110

TRENCH WIDTH AT TOP OF PIPE

H	10'-0"	10'-6"	11'-0"	11'-6"	12'-0"	13'-0"	14'-0"	15'-0"	16'-0"	17'-0"	TRANSITION WIDTH
5	4384										9'- 3"
6	5395										9'- 7"
7	6457										9'-11"
8	7335	7570									10'- 3"
9	8165	8612	8739								10'- 8"
10	8976	9472	9966								11'- 0"
11	9770	10320	10860	11250							11'- 5"
12	10550	11140	11740	12330	12600						11'- 9"
13	11310	11950	12590	13240	13880	14020					12'- 1"
14	12050	12740	13430	14120	14820	15510					12'- 6"
15	12780	13520	14250	15000	15740	16890					12'-11"
16	13490	14270	15060	15850	16640	18080					13'- 1"
17	14180	15020	15850	16690	17530	19200	19250				13'- 2"
18	14860	15740	16630	17510	18400	20170	20430				13'- 5"
19	15530	16460	17390	18320	19250	21120	21600				13'- 5"
20	16180	17160	18130	19110	20090	22060	22780				13'- 7"
21	16820	17840	18860	19890	20920	22980	23940				13'- 9"
22	17440	18510	19580	20650	21720	23880	25110				13'-11"
23	18050	19160	20280	21400	22520	24770	26280				13'-11"
24	18650	19800	20970	22130	23300	25640	27450				14'- 1"
25	19230	20430	21640	22850	24060	26500	28610				14'- 2"
26	19800	21050	22300	23560	24820	27340	29780				14'- 4"
27	20360	21650	22950	24250	25560	28170	30800	30940			14'- 5"
28	20900	22240	23580	24930	26280	28990	31710	32120			14'- 6"
29	21440	22820	24200	25600	26990	29790	32610	33280			14'- 8"
30	21960	23380	24820	26250	27690	30580	33490	34460			14'- 9"
31	22470	23940	25410	26890	28380	31360	34360	35600			14'-10"
32	22970	24480	26000	27520	29050	32120	35210	36770			14'-11"
33	23460	25010	26570	28140	29710	32870	36050	37950			15'- 0"
34	23940	25530	27140	28740	30360	33610	36880	39100			15'- 1"
35	24410	26040	27690	29340	31000	34330	37690	40290			15'- 2"
36	24870	26540	28230	29920	31620	35050	38490	41460			
37	25310	27030	28760	30490	32240	35750	39280	42600			
38	25750	27510	29280	31060	32840	36440	40060	43760			
39	26180	27980	29790	31610	33430	37110	40820	44550	44940		
40	26600	28440	30290	32150	34020	37780	41570	45390	46100		

C — ORDINARY CLAY Kμ'—0.130

TRENCH WIDTH AT TOP OF PIPE

H	10'-0"	10'-6"	11'-0"	11'-6"	12'-0"	13'-0"	14'-0"	15'-0"	16'-0"	17'-0"	TRANSITION WIDTH
5	4384										9'- 5"
6	5395										9'- 9"
7	6399	6457									10'- 1"
8	7222	7570									10'- 5"
9	8024	8471	8739								10'- 9"
10	8805	9300	9796	9966							11'- 2"
11	9566	10110	10650	11250							11'- 6"
12	10310	10900	11490	12090	12600						11'-11"
13	11030	11670	12310	12950	13600	14020					12'- 4"
14	11730	12420	13110	13800	14490	15510					12'- 9"
15	12420	13160	13890	14630	15370	16850	16890				13'- 1"
16	13090	13870	14650	15440	16220	17800	18080				13'- 2"
17	13740	14570	15400	16230	17060	18730	19250				13'- 4"
18	14370	15250	16130	17000	17890	19650	20430				13'- 5"
19	14990	15910	16840	17760	18690	20550	21600				13'- 7"
20	15600	16560	17530	18500	19480	21430	22780				13'- 8"
21	16180	17190	18210	19230	20240	22290	23940				13'-10"
22	16750	17810	18870	19930	21000	23140	25110				13'-11"
23	17310	18410	19520	20620	21740	23970	26200	26280			14'- 1"
24	17850	19000	20150	21300	22460	24780	27110	27450			14'- 2"
25	18380	19570	20760	21960	23160	25580	28000	28610			14'- 3"
26	18900	20130	21370	22610	23850	26360	28870	29780			14'- 4"
27	19400	20670	21950	23240	24530	27120	29730	30940			14'- 5"
28	19890	21200	22530	23860	25190	27870	30570	32120			14'- 7"
29	20370	21720	23090	24460	25840	28610	31390	33280			14'- 8"
30	20830	22230	23640	25050	26470	29330	32200	34460			14'- 9"
31	21280	22720	24170	25630	27090	30030	33000	35600			14'-11"
32	21720	23200	24690	26190	27700	30720	33780	36770			15'- 0"
33	22150	23670	25200	26740	28290	31400	34540	37700	37950		15'- 1"
34	22570	24130	25700	27280	28870	32070	35290	38540	39100		15'- 2"
35	22980	24580	26190	27810	29440	32720	36030	39360	40290		15'- 3"
36	23380	25020	26660	28320	30000	33360	36750	40170	41460		15'- 5"
37	23760	25440	27130	28830	30540	33990	37460	40970	42600		15'- 5"
38	24140	25860	27580	29320	31070	34600	38160	41750	43760		15'- 7"
39	24510	26260	28020	29800	31590	35200	38850	42520	44520	44940	15'- 8"
40	24870	26660	28460	30270	32100	35790	39520	43280	45390	46100	

* For backfill weighing 110 pounds per cubic foot, increase loads 10%; for 120 pounds per cubic foot, increase 20%; etc.

▲ Transition loads (**bold type**) and widths based on Kμ—0.19, fsdP—0.5 in the embankment equation

Interpolate for intermediate heights of backfill and/or trench widths

TABLE 32

84″

BACKFILL LOADS ON CIRCULAR PIPE IN TRENCH INSTALLATION

*100 POUNDS PER CUBIC FOOT BACKFILL MATERIAL — LOADS IN POUNDS PER LINEAR FOOT

A — SAND AND GRAVEL Kµ'—0.165

TRENCH WIDTH AT TOP OF PIPE

H	10'-6"	11'-0"	11'-6"	12'-0"	13'-0"	14'-0"	15'-0"	16'-0"	17'-0"	18'-0"	TRANSITION WIDTH
5	4671										10'- 2"
6	5738										10'- 6"
7	6597	6854									10'-11"
8	7427	7823	8021								11'- 3"
9	8231	8676	9121	9242							11'- 8
10	9010	9503	9997	10520							12'- 0"
11	9764	10310	10850	11390	11860						12'- 5"
12	10500	11080	11670	12260	13250						12'-10"
13	11200	11840	12480	13120	14390	14710					13'- 3"
14	11890	12570	13260	13940	15320	16240					13'- 8"
15	12560	13290	14020	14750	16220	17690	17840				14'- 1"
16	13200	13980	14750	15530	17090	18660	19360				14'- 5"
17	13830	14650	15470	16300	17950	19610	20630				14'- 8"
18	14430	15300	16170	17040	18780	20540	21900				14'- 9"
19	15020	15930	16840	17760	19600	21440	23160				14'-11"
20	15590	16540	17500	18460	20390	22320	24270	24420			15'- 1"
21	16140	17140	18140	19140	21160	23190	25220	25680			15'- 3"
22	16680	17720	18760	19810	21910	24030	26160	26940			15'- 4"
23	17190	18280	19360	20450	22650	24860	27070	28200			15'- 6"
24	17700	18820	19950	21080	23360	25660	27970	29460			15'- 8"
25	18180	19350	20520	21690	24060	26450	28840	30720			15'- 9"
26	18650	19860	21070	22290	24740	27210	29700	31970			15'-11"
27	19110	20360	21610	22870	25410	27960	30540	33120	33230		16'- 1"
28	19550	20840	22130	23430	26050	28700	31360	34030	34470		16'- 2"
29	19980	21300	22640	23980	26680	29410	32160	34920	35740		16'- 4"
30	20400	21760	23130	24510	27300	30110	32940	35790	36970		16'- 5"
31	20800	22200	23610	25030	27900	30790	33710	36640	38250		16'- 7"
32	21190	22630	24080	25540	28480	31460	34460	37480	39490		16'- 8"
33	21570	23040	24530	26030	29050	32110	35190	38300	40720		16'- 9"
34	21930	23440	24970	26500	29610	32740	35910	39100	42000		16'-11"
35	22290	23840	25400	26970	30150	33360	36610	39890	43240		17'- 0"
36	22630	24210	25810	27420	30680	33970	37300	40660	44040	44500	17'- 2"
37	22960	24580	26210	27860	31190	34560	37970	41410	44870	45770	17'- 3"
38	23290	24940	26610	28290	31690	35140	38630	42150	45690	47010	17'- 5"
39	23600	25290	26990	28710	32180	35710	39270	42870	46500	48270	17'- 6"
40	23900	25620	27360	29110	32660	36260	39900	43580	47290	49500	17'- 7"

B — SATURATED TOP SOIL Kµ'—0.150

TRENCH WIDTH AT TOP OF PIPE

H	10'-6"	11'-0"	11'-6"	12'-0"	13'-0"	14'-0"	15'-0"	16'-0"	17'-0"	18'-0"	TRANSITION WIDTH
5	4671										10'- 1"
6	5738										10'- 5"
7	6661	6854									10'- 9"
8	7509	7906	8021								11'- 2"
9	8332	8778	9242								11'- 6"
10	9133	9627	10120	10520							11'-11"
11	9911	10450	11000	11540							12'- 3"
12	10670	11260	11850	12440	11860						12'-10"
13	11400	12040	12680	13320	13250	14710					13'- 1"
14	12120	12800	13490	14170	14600	16240					13'- 6"
15	12810	13540	14280	15010	15550	17840	19360				13'-11"
16	13480	14260	15040	15820	16480	18960	20630				14'- 1"
17	14140	14960	15790	16620	17390	19950	21900				14'- 5"
18	14780	15650	16520	17390	18280	20910	23160				14'- 7"
19	15400	16310	17230	18150	19150	21850	24420				14'- 8"
20	16000	16960	17920	18890	20000	22770	25680	26940			14'-10"
21	16580	17580	18590	19600	20820	23670	26700	28200			15'- 0"
22	17150	18200	19250	20310	21640	24560	27650	29460			15'- 1"
23	17700	18790	19890	20990	22430	25420	28590	30720			15'- 3"
24	18240	19370	20510	21660	23200	26270	29510	31970			15'- 4"
25	18760	19940	21120	22310	23960	27100	30410	33230			15'- 6"
26	19270	20480	21710	22940	24700	27910	31290	34470			15'- 8"
27	19760	21020	22290	23560	25420	28700	32160	35740			15'- 9"
28	20240	21540	22850	24160	26120	29480	33010	36710			15'-11"
29	20700	22040	23400	24750	26810	30240	33840	37620			16'- 1"
30	21150	22540	23930	25330	27480	30980	34650	38500	36970		16'- 2"
31	21590	23020	24450	25890	28140	31710	35450	39370	38250		16'- 4"
32	22020	23480	24950	26430	28790	32420	36240	40220	39490		16'- 5"
33	22440	23940	25440	26960	29410	33120	37000	41060	40720		16'- 7"
34	22840	24380	25920	27480	30030	33800	37760	41880	42000		16'- 8"
35	23230	24800	26390	27990	30630	34470	38490	42690	43240		16'- 9"
36	23610	25220	26850	28480	31220	35130	39220	43480	44500		16'-11"
37	23980	25630	27290	28970	31790	35770	39920	44260	45770		17'- 0"
38	24340	26020	27720	29440	32350	36390	40620	45020	47010	48270	17'- 1"
39	24690	26410	28140	29890	32900	37010	41300		47930	48270	17'- 3"
40	25030	26780	28560	30340	33430	37610			48780	49500	

D — SATURATED CLAY $K\mu'$-0.110

HEIGHT OF BACKFILL H ABOVE TOP OF PIPE, FEET / TRENCH WIDTH AT TOP OF PIPE

H	10'-6"	11'-0"	11'-6"	12'-0"	13'-0"	14'-0"	15'-0"	16'-0"	17'-0"	18'-0"	▲Transition Width
5	**4671**										9'-10"
6	**5738**										10'-2"
7	**6854**										10'-6"
8	7733	**8021**									10'-10"
9	8612	9060	**9242**								11'-3"
10	9472	9969	**10520**								11'-6"
11	10320	10860	11410	**11860**							11'-11"
12	11140	11740	12330	12930	**13250**						12'-3"
13	11950	12590	13240	13880	**14710**						12'-8"
14	12740	13430	14120	14820	**16240**						13'-0"
15	13520	14250	15000	15740	17220	**17840**					13'-5"
16	14270	15060	15850	16640	18220	**19360**					13'-9"
17	15020	15850	16690	17530	19200	**20630**					13'-10"
18	15740	16630	17510	18400	20170	**21900**					14'-0"
19	16460	17390	18320	19250	21120	23000	**23160**				14'-1"
20	17160	18130	19110	20090	22060	24030	**24420**				14'-3"
21	17840	18860	19890	20920	22980	25040	**25680**				14'-4"
22	18510	19580	20650	21720	23880	26040	**26940**				14'-5"
23	19160	20280	21400	22520	24770	27020	**28200**				14'-6"
24	19800	20970	22130	23300	25640	27990	**29460**				14'-8"
25	20430	21640	22850	24060	26490	28940	**30720**				14'-9"
26	21050	22300	23560	24820	27340	29880	**31970**				14'-10"
27	21650	22950	24250	25560	28170	30800	**33230**				14'-11"
28	22240	23580	24930	26280	28990	31710	**34470**				15'-0"
29	22820	24200	25600	26990	29790	32610	35430	**35740**			15'-1"
30	23380	24820	26250	27690	30580	33490	36400	**36970**			15'-2"
31	23940	25410	26890	28380	31360	34360	37360	**38250**			15'-3"
32	24480	26000	27520	29050	32120	35210	38310	**39490**			15'-5"
33	25010	26570	28140	29710	32870	36050	39240	**40720**			15'-6"
34	25530	27140	28740	30360	33610	36880	40160	**42000**			15'-7"
35	26040	27690	29340	31000	34330	37690	41060	**43240**			15'-8"
36	26540	28230	29920	31620	35050	38490	41950	**44500**			15'-9"
37	27030	28760	30490	32240	35750	39280	42830	**45770**			15'-10"
38	27510	29280	31060	32840	36440	40060	43700	**47010**			15'-11"
39	27980	29790	31610	33430	37110	40830	44550	**48270**			16'-0"
40	28440	30290	32150	34020	37780	41570	45390	49230	**49500**		16'-1"

C — ORDINARY CLAY $K\mu'$-0.130

TRENCH WIDTH AT TOP OF PIPE / HEIGHT OF BACKFILL H ABOVE TOP OF PIPE, FEET

H	10'-6"	11'-0"	11'-6"	12'-0"	13'-0"	14'-0"	15'-0"	16'-0"	17'-0"	18'-0"	▲Transition Width
5	**4671**										10'-0"
6	5738	**6854**									10'-4"
7	7620	**8021**									10'-8"
8	8471	8917	**9242**								11'-0"
9	9300	9796	10290	**10520**							11'-4"
10	10110	10650	11200	11740	**11860**						11'-9"
11	10900	11490	12090	12680	**13250**						12'-1"
12	11670	12310	12950	13600	**14710**						12'-6"
13	12420	13110	13800	14490	15870	**16240**					12'-11"
14	13160	13890	14630	15370	16850	**17840**					13'-3"
15	13870	14650	15440	16220	17800	**19360**					13'-8"
16	14570	15400	16230	17060	18730	20410	**20630**				14'-0"
17	15250	16130	17000	17890	19650	21420	**21900**				14'-2"
18	15910	16840	17760	18690	20550	22410	**23160**				14'-3"
19	16560	17530	18500	19480	21430	23390	**24420**				14'-5"
20	17190	18210	19230	20240	22290	24340	**25680**				14'-6"
21	17810	18870	19930	21000	23140	25280	**26940**				14'-8"
22	18410	19520	20620	21740	23970	26200	**28200**				14'-9"
23	19000	20150	21300	22460	24780	27110	**29460**				14'-10"
24	19570	20760	21960	23160	25580	28000	30430	**30720**			15'-0"
25	20130	21370	22610	23850	26360	28870	31400	**31970**			15'-3"
26	20670	21950	23240	24530	27120	29730	32340	**33230**			15'-4"
27	21200	22530	23860	25190	27870	30570	33270	**34470**			15'-6"
28	21720	23090	24460	25840	28610	31390	34190	**35740**			15'-8"
29	22230	23640	25050	26470	29330	32200	35090	**36970**			15'-9"
30	22730	24170	25630	27090	30030	33000	35970	**38250**			15'-11"
31	23200	24690	26190	27700	30720	33780	36840	**39490**			16'-1"
32	23670	25200	26740	28290	31400	34540	37700	**40720**			16'-2"
33	24130	25700	27280	28870	32070	35290	38540	41800	**42000**		16'-4"
34	24580	26190	27810	29440	32720	36030	39360	42710	**43240**		16'-5"
35	25020	26660	28320	30000	33360	36750	40170	43610	**44500**		16'-7"
36	25440	27130	28830	30540	33990	37460	40970	44490	**45770**		16'-8"
37	25850	27580	29320	31070	34600	38160	41750	45360	**47010**		
38	26260	28020	29800	31590	35200	38850	42520	46220	**48270**		
39	26660	28460	30270	32100	35790	39520	43280	47060	**49500**		

* For backfill weighing 110 pounds per cubic foot; for 120 pounds per cubic foot, increase loads 10%; for 130 pounds per cubic foot, increase 20%, etc.

▲ Transition loads (**bold type**) and widths based on $K\mu$—0.19, $r_{sd}p$—0.5 in the embankment equation

Interpolate for intermediate heights of backfill and/or trench widths

TABLE 33

BACKFILL LOADS ON CIRCULAR PIPE IN TRENCH INSTALLATION

*100 POUNDS PER CUBIC FOOT BACKFILL MATERIAL — LOADS IN POUNDS PER LINEAR FOOT

90″ — SAND AND GRAVEL Kμ′–0.165

A — HEIGHT OF BACKFILL H ABOVE TOP OF PIPE, FEET / TRENCH WIDTH AT TOP OF PIPE

H	Transition Width	11'-0"	12'-0"	13'-0"	14'-0"	15'-0"	16'-0"	17'-0"	18'-0"	19'-0"
5	10'-9"	**4963**								
6	11'-1"	6040	**6087**							
7	11'-5"	6945	**7260**							
8	11'-10"	7823	**8482**							
9	12'-2"	8676	9567	**9757**						
10	12'-7"	9503	10490	**11090**						
11	13'-0"	10310	11390	**12470**						
12	13'-5"	11080	12260	13450	**13920**					
13	13'-10"	11840	13120	14390	**15430**					
14	14'-3"	12570	13940	15320	16690	**17000**				
15	14'-8"	13290	14750	16220	17690	**18640**				
16	15'-1"	13980	15530	17090	18660	20230	**20340**			
17	15'-6"	14650	16300	17950	19610	21270	**22010**			
18	15'-7"	15300	17040	18780	20540	22290	**23380**			
19	15'-9"	15930	17760	19600	21440	23290	**24740**			
20	15'-11"	16540	18460	20390	22320	24270	**26090**			
21	16'-1"	17140	19140	21160	23190	25220	27270	**27440**		
22	16'-3"	17720	19810	21910	24030	26160	28300	**28790**		
23	16'-4"	18280	20450	22650	24860	27070	29300	**30150**		
24	16'-6"	18820	21080	23360	25660	27970	30290	**31500**		
25	16'-8"	19350	21690	24060	26450	28840	31250	**32840**		
26	16'-10"	19860	22290	24740	27210	29700	32200	**34180**		
27	16'-11"	20360	22870	25410	27960	30540	33120	**35520**		
28	17'-1"	20840	23430	26050	28700	31360	34030	36720	**36860**	
29	17'-2"	21300	23980	26680	29410	32160	34920	37700	**38220**	
30	17'-4"	21760	24510	27300	30110	32940	35790	38660	**39560**	
31	17'-5"	22200	25030	27900	30790	33710	36640	39600	**40880**	
32	17'-7"	22630	25540	28480	31460	34460	37480	40520	**42230**	
33	17'-8"	23040	26030	29050	32110	35190	38300	41420	**43560**	
34	17'-9"	23440	26500	29610	32740	35910	39100	42310	**44940**	
35	17'-11"	23840	26970	30150	33360	36610	39890	43180	**46280**	
36	18'-0"	24210	27420	30680	33970	37300	40640	44040	**47620**	
37	18'-2"	24580	27860	31190	34560	37970	41410	44870	48360	**48940**
38	18'-4"	24940	28290	31690	35140	38630	42150	45690	49260	**50310**
39	18'-5"	25290	28710	32180	35710	39270	42870	46500	50150	**51650**
40	18'-6"	25620	29110	32660	36260	39990	43580	47290	51020	**52960**

90″ — SATURATED TOP SOIL Kμ′–0.150

B — HEIGHT OF BACKFILL H ABOVE TOP OF PIPE, FEET / TRENCH WIDTH AT TOP OF PIPE

H	Transition Width	11'-0"	12'-0"	13'-0"	14'-0"	15'-0"	16'-0"	17'-0"	18'-0"	19'-0"
5	10'-8"	**4963**								
6	11'-0"	6040	**6087**							
7	11'-4"	6945	**7260**							
8	11'-8"	7823	**8482**							
9	12'-1"	8778	9671	**9757**						
10	12'-6"	9627	10620	**11090**						
11	12'-10"	10450	11540	**12470**						
12	13'-3"	11260	12440	13630	**13920**					
13	13'-8"	12040	13320	14600	**15430**					
14	14'-1"	12800	14170	15550	16930	**17000**				
15	14'-5"	13540	15010	16480	17960	**18640**				
16	14'-11"	14260	15820	17390	18960	**20340**				
17	15'-3"	14960	16620	18280	19950	21620	**22010**			
18	15'-5"	15650	17390	19150	20910	22670	**23380**			
19	15'-9"	16310	18150	20000	21850	23710	**24740**			
20	15'-9"	16960	18890	20820	22770	24720	**26090**			
21	15'-10"	17580	19600	21640	23670	25720	**27440**			
22	16'-0"	18200	20310	22430	24560	26700	**28790**			
23	16'-1"	18790	20990	23200	25420	27650	29890	**30150**		
24	16'-3"	19370	21660	23960	26270	28590	30920	**31500**		
25	16'-4"	19940	22310	24700	27100	29510	31930	**32840**		
26	16'-6"	20480	22940	25420	27910	30410	32920	**34180**		
27	16'-8"	21020	23560	26120	28700	31290	33900	**35520**		
28	16'-9"	21540	24160	26810	29480	32160	34850	**36860**		
29	16'-11"	22040	24750	27480	30240	33010	35790	**38220**		
30	17'-0"	22540	25330	28140	30980	33840	36710	**39560**		
31	17'-1"	23020	25890	28790	31710	34650	37620	40590	**40880**	
32	17'-2"	23480	26430	29410	32420	35450	38500	41560	**42230**	
33	17'-4"	23940	26960	30030	33120	36240	39370	42520	**43560**	
34	17'-5"	24380	27480	30630	33800	37000	40220	43460	**44940**	
35	17'-7"	24800	27990	31220	34470	37760	41060	44390	**46280**	
36	17'-8"	25220	28480	31790	35130	38490	41880	45300	**47620**	
37	17'-9"	25630	28970	32350	35770	39220	42690	46190	**48940**	
38	17'-11"	26020	29440	32900	36390	39920	43480	47070	**50310**	
39	18'-0"	26410	29890	33430	37010	40620	44260	47930	**51650**	
40	18'-1"	26780	30340	33950	37610	41300	45020	48780	52550	**52960**

HEIGHT OF BACKFILL H ABOVE TOP OF PIPE, FEET

D — SATURATED CLAY Kμ'–0.110

Trench width at top of pipe (loads in pounds). Transition loads shown in **bold**.

H	11'-0"	12'-0"	13'-0"	14'-0"	15'-0"	16'-0"	17'-0"	18'-0"	19'-0"	TRANSITION WIDTH
5	**4963**									10'-5"
6	**6087**									10'-9"
7	7185	**7260**								11'-1"
8	8132	**8482**								11'-5"
9	9060	**9757**								11'-9"
10	9969	10960	**11090**							12'-2"
11	10860	11950	**12470**							12'-6"
12	11740	12930	**13920**							12'-10"
13	12590	13880	15170	**15430**						13'-3"
14	13430	14820	16200	**17000**						13'-6"
15	14250	15740	17220	**18640**						13'-11"
16	15060	16640	18220	19800	**20340**					14'-4"
17	15850	17530	19200	20890	**22010**					14'-8"
18	16630	18400	20170	21950	**23380**					14'-10"
19	17390	19250	21120	23000	**24740**					15'-0"
20	18130	20090	22060	24030	**26090**					15'-0"
21	18860	20920	22980	25040	27110	**27440**				15'-2"
22	19580	21720	23880	26040	28200	**28790**				15'-3"
23	20280	22520	24770	27020	29280	**30150**				15'-5"
24	20970	23300	25640	27990	30350	**31500**				15'-6"
25	21640	24060	26500	28940	31390	**32840**				15'-7"
26	22300	24820	27340	29880	32420	**34180**				15'-8"
27	22950	25560	28170	30800	33440	**35520**				15'-9"
28	23580	26280	28990	31710	34440	**36860**				15'-10"
29	24200	26990	29790	32610	35430	**38220**				16'-0"
30	24820	27690	30580	33490	36400	39330	**39560**			16'-1"
31	25410	28380	31360	34360	37360	40380	**40880**			16'-2"
32	26000	29050	32120	35210	38310	41420	**42230**			16'-3"
33	26570	29710	32870	36050	39240	42440	**43560**			16'-4"
34	27140	30360	33610	36880	40160	43450	**44940**			16'-5"
35	27690	31000	34330	37690	41060	44450	**46280**			16'-7"
36	28230	31620	35050	38490	41950	45430	**47620**			16'-8"
37	28760	32240	35750	39280	42830	46400	**48940**			16'-8"
38	29280	32840	36440	40060	43700	47360	**50310**			16'-10"
39	29790	33430	37110	40820	44550	48300	**51650**			16'-11"
40	30290	34020	37780	41570	45390	49230	**52960**			16'-11"

C — ORDINARY CLAY Kμ'–0.130

Trench width at top of pipe (loads in pounds). Transition loads shown in **bold**.

H	11'-0"	12'-0"	13'-0"	14'-0"	15'-0"	16'-0"	17'-0"	18'-0"	19'-0"	TRANSITION WIDTH
5	**4963**									10'-7"
6	**6087**									10'-11"
7	7096	**7260**								11'-3"
8	8018	**8482**								11'-7"
9	8917	**9757**								11'-11"
10	9796	10790	**11090**							12'-3"
11	10650	11740	**12470**							12'-8"
12	11490	12680	**13920**							13'-0"
13	12310	13600	14880	**15430**						13'-5"
14	13110	14490	15870	**17000**						13'-10"
15	13890	15370	16850	18330	**18640**					14'-2"
16	14650	16220	17800	19380	**20340**					14'-8"
17	15400	17060	18730	20410	**22010**					15'-0"
18	16130	17890	19650	21420	23190	**23380**				15'-1"
19	16840	18690	20550	22410	24280	**24740**				15'-3"
20	17530	19480	21430	23390	25350	**26090**				15'-5"
21	18210	20240	22290	24340	26400	**27440**				15'-6"
22	18870	21140	23140	25280	27440	**28790**				15'-7"
23	19520	21740	23970	26200	28450	**30250**				15'-9"
24	20150	22460	24780	27110	29450	**31500**				15'-10"
25	20760	23160	25580	28000	30430	**32840**				16'-0"
26	21370	23850	26360	28870	31400	33930	**34180**			16'-0"
27	21950	24530	27120	29730	32340	34970	**35520**			16'-3"
28	22530	25190	27870	30570	33270	35990	**36860**			16'-4"
29	23090	25840	28610	31390	34190	37000	**38220**			16'-5"
30	23640	26470	29330	32200	35090	37970	**39560**			16'-7"
31	24170	27090	30030	33000	35970	38960	**40880**			16'-8"
32	24690	27700	30720	33780	36840	39920	**42230**			16'-9"
33	25200	28290	31400	34540	37700	40870	**43560**			16'-10"
34	25700	28870	32070	35290	38540	41800	**44940**			16'-11"
35	26190	29440	32720	36030	39360	42710	46070	**46280**		17'-1"
36	26660	30000	33360	36750	40170	43610	47060	**47620**		17'-2"
37	27130	30540	33990	37460	40970	44490	48030	**48940**		17'-3"
38	27580	31070	34600	38160	41750	45360	48990	**50310**		17'-4"
39	28020	31590	35200	38850	42520	46220	49940	**51650**		17'-5"
40	28460	32100	35790	39520	43280	47060	50860	**52960**		17'-6"

* For backfill weighing 110 pounds per cubic foot, increase loads 10%; for 120 pounds per cubic foot, increase 20%; etc.

▲ Transition loads (**bold type**) and widths based on Kμ—0.19, f_{sdp}—0.5 in the embankment equation

Interpolate for intermediate heights of backfill and/or trench widths

TABLE 34

96"

BACKFILL LOADS ON CIRCULAR PIPE IN TRENCH INSTALLATION

*100 POUNDS PER CUBIC FOOT BACKFILL MATERIAL — LOADS IN POUNDS PER LINEAR FOOT

A — SAND AND GRAVEL Kμ'—0.165

HEIGHT OF BACKFILL H ABOVE TOP OF PIPE, FEET	TRENCH WIDTH AT TOP OF PIPE									▲TRANSITION WIDTH
	12'-0"	13'-0"	14'-0"	15'-0"	16'-0"	17'-0"	18'-0"	19'-0"	20'-0"	
5	5251									11'-3"
6	6432									11'-8"
7	7659									12'-0"
8	8617	8937								12'-5"
9	9567	10260								12'-9"
10	10490	11480	11650							13'-2"
11	11390	12480	13080							13'-7"
12	12260	13450	14580							13'-11"
13	13120	14390	15680	16130						14'-4"
14	13940	15320	16690	17750						14'-9"
15	14750	16220	17690	19160	19430					15'-2"
16	15530	17090	18660	20230	21180					15'-7"
17	16300	17950	19610	21270	22940	23000				16'-1"
18	17040	18780	20540	22290	24060	24820				16'-5"
19	17760	19600	21440	23290	25150	26270				16'-7"
20	18460	20390	22320	24270	26220	27720				16'-9"
21	19140	21160	23190	25220	27270	29160				17'-0"
22	19810	21910	24030	26160	28300	30440	30600			17'-1"
23	20450	22650	24860	27070	29300	31540	32040			17'-3"
24	21080	23360	25660	27960	30290	32610	33470			17'-4"
25	21690	24060	26450	28840	31250	33670	34910			17'-6"
26	22290	24740	27210	29700	32200	34710	36340			17'-8"
27	22870	25410	27960	30540	33120	35720	37790			17'-9"
28	23430	26050	28700	31360	34030	36720	39200			17'-11"
29	24060	26680	29410	32160	34920	37700	40490	40650		18'-1"
30	24510	27300	30110	32940	35790	38660	41540	42080		18'-2"
31	25030	27900	30790	33700	36640	39600	42560	43520		18'-4"
32	25540	28480	31460	34460	37480	40520	43580	44940		18'-5"
33	26040	29050	32110	35190	38300	41420	44570	46380		18'-7"
34	26500	29610	32740	35910	39100	42310	45540	47810		18'-9"
35	26970	30150	33360	36610	39890	43180	46500	49210		18'-10"
36	27420	30680	33970	37300	40660	44040	47440	50640		18'-11"
37	27860	31190	34560	37970	41410	44870	48360	51860	52090	19'-2"
38	28290	31690	35140	38630	42150	45690	49260	52850	53490	19'-3"
39	28710	32180	35710	39270	42870	46500	50150	53830	54920	19'-5"
40	29110	32660	36260	39900	43580	47290	51020	54780	56360	19'-5"

B — SATURATED TOP SOIL Kμ'—0.150

HEIGHT OF BACKFILL H ABOVE TOP OF PIPE, FEET	TRENCH WIDTH AT TOP OF PIPE									▲TRANSITION WIDTH
	12'-0"	13'-0"	14'-0"	15'-0"	16'-0"	17'-0"	18'-0"	19'-0"	20'-0"	
5	5251									11'-3"
6	6432									11'-7"
7	7659									11'-11"
8	8700	8937								12'-4"
9	9671	10260								12'-8"
10	10620	11650								13'-0"
11	11540	12630	13080							13'-5"
12	12440	13630	14580							13'-11"
13	13320	14600	15680	16130						14'-3"
14	14170	15550	16930	17750						14'-7"
15	15010	16480	17960	19430						15'-0"
16	15820	17390	18960	20540	21180					15'-5"
17	16620	18280	19950	21620	23000					15'-10"
18	17390	19150	20910	22670	24440	24820				16'-2"
19	18150	20000	21850	23710	25570	26270				16'-4"
20	18890	20820	22770	24720	26680	27720				16'-7"
21	19600	21640	23670	25720	27770	29160				16'-8"
22	20310	22430	24560	26700	28840	30600				16'-10"
23	20990	23200	25420	27650	29890	32040				17'-0"
24	21660	23960	26270	28590	30920	33260	33470			17'-1"
25	22310	24700	27100	29510	31930	34360	34910			17'-3"
26	22940	25420	27910	30410	32920	35450	36340			17'-4"
27	23560	26120	28700	31290	33900	36510	37790			17'-6"
28	24160	26810	29480	32160	34850	37560	39200			17'-8"
29	24750	27480	30240	33010	35770	38590	40650			17'-9"
30	25330	28140	30980	33840	36710	39600	42080			17'-10"
31	25890	28790	31710	34650	37560	40590	43520			18'-0"
32	26430	29410	32420	35450	38500	41560	44640	44940		18'-1"
33	26960	30030	33120	36240	39370	42520	45690	46380		18'-2"
34	27480	30630	33800	37000	40220	43460	46720	47810		18'-4"
35	27990	31220	34470	37760	41060	44390	47730	49210		18'-5"
36	28480	31790	35130	38490	41880	45300	48730	50640		18'-6"
37	28970	32350	35770	39220	42690	46190	49710	52090		18'-8"
38	29440	32900	36390	39920	43480	47070	50670	53490		18'-10"
39	29890	33430	37010	40620	44260	47930	51620	54920		18'-10"
40	30340	33950	37610	41300	45020	48780	52550	56360		19'-0"

HEIGHT OF BACKFILL H ABOVE TOP OF PIPE, FEET

C — ORDINARY CLAY Kμ'−0.130

Trench width at top of pipe.

H	12'-0"	13'-0"	14'-0"	15'-0"	16'-0"	17'-0"	18'-0"	19'-0"	20'-0"	Transition Width
5	5251									11'-2"
6	6432									11'-5"
7	7659									11'-9"
8	8814	**8937**								12'-2"
9	9812	**10260**								12'-6"
10	10790	**11650**								12'-10"
11	11740	12840	**13080**							13'-3"
12	12680	13870	**14580**							13'-7"
13	13600	14880	**16130**							13'-11"
14	14490	15870	17260	**17750**						14'-4"
15	15370	16850	18330	**19430**						14'-9"
16	16220	17800	19380	20960	**21180**					15'-1"
17	17060	18730	20410	22090	**23000**					15'-6"
18	17890	19650	21420	23190	**24820**					15'-11"
19	18690	20550	22410	24280	26150	**26270**				16'-2"
20	19480	21430	23390	25350	27320	**27720**				16'-4"
21	20240	22290	24340	26400	28470	**29160**				16'-6"
22	21000	23140	25280	27440	29600	**30600**				16'-7"
23	21740	23970	26200	28450	30700	**32040**				16'-8"
24	22460	24780	27110	29450	31800	**33470**				16'-10"
25	23160	25580	28010	30430	32870	**34910**				17'-0"
26	23850	26360	28870	31400	33930	**36340**				17'-1"
27	24530	27120	29730	32340	34970	37600	**37790**			17'-2"
28	25190	27870	30570	33270	35990	38720	**39200**			17'-4"
29	25840	28610	31390	34180	37000	39820	**40650**			17'-5"
30	26470	29330	32200	35090	37990	40900	**42080**			17'-6"
31	27090	30030	33000	35980	38960	41970	**43520**			17'-8"
32	27700	30720	33780	36840	39920	43020	**44940**			17'-9"
33	28290	31400	34540	37700	40870	44050	**46380**			17'-10"
34	28870	32070	35290	38540	41800	45070	**47810**			17'-11"
35	29440	32720	36030	39360	42710	46070	**49210**			18'-1"
36	30000	33360	36750	40170	43610	47060	50530	**50640**		18'-3"
37	30540	33990	37460	40970	44490	48030	51590	**52090**		18'-4"
38	31070	34600	38160	41750	45360	48990	52640	**53490**		18'-5"
39	31590	35210	38850	42520	46220	49940	53670	**54920**		
40	32100	35790	39520	43280	47060	50860	54690	**56360**		

D — SATURATED CLAY Kμ'−0.110

Trench width at top of pipe.

H	12'-0"	13'-0"	14'-0"	15'-0"	16'-0"	17'-0"	18'-0"	19'-0"	20'-0"	Transition Width
5	5251									11'-0"
6	6432									11'-4"
7	7659									11'-8"
8	8937									12'-0"
9	9956	**10260**								12'-4"
10	10960	**11650**								12'-8"
11	11950	**13080**								13'-0"
12	12930	14120	**14580**							13'-5"
13	13880	15170	**16130**							13'-9"
14	14820	16200	17590	**17750**						14'-1"
15	15740	17220	18710	**19430**						14'-6"
16	16640	18220	19800	21180	**23000**					14'-10"
17	17530	19200	20890	22570	**24820**					15'-3"
18	18400	20170	21950	23730	**26270**					15'-7"
19	19250	21120	23000	24870	**27720**					15'-9"
20	20090	22060	24030	26000	**29160**					15'-10"
21	20920	22980	25040	27110	30370					16'-0"
22	21720	23880	26040	28200	31550	**30600**				16'-2"
23	22520	24770	27020	29280	32710	**32040**				16'-3"
24	23300	25640	27990	30350	33850	**33470**				16'-4"
25	24060	26500	28940	31390	34980	**34910**				16'-5"
26	24820	27340	29880	32420	36090	**36340**				16'-7"
27	25560	28170	30800	33440	37180	**37790**				16'-7"
28	26280	28990	31710	34440	38260	**39200**				16'-8"
29	26990	29790	32610	35430	39330	**40650**				16'-10"
30	27690	30580	33490	36400	40380	**42080**				17'-0"
31	28380	31360	34360	37360	41420	43520				17'-0"
32	29050	32120	35210	38310	42440	44540	**44940**			17'-1"
33	29710	32870	36050	39240	43450	45660	**46380**			17'-3"
34	30360	33610	36880	40160	44450	46760	**47810**			17'-4"
35	31000	34330	37690	41060	45430	47850	**49210**			17'-5"
36	31620	35050	38490	41950	46400	48920	**50640**			17'-6"
37	32240	35750	39280	42830	47360	49980	**52090**			17'-7"
38	32840	36440	40060	43700	48300	51030	**53490**			17'-8"
39	33430	37110	40820	44550	49230	52060	**54920**			17'-9"
40	34020	37780	41570	45390		53080	**56360**			17'-10"

* For backfill weighing 110 pounds per cubic foot, increase loads 10%; for 120 pounds per cubic foot, increase 20%; etc.

▲ Transition loads (**bold type**) and widths based on Kμ−0.19, $r_{sd}p$−0.5 in the embankment equation

Interpolate for intermediate heights of backfill and/or trench widths

TABLE 35

BACKFILL LOADS ON CIRCULAR PIPE IN TRENCH INSTALLATION

LOADS IN POUNDS PER LINEAR FOOT

102" — SAND AND GRAVEL Kμ'=0.165
*100 POUNDS PER CUBIC FOOT BACKFILL MATERIAL

HEIGHT OF BACKFILL **H** ABOVE TOP OF PIPE, FEET / TRENCH WIDTH AT TOP OF PIPE

H	12'-0"	13'-0"	14'-0"	15'-0"	16'-0"	17'-0"	18'-0"	19'-0"	20'-0"	22'-0"	Transition Width
5	5539										11'-10"
6	6637	6776									12'-3"
7	7640	8060									12'-7"
8	8617	9392									13'-0"
9	9567	10460	10780								13'-4"
10	10490	11480	12210								13'-9"
11	11390	12480	13560	13700							14'-0"
12	12260	13450	14630	15240							14'-6"
13	13120	14390	15680	16850	18510						14'-11"
14	13940	15320	16690	18070	20240						15'-4"
15	14750	16220	17690	19160	21800						15'-9"
16	15530	17090	18660	20230	22940	22030					16'-2"
17	16300	17950	19610	21270	24060	23890					16'-6"
18	17040	18780	20540	22290	25150	25820	27780				17'-0"
19	17760	19600	21440	23290	26220	27010	29330				17'-5"
20	18460	20390	22320	24260	27270	28180	30870				17'-7"
21	19140	21160	23190	25220	28300	29320	32400				17'-11"
22	19810	21910	24030	26160	29300	30440	33780				18'-1"
23	20450	22650	24860	27070	30290	31540	34950	33940			18'-3"
24	21080	23360	25660	27970	31250	32610	36100	35460			18'-6"
25	21690	24060	26440	28840	32200	33670	37220	36980			18'-8"
26	22290	24740	27200	29700	33120	34710	38330	38500			18'-11"
27	22870	25410	27940	30540	34030	35720	39420	40020			19'-1"
28	23430	26050	28670	31360	34920	36720	40490	41540			19'-3"
29	23980	26680	29380	32160	35790	37700	41540	43070			19'-5"
30	24510	27300	30080	32940	36640	38660	42560	44590	44590		19'-7"
31	25030	27900	30760	33710	37480	39600	43580	45540	46110		19'-7"
32	25540	28480	31430	34460	38300	40520	44570	46640	47640		19'-10"
33	26030	29050	32090	35190	39100	41420	45540	47720	49150		19'-11"
34	26500	29610	32740	35910	39900	42310	46510	48780	50650		20'-1"
35	26970	30150	33360	36610	40660	43180	47440	49830	52180		20'-2"
36	27420	30680	33970	37300	41410	44040	48360	50850	53710		20'-4"
37	27860	31190	34560	37970	42150	44870	49260	51860	55200		
38	28290	31690	35140	38630	42870	45690	50150	52850	56460	56740	
39	28710	32180	35710	39270	43580	46500	51020	53830	57520	58250	
40	29110	32660	36260	39900	44280	47290	51870	54780	58560	59770	

102" — SATURATED TOP SOIL Kμ'=0.150

HEIGHT OF BACKFILL **H** ABOVE TOP OF PIPE, FEET / TRENCH WIDTH AT TOP OF PIPE

H	12'-0"	13'-0"	14'-0"	15'-0"	16'-0"	17'-0"	18'-0"	19'-0"	20'-0"	22'-0"	Transition Width
5	5539										11'-9"
6	6686	6776									12'-2"
7	7706	8060									12'-6"
8	8700	9392									12'-10"
9	9671	10560	10780								13'-3"
10	10620	11610	12210								13'-7"
11	11540	12630	13700								14'-0"
12	12440	13630	14810	15240							14'-4"
13	13320	14600	15880	16850							14'-9"
14	14170	15550	16930	18320							15'-2"
15	15010	16480	17960	19440	18510						15'-6"
16	15820	17390	18960	20540	20240						16'-0"
17	16620	18280	19950	21620	22030	23890					16'-5"
18	17390	19150	20910	22670	23390	25820	27780				16'-9"
19	18150	20000	21850	23710	24440	27440	29330				17'-2"
20	18890	20820	22770	24720	25570	28650	30870				17'-4"
21	19600	21640	23670	25720	26660	29830	32400				17'-6"
22	20310	22430	24560	26700	27770	30990	33940				17'-8"
23	20990	23200	25420	27650	28840	32140	35460				17'-9"
24	21660	23960	26270	28590	29890	33260	36800				17'-11"
25	22310	24700	27100	29520	30920	34360	37980	36980			18'-1"
26	22940	25420	27910	30410	31930	35450	39140	38500			18'-3"
27	23560	26120	28700	31290	32920	36510	40270	40020			18'-4"
28	24160	26810	29480	32160	33900	37560	41390	41540			18'-6"
29	24750	27480	30240	33000	34850	38590	42490	43070			18'-7"
30	25330	28140	30980	33830	35790	39600	43580	44590			18'-9"
31	25890	28790	31710	34650	36710	40590	44640	46110			18'-10"
32	26430	29410	32420	35450	37620	41560	45690	47640			18'-11"
33	26960	30030	33120	36240	38490	42520	46720	48870	49150		19'-1"
34	27480	30630	33800	37000	39370	43460	47730	49990	50650		19'-3"
35	27990	31220	34470	37760	40220	44390	48730	51090	52180		19'-4"
36	28480	31790	35130	38490	41060	45300	49710	52180	53710		19'-5"
37	28970	32350	35770	39220	41880	46190	50670	53240	55200		19'-7"
38	29440	32900	36390	39920	42690	47070	51620	54290	56740		19'-8"
39	29890	33430	37010	40620	43480	47930	52550	55330	58250		19'-10"
40	30340	33950	37610	41300	45020	48780	53470	56340	59770		19'-11"

C   ORDINARY CLAY Kμ'—0.130

TRENCH WIDTH AT TOP OF PIPE

H (ft)	12'-0"	13'-0"	14'-0"	15'-0"	16'-0"	17'-0"	18'-0"	19'-0"	20'-0"	22'-0"	▲TRAN-SITION WIDTH
5	5539										11'- 9"
6	6776										12'- 0"
7	7794	**8060**									12'- 4"
8	8814	9392									12'- 9"
9	9812	10710	**10780**								13'- 1"
10	10790	11780	12210								13'- 5"
11	11740	12840	**13700**								13'- 9"
12	12680	13870	15060	**15240**							14'- 2"
13	13600	14880	16170	16850							14'- 6"
14	14490	15870	17260	18510							14'-10"
15	15370	16850	18330	19810	**20240**						15'- 4"
16	16220	17800	19380	20960	22030						15'- 8"
17	17060	18730	20410	22090	23770	**23890**					16'- 1"
18	17890	19650	21420	23190	24970	25820					16'- 6"
19	18690	20550	22410	24280	26150	27780					16'-11"
20	19480	21430	23390	25350	27320	29290	**29330**				17'- 1"
21	20240	22290	24340	26400	28470	30530	30870				17'- 2"
22	21000	23140	25280	27440	29600	31760	32400				17'- 3"
23	21740	23970	26200	28450	30700	32960	33940				17'- 5"
24	22460	24780	27110	29450	31800	34150	35460				17'- 7"
25	23160	25580	28000	30430	32870	35320	36980				17'- 8"
26	23850	26360	28870	31400	33930	36470	38500				17'- 9"
27	24530	27120	29730	32340	34970	37600	40020				17'-11"
28	25190	27870	30570	33270	35990	38720	41450	41540			18'- 1"
29	25840	28610	31390	34190	36990	39820	42650	43070			18'- 2"
30	26470	29330	32200	35090	37990	40900	43820	44590			18'- 3"
31	27090	30030	33000	35970	38960	41970	44980	46110			18'- 4"
32	27700	30720	33780	36840	39920	43020	46120	47640			18'- 6"
33	28290	31400	34540	37700	40870	44050	47250	49150			18'- 7"
34	28870	32070	35290	38540	41800	45070	48360	50650			18'- 9"
35	29440	32720	36030	39360	42710	46070	49450	52180			18'- 9"
36	30000	33360	36750	40170	43610	47060	50530	53710			18'-11"
37	30540	33990	37460	40970	44490	48030	51590	55200			19'- 0"
38	31070	34600	38160	41750	45360	48990	52640	56300	56740		19'- 2"
39	31590	35200	38850	42520	46220	49940	53670	57420	58250		19'- 3"
40	32100	35790	39520	43280	47060	50860	54690	58530	59770		19'- 4"

HEIGHT OF BACKFILL H ABOVE TOP OF PIPE, FEET

D   SATURATED CLAY Kμ'—0.110

HEIGHT OF BACKFILL H ABOVE TOP OF PIPE, FEET

TRENCH WIDTH AT TOP OF PIPE

H (ft)	12'-0"	13'-0"	14'-0"	15'-0"	16'-0"	17'-0"	18'-0"	19'-0"	20'-0"	22'-0"	▲TRAN-SITION WIDTH
5	5539										11'- 7"
6	6776										11'-11"
7	7883	**8060**									12'- 3"
8	8929	9392									12'- 7"
9	9956	10780									12'-11"
10	10960	11960	**12210**								13'- 3"
11	11950	13050	**13700**								13'- 7"
12	12930	14120	15240								13'-11"
13	13880	15170	16460	**16850**							14'- 3"
14	14820	16200	17590	18510							14'- 8"
15	15740	17220	18710	20240							15'- 0"
16	16640	18220	19800	21390	**22030**						15'- 5"
17	17530	19200	20890	22570	23890						15'-10"
18	18400	20170	21950	23730	25510	25820					16'- 2"
19	19250	21120	22980	24870	26750	27780					16'- 6"
20	20090	22060	24030	26000	27980	29330					16'- 8"
21	20920	22980	25040	27110	29180	30870					16'-10"
22	21720	23880	26040	28200	30370	32400					16'-11"
23	22520	24770	27020	29280	31550	33820	33940				17'- 1"
24	23300	25640	27990	30350	32710	35070	35460				17'- 2"
25	24060	26500	28940	31390	33850	36310	36980				17'- 3"
26	24820	27340	29880	32420	34980	37530	38500				17'- 5"
27	25560	28170	30800	33440	36090	38740	40020				17'- 6"
28	26280	28990	31710	34440	37180	39930	41540				17'- 7"
29	26990	29790	32610	35430	38260	41100	43070				17'- 8"
30	27690	30580	33490	36400	39330	42260	44590				17'- 9"
31	28380	31360	34360	37360	40380	43410	46110				17'-11"
32	29050	32120	35210	38310	41420	44540	47640				18'- 0"
33	29710	32870	36050	39240	42440	45660	48880	49150			18'- 1"
34	30360	33610	36880	40160	43450	46760	50080	50650			18'- 3"
35	31000	34330	37690	41060	44450	47850	51260	52180			18'- 3"
36	31620	35050	38490	41950	45430	48920	52420	53710			18'- 4"
37	32240	35750	39280	42830	46400	49980	53580	55200			18'- 5"
38	32840	36440	40060	43700	47360	51030	54710	56740			18'- 7"
39	33430	37110	40820	44550	48300	52060	55840	58250			18'- 8"
40	34020	37780	41570	45390	49230	53080	56950	59770			18'- 9"

---

* For backfill weighing 110 pounds per cubic foot, increase loads 10%; for 120 pounds per cubic foot, increase 20%; etc.
*▲Transition loads (**bold type**) and widths based on Kμ—0.19, $r_{sd}p$—0.5 in the embankment equation*
Interpolate for intermediate heights of backfill and/or trench widths

TABLE 36

108"

BACKFILL LOADS ON CIRCULAR PIPE IN TRENCH INSTALLATION

*100 POUNDS PER CUBIC FOOT BACKFILL MATERIAL

LOADS IN POUNDS PER LINEAR FOOT

A — SAND AND GRAVEL Kμ'—0.165

TRENCH WIDTH AT TOP OF PIPE

HEIGHT OF BACKFILL H ABOVE TOP OF PIPE, FEET	13'-0"	14'-0"	15'-0"	16'-0"	17'-0"	18'-0"	19'-0"	20'-0"	21'-0"	22'-0"	TRANSITION WIDTH
5	**5833**										12'- 5"
6	**7127**										12'-10"
7	8337	**8468**									13'- 3"
8	9411	**9857**									13'- 7"
9	10460	**11300**									13'-11"
10	11480	12470	**12780**								14'- 4"
11	12480	13560	**14330**								14'- 8"
12	13450	14630	15820	**15920**							15'- 1"
13	14390	15680	16960	**17580**							15'- 6"
14	15320	16690	18070	**19290**							15'-11"
15	16220	17690	19160	20640	**21070**						16'- 3"
16	17090	18680	20230	21800	**22910**						16'- 8"
17	17950	19610	21270	22940	23930	**24810**					17'- 1"
18	18780	20540	22290	24060	24940	**26780**					17'- 6"
19	19600	21440	23290	25150	25960	**28820**					18'- 0"
20	20390	22320	24270	26220	26970	29880	**30940**				18'- 5"
21	21160	23190	25220	27260	27990	30930	**32580**				18'- 7"
22	21910	24030	26160	28300	29000	31990	**34220**				18'- 9"
23	22650	24860	27070	29300	30020	33050	**35840**				18'-11"
24	23360	25660	27970	30290	31040	34110	**37460**				19'- 0"
25	24060	26450	28840	31250	32050	35160	38610	**39080**			19'- 2"
26	24740	27210	29700	32200	33070	36220	39750	**40690**			19'- 4"
27	25410	27960	30540	33120	34080	37280	40950	**42310**			19'- 6"
28	26050	28700	31360	34030	35100	38330	42130	**43920**			19'- 8"
29	26680	29410	32160	34920	36110	39390	43390	**45530**			19'-10"
30	27300	30110	32940	35790	37130	40450	44540	**47130**			20'- 0"
31	27900	30790	33710	36640	38150	41510	45540	48530	**48740**		20'- 1"
32	28480	31460	34460	37480	39160	42560	46640	49720	**50350**		20'- 2"
33	29050	32110	35190	38310	40180	43620	47720	50890	**51950**		20'- 4"
34	29610	32740	35910	39100	41190	44680	48780	52040	**53550**		20'- 5"
35	30150	33360	36610	39890	42210	45740	49830	53180	**55190**		20'- 7"
36	30680	33970	37300	40660	43230	46790	50850	54290	**56780**		20'- 9"
37	31190	34560	37970	41410	44240	47850	51860	55380	**58400**		20'-11"
38	31690	35140	38630	42150	45260	48910	52850	56460	**59990**		21'- 0"
39	32180	35710	39270	42870	46270	49960	53830	57520	61230	**61590**	21'- 1"
40	32660	36260	39900	43580	47290	51020	54780	58560	62360	**63190**	21'- 2"

B — SATURATED TOP SOIL Kμ'—0.150

TRENCH WIDTH AT TOP OF PIPE

HEIGHT OF BACKFILL H ABOVE TOP OF PIPE, FEET	13'-0"	14'-0"	15'-0"	16'-0"	17'-0"	18'-0"	19'-0"	20'-0"	21'-0"	22'-0"	TRANSITION WIDTH
5	**5833**										12'- 5"
6	**7127**										12'- 9"
7	8403	**8468**									13'- 1"
8	9496	**9857**									13'- 5"
9	10560	**11300**									13'-10"
10	11610	12600	**12780**								14'- 2"
11	12630	13720	**14330**								14'- 7"
12	13630	14810	**15920**								14'-11"
13	14600	15880	17170	**17580**							15'- 4"
14	15550	16930	18320	**19290**							15'- 9"
15	16480	17960	19440	20920	**21070**						16'- 3"
16	17390	18960	20540	22120	**22910**						16'- 6"
17	18280	19950	21620	23290	**24810**						16'-11"
18	19150	20910	22670	24440	26220	**26780**					17'- 4"
19	20000	21850	23710	25570	27440	**28820**					17'- 9"
20	20820	22770	24720	26680	28650	30610	**30940**				18'- 2"
21	21640	23670	25720	27770	29830	31890	**32580**				18'- 4"
22	22430	24560	26700	28840	30990	33150	**34220**				18'- 6"
23	23200	25420	27650	29890	32140	34390	**35840**				18'- 8"
24	23960	26270	28590	30920	33260	35600	**37460**				18'-10"
25	24700	27100	29510	31930	34360	36800	**39080**				19'- 0"
26	25420	27910	30410	32920	35450	37980	40520	**40690**			19'- 1"
27	26120	28700	31290	33900	36510	39140	41770	**42310**			19'- 2"
28	26810	29480	32160	34850	37560	40270	43000	**43920**			19'- 4"
29	27480	30240	33010	35790	38590	41390	44210	**45530**			19'- 6"
30	28140	30980	33840	36710	39600	42490	45400	**47130**			19'- 7"
31	28790	31710	34650	37620	40590	43580	46580	**48740**			19'- 9"
32	29410	32420	35450	38490	41560	44640	47730	**50350**			19'-10"
33	30030	33120	36240	39370	42520	45690	48870	**51950**			20'- 0"
34	30630	33800	37000	40220	43460	46720	49990	53270	**53550**		20'- 1"
35	31220	34470	37760	41060	44390	47730	51090	54460	**55190**		20'- 2"
36	31790	35130	38490	41880	45300	48730	52170	55680	**56780**		20'- 5"
37	32350	35770	39220	42690	46190	49710	53240	56790	**58400**		20'- 7"
38	32900	36390	39920	43480	47070	50670	54290	57930	**59990**		20'- 8"
39	33430	37010	40620	44260	47930	51620	55330	59050	**61590**		20'-10"
40	33950	37610	41300	45020	48780	52550	56340	60160	**63190**		21'- 0"

HEIGHT OF BACKFILL H ABOVE TOP OF PIPE, FEET

D — SATURATED CLAY Kμ'—0.110

TRENCH WIDTH AT TOP OF PIPE

H	13'-0"	14'-0"	15'-0"	16'-0"	17'-0"	18'-0"	19'-0"	20'-0"	21'-0"	22'-0"	TRANSITION WIDTH
5	5833										12'- 3"
6	7127										12'- 6"
7	8468										12'-10"
8	9726	9857									13'- 2"
9	10850	11300									13'- 6"
10	11960	12780									13'-10"
11	13050	14140	**14330**								14'- 2"
12	14120	15310	**15920**								14'- 6"
13	15170	16460	17460	**17580**							14'-10"
14	16200	17590	18980	**19290**							15'- 3"
15	17220	18710	20200	**21070**							15'- 7"
16	18220	19800	21390	**22910**							16'- 0"
17	19200	20890	22570	24250	**24810**						16'- 4"
18	20170	21950	23730	25510	**26780**						16'- 9"
19	21120	23000	24870	26750	**28820**						17'- 1"
20	22060	24030	26000	27980	**30940**						17'- 4"
21	22980	25040	27110	29210	**32580**						17'- 7"
22	23880	26040	28200	30370	32530	**34220**					17'-10"
23	24770	27020	29280	31530	33780	**35840**					18'- 1"
24	25640	27990	30350	32710	35070	**37460**					18'- 1"
25	26500	28940	31390	33830	36270	**39080**					18'- 2"
26	27340	29880	32420	34960	37500	**40690**					18'- 4"
27	28170	30800	33430	36060	38690	**42310**					18'- 5"
28	28990	31710	34440	37180	39930	42680	**43920**				18'- 7"
29	29790	32610	35430	38260	41100	43950	**45530**				18'- 8"
30	30580	33490	36410	39330	42260	45210	**47130**				18'- 9"
31	31360	34360	37360	40380	43410	46450	**48740**				18'-11"
32	32120	35210	38310	41420	44540	47670	**50350**				19'- 0"
33	32870	36050	39240	42440	45660	48880	**51950**				19'- 1"
34	33610	36880	40160	43450	46760	50080	53400	**53550**			19'- 1"
35	34330	37690	41060	44450	47850	51250	54670	**55190**			19'- 3"
36	35050	38490	41950	45430	48920	52420	55930	**56780**			19'- 3"
37	35750	39280	42830	46400	49980	53580	57180	**58400**			19'- 5"
38	36440	40060	43700	47360	51030	54710	58410	**59990**			19'- 6"
39	37110	40820	44550	48300	52060	55840	59630	**61590**			19'- 7"
40	37780	41570	45390	49230	53080	56950	60830	**63190**			19'- 7"

C — ORDINARY CLAY Kμ'—0.130

TRENCH WIDTH AT TOP OF PIPE

H	13'-0"	14'-0"	15'-0"	16'-0"	17'-0"	18'-0"	19'-0"	20'-0"	21'-0"	22'-0"	TRANSITION WIDTH
5	5833										12'- 3"
6	7127										12'- 6"
7	8468										13'- 0"
8	9610	9857									13'- 4"
9	10710	11300									13'- 8"
10	11780	12780									14'- 0"
11	12840	13930	**14330**								14'- 4"
12	13870	15060	**15920**								14'- 9"
13	14880	16170	17460	**17580**							15'- 1"
14	15870	17260	18650	**19290**							15'- 6"
15	16850	18330	19810	**21070**							15'-10"
16	17800	19380	20960	22540	**22910**						16'- 2"
17	18730	20410	22090	23770	**24810**						16'- 7"
18	19650	21420	23190	24970	26750	**26780**					17'- 1"
19	20550	22410	24280	26150	28030	**28820**					17'- 5"
20	21430	23390	25350	27320	29290	**30940**					17'-10"
21	22290	24340	26400	28470	30530	**32580**					18'- 0"
22	23140	25280	27440	29600	31760	33920	**34220**				18'- 1"
23	23970	26200	28450	30700	32960	35220	**35840**				18'- 3"
24	24780	27110	29450	31800	34150	36510	**37460**				18'- 5"
25	25580	28000	30430	32870	35320	37770	**39080**				18'- 6"
26	26360	28870	31400	33930	36470	39010	**40690**				18'- 8"
27	27120	29730	32340	34970	37600	40240	**42310**				18'-10"
28	27870	30570	33270	35990	38780	41450	**43920**				18'-11"
29	28610	31390	34190	36990	39840	42640	**45530**				19'- 0"
30	29330	32200	35090	37990	40900	43820	46750	**47130**			19'- 3"
31	30000	33000	35970	38960	41970	44980	48000	**48740**			19'- 4"
32	30720	33780	36840	39920	43020	46120	49240	**50350**			19'- 5"
33	31400	34540	37700	40870	44050	47250	50450	**51950**			19'- 7"
34	32070	35290	38540	41800	45070	48360	51650	**53550**			19'- 8"
35	32720	36030	39360	42710	46070	49450	52840	**55190**			19'-10"
36	33360	36750	40170	43610	47060	50530	54010	**56780**			19'-11"
37	33990	37460	40970	44490	48030	51590	55160	**58400**			20'- 0"
38	34600	38160	41750	45360	48990	52640	56300	**59990**			20'- 1"
39	35200	38850	42520	46220	49940	53670	57420	61180	**61590**		20'- 2"
40	35790	39520	43280	47060	50860	54690	58530	62380	**63190**		

* For backfill weighing 110 pounds per cubic foot, increase loads 10%; for 120 pounds per cubic foot, increase 20%; etc.
▲Transition loads (**bold type**) and widths based on Kμ—0.19, rsdp—0.5 in the embankment equation
Interpolate for intermediate heights of backfill and/or trench widths

TABLE 37

BACKFILL LOADS ON CIRCULAR PIPE IN TRENCH INSTALLATION

*100 POUNDS PER CUBIC FOOT BACKFILL MATERIAL

LOADS IN POUNDS PER LINEAR FOOT

114″

A — SAND AND GRAVEL Kμ'—0.165

HEIGHT OF BACKFILL **H** ABOVE TOP OF PIPE, FEET

TRENCH WIDTH AT TOP OF PIPE

H	14'-0"	15'-0"	16'-0"	17'-0"	18'-0"	19'-0"	20'-0"	21'-0"	22'-0"	23'-0"	TRANS. WIDTH
5	6121										13'-0"
6	7472										13'-3"
7	8870										13'-9"
8	10210	10310									14'-2"
9	11350	11810									14'-6"
10	12470	13350									14'-11"
11	13560	14660	14950								15'-3"
12	14630	15820	16600								15'-8"
13	15680	16960	18300								16'-0"
14	16690	18070	19460	20070							16'-5"
15	17690	19160	20640	21890							16'-10"
16	18660	20230	21800	23380	23770						17'-3"
17	19610	21270	22940	24620	25720						17'-8"
18	20540	22290	24060	25820	27600						18'-1"
19	21440	23290	25150	27010	28880	29820					18'-6"
20	22320	24270	26220	28180	30140	31970					18'-11"
21	23190	25220	27270	29320	31370	33430	34190				19'-4"
22	24030	26160	28300	30440	32590	34740	35980				19'-7"
23	24860	27070	29300	31540	33780	36030	37700				19'-9"
24	25660	27970	30290	32610	34950	37290	39410				19'-11"
25	26450	28840	31250	33670	36100	38530	40970	41120			20'-1"
26	27210	29700	32200	34710	37220	39750	42280	42820			20'-3"
27	27960	30540	33120	35720	38330	40950	43580	44540			20'-5"
28	28700	31360	34030	36720	39420	42130	44840	46240			20'-6"
29	29410	32160	34920	37700	40490	43290	46100	47940			20'-8"
30	30110	32940	35790	38650	41540	44430	47320	49640			20'-10"
31	30790	33710	36640	39600	42560	45540	48530	51320			21'-0"
32	31460	34460	37480	40520	43580	46640	49720	52810	53030		21'-1"
33	32110	35190	38300	41420	44570	47720	50890	54070	54730		21'-4"
34	32740	35910	39100	42310	45540	48780	52040	55310	56420		21'-5"
35	33360	36610	39890	43180	46500	49830	53180	56530	58120		21'-7"
36	33970	37300	40660	44040	47440	50850	54290	57740	59810		21'-8"
37	34560	37970	41410	44870	48360	51860	55380	58920	61490		21'-10"
38	35140	38630	42150	45690	49260	52850	56460	60080	63220		22'-0"
39	35710	39270	42870	46500	50150	53830	57520	61230	64900		22'-1"
40	36260	39900	43580	47290	51020	54780	58560	62360	66170	66590	22'-1"

114″

B — SATURATED TOP SOIL Kμ'—0.150

TRENCH WIDTH AT TOP OF PIPE

H	14'-0"	15'-0"	16'-0"	17'-0"	18'-0"	19'-0"	20'-0"	21'-0"	22'-0"	23'-0"	TRANS. WIDTH
5	6121										12'-11"
6	7472										13'-4"
7	8870										13'-8"
8	10310										14'-0"
9	11460	11810									14'-4"
10	12600	13350									14'-9"
11	13720	14810	14950								15'-2"
12	14810	16000	16600								15'-5"
13	15880	17170	18300								15'-11"
14	16930	18320	19700	20070							16'-3"
15	17960	19440	20920	21890							16'-8"
16	18960	20540	22120	23700	23770						17'-1"
17	19610	21620	23290	24970	25720						17'-6"
18	20910	22670	24440	26220	27740						17'-11"
19	21850	23710	25570	27440	29310	29820					18'-4"
20	22770	24720	26680	28650	30610	31970					18'-8"
21	23670	25720	27770	29830	31890	33960	34190				19'-1"
22	24560	26700	28840	30990	33150	35310	35980				19'-3"
23	25420	27650	29890	32140	34390	36640	37700				19'-5"
24	26270	28590	30920	33260	35600	37960	39410				19'-7"
25	27100	29510	31930	34360	36800	39240	41120				19'-9"
26	27910	30410	32920	35450	37980	40520	42820				19'-11"
27	28700	31290	33900	36510	39140	41770	44400	44540			20'-1"
28	29480	32160	34850	37560	40270	43000	45730	46240			20'-2"
29	30240	33010	35790	38590	41390	44210	47030	47940			20'-4"
30	30980	33840	36710	39600	42490	45400	48320	49640			20'-6"
31	31710	34650	37620	40590	43580	46580	49580	51320			20'-7"
32	32420	35450	38500	41560	44640	47730	50830	53030			20'-9"
33	33120	36240	39370	42520	45690	48870	52060	54730			20'-10"
34	33800	37000	40220	43460	46720	49990	53270	56420			21'-0"
35	34470	37760	41060	44390	47730	51090	54460	57840	58120		21'-1"
36	35130	38490	41880	45300	48730	52170	55630	59100	59810		21'-3"
37	35770	39220	42690	46190	49710	53240	56790	60350	61490		21'-5"
38	36390	39920	43480	47070	50670	54290	57930	61580	63220		21'-6"
39	37010	40620	44260	47930	51620	55330	59050	62790	64900		21'-8"
40	37610	41300	45020	48780	52550	56340	60160	63990	66590		

HEIGHT OF BACKFILL H ABOVE TOP OF PIPE, FEET

D — SATURATED CLAY Kμ'—0.110

TRENCH WIDTH AT TOP OF PIPE

H	14'-0"	15'-0"	16'-0"	17'-0"	18'-0"	19'-0"	20'-0"	21'-0"	22'-0"	23'-0"	▲TRANSITION WIDTH
5	**6121**										12'-9"
6	**7472**										13'-1"
7	**8870**										13'-5"
8	**10310**										13'-9"
9	**11810**										14'-0"
10	12960	**13350**									14'-5"
11	14140	**14950**									14'-9"
12	15310	16500	**16600**								15'-1"
13	16460	17750	**18300**								15'-5"
14	17590	18980	**20070**								15'-9"
15	18710	20200	21690	**21890**							16'-2"
16	19800	21390	22980	**23770**							16'-6"
17	20890	22570	24250	**25720**							16'-10"
18	21950	23730	25510	27300	**27740**						17'-3"
19	23000	24870	26750	28640	**29820**						17'-8"
20	24030	26000	27980	29960	31940	**31970**					18'-1"
21	25040	27110	29180	31260	33340	**34190**					18'-5"
22	26040	28200	30370	32550	34720	**35980**					18'-6"
23	27020	29280	31550	33820	36090	**37700**					18'-8"
24	27990	30350	32710	35070	37440	**39410**					18'-10"
25	28940	31390	33850	36310	38770	**41120**					18'-11"
26	29880	32420	34980	37530	40090	**42820**					19'-0"
27	30800	33440	36090	38740	41390	44060	**44540**				19'-2"
28	31710	34440	37180	39930	42680	45440	**46240**				19'-3"
29	32610	35430	38260	41100	43950	46800	**47940**				19'-5"
30	33490	36400	39330	42260	45210	48150	**49640**				19'-6"
31	34360	37360	40380	43410	46450	49490	**51320**				19'-7"
32	35210	38310	41420	44540	47670	50810	**53030**				19'-8"
33	36050	39240	42440	45660	48880	52110	**54730**				19'-10"
34	36880	40160	43450	46760	50080	53400	**56420**				19'-11"
35	37690	41060	44450	47850	51260	54670	**58120**				20'-0"
36	38490	41950	45430	48920	52420	55930	59450	**59810**			20'-1"
37	39280	42830	46400	49980	53580	57180	60790	**61490**			20'-2"
38	40060	43700	47360	51030	54710	58410	62120	**63220**			20'-4"
39	40820	44550	48300	52060	55840	59630	63420	**64900**			20'-5"
40	41570	45390	49230	53080	56950	60830	64720	**66590**			20'-6"

C — ORDINARY CLAY Kμ'—0.130

TRENCH WIDTH AT TOP OF PIPE

H	14'-0"	15'-0"	16'-0"	17'-0"	18'-0"	19'-0"	20'-0"	21'-0"	22'-0"	23'-0"	▲TRANSITION WIDTH
5	**6121**										12'-10"
6	**7472**										13'-2"
7	**8870**										13'-7"
8	**10310**										13'-11"
9	11600	**11810**									14'-3"
10	12780	**13350**									14'-7"
11	13930	**14950**									14'-11"
12	15060	16250	**16600**								15'-4"
13	16170	17460	**18300**								15'-8"
14	17260	18650	**20070**								16'-0"
15	18330	19810	21300	**21890**							16'-5"
16	19380	20960	22540	**23770**							16'-9"
17	20410	22090	23770	25450							17'-2"
18	21420	23190	24970	26750	**27740**						17'-7"
19	22410	24280	26150	28030	**29820**						18'-0"
20	23390	25350	27320	29290	31270	**31970**					18'-5"
21	24340	26400	28470	30530	32600	**34190**					18'-9"
22	25280	27440	29600	31760	33920	**35980**					18'-11"
23	26200	28450	30700	32960	35220	37490	**37700**				19'-1"
24	27110	29450	31800	34150	36510	38870	**39410**				19'-3"
25	28000	30430	32870	35320	37770	40230	**41120**				19'-4"
26	28870	31400	33930	36470	39020	41570	**42820**				19'-6"
27	29730	32340	34970	37600	40240	42890	**44540**				19'-7"
28	30570	33270	35990	38720	41450	44190	**46240**				19'-9"
29	31390	34190	37000	39820	42650	45480	**47940**				19'-10"
30	32200	35090	37990	40900	43820	46750	**49640**				20'-0"
31	33000	35970	38960	41970	44980	48000	51030	**51320**			20'-1"
32	33780	36840	39920	43020	46120	49240	52360	**53030**			20'-3"
33	34540	37700	40870	44050	47250	50450	53670	**54730**			20'-4"
34	35290	38540	41800	45070	48360	51650	54960	**56420**			20'-5"
35	36030	39360	42710	46070	49450	52840	56240	**58120**			20'-7"
36	36750	40170	43610	47060	50530	54010	57500	**59810**			20'-8"
37	37460	40970	44490	48030	51590	55160	58740	**61490**			20'-9"
38	38160	41750	45360	48990	52640	56300	59970	**63220**			20'-11"
39	38850	42520	46220	49940	53670	57420	61180	**64900**			21'-0"
40	39520	43280	47060	50860	54690	58530	62380	66250	**66590**		21'-1"

* For backfill weighing 110 pounds per cubic foot; increase loads 10%; for 120 pounds per cubic foot, increase 20%; etc.

▲ Transition loads (**bold type**) and widths based on Kμ—0.19, rsdP—0.5 in the embankment equation

Interpolate for intermediate heights of backfill and/or trench widths

TABLE 38

BACKFILL LOADS ON CIRCULAR PIPE IN TRENCH INSTALLATION
LOADS IN POUNDS PER LINEAR FOOT

HEIGHT OF BACKFILL H ABOVE TOP OF PIPE, FEET

B — 120" SATURATED TOP SOIL Kμ'—0.150

TRENCH WIDTH AT TOP OF PIPE

H	14'-0"	15'-0"	16'-0"	17'-0"	18'-0"	19'-0"	20'-0"	21'-0"	22'-0"	23'-0"	TRANSITION WIDTH
5	6330										13'- 5"
6	7723										13'- 9"
7	9100	9161									14'- 1"
8	10290	10650									14'- 5"
9	11460	12180									14'-10"
10	12600	13600	13760								15'- 2"
11	13720	14810	15400								15'- 6"
12	14810	16000	17090								15'-11"
13	15680	17170	18460	18830							16'- 3"
14	16930	18320	19700	20630							16'- 8"
15	17960	19440	20920	22400	22490						17'- 1"
16	18960	20540	22120	23700	24410						17'- 6"
17	19950	21620	23290	24970	26390						17'-10"
18	20910	22670	24440	26220	27990	28430					18'- 3"
19	21850	23710	25570	27440	29310	30540					18'- 8"
20	22770	24720	26680	28650	30610	32580	32730				19'- 1"
21	23670	25720	27770	29830	31890	33960	34980				19'- 6"
22	24560	26700	28840	30990	33150	35310	37240				19'-11"
23	25420	27650	29890	32140	34390	36640	38900	39040			20'- 2"
24	26270	28590	30920	33260	35600	37960	40310	40820			20'- 3"
25	27100	29510	31930	34360	36800	39240	41690	42600			20'- 5"
26	27910	30410	32920	35450	37980	40520	43060	44370			20'- 6"
27	28700	31290	33900	36510	39140	41770	44400	46140			20'- 8"
28	29480	32160	34850	37560	40270	43000	45730	47900			20'-11"
29	30240	33010	35790	38590	41390	44210	47030	49660			20'-11"
30	30980	33840	36710	39690	42490	45400	48320	51240	51430		21'- 1"
31	31710	34650	37620	40590	43580	46580	49580	52600	53200		21'- 2"
32	32420	35450	38500	41560	44640	47730	50830	53940	54960		21'- 4"
33	33120	36240	39370	42520	45690	48870	52060	55260	56710		21'- 5"
34	33800	37000	40220	43460	46720	49990	53270	56560	58470		21'- 7"
35	34470	37760	41060	44370	47730	51090	54460	57840	60240		21'- 8"
36	35130	38490	41880	45300	48730	52170	55630	59100	61990		21'-10"
37	35770	39220	42690	46190	49710	53240	56790	60350	63740		21'-11"
38	36390	39920	43480	47070	50670	54290	57930	61580	65240	65510	22'- 1"
39	37010	40620	44260	47930	51620	55330	59050	62790	66540	67250	22'- 2"
40	37610	41300	45020	48780	52550	56340	60160	63990	67830	69040	22'- 4"

A — 120" SAND AND GRAVEL Kμ'—0.165
*100 POUNDS PER CUBIC FOOT BACKFILL MATERIAL

TRENCH WIDTH AT TOP OF PIPE

H	14'-0"	15'-0"	16'-0"	17'-0"	18'-0"	19'-0"	20'-0"	21'-0"	22'-0"	23'-0"	TRANSITION WIDTH
5	6330										13'- 5"
6	7723										13'-10"
7	9034	9161									14'- 2"
8	10210	10650									14'- 7"
9	11350	12180									14'-11"
10	12470	13460	13760								15'- 3"
11	13560	14660	15400								15'- 8"
12	14630	15820	17010	17090							16'- 1"
13	15680	16960	18240	18830							16'- 5"
14	16690	18070	19460	20630							16'-10"
15	17690	19160	20640	22120	22490						17'- 3"
16	18660	20230	21800	23380	24410						17'- 8"
17	19610	21270	22940	24620	26290	26390					18'- 1"
18	20540	22290	24060	25820	27600	28430					18'- 6"
19	21440	23290	25150	27010	28880	30540					18'-11"
20	22320	24270	26220	28180	30140	32100	32730				19'- 4"
21	23190	25220	27270	29320	31370	33430	34980				19'- 9"
22	24030	26160	28290	30440	32590	34740	36900	37240			20'- 2"
23	24860	27070	29300	31540	33780	36030	38280	39040			20'- 4"
24	25660	27970	30290	32610	34950	37290	39640	40820			20'- 6"
25	26450	28840	31250	33670	36100	38530	40970	42600			20'- 8"
26	27210	29700	32200	34710	37220	39750	42280	44370			20'-10"
27	27960	30540	33120	35720	38330	40950	43580	46140			21'- 0"
28	28700	31360	34030	36720	39420	42130	44840	47570	47900		21'- 1"
29	29410	32160	34920	37700	40490	43290	46100	48910	49660		21'- 3"
30	30110	32940	35790	38660	41540	44420	47320	50230	51430		21'- 5"
31	30790	33710	36640	39600	42560	45540	48530	51530	53200		21'- 7"
32	31460	34460	37480	40520	43580	46640	49720	52810	54960		21'- 8"
33	32110	35190	38300	41420	44570	47720	50890	54070	56710		21'-10"
34	32740	35910	39100	42310	45540	48780	52040	55310	58470		21'-11"
35	33360	36610	39890	43180	46500	49830	53180	56530	59900	60240	22'- 1"
36	33970	37300	40660	44040	47440	50850	54290	57740	61200	61990	22'- 3"
37	34560	37970	41410	44870	48360	51860	55380	58920	62470	63740	22'- 4"
38	35140	38630	42150	45690	49260	52850	56460	60080	63720	65510	22'- 6"
39	35710	39270	42860	46500	50150	53810	57520	61230	64960	67250	22'- 7"
40	36260	39900	43580	47290	51020	54780	58560	62360	66170	69040	22'- 9"

D — SATURATED CLAY Kμ'—0.110

HEIGHT OF BACKFILL H ABOVE TOP OF PIPE, FEET											
TRENCH WIDTH AT TOP OF PIPE										▲TRAN-SITION WIDTH	H
14'-0"	15'-0"	16'-0"	17'-0"	18'-0"	19'-0"	20'-0"	21'-0"	22'-0"	23'-0"		
6330										13'-2"	5
7723	**10650**									13'-6"	6
9161	**12180**									13'-10"	7
10520	**13760**	**15400**								14'-2"	8
11750	15020	**17090**								14'-6"	9
12960	16500	**18830**								14'-10"	10
14140	17750	20380	**20630**							15'-2"	11
15310	18990	21690	**22490**							15'-6"	12
16460	20200	22980	24410	**24410**						15'-10"	13
17590	21390	24250	25940	**26390**						16'-2"	14
18710	22570	25510	27300	**28430**						16'-6"	15
19800	23730	26750	28640	30540						16'-11"	16
20890	24870	27980	29960	31940	**32730**					17'-4"	17
21950	26000	29180	31260	33340	**34980**					17'-8"	18
23000	27110	30370	32550	34720	36900	**37240**				18'-0"	19
24030	28200	31550	33820	36090	38360	**39040**				18'-5"	20
25040	29280	32710	35070	37440	39810	**40820**				18'-10"	21
26040	30370	33850	36310	38770	41240	**42600**				19'-2"	22
27020	31390	34980	37530	40090	42660	**44370**				19'-4"	23
27990	32420	36090	38740	41390	44060	**46140**				19'-6"	24
28940	33440	37180	39930	42680	45440	**47900**				19'-7"	25
29880	34480	38260	41100	43950	46800	**49660**				19'-8"	26
30800	35430	39330	42260	45210	48150	51100	**51430**			19'-11"	27
31710	36400	40380	43410	46450	49490	52530	**53200**			20'-0"	28
32610	37360	41420	44540	47670	50810	53950	**54960**			20'-2"	29
33490	38310	42440	45660	48880	52110	55350	**56710**			20'-3"	30
34360	39240	43450	46760	50080	53400	56730	**58470**			20'-4"	31
35210	40160	44450	47850	51260	54670	58100	**60240**			20'-6"	32
36050	41060	45430	48920	52420	55930	59450	61990	**61990**		20'-8"	33
36880	41950	46360	49980	53580	57180	60790	63740	**63740**		20'-9"	34
37690	42830	47360	51030	54710	58410	62120	65510	**65510**		20'-10"	35
38490	43700	48300	52060	55840	59630	63420	67250	**67250**		20'-11"	36
39280	44550	49230	53080	56950	60830	64720	68620	**68620**		21'-0"	37
40060	45390							69040		21'-1"	38
40820											39
41570											40

C — ORDINARY CLAY Kμ'—0.130

HEIGHT OF BACKFILL H ABOVE TOP OF PIPE, FEET											
H	**TRENCH WIDTH AT TOP OF PIPE**										▲TRAN-SITION WIDTH
	14'-0"	15'-0"	16'-0"	17'-0"	18'-0"	19'-0"	20'-0"	21'-0"	22'-0"	23'-0"	
5	6330										13'-4"
6	7723	**10650**									13'-7"
7	9161	**12180**									13'-11"
8	10410	**13760**	**15400**								14'-4"
9	11600	15020	**17090**								14'-8"
10	12780	16250	**18750**	**18830**							15'-0"
11	13930	17460	20030	**20630**							15'-4"
12	15060	18650	21300	**22490**							15'-8"
13	16170	19810	22540	24130	**24400**						16'-0"
14	17260	20960	24130?	24970	**26390**						16'-5"
15	18330	22090	24970	26750	**28430**						16'-10"
16	19380	23190	26150	28030	29910						17'-3"
17	20410	24280	26750	29450?	30540						17'-7"
18	21420	25350	28030	30350?	31270	**30540**					18'-0"
19	22410	26400	29290	31270	34680?	**32730**					18'-4"
20	23390	27320	30350	32620	34680	34680					18'-9"
21	24340	28470	30530	33920	36090?	36090	**34980**				19'-2"
22	25280	29450	31760	35220	33920	37490	**37240**				19'-7"
23	26200	30700	32960	34150	35220	38870	**39040**				19'-8"
24	27110	31800	34150	36510	38870	40230	**40820**				19'-10"
25	28000	32870	35320	37770	40230	42600	**42600**				20'-0"
26	28870	33930	36470	39020	41570	44120	**44370**	**44370**			20'-1"
27	29730	34970	37620	40240	42890	45540	44120	**46140**			20'-3"
28	30570	35990	38720	41450	44190	46940	45480	**47900**			20'-4"
29	31390	37000	39820	42650	45480	48320	49680	**49660**			20'-6"
30	32200	37990	40900	43820	46750	49680	51030	**51430**			20'-7"
31	33000	38960	41970	44980	48000	51030	52360	**53200**			20'-9"
32	33780	39920	43020	46120	49240	52360	53670	**54960**			20'-10"
33	34540	40870	44050	47250	50450	53670	55650	**56710**			20'-11"
34	35290	41800	45070	48360	51650	54960	56240	**58470**	**58470**		21'-1"
35	36030	42710	46070	49450	52840	56240	57500	59650	**60240**		21'-2"
36	36750	43610	47060	50530	54010	57500	58740	61000	**61990**		21'-3"
37	37460	44490	48030	51590	55160	58740	60530	62340	**63740**		21'-5"
38	38160	45360	48990	52640	56300	59970	61180	63660	**65510**		21'-6"
39	38850	46220	49940	53670	57420	61180	62380	64960	**67250**		21'-7"
40	39520	47060	50860	54690	58530	62380	63500	66250	**69040**		21'-9"

* For backfill weighing 110 pounds per cubic foot. For backfill weighing 100 pounds per cubic foot, increase loads 10%; for 120 pounds per cubic foot, increase 20%; etc.
▲Transition loads (bold type) and widths based on Kμ—0.19, r_{sdp}—0.5 in the embankment equation
Interpolate for intermediate heights of backfill and/or trench widths

TABLE 39

BACKFILL LOADS ON CIRCULAR PIPE IN TRENCH INSTALLATION

LOADS IN POUNDS PER LINEAR FOOT

A — 126″ — SAND AND GRAVEL Ku′−0.165
*100 POUNDS PER CUBIC FOOT BACKFILL MATERIAL

TRENCH WIDTH AT TOP OF PIPE

H (ft)	15′-0″	16′-0″	17′-0″	18′-0″	19′-0″	20′-0″	21′-0″	22′-0″	23′-0″	24′-0″	▲Transition Width
5	**6619**										14′-0″
6	**8068**										14′-5″
7	**9563**										14′-9″
8	11000	**11100**									15′-1″
9	12250	**12690**									15′-6″
10	13460	**14330**									15′-10″
11	14660	15750	**16020**								16′-3″
12	15820	17010	**17760**								16′-7″
13	16960	18240	**19560**								17′-0″
14	18070	19460	20840	**21410**							17′-5″
15	19160	20640	22120	**23320**							17′-10″
16	20230	21800	23380	24960	**25280**						18′-3″
17	21270	22940	24620	26290	**27310**						18′-7″
18	22290	24060	25820	27600	29370	**29400**					19′-1″
19	23290	25150	27010	28880	30750	**31560**					19′-5″
20	24270	26220	28180	30140	32100	**33780**					19′-10″
21	25220	27270	29320	31370	33430	35500	**36070**				20′-3″
22	26160	28300	30440	32590	34740	36900	**38440**				20′-7″
23	27070	29300	31540	33780	36030	38280	40530	**40860**			21′-2″
24	27970	30290	32610	34950	37290	39640	41990	**42740**			21′-4″
25	28840	31250	33670	36100	38530	40970	43420	**44620**			21′-6″
26	29700	32200	34710	37220	39750	42280	44820	**46490**			21′-8″
27	30540	33120	35720	38330	40950	43580	46210	**48340**			21′-9″
28	31360	34030	36720	39420	42130	44840	47570	**50210**			21′-11″
29	32160	34920	37700	40490	43290	46100	48910	51730	**52060**		22′-2″
30	32940	35790	38660	41540	44420	47320	50230	53150	**53910**		22′-4″
31	33710	36640	39600	42560	45540	48530	51530	54540	**55770**		22′-5″
32	34460	37480	40520	43580	46640	49720	52810	55900	**57630**		22′-7″
33	35190	38300	41420	44570	47720	50890	54070	57260	**59470**		22′-8″
34	35910	39100	42310	45540	48780	52040	55310	58590	**61320**		22′-10″
35	36610	39890	43180	46500	49830	53180	56530	59900	**63160**		22′-11″
36	37300	40660	44040	47440	50850	54290	57740	61200	64670	**64990**	23′-1″
37	37970	41410	44870	48360	51860	55380	58920	62470	66030	**66840**	23′-2″
38	38630	42150	45690	49260	52850	56460	60080	63720	67370	**68710**	23′-4″
39	39270	42870	46500	50150	53830	57520	61230	64960	68700	**70540**	23′-5″
40	39900	43580	47290	51020	54780	58560	62360	66170	70000	**72370**	23′-8″

B — 126″ — SATURATED TOP SOIL Ku′−0.150

HEIGHT OF BACKFILL H ABOVE TOP OF PIPE, FEET

TRENCH WIDTH AT TOP OF PIPE

H (ft)	15′-0″	16′-0″	17′-0″	18′-0″	19′-0″	20′-0″	21′-0″	22′-0″	23′-0″	24′-0″	▲Transition Width
5	**6619**										14′-0″
6	**8068**										14′-4″
7	**9563**										14′-8″
8	**11100**										15′-0″
9	12350	**12690**									15′-5″
10	13600	**14330**									15′-9″
11	14810	15900	**16020**								16′-1″
12	16000	17190	**17760**								16′-6″
13	17170	18460	**19560**								16′-10″
14	18320	19700	21090	**21410**							17′-3″
15	19440	20920	22400	**23320**							17′-8″
16	20540	22120	23700	**25280**							18′-0″
17	21620	23290	24970	26650	**27310**						18′-5″
18	22670	24440	26220	27990	**29400**						18′-9″
19	23710	25570	27440	29310	31190	**31560**					19′-3″
20	24720	26680	28650	30610	32580	**33780**					19′-7″
21	25720	27770	29830	31890	33960	**36070**					20′-0″
22	26700	28840	30990	33150	35310	37480	**38440**				20′-5″
23	27650	29890	32140	34390	36640	38900	**40860**				20′-11″
24	28590	30920	33260	35600	37960	40310	42670	**42740**			21′-1″
25	29510	31930	34360	36800	39240	41690	44150	**44620**			21′-2″
26	30410	32920	35450	37980	40520	43060	45610	**46490**			21′-4″
27	31290	33900	36510	39140	41770	44400	47040	**48340**			21′-6″
28	32160	34850	37560	40270	43000	45730	48460	**50210**			21′-8″
29	33010	35790	38590	41390	44210	47030	49860	**52060**			21′-9″
30	33840	36710	39600	42490	45400	48320	51240	**53910**			21′-11″
31	34650	37620	40590	43580	46580	49580	52600	**55770**			22′-0″
32	35450	38500	41560	44640	47730	50830	53940	57050	**57630**		22′-3″
33	36240	39370	42520	45690	48870	52060	55260	58460	**59470**		22′-4″
34	37000	40220	43460	46720	49990	53270	56560	59860	**61320**		22′-6″
35	37760	41060	44390	47730	51090	54460	57840	61230	**63160**		22′-8″
36	38490	41880	45300	48730	52170	55630	59100	62590	**64990**		22′-10″
37	39220	42690	46190	49710	53240	56790	60350	63920	**66840**		22′-11″
38	39920	43480	47070	50670	54290	57930	61580	65240	**68710**		23′-1″
39	40620	44260	47930	51620	55330	59050	62790	66540	70310	**70540**	23′-2″
40	41300	45020	48780	52550	56340	60160	63990	67830	71680	**72370**	23′-4″

HEIGHT OF BACKFILL H ABOVE TOP OF PIPE, FEET

C — ORDINARY CLAY Kμ'=0.130

TRENCH WIDTH AT TOP OF PIPE

H	15'-0"	16'-0"	17'-0"	18'-0"	19'-0"	20'-0"	21'-0"	22'-0"	23'-0"	24'-0"	▲TRANSITION WIDTH
5	6619										13'-11"
6	8068										14'- 2"
7	9563										14'- 6"
8	11100										14'-10"
9	12500	**12690**									15'- 2"
10	13770	**14330**									15'- 7"
11	15020	**16020**									15'-11"
12	16250	17440	**17760**								16'- 3"
13	17460	18750	**19560**								16'- 7"
14	18650	20030	**21410**								17'- 0"
15	19810	21300	22790	**23320**							17'- 4"
16	20960	22540	24130	**25280**							17'- 9"
17	22090	23770	25450	27130	**27310**						18'- 1"
18	23190	24970	26750	28530	**29400**						18'- 6"
19	24280	26150	28030	29910	**31560**						18'-10"
20	25350	27320	29290	31270	33240	**33780**					19'- 4"
21	26400	28470	30530	32600	34680	**36070**					19'- 8"
22	27440	29600	31760	33920	36090	38270	**38440**				20'- 5"
23	28450	30700	32960	35220	37490	39760	**40860**				20'- 8"
24	29450	31800	34150	36510	38870	41230	**42740**				20'-10"
25	30430	32870	35320	37770	40230	42690	**44620**				20'-11"
26	31400	33930	36470	39020	41570	44120	**46490**				21'- 1"
27	32340	34970	37600	40240	42890	45540	48200	**48340**			21'- 4"
28	33270	35990	38720	41450	44190	46940	49690	**50210**			21'- 5"
29	34190	37000	39820	42650	45480	48320	51160	**52060**			21'- 8"
30	35090	37990	40900	43820	46750	49680	52620	**53910**			21'- 9"
31	35970	38960	41970	44980	48000	51030	54060	**55770**			21'-11"
32	36840	39920	43020	46120	49240	52360	55480	**57630**			22'- 2"
33	37700	40870	44050	47250	50450	53670	56890	**59470**			22'- 3"
34	38540	41800	45070	48360	51650	54960	58280	**61320**			22'- 5"
35	39360	42710	46070	49450	52840	56240	59650	**63160**			22'- 6"
36	40170	43610	47060	50530	54010	57500	61000	64510	**64990**		22'- 7"
37	40970	44490	48030	51590	55160	58740	62340	65940	**66840**		
38	41750	45360	48990	52640	56300	59970	63660	67350	**68710**		
39	42520	46220	49940	53670	57420	61180	64960	68740	**70540**		
40	43280	47060	50860	54690	58530	62380	66250	70120	**72370**		

D — SATURATED CLAY Kμ'=0.110

TRENCH WIDTH AT TOP OF PIPE

H	15'-0"	16'-0"	17'-0"	18'-0"	19'-0"	20'-0"	21'-0"	22'-0"	23'-0"	24'-0"	▲TRANSITION WIDTH
5	6619										13'- 9"
6	8068										14'- 1"
7	9563										14'- 5"
8	11100										14'- 9"
9	12650	**12690**									15'- 1"
10	13950	**14330**									15'- 5"
11	15240	**16020**									15'- 9"
12	16500	**17760**									16'- 0"
13	17750	19050	**19560**								16'- 5"
14	18980	20380	**21410**								16'- 9"
15	20200	21690	23180	**23320**							17'- 1"
16	21390	22980	24570	**25280**							17'- 5"
17	22570	24250	25940	**27310**							17'-10"
18	23730	25510	27300	29080	**29400**						18'- 2"
19	24870	26750	28640	30520	**31560**						18'- 6"
20	26000	27980	29960	31940	**33780**						18'-11"
21	27110	29180	31260	33420	35420	**36070**					19'- 4"
22	28200	30370	32550	34720	36900	**38440**					19'- 9"
23	29280	31550	33820	36090	38360	40640	**40860**				20'- 1"
24	30350	32710	35070	37440	39810	42190	**42740**				20'- 3"
25	31390	33850	36310	38770	41240	43710	**44620**				20'- 4"
26	32420	34980	37530	40090	42660	45220	**46490**				20'- 5"
27	33440	36090	38740	41390	44060	46720	**48340**				20'- 8"
28	34440	37180	39930	42680	45440	48200	**50210**				20'-10"
29	35430	38260	41100	43950	46800	49660	**52060**				21'- 0"
30	36400	39330	42260	45210	48150	51100	**53910**				21'- 1"
31	37360	40380	43410	46450	49490	52530	55590	**55770**			21'- 3"
32	38310	41420	44540	47670	50810	53950	57100	**57630**			21'- 4"
33	39240	42440	45660	48880	52110	55350	58590	**59470**			21'- 6"
34	40160	43450	46760	50080	53400	56730	60070	**61320**			21'- 8"
35	41060	44450	47850	51260	54670	58100	61530	**63160**			21'- 9"
36	41950	45430	48920	52420	55930	59450	62980	**64990**			21'-11"
37	42830	46400	49980	53580	57180	60790	64410	**66840**			
38	43700	47360	51030	54710	58410	62120	65830	**68710**			
39	44550	48300	52060	55860	59630	63440	67230	**70540**			
40	45390	49230	53080	56950	60830	64720	68620	**72370**			

* For backfill weighing 110 pounds per cubic foot; increase loads 10%; for 120 pounds per cubic foot, increase 20%; etc.
▲Transition loads (**bold type**) and widths based on Kμ—0.19, r_sd p—0.5 in the embankment equation
Interpolate for intermediate heights of backfill and/or trench widths

TABLE 40

BACKFILL LOADS ON CIRCULAR PIPE IN TRENCH INSTALLATION
*100 POUNDS PER CUBIC FOOT BACKFILL MATERIAL
LOADS IN POUNDS PER LINEAR FOOT

HEIGHT OF BACKFILL H ABOVE TOP OF PIPE, FEET

132″ — SAND AND GRAVEL Kμ'—0.165

H	TRENCH WIDTH AT TOP OF PIPE 15'-0"	16'-0"	17'-0"	18'-0"	19'-0"	20'-0"	21'-0"	22'-0"	23'-0"	25'-0"	TRANSITION WIDTH
5	6908										14'-8"
6	8414										14'-11"
7	9731	9966									15'-4"
8	11000	11560									15'-8"
9	12250	13140	13210								16'-1"
10	13460	14460	14900								16'-5"
11	14660	15750	16640								16'-10"
12	15820	17010	18200	18400							17'-3"
13	16960	18240	19530	20290							17'-7"
14	18070	19460	20840	22190							18'-0"
15	19160	20640	22120	23600	24150						18'-4"
16	20230	21800	23380	24960	26170						18'-9"
17	21270	22940	24620	26290	27970	28240					19'-2"
18	22290	24060	25820	27600	29370	30380					19'-7"
19	23290	25150	27010	28880	30750	32580					19'-11"
20	24270	26220	28180	30140	32100	34070	34850				20'-5"
21	25220	27270	29320	31370	33430	35500	37180				20'-9"
22	26160	28300	30440	32590	34740	36900	39060	39580			21'-3"
23	27070	29300	31540	33780	36030	38280	40530	42060			21'-8"
24	27970	30290	32610	34950	37290	39640	41990	44340	44600		22'-1"
25	28840	31250	33670	36100	38530	40970	43420	45860	46620		22'-4"
26	29700	32200	34710	37220	39750	42280	44820	47360	48580		22'-5"
27	30540	33120	35720	38330	40950	43580	46210	48840	50540		22'-7"
28	31360	34030	36720	39420	42130	44840	47570	50300	52490		22'-10"
29	32160	34920	37700	40490	43290	46100	48910	51730	54440		23'-0"
30	32940	35790	38660	41540	44420	47320	50230	53150	56070	56390	23'-1"
31	33710	36640	39600	42560	45540	48530	51530	54540	57550	58320	23'-3"
32	34460	37480	40520	43580	46640	49720	52810	55910	59020	60260	23'-4"
33	35190	38300	41420	44570	47720	50890	54070	57260	60460	62210	23'-7"
34	35910	39100	42310	45540	48780	52040	55310	58590	61880	64150	23'-9"
35	36610	39890	43180	46500	49830	53180	56530	59900	63280	66080	23'-10"
36	37300	40700	44040	47440	50850	54290	57740	61200	64670	68020	24'-0"
37	37970	41410	44870	48360	51860	55380	58920	62470	66030	69930	24'-1"
38	38630	42150	45690	49260	52850	56460	60080	63720	67370	71870	24'-2"
39	39270	42870	46500	50150	53830	57520	61230	64960	68700	73800	24'-5"
40	39900	43580	47290	51020	54780	58560	62360	66170	70000	75770	24'-6"

132″ — SATURATED TOP SOIL Kμ'—0.150

H	TRENCH WIDTH AT TOP OF PIPE 15'-0"	16'-0"	17'-0"	18'-0"	19'-0"	20'-0"	21'-0"	22'-0"	23'-0"	25'-0"	TRANSITION WIDTH
5	6908										14'-6"
6	8414										14'-11"
7	9798	9966									15'-3"
8	11090	11560									15'-7"
9	12350	13210									16'-0"
10	13600	14590	14900								16'-3"
11	14810	15900	16640								16'-8"
12	16000	17190	18440								17'-0"
13	17170	18460	19750	20290							17'-5"
14	18320	19700	21090	22190							17'-9"
15	19440	20920	22400	23890	24150						18'-2"
16	20540	22120	23700	25280	26170						18'-7"
17	21620	23290	24970	26650	28240						18'-11"
18	22670	24440	26220	27990	29770	30380					19'-5"
19	23710	25570	27440	29310	31190	32580					19'-9"
20	24720	26680	28650	30610	32580	34560	34850				20'-2"
21	25720	27770	29830	31890	33960	36030	37180				20'-7"
22	26700	28840	30990	33150	35310	37480	39580				21'-0"
23	27650	29890	32140	34390	36640	38900	41170	42060			21'-5"
24	28590	30920	33260	35600	37960	40310	42670	44600			21'-9"
25	29510	31930	34390	36800	39240	41690	44150	46620			22'-0"
26	30410	32920	35450	37980	40520	43060	45610	48160	48580		22'-2"
27	31290	33900	36510	39140	41770	44400	47040	49690	50540		22'-4"
28	32160	34850	37560	40270	43000	45730	48460	51200	52490		22'-5"
29	33010	35790	38590	41390	44210	47030	49860	52700	54440		22'-7"
30	33840	36710	39600	42490	45400	48320	51240	54170	56390		22'-9"
31	34650	37620	40590	43580	46580	49580	52600	55620	58320		22'-11"
32	35450	38500	41560	44660	47730	50830	53940	57050	60260		23'-1"
33	36240	39370	42520	45690	48870	52060	55260	58460	61680	62210	23'-2"
34	37000	40220	43460	46720	49990	53270	56560	59860	63160	64150	23'-3"
35	37760	41060	44390	47730	51090	54460	57840	61230	64630	66080	23'-5"
36	38490	41880	45300	48730	52170	55630	59100	62590	66080	68020	23'-7"
37	39220	42690	46190	49710	53240	56790	60350	63920	67500	69930	23'-8"
38	39920	43480	47070	50670	54290	57930	61580	65240	68920	71870	23'-10"
39	40620	44260	47930	51620	55330	59050	62790	66540	70310	73800	23'-11"
40	41300	45020	48780	52550	56340	60160	63990	67830	71680	75770	24'-1"

HEIGHT OF BACKFILL H ABOVE TOP OF PIPE, FEET

D. SATURATED CLAY Kµ'−0.110

H	15'-0"	16'-0"	17'-0"	18'-0"	19'-0"	20'-0"	21'-0"	22'-0"	23'-0"	25'-0"	TRANSITION WIDTH
5	6908										14'-4"
6	8414										14'-8"
7	9966										15'-0"
8	11320	**11560**									15'-4"
9	12650	**13210**									15'-8"
10	13950	**14900**									16'-0"
11	15240	16330	**16640**								16'-3"
12	16500	17700	**18440**								16'-7"
13	17750	19050	**20290**								16'-11"
14	18980	20380	21770	**22190**							17'-4"
15	20200	21690	23180	**24150**							17'-8"
16	21390	22980	24570	**26170**							18'-0"
17	22570	24250	25940	27630	**28240**						18'-4"
18	23730	25510	27300	29080	**30380**						18'-9"
19	24870	26750	28640	30520	32400	**32580**					19'-1"
20	26000	27980	29960	31940	33920	**34850**					19'-6"
21	27110	29180	31260	33340	35420	**37180**					19'-10"
22	28200	30370	32550	34720	36900	39080	**39580**				20'-3"
23	29280	31550	33820	36090	38360	40640	**42060**				20'-7"
24	30350	32710	35070	37440	39810	42190	44560	**44600**			21'-1"
25	31390	33850	36310	38770	41240	43710	46190	**46620**			21'-2"
26	32420	34980	37530	40090	42660	45220	47800	**48580**			21'-4"
27	33440	36090	38740	41390	44060	46720	49390	**50540**			21'-5"
28	34440	37180	39930	42680	45440	48200	50960	**52490**			21'-6"
29	35430	38260	41100	43950	46800	49660	52520	**54440**			21'-8"
30	36400	39330	42260	45210	48150	51100	54060	**56390**			21'-11"
31	37360	40380	43410	46450	49490	52530	55590	**58320**			22'-0"
32	38310	41420	44540	47670	50810	53950	57100	**60260**			22'-2"
33	39240	42440	45660	48880	52110	55330	58590	61840	**62210**		22'-5"
34	40160	43450	46760	50080	53400	56730	60070	63410	**64150**		22'-6"
35	41060	44450	47850	51260	54670	58100	61530	64970	**66080**		22'-8"
36	41950	45430	48920	52420	55930	59450	62980	66510	**68020**		22'-10"
37	42830	46450	49980	53580	57180	60790	64410	68040	**69930**		
38	43700	47360	51030	54710	58410	62120	65830	69550	**71870**		
39	44550	48300	52060	55840	59630	63420	67230	71050	**73800**		
40	45390	49230	53080	56950	60830	64720	68620	72530	**75770**		

C. ORDINARY CLAY Kµ'−0.130

H	15'-0"	16'-0"	17'-0"	18'-0"	19'-0"	20'-0"	21'-0"	22'-0"	23'-0"	25'-0"	TRANSITION WIDTH
5	6908										14'-5"
6	8414										14'-9"
7	9887	**9966**									15'-1"
8	11200	**11560**									15'-5"
9	12500	**13210**									15'-9"
10	13770	14770	**14900**								16'-2"
11	15020	16120	**16640**								16'-6"
12	16250	17440	**18440**								16'-10"
13	17460	18750	20040	**20290**							17'-2"
14	18650	20030	21420	**22190**							17'-6"
15	19810	21300	22790	**24150**							17'-11"
16	20960	22540	24130	25710	**26170**						18'-3"
17	22090	23770	25450	27130	**28240**						18'-8"
18	23190	24970	26750	28530	**30380**						19'-0"
19	24280	26150	28030	29910	31790	**32580**					19'-5"
20	25350	27320	29290	31270	33240	**34850**					19'-10"
21	26400	28470	30530	32600	34680	36750	**37180**				20'-3"
22	27440	29600	31760	33920	36090	38270	**39580**				20'-7"
23	28450	30700	32960	35200	37490	39760	42030	**42060**			21'-1"
24	29450	31800	34150	36510	38870	41230	43600	**44600**			21'-1"
25	30430	32870	35320	37770	40230	42690	45150	**46620**			21'-5"
26	31400	33930	36470	39020	41570	44120	46680	**48580**			21'-7"
27	32340	34970	37600	40240	42890	45540	48200	**50540**			21'-8"
28	33270	35990	38720	41450	44190	46940	49690	**52490**			22'-0"
29	34190	37000	39820	42650	45480	48320	51160	54020	**54440**		22'-2"
30	35090	37990	40900	43820	46750	49680	52620	55570	**56390**		22'-3"
31	35970	38980	41970	44980	48000	51030	54060	57100	**58320**		22'-6"
32	36840	39920	43020	46120	49240	52360	55480	58620	**60260**		22'-7"
33	37700	40870	44050	47250	50450	53670	56890	60110	**62210**		22'-10"
34	38540	41800	45070	48360	51650	54960	58280	61600	**64150**		22'-11"
35	39360	42710	46070	49450	52840	56240	59650	63060	**66080**		23'-0"
36	40170	43610	47060	50530	54010	57500	61000	64510	**68020**		23'-1"
37	40970	44490	48030	51590	55160	58740	62340	65940	**69930**		23'-2"
38	41750	45360	48990	52640	56300	59970	63660	67350	**71870**		23'-4"
39	42520	46220	49940	53670	57420	61180	64960	68740	**73800**		23'-5"
40	43280	47060	50860	54690	58530	62380	66250	70120	**75770**		

HEIGHT OF BACKFILL H ABOVE TOP OF PIPE, FEET

* For backfill weighing 110 pounds per cubic foot, increase loads 10%; for 120 pounds per cubic foot, increase 20%; etc.
▲Transition loads (**bold type**) and widths based on Kµ−0.19, rsdp−0.5 in the embankment equation
Interpolate for intermediate heights of backfill and/or trench widths

TABLE 41

138″

BACKFILL LOADS ON CIRCULAR PIPE IN TRENCH INSTALLATION

A — *100 POUNDS PER CUBIC FOOT BACKFILL MATERIAL — SAND AND GRAVEL Kμ'—0.165

HEIGHT OF BACKFILL **H** ABOVE TOP OF PIPE, FEET — TRENCH WIDTH AT TOP OF PIPE

H	16'-0"	17'-0"	18'-0"	19'-0"	20'-0"	21'-0"	22'-0"	23'-0"	24'-0"	26'-0"	TRANSITION WIDTH
5	7202										15'-3"
6	8767										15'-7"
7	10380										15'-11"
8	11800	12031									16'-3"
9	13140	13730									16'-8"
10	14460	15450	15480								17'-1"
11	15750	16840	17280								17'-5"
12	17010	18200	19130								17'-9"
13	18240	19530	20820	21030							18'-2"
14	19460	20840	22220	22990							18'-6"
15	20640	22120	23600	25000							18'-11"
16	21800	23370	24960	26540	27070						19'-4"
17	22940	24620	26290	27970	29200						19'-8"
18	24060	25820	27600	29370	31150	31380					20'-1"
19	25150	27010	28880	30750	32620	33630					20'-7"
20	26220	28180	30140	32100	34070	35940					21'-0"
21	27270	29320	31370	33430	35500	37560	38320				21'-4"
22	28300	30440	32590	34740	36900	39060	40770				21'-10"
23	29300	31540	33780	36020	38280	40530	42790	43280			22'-5"
24	30290	32610	34950	37290	39640	41990	44340	45860			22'-7"
25	31250	33670	36100	38530	40970	43420	45860	48320	48520		23'-1"
26	32200	34710	37220	39740	42280	44820	47360	49910	50700		23'-3"
27	33120	35720	38330	40950	43580	46210	48840	51480	52750		23'-6"
28	34030	36720	39420	42130	44840	47570	50300	53040	54800		23'-8"
29	34920	37700	40490	43290	46100	48910	51730	54560	56850		23'-9"
30	35790	38660	41540	44420	47320	50230	53150	56070	58890		23'-11"
31	36640	39600	42560	45540	48530	51530	54540	57550	60580	60920	24'-2"
32	37480	40520	43580	46640	49720	52810	55910	59020	62130	62940	24'-3"
33	38300	41420	44540	47720	50890	54070	57260	60460	63670	64970	24'-5"
34	39100	42310	45540	48780	52040	55310	58590	61880	65180	67010	24'-6"
35	39890	43180	46500	49830	53180	56530	59900	63280	66670	69040	24'-9"
36	40660	44040	47440	50850	54290	57740	61200	64670	68150	71060	24'-10"
37	41410	44870	48360	51860	55380	58920	62470	66030	69600	73090	25'-0"
38	42150	45690	49260	52850	56460	60080	63720	67370	71030	75100	25'-1"
39	42870	46500	50150	53830	57520	61230	64960	68700	72450	77130	25'-3"
40	43580	47290	51020	54780	58560	62360	66170	70000	73840	79150	25'-5"

138″

B — LOADS IN POUNDS PER LINEAR FOOT — SATURATED TOP SOIL Kμ'—0.150

HEIGHT OF BACKFILL **H** ABOVE TOP OF PIPE, FEET — TRENCH WIDTH AT TOP OF PIPE

H	16'-0"	17'-0"	18'-0"	19'-0"	20'-0"	21'-0"	22'-0"	23'-0"	24'-0"	26'-0"	TRANSITION WIDTH
5	7202										15'-1"
6	8767										15'-6"
7	10380										15'-10"
8	11890	12030									16'-2"
9	13250	13730									16'-7"
10	14590	15480									16'-11"
11	15900	17000	17280								17'-3"
12	17190	18380	19130								17'-7"
13	18460	19750	21030								18'-0"
14	19700	21090	22480	22990							18'-4"
15	20920	22400	23890	25000							18'-9"
16	22120	23700	25280	26860	27070						19'-1"
17	23290	24970	26650	28330	29200						19'-6"
18	24440	26220	27990	29770	31380						19'-11"
19	25570	27440	29310	31190	33060	33630					20'-3"
20	26680	28650	30610	32580	34560	35940					20'-8"
21	27770	29830	31890	33960	36030	38100	38320				21'-2"
22	28840	30990	33150	35310	37480	39640	40770				21'-6"
23	29890	32140	34390	36640	38900	41170	43280				21'-11"
24	30920	33260	35600	37960	40310	42670	45030	45860			22'-4"
25	31930	34360	36800	39240	41690	44150	46600	48520			22'-9"
26	32920	35450	37980	40520	43060	45610	48160	50700			23'-0"
27	33900	36510	39140	41770	44400	47040	49690	52340	52750		23'-2"
28	34850	37560	40270	43000	45730	48460	51200	53950	54800		23'-3"
29	35790	38590	41390	44210	47030	49860	52700	55540	56850		23'-6"
30	36710	39600	42490	45400	48320	51240	54170	57100	58890		23'-7"
31	37620	40590	43580	46580	49580	52600	55620	58650	60920		23'-9"
32	38500	41560	44640	47730	50830	53940	57050	60170	62940		23'-10"
33	39370	42520	45680	48870	52060	55260	58460	61680	64900	64970	24'-1"
34	40220	43460	46720	49990	53260	56560	59860	63160	66480	67010	24'-2"
35	41060	44390	47730	51090	54460	57840	61230	64630	68040	69040	24'-4"
36	41880	45300	48730	52170	55630	59120	62590	66060	69580	71060	24'-5"
37	42690	46190	49710	53240	56790	60350	63920	67500	71100	73090	24'-6"
38	43480	47070	50670	54290	57930	61580	65240	68920	72600	75100	24'-9"
39	44260	47930	51620	55330	59050	62790	66540	70310	74080	77130	24'-10"
40	45020	48780	52550	56340	60160	63990	67830	71680	75550	79150	24'-11"

HEIGHT OF BACKFILL H ABOVE TOP OF PIPE, FEET

D — SATURATED CLAY Kμ'−0.110 — TRENCH WIDTH AT TOP OF PIPE

H	16'-0"	17'-0"	18'-0"	19'-0"	20'-0"	21'-0"	22'-0"	23'-0"	24'-0"	26'-0"	▲TRAN- SITION WIDTH
5	7202										14'-11"
6	8767										15'-3"
7	10380										15'-7"
8	12030										15'-11"
9	13540	13730									16'-3"
10	14950	15480									16'-6"
11	16330	17280	**19130**								16'-10"
12	17700	18890	**21030**								17'-2"
13	19050	20340	**22990**								17'-6"
14	20380	21770	**25000**								17'-10"
15	21690	23180	26160	**27070**							18'-2"
16	22980	24570	27630	**29200**							18'-7"
17	24250	25940	29080	**31380**							18'-11"
18	25510	27300	30520	32400	**33630**						19'-3"
19	26750	28640	31940	33920	**35940**						19'-7"
20	27980	29960	33340	35420	**38320**						20'-0"
21	29180	31260	34720	36900	39080	**40770**					20'-5"
22	30370	32550	36090	38360	40640	**43280**					20'-9"
23	31550	33820	37440	39810	42190	44560	**45860**				21'-2"
24	32710	35070	38770	41240	43710	46190	**48520**				21'-6"
25	33850	36310	40090	42660	45220	47800	**50700**				21'-11"
26	34980	37530	41390	44060	46720	49390	52060	**52750**			22'-1"
27	36090	38740	42680	45440	48200	50960	53730	**54800**			22'-3"
28	37180	39930	43950	46800	49660	52520	55380	**56850**			22'-5"
29	38260	41100	45210	48150	51100	54060	57020	**58890**			22'-6"
30	39330	42260	46450	49490	52530	55590	58640	**60920**			22'-7"
31	40380	43410	47670	50810	53950	57100	60250	**62940**			22'-8"
32	41420	44540	48880	52110	55350	58590	61840	**64970**			22'-11"
33	42440	45660	50080	53400	56730	60070	63410	**67010**			23'-0"
34	43450	46760	51260	54670	58100	61540	64970	68410	**69040**		23'-1"
35	44450	47850	52420	55930	59450	62980	66530	70050	**71060**		23'-2"
36	45430	48920	53580	57180	60790	64410	68040	71670	**73090**		23'-3"
37	46400	49980	54710	58410	62120	65830	69550	73280	**75100**		23'-4"
38	47360	51030	55840	59630	63420	67230	71050	74870	**77130**		23'-6"
39	48300	52060	56950	60830	64720	68620	72530	76440	**79150**		23'-7"
40	49230	53080									23'-8"

C — ORDINARY CLAY Kμ'−0.130 — TRENCH WIDTH AT TOP OF PIPE

H	16'-0"	17'-0"	18'-0"	19'-0"	20'-0"	21'-0"	22'-0"	23'-0"	24'-0"	26'-0"	▲TRAN- SITION WIDTH
5	7202										15'-0"
6	8767										15'-4"
7	10380										15'-8"
8	12030										16'-0"
9	13400	13730									16'-4"
10	14770	15480									16'-9"
11	16120	17280	**19130**								17'-0"
12	17440	18640	**21030**								17'-5"
13	18750	20040	**22990**								17'-9"
14	20030	21420	24280	**25000**							18'-1"
15	21300	22790	25710	**27070**							18'-6"
16	22540	24130	27130	**29200**							18'-10"
17	23770	25450	28530	30310	**31380**						19'-3"
18	24970	26750	29910	31790	**33630**						19'-7"
19	26150	28030	31270	33240	**35940**						20'-0"
20	27320	29290	32600	34680	36750	**38320**					20'-5"
21	28470	30530	33920	36090	38270	**40770**					20'-9"
22	29600	31760	35220	37490	39760	42030	**43280**				21'-2"
23	30700	32960	36510	38870	41230	43600	**45860**				21'-6"
24	31800	34150	37770	40230	42690	45150	**48520**				21'-11"
25	32870	35320	39020	41570	44120	46680	49250	**50700**			22'-5"
26	33930	36470	40240	42890	45540	48200	50860	**52750**			22'-7"
27	34970	37600	41450	44190	46940	49690	52440	**54800**			22'-8"
28	35990	38720	42650	45480	48320	51160	54020	**56850**			22'-11"
29	37000	39820	43820	46750	49680	52620	55570	**58890**			23'-0"
30	37990	40900	44980	48000	51030	54060	57100	60150	**60920**		23'-1"
31	38960	41970	46120	49240	52360	55480	58620	61760	**62940**		23'-3"
32	39920	43020	47250	50450	53670	56890	60110	63350	**64970**		23'-4"
33	40870	44050	48360	51650	54960	58280	61600	64920	**67010**		23'-6"
34	41800	45070	49450	52840	56240	59650	63060	66480	**69040**		23'-8"
35	42710	46070	50530	54010	57500	61000	64510	68020	**71060**		23'-9"
36	43610	47060	51590	55160	58730	62340	65940	69550	73090		23'-10"
37	44490	48030	52640	56300	59970	63660	67350	71050	74760		23'-11"
38	45360	48990	53670	57420	61180	64980	68740	72540	75100		24'-1"
39	46220	49940	54690	58530	62380	66250	70120	74010	77130		24'-3"
40	47060	50860						77900	79150		24'-4"

* For backfill weighing 110 pounds per cubic foot; increase loads 10%; for 120 pounds per cubic foot, increase 20%; etc.
▲ Transition loads (**bold type**) and widths based on Kμ'−0.19, fsdP−0.5 in the embankment equation
Interpolate for intermediate heights of backfill and/or trench widths

TABLE 42

144"

BACKFILL LOADS ON CIRCULAR PIPE IN TRENCH INSTALLATION

LOADS IN POUNDS PER LINEAR FOOT

A — SAND AND GRAVEL Ku'—0.165

*100 POUNDS PER CUBIC FOOT BACKFILL MATERIAL

HEIGHT OF BACKFILL H ABOVE TOP OF PIPE, FEET	TRENCH WIDTH AT TOP OF PIPE										TRANSITION WIDTH
	17'-0"	18'-0"	19'-0"	20'-0"	21'-0"	22'-0"	23'-0"	24'-0"	25'-0"	26'-0"	
5	7491										15'- 9"
6	9113										16'- 1"
7	10780										16'- 6"
8	12490										16'-10"
9	14040	14250									17'- 3"
10	15450	16050									17'- 8"
11	16840	17910									18'- 0"
12	18200	19390	19810								18'- 4"
13	19530	20820	21770								18'- 9"
14	20840	22220	23610	23780							19'- 2"
15	22120	23600	25090	25840							19'- 6"
16	23380	24960	26540	27960							19'-11"
17	24620	26290	27970	29650	30140						20'- 4"
18	25820	27600	29370	31150	32370						20'- 8"
19	27010	28880	30750	32620	34490	34670					21'- 1"
20	28180	30140	32100	34070	36040	37030					21'- 5"
21	29320	31370	33430	35500	37560	39450					22'- 0"
22	30440	32590	34740	36900	39060	41220	41940				22'- 4"
23	31540	33780	36030	38280	40530	42790	44490				22'- 9"
24	32610	34950	37290	39640	41990	44340	46700	47120			23'- 2"
25	33670	36100	38530	40970	43420	45860	48320	49810			23'- 7"
26	34710	37220	39750	42280	44820	47360	49910	52460	52580		24'- 1"
27	35720	38330	40950	43580	46210	48840	51480	54130	54910		24'- 3"
28	36720	39420	42130	44840	47570	50300	53040	55780	57050		24'- 6"
29	37700	40490	43290	46100	48910	51730	54560	57400	59190		24'- 7"
30	38660	41540	44420	47320	50120	53150	56070	59000	61320		24'- 9"
31	39600	42560	45540	48530	51530	54540	57550	60580	63440		25'- 0"
32	40520	43580	46640	49720	52810	55910	59020	62130	65250	65580	25'- 1"
33	41420	44570	47720	50890	54070	57260	60460	63670	66680	67690	25'- 3"
34	42310	45540	48780	52040	55310	58590	61880	65180	68490	69810	25'- 5"
35	43180	46500	49830	53180	56530	59900	63280	66670	70070	71930	25'- 7"
36	44040	47440	50850	54290	57740	61200	64670	68150	71640	74050	25'- 8"
37	44870	48360	51860	55380	58920	62470	66030	69600	73180	76160	25'- 9"
38	45690	49260	52850	56460	60080	63720	67370	71030	74700	78280	26'- 0"
39	46500	50150	53830	57520	61230	64960	68700	72450	76210	80380	26'- 1"
40	47290	51020	54780	58560	62360	66170	70000	73840	77690	82500	26'- 2"

B — SATURATED TOP SOIL Ku'—0.150

HEIGHT OF BACKFILL H ABOVE TOP OF PIPE, FEET	TRENCH WIDTH AT TOP OF PIPE										TRANSITION WIDTH
	17'-0"	18'-0"	19'-0"	20'-0"	21'-0"	22'-0"	23'-0"	24'-0"	25'-0"	26'-0"	
5	7491										15'- 9"
6	9113										16'- 1"
7	10780										16'- 5"
8	12490										16'- 9"
9	14150	14250									17'- 1"
10	15580	16050									17'- 6"
11	17000	17910									17'-10"
12	18380	19580	19810								18'- 2"
13	19750	21040	21770								18'- 7"
14	21090	22480	23780								18'-11"
15	22400	23890	25380	25840							19'- 3"
16	23700	25280	26860	27960							19'- 8"
17	24970	26650	28330	30010	30140						20'- 1"
18	26220	27990	29770	31550	32370						20'- 5"
19	27440	29310	31190	33060	34670						20'-10"
20	28650	30610	32580	34560	36530	37030					21'- 3"
21	29830	31890	33960	36030	38100	39450					21'- 8"
22	30990	33150	35310	37480	39640	41810	41940				22'- 1"
23	32140	34390	36640	38900	41170	43430	44490				22'- 6"
24	33260	35600	37960	40310	42670	45030	47120				22'-10"
25	34360	36800	39240	41690	44150	46600	49070	49810			23'- 3"
26	35450	37980	40520	43060	45610	48160	50720	52580			23'- 8"
27	36510	39140	41770	44400	47040	49690	52340	54910			24'- 0"
28	37560	40270	43000	45730	48460	51200	53950	56700	57050		24'- 1"
29	38590	41390	44210	47030	49860	52700	55540	58380	59190		24'- 3"
30	39600	42490	45400	48320	51240	54170	57100	60040	61320		24'- 6"
31	40590	43580	46580	49580	52600	55620	58650	61680	63440		24'- 8"
32	41560	44640	47730	50830	53940	57050	60170	63300	65580		24'-11"
33	42520	45690	48870	52060	55260	58460	61680	64900	67690		25'- 0"
34	43460	46720	49990	53270	56560	59860	63160	66480	69810		25'- 3"
35	44390	47730	51090	54460	57840	61230	64630	68040	71450	71930	25'- 5"
36	45300	48730	52170	55630	59100	62590	66080	69580	73080	74050	25'- 6"
37	46190	49710	53240	56790	60350	63920	67500	71100	74690	76160	25'- 8"
38	47070	50670	54290	57930	61580	65240	68920	72600	76290	78280	25'- 9"
39	47930	51620	55330	59050	62790	66540	70310	74080	77860	80380	25'- 8"
40	48780	52550	56340	60160	63990	67830	71680	75550	79420	82500	25'- 9"

144"

HEIGHT OF BACKFILL H ABOVE TOP OF PIPE, FEET

D. SATURATED CLAY Kμ'—0.110 — TRENCH WIDTH AT TOP OF PIPE

H	17'-0"	18'-0"	19'-0"	20'-0"	21'-0"	22'-0"	23'-0"	24'-0"	25'-0"	26'-0"	▲TRANSITION WIDTH
5	7491										15'- 6"
6	9113										15'-10"
7	**10780**										16'- 2"
8	12490										16'- 6"
9	14250										16'- 9"
10	15940	16050									17'- 1"
11	17430	17910									17'- 5"
12	18890	19810									17'- 9"
13	20340	21330	**21770**								18'- 1"
14	21770	23160	**23780**								18'- 5"
15	23180	24670	**25840**								18'- 9"
16	24570	26160	27750	**27960**							19'- 2"
17	25940	27630	29320	**30140**							19'- 6"
18	27300	29080	30870	**32370**							19'-10"
19	28640	30520	32400	34290	**34670**						20'- 2"
20	29960	31940	33920	35900	**37030**						20'- 7"
21	31260	33340	35420	37500	**39450**						21'- 0"
22	32550	34720	36900	39080	41260	**41940**					21'- 4"
23	33820	36090	38360	40640	42920	**44490**					21'- 8"
24	35070	37440	39810	42190	44560	46940	**47120**				22'- 1"
25	36310	38770	41240	43710	46190	48660	**49810**				22'- 6"
26	37530	40090	42660	45220	47800	50370	**52580**				22'-10"
27	38740	41390	44060	46720	49390	52060	54730	**54910**			23'- 1"
28	39930	42680	45440	48200	50960	53730	56500	**57050**			23'- 4"
29	41100	43950	46800	49660	52520	55380	58250	**59190**			23'- 6"
30	42260	45210	48150	51100	54060	57020	59980	**61320**			23'- 7"
31	43410	46450	49490	52530	55590	58640	61700	**63440**			23'- 8"
32	44540	47670	50810	53950	57100	60250	63400	**65580**			23'- 9"
33	45660	48880	52110	55350	58590	61840	65090	**67690**			23'-11"
34	46760	50080	53400	56730	60070	63410	66760	**69810**			24'- 0"
35	47850	51260	54670	58100	61530	64970	68410	**71930**			24'- 1"
36	48920	52420	55930	59450	62980	66510	70050	73590	**74050**		24'- 3"
37	49980	53580	57180	60790	64410	68040	71670	75310	**76160**		24'- 5"
38	51030	54710	58410	62120	65830	69550	73280	77010	**78280**		24'- 6"
39	52060	55840	59630	63420	67230	71050	74870	78700	**80380**		24'- 7"
40	53080	56950	60830	64720	68620	72530	76440	80370	**82500**		24'- 7"

C. ORDINARY CLAY Kμ'—0.130 — TRENCH WIDTH AT TOP OF PIPE

H	17'-0"	18'-0"	19'-0"	20'-0"	21'-0"	22'-0"	23'-0"	24'-0"	25'-0"	26'-0"	▲TRANSITION WIDTH
5	7491										15'- 7"
6	9113										16'- 0"
7	**10780**										16'- 3"
8	12490										16'- 7"
9	14250										17'- 0"
10	15760	16050									17'- 3"
11	17210	17910									17'- 8"
12	18640	19810									18'- 0"
13	20040	21330	**21770**								18'- 4"
14	21420	22820	**23780**								18'- 8"
15	22790	24280	25760	**25840**							19'- 1"
16	24130	25710	27300	**27960**							19'- 5"
17	25450	27130	28820	**30140**							19'-10"
18	26750	28530	30310	32100	**32370**						20'- 2"
19	28030	29910	31790	33670	**34670**						20'- 7"
20	29290	31270	33240	35220	**37030**						21'- 0"
21	30530	32600	34680	36750	38830	**39450**					21'- 3"
22	31760	33920	36090	38270	40440	**41940**					21'- 8"
23	32960	35220	37490	39760	42040	44300	**44490**				22'- 1"
24	34150	36510	38870	41230	43600	45970	**47120**				22'- 6"
25	35320	37770	40230	42690	45150	47620	**49810**				22'-10"
26	36470	39020	41570	44120	46680	49250	51810	**52580**			23'- 1"
27	37600	40240	42890	45540	48200	50860	53520	**54910**			23'- 6"
28	38720	41450	44190	46940	49690	52440	55200	**57050**			23'- 8"
29	39820	42650	45480	48320	51160	54020	56870	**59190**			23'- 9"
30	40900	43820	46750	49680	52620	55570	58520	**61320**			24'- 0"
31	41970	44980	48000	51030	54060	57100	60150	63200	**63440**		24'- 1"
32	43020	46120	49240	52360	55480	58620	61760	64900	**65580**		24'- 5"
33	44050	47250	50450	53670	56890	60120	63350	66590	**67690**		24'- 6"
34	45070	48360	51650	54960	58280	61600	64920	68260	**69810**		24'- 7"
35	46070	49450	52840	56240	59650	63060	66480	69910	**71930**		24'- 8"
36	47060	50530	54010	57500	61000	64510	68020	71540	**74050**		24'- 9"
37	48030	51590	55160	58740	62340	65940	69540	73160	**76160**		25'- 0"
38	48990	52640	56300	59970	63660	67350	71050	74760	**78280**		25'- 1"
39	49940	53670	57420	61180	64960	68740	72540	76340	80150	**80380**	25'- 1"
40	50860	54690	58530	62380	66250	70120	74010	77900	81810	**82500**	25'- 2"

* For backfill weighing 110 pounds per cubic foot, increase loads 10%; for 120 pounds per cubic foot, increase 20%; etc.

▲Transition loads (**bold type**) and widths based on $K\mu$—0.19, $r_{sd}p$—0.5 in the embankment equation

Interpolate for intermediate heights of backfill and/or trench widths

TABLE 43

DESIGN VALUES OF SETTLEMENT RATIO

Installation and Foundation Condition	Settlement Ratio r_{sd}	
	Usual Range	Design Value
Positive Projecting..	0.0 to +1.0	
Rock or Unyielding Soil	+1.0	+1.0
*Ordinary Soil	+0.5 to +0.8	+0.7
Yielding Soil	0.0 to +0.5	+0.3
Zero Projecting...		0.0
Negative Projecting..	−1.0 to 0.0	
$p' = 0.5$		−0.1
$p' = 1.0$		−0.3
$p' = 1.5$		−0.5
$p' = 2.0$		−1.0
Induced Trench	−2.0 to 0.0	
$p' = 0.5$		−0.5
$p' = 1.0$		−0.7
$p' = 1.5$		−1.0
$p' = 2.0$		−2.0

*The value of the settlement ratio depends on the degree of compaction of the fill material adjacent to the sides of the pipe. With good construction methods resulting in proper compaction of bedding and sidefill materials, a settlement ratio design value of +0.5 is recommended.

TABLE 44

DESIGN VALUES OF COEFFICIENT OF COHESION

Type of Soil	Values of c
Clay	
Soft..	40
Medium	250
Hard...	1000
Sand	
Loose Dry...	0
Silty	100
Dense...	300
Top Soil	
Saturated..	100

TABLE 45

HIGHWAY LOADS ON CIRCULAR PIPE
POUNDS PER LINEAR FOOT

PIPE SIZE **D** IN INCHES

PIPE SIZE D IN INCHES	B_c (ft.)	HEIGHT OF FILL H ABOVE TOP OF PIPE IN FEET												
		0.5	1.0	1.5	2.0	2.5	3.0	3.5	4.0	5.0	6.0	7.0	8.0	9.0
12	1.33	3780	2080	1470	1080	760	550	450	380	290	230	190	160	130
15	1.63	4240	2360	1740	1280	900	660	540	450	350	280	230	190	160
18	1.92	4110	2610	1970	1460	1030	750	620	520	400	320	260	220	190
21	2.21	3920	2820	2190	1620	1150	840	690	580	450	360	300	250	210
24	2.50	4100	3010	2400	1780	1270	930	760	640	500	400	330	280	240
27	2.79	3880	2940	2590	1930	1380	1010	830	700	560	440	360	300	260
30	3.08	3620	2830	2770	2070	1480	1080	890	750	590	480	390	330	280
33	3.38	3390	2930	2950	2200	1580	1160	960	810	630	510	420	360	300
36	3.67	3190	2810	2930	2330	1670	1230	1020	860	670	550	450	380	330
39	3.96	3010	2670	2850	2440	1760	1290	1070	910	710	580	480	410	350
42	4.25	2860	2550	2770	2560	1840	1360	1130	950	750	610	510	430	370
48	4.83	2590	2330	2620	2480	1990	1470	1230	1040	820	670	560	470	410
54	5.42	2360	2150	2490	2360	2050	1580	1320	1120	890	730	610	520	440
60	6.00	2170	1990	2450	2250	1960	1680	1400	1190	950	780	650	560	480
66	6.58	2010	1850	2520	2160	1880	1640	1480	1260	1010	830	700	590	510
72	7.17	1870	1730	2580	2190	1810	1570	1510	1330	1060	880	740	630	540
78	7.75	1750	1630	2630	2240	1770	1520	1510	1390	1110	920	780	660	570
84	8.33	1650	1540	2730	2290	1810	1460	1410	1360	1160	960	810	690	600
90	8.92	1550	1460	2530	2330	1850	1470	1360	1310	1210	1000	850	720	630
96	9.50	1470	1380	2410	2290	1880	1500	1330	1270	1250	1040	880	750	650
102	10.08	1390	1320	2300	2190	1910	1530	1350	1240	1290	1070	910	780	680
108	10.67	1320	1260	2200	2090	1830	1560	1380	1230	1330	1110	940	810	700
114	11.25	1260	1200	2110	2010	1760	1540	1410	1260	1362	1140	970	830	730
120	11.83	1210	1150	2020	1930	1700	1480	1420	1280	1400	1170	990	860	750
126	12.42	1160	1100	1940	1860	1640	1430	1380	1300	1430	1200	1020	880	770
132	13.00	1110	1060	1870	1800	1580	1380	1330	1290	1460	1220	1040	900	790
138	13.58	1070	1020	1800	1730	1530	1340	1290	1250	1490	1250	1070	920	810
144	14.17	1020	980	1740	1670	1480	1300	1250	1210	1470	1280	1090	940	830

DATA:
1. Unsurfaced roadway.
2. Loads — AASHTO HS 20, two 16,000 lb dual-tired wheels, 4 ft. on centers, or alternate loading, four 12,000 lb. dual-tired wheels, 4 ft. on centers.

NOTES:
1. Interpolate for intermediate pipe sizes and/or fill heights.
2. Critical loads:
   a. For H = 0.5 and 1.0 ft., a single 16,000 lb. dual-tired wheel.
   b. For H = 1.5 through 4.0 ft., two 16,000 lb. dual-tired wheels, 4 ft. on centers.
   c. For H > 4.0 ft. alternate loading.
3. Truck live loads for H = 10.0 ft. or more are insignificant.

TABLE 46

HIGHWAY LOADS ON HORIZONTAL ELLIPTICAL PIPE
POUNDS PER LINEAR FOOT

PIPE SIZE S X R IN INCHES

Pipe Size S×R (in.)	Equiv. Dia. (in.)	HEIGHT OF FILL H ABOVE TOP OF PIPE IN FEET												
		0.5	1.0	1.5	2.0	2.5	3.0	3.5	4.0	5.0	6.0	7.0	8.0	9.0
23×14	18	4940	3380	2490	1840	1300	940	770	950	500	400	330	270	230
30×19	24	4610	3450	3060	2270	1610	1170	960	810	630	510	420	350	290
34×22	27	4300	3640	3330	2470	1750	1280	1050	880	690	550	460	380	320
38×24	30	4040	3450	3270	2650	1890	1380	1140	960	750	600	500	420	350
42×27	33	3840	3310	3200	2820	2010	1470	1210	1020	800	640	530	450	380
45×29	36	3560	3100	3090	2890	2160	1580	1310	1100	860	700	580	490	410
49×32	39	3380	2960	3010	2820	2280	1670	1380	1170	920	740	610	520	440
53×34	42	3210	2830	2950	2750	2380	1760	1460	1230	970	780	650	550	470
60×38	48	2930	2610	3110	2630	2280	1920	1590	1350	1060	860	720	610	520
68×43	54	2690	2410	3250	2690	2190	1890	1720	1460	1150	940	780	660	570
76×48	60	2480	2250	3380	2810	2180	1820	1680	1560	1240	1010	840	710	610
83×53	66	2310	2100	3480	2910	2270	1770	1620	1600	1320	1080	900	770	660
91×58	72	2160	1980	3370	3010	2350	1840	1660	1550	1390	1140	960	810	700
98×63	78	2020	1860	3190	2980	2420	1900	1720	1510	1460	1210	1010	860	740
106×68	84	1910	1760	3030	2840	2440	1960	1770	1520	1530	1260	1060	900	780
113×72	90	1800	1670	2890	2710	2340	2010	1820	1560	1600	1320	1110	950	820
121×77	96	1710	1590	2760	2590	2240	1930	1780	1610	1660	1370	1150	990	850
128×82	102	1630	1530	2650	2500	2160	1870	1720	1650	1710	1420	1200	1020	890
136×87	108	1560	1460	2540	2400	2090	1810	1660	1640	1760	1460	1240	1060	920
143×92	114	1490	1400	2440	2310	2010	1740	1610	1590	1800	1510	1280	1090	950
151×97	120	1420	1340	2350	2230	1940	1690	1510	1540	1810	1550	1320	1130	980
166×106	132	1310	1240	2180	2080	1820	1580	1510	1450	1730	1600	1390	1190	1040
180×116	144	1210	1150	2030	1940	1700	1490	1430	1370	1650	1560	1440	1250	1090

PIPE SIZE S X R IN INCHES

DATA:
1. Unsurfaced roadway.
2. Loads— AASHTO HS 20, two 16,000 lb dual-tired wheels, 4 ft. on centers, or alternate loading, four 12,000 lb. dual-tired wheels, 4 ft. on centers.

NOTES:
1. Interpolate for intermediate pipe sizes and/or fill heights.
2. Critical loads:
   a. For H = 0.5 and 1.0 ft., a single 16,000 lb. dual-tired wheel.
   b. For H = 1.5 through 4.0 ft., two 16,000 lb. dual-tired wheels, 4 ft. on centers.
   c. For H > 4.0 ft. alternate loading.
3. Truck live loads for H = 10.0 ft. or more are insignificant.

TABLE 47

HIGHWAY LOADS ON VERTICAL ELLIPTICAL PIPE

POUNDS PER LINEAR FOOT

PIPE SIZE
S X R IN INCHES

PIPE SIZE S X R IN INCHES	Equiv. Dia. (in.)	HEIGHT OF FILL H ABOVE TOP OF PIPE IN FEET												
		0.5	1.0	1.5	2.0	2.5	3.0	3.5	4.0	5.0	6.0	7.0	8.0	9.0
29X45	36	2720	2250	2460	1850	1330	980	820	690	550	450	370	310	270
32X49	39	2560	2290	2560	1930	1390	1030	860	730	580	470	390	330	280
34X53	42	2420	2200	2530	2010	1450	1070	900	760	600	490	410	350	300
38X60	48	2180	2000	2380	2150	1550	1160	970	820	650	540	450	380	330
43X68	54	1990	1840	2250	2140	1650	1230	1030	880	700	580	480	410	360
48X76	60	1830	1700	2140	2040	1740	1300	1090	930	750	620	520	440	380
53X83	66	1690	1570	2040	1940	1700	1360	1140	980	790	650	550	470	410
58X91	72	1570	1470	1930	1850	1630	1420	1190	1020	820	680	580	490	430
63X98	78	1460	1380	1900	1770	1560	1370	1240	1060	860	710	600	520	450
68X106	84	1370	1300	1920	1700	1500	1310	1270	1100	890	740	630	540	470
72X113	90	1290	1230	1950	1680	1440	1270	1220	1130	920	770	650	560	490
77X121	96	1220	1160	1970	1700	1390	1220	1160	1140	950	790	680	580	510
82X128	102	1160	1110	1950	1720	1380	1180	1140	1110	970	820	690	600	520
87X136	108	1110	1060	1870	1730	1390	1180	1110	1080	1000	840	710	620	540
92X143	114	1060	1010	1790	1720	1410	1140	1070	1040	1020	860	730	630	550
97X151	120	1010	970	1710	1650	1430	1150	1040	1010	1040	880	750	650	570
106X166	132	920	890	1580	1530	1350	1180	1060	960	1080	910	780	680	600
116X180	144	850	820	1470	1420	1260	1110	1080	970	1120	950	810	710	620

DATA:

1. Unsurfaced roadway.
2. Loads — AASHTO HS 20, two 16,000 lb dual-tired wheels, 4 ft. on centers, or alternate loading, four 12,000 lb. dual-tired wheels, 4 ft. on centers.

NOTES:

1. Interpolate for intermediate pipe sizes and/or fill heights.
2. Critical loads:
   a. For H = 0.5 and 1.0 ft., a single 16,000 lb. dual-tired wheel.
   b. For H = 1.5 through 4.0 ft., two 16,000 lb. dual-tired wheels, 4 ft. on centers.
   c. For H > 4.0 ft. alternate loading.
3. Truck live loads for H = 10.0 ft. or more are insignificant.

TABLE 48

HIGHWAY LOADS ON ARCH PIPE

POUNDS PER LINEAR FOOT

Pipe Size S X R in inches	Equiv. Dia. (in.)	\multicolumn{13}{c}{HEIGHT OF FILL H ABOVE TOP OF PIPE IN FEET}
		0.5	1.0	1.5	2.0	2.5	3.0	3.5	4.0	5.0	6.0	7.0	8.0	9.0
18X11	15	4910	2960	2090	1530	1080	780	640	530	410	330	270	220	190
22X13	18	4930	3330	2420	1780	1260	910	750	630	480	390	320	260	220
26X15	21	5200	3640	2750	2030	1440	1050	860	720	560	450	360	300	260
29X18	24	4800	3440	2930	2160	1530	1120	920	770	600	480	400	330	280
36X22	30	4220	3580	3330	2580	1840	1340	1110	930	720	580	480	400	340
44X27	36	3790	3270	3180	2950	2110	1540	1270	1070	840	680	560	470	400
51X31	42	3400	2980	3020	2830	2340	1720	1420	1200	940	760	630	530	450
58X36	48	3090	2730	3110	2700	2330	1880	1560	1320	1040	840	700	590	500
65X40	54	2860	2550	3250	2680	2250	1940	1680	1420	1120	910	760	640	550
73X45	60	2620	2360	3380	2810	2170	1870	1770	1530	1210	990	820	700	600
88X54	72	2280	2080	3530	3020	2360	1840	1660	1590	1370	1130	940	800	690
102X62	84	2030	1870	3200	2990	2510	1970	1720	1520	1510	1250	1040	890	770
115X72	90	1820	1690	2910	2730	2360	2020	1790	1580	1610	1330	1120	950	820
122X78	96	1710	1600	2760	2600	2250	1940	1820	1610	1660	1370	1160	990	850
138X88	108	1550	1450	2530	2390	2080	1800	1710	1640	1780	1480	1250	1070	930
154X97	120	1410	1330	2330	2220	1930	1680	1600	1540	1810	1570	1330	1140	990
169X106	132	1340	1270	2220	2110	1850	1610	1540	1480	1750	1600	1390	1200	1040

DATA:
1. Unsurfaced roadway.
2. Loads — AASHTO HS 20, two 16,000 lb dual-tired wheels, 4 ft. on centers, or alternate loading, four 12,000 lb. dual-tired wheels, 4 ft. on centers.

NOTES:
1. Interpolate for intermediate pipe sizes and/or fill heights.
2. Critical loads:
    a. For H = 0.5 and 1.0 ft., a single 16,000 lb. dual-tired wheel.
    b. For H = 1.5 through 4.0 ft., two 16,000 lb. dual-tired wheels, 4 ft. on centers.
    c. For H > 4.0 ft. alternate loading.
3. Truck live loads for H = 10.0 ft. or more are insignificant.

TABLE 49

PRESSURE COEFFICIENTS FOR A SINGLE LOAD

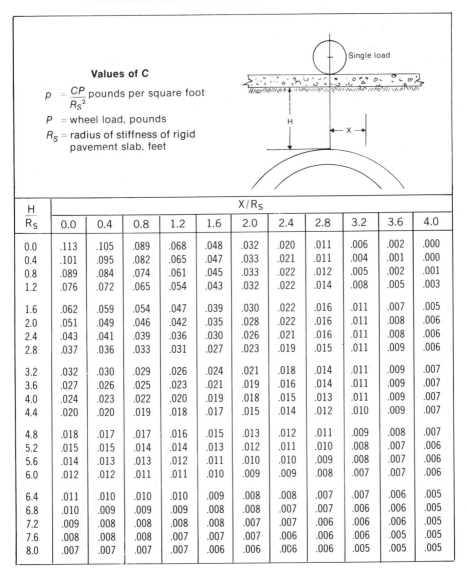

Values of C

$p = \dfrac{CP}{R_S^2}$ pounds per square foot

P = wheel load, pounds

R_S = radius of stiffness of rigid pavement slab, feet

$\dfrac{H}{R_S}$	X/R_S										
	0.0	0.4	0.8	1.2	1.6	2.0	2.4	2.8	3.2	3.6	4.0
0.0	.113	.105	.089	.068	.048	.032	.020	.011	.006	.002	.000
0.4	.101	.095	.082	.065	.047	.033	.021	.011	.004	.001	.000
0.8	.089	.084	.074	.061	.045	.033	.022	.012	.005	.002	.001
1.2	.076	.072	.065	.054	.043	.032	.022	.014	.008	.005	.003
1.6	.062	.059	.054	.047	.039	.030	.022	.016	.011	.007	.005
2.0	.051	.049	.046	.042	.035	.028	.022	.016	.011	.008	.006
2.4	.043	.041	.039	.036	.030	.026	.021	.016	.011	.008	.006
2.8	.037	.036	.033	.031	.027	.023	.019	.015	.011	.009	.006
3.2	.032	.030	.029	.026	.024	.021	.018	.014	.011	.009	.007
3.6	.027	.026	.025	.023	.021	.019	.016	.014	.011	.009	.007
4.0	.024	.023	.022	.020	.019	.018	.015	.013	.011	.009	.007
4.4	.020	.020	.019	.018	.017	.015	.014	.012	.010	.009	.007
4.8	.018	.017	.017	.016	.015	.013	.012	.011	.009	.008	.007
5.2	.015	.015	.014	.014	.013	.012	.011	.010	.008	.007	.006
5.6	.014	.013	.013	.012	.011	.010	.010	.009	.008	.007	.006
6.0	.012	.012	.011	.011	.010	.009	.009	.008	.007	.007	.006
6.4	.011	.010	.010	.010	.009	.008	.008	.007	.007	.006	.005
6.8	.010	.009	.009	.009	.008	.008	.007	.007	.006	.006	.005
7.2	.009	.008	.008	.008	.008	.007	.007	.006	.006	.006	.005
7.6	.008	.008	.008	.007	.007	.007	.006	.006	.006	.005	.005
8.0	.007	.007	.007	.007	.006	.006	.006	.006	.005	.005	.005

TABLE 50

PRESSURE COEFFICIENTS FOR TWO LOADS SPACED 0.8R$_S$ APART

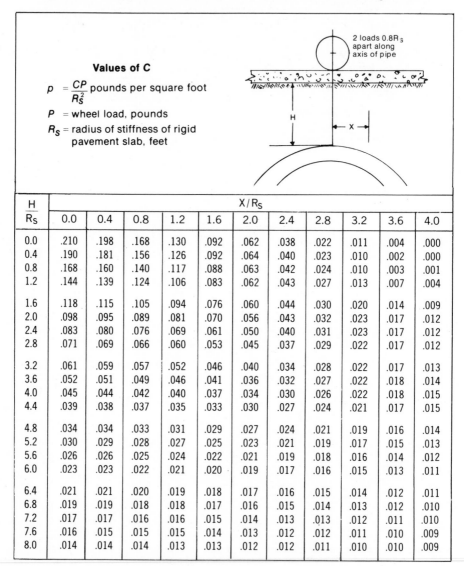

Values of C

$p = \dfrac{CP}{R_S^2}$ pounds per square foot

P = wheel load, pounds

R_S = radius of stiffness of rigid pavement slab, feet

2 loads 0.8R$_S$ apart along axis of pipe

$\dfrac{H}{R_S}$	X/R_S										
	0.0	0.4	0.8	1.2	1.6	2.0	2.4	2.8	3.2	3.6	4.0
0.0	.210	.198	.168	.130	.092	.062	.038	.022	.011	.004	.000
0.4	.190	.181	.156	.126	.092	.064	.040	.023	.010	.002	.000
0.8	.168	.160	.140	.117	.088	.063	.042	.024	.010	.003	.001
1.2	.144	.139	.124	.106	.083	.062	.043	.027	.013	.007	.004
1.6	.118	.115	.105	.094	.076	.060	.044	.030	.020	.014	.009
2.0	.098	.095	.089	.081	.070	.056	.043	.032	.023	.017	.012
2.4	.083	.080	.076	.069	.061	.050	.040	.031	.023	.017	.012
2.8	.071	.069	.066	.060	.053	.045	.037	.029	.022	.017	.012
3.2	.061	.059	.057	.052	.046	.040	.034	.028	.022	.017	.013
3.6	.052	.051	.049	.046	.041	.036	.032	.027	.022	.018	.014
4.0	.045	.044	.042	.040	.037	.034	.030	.026	.022	.018	.015
4.4	.039	.038	.037	.035	.033	.030	.027	.024	.021	.017	.015
4.8	.034	.034	.033	.031	.029	.027	.024	.021	.019	.016	.014
5.2	.030	.029	.028	.027	.025	.023	.021	.019	.017	.015	.013
5.6	.026	.026	.025	.024	.022	.021	.019	.018	.016	.014	.012
6.0	.023	.023	.022	.021	.020	.019	.017	.016	.015	.013	.011
6.4	.021	.021	.020	.019	.018	.017	.016	.015	.014	.012	.011
6.8	.019	.019	.018	.018	.017	.016	.015	.014	.013	.012	.010
7.2	.017	.017	.016	.016	.015	.014	.013	.013	.012	.011	.010
7.6	.016	.015	.015	.015	.014	.013	.012	.012	.011	.010	.009
8.0	.014	.014	.014	.013	.013	.012	.012	.011	.010	.010	.009

TABLE 51

PRESSURE COEFFICIENTS FOR TWO LOADS SPACED 1.6R$_S$ APART

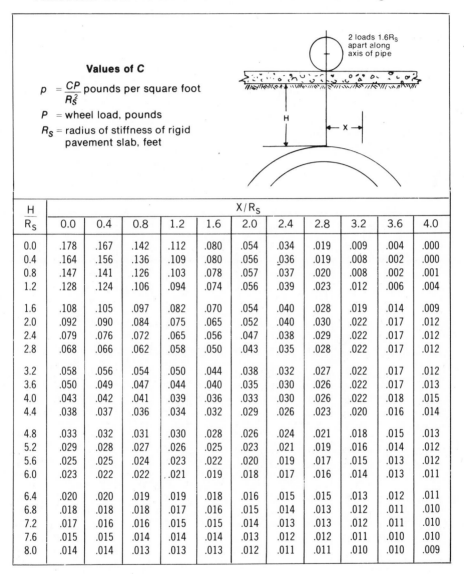

Values of C

$p = \dfrac{CP}{R_s^2}$ pounds per square foot

P = wheel load, pounds

R_S = radius of stiffness of rigid pavement slab, feet

$\dfrac{H}{R_S}$	X/R_S										
	0.0	0.4	0.8	1.2	1.6	2.0	2.4	2.8	3.2	3.6	4.0
0.0	.178	.167	.142	.112	.080	.054	.034	.019	.009	.004	.000
0.4	.164	.156	.136	.109	.080	.056	.036	.019	.008	.002	.000
0.8	.147	.141	.126	.103	.078	.057	.037	.020	.008	.002	.001
1.2	.128	.124	.106	.094	.074	.056	.039	.023	.012	.006	.004
1.6	.108	.105	.097	.082	.070	.054	.040	.028	.019	.014	.009
2.0	.092	.090	.084	.075	.065	.052	.040	.030	.022	.017	.012
2.4	.079	.076	.072	.065	.056	.047	.038	.029	.022	.017	.012
2.8	.068	.066	.062	.058	.050	.043	.035	.028	.022	.017	.012
3.2	.058	.056	.054	.050	.044	.038	.032	.027	.022	.017	.012
3.6	.050	.049	.047	.044	.040	.035	.030	.026	.022	.017	.013
4.0	.043	.042	.041	.039	.036	.033	.030	.026	.022	.018	.015
4.4	.038	.037	.036	.034	.032	.029	.026	.023	.020	.016	.014
4.8	.033	.032	.031	.030	.028	.026	.024	.021	.018	.015	.013
5.2	.029	.028	.027	.026	.025	.023	.021	.019	.016	.014	.012
5.6	.025	.025	.024	.023	.022	.020	.019	.017	.015	.013	.012
6.0	.023	.022	.022	.021	.019	.018	.017	.016	.014	.013	.011
6.4	.020	.020	.019	.019	.018	.016	.015	.015	.013	.012	.011
6.8	.018	.018	.018	.017	.016	.015	.014	.013	.012	.011	.010
7.2	.017	.016	.016	.015	.015	.014	.013	.013	.012	.011	.010
7.6	.015	.015	.014	.014	.014	.013	.012	.012	.011	.010	.010
8.0	.014	.014	.013	.013	.013	.012	.011	.011	.010	.010	.009

TABLE 52

PRESSURE COEFFICIENTS FOR TWO LOADS SPACED 2.4R$_S$ APART

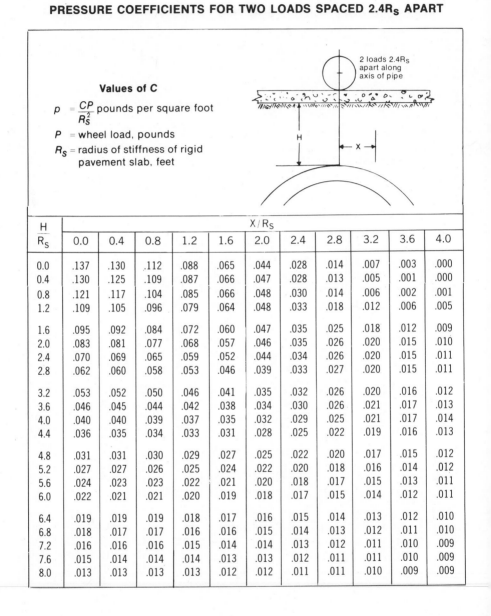

Values of C

$p = \dfrac{CP}{R_S^2}$ pounds per square foot

P = wheel load, pounds

R_S = radius of stiffness of rigid pavement slab, feet

2 loads 2.4R$_S$ apart along axis of pipe

$\dfrac{H}{R_S}$	X/R_S										
	0.0	0.4	0.8	1.2	1.6	2.0	2.4	2.8	3.2	3.6	4.0
0.0	.137	.130	.112	.088	.065	.044	.028	.014	.007	.003	.000
0.4	.130	.125	.109	.087	.066	.047	.028	.013	.005	.001	.000
0.8	.121	.117	.104	.085	.066	.048	.030	.014	.006	.002	.001
1.2	.109	.105	.096	.079	.064	.048	.033	.018	.012	.006	.005
1.6	.095	.092	.084	.072	.060	.047	.035	.025	.018	.012	.009
2.0	.083	.081	.077	.068	.057	.046	.035	.026	.020	.015	.010
2.4	.070	.069	.065	.059	.052	.044	.034	.026	.020	.015	.011
2.8	.062	.060	.058	.053	.046	.039	.033	.027	.020	.015	.011
3.2	.053	.052	.050	.046	.041	.035	.032	.026	.020	.016	.012
3.6	.046	.045	.044	.042	.038	.034	.030	.026	.021	.017	.013
4.0	.040	.040	.039	.037	.035	.032	.029	.025	.021	.017	.014
4.4	.036	.035	.034	.033	.031	.028	.025	.022	.019	.016	.013
4.8	.031	.031	.030	.029	.027	.025	.022	.020	.017	.015	.012
5.2	.027	.027	.026	.025	.024	.022	.020	.018	.016	.014	.012
5.6	.024	.023	.023	.022	.021	.020	.018	.017	.015	.013	.011
6.0	.022	.021	.021	.020	.019	.018	.017	.015	.014	.012	.011
6.4	.019	.019	.019	.018	.017	.016	.015	.014	.013	.012	.010
6.8	.018	.017	.017	.016	.016	.015	.014	.013	.012	.011	.010
7.2	.016	.016	.016	.015	.014	.014	.013	.012	.011	.010	.009
7.6	.015	.014	.014	.014	.013	.013	.012	.011	.011	.010	.009
8.0	.013	.013	.013	.013	.012	.012	.011	.011	.010	.009	.009

TABLE 53

PRESSURE COEFFICIENTS FOR TWO LOADS SPACED 3.2R$_S$ APART

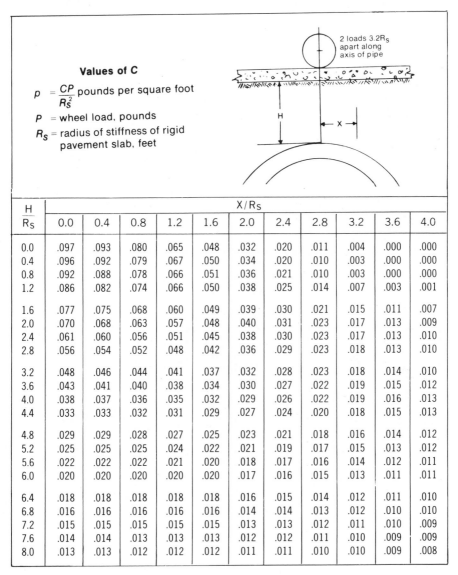

Values of C

$p = \dfrac{CP}{R_S^2}$ pounds per square foot

P = wheel load, pounds

R_S = radius of stiffness of rigid pavement slab, feet

2 loads 3.2R$_S$ apart along axis of pipe

$\dfrac{H}{R_S}$	X/R_S										
	0.0	0.4	0.8	1.2	1.6	2.0	2.4	2.8	3.2	3.6	4.0
0.0	.097	.093	.080	.065	.048	.032	.020	.011	.004	.000	.000
0.4	.096	.092	.079	.067	.050	.034	.020	.010	.003	.000	.000
0.8	.092	.088	.078	.066	.051	.036	.021	.010	.003	.000	.000
1.2	.086	.082	.074	.066	.050	.038	.025	.014	.007	.003	.001
1.6	.077	.075	.068	.060	.049	.039	.030	.021	.015	.011	.007
2.0	.070	.068	.063	.057	.048	.040	.031	.023	.017	.013	.009
2.4	.061	.060	.056	.051	.045	.038	.030	.023	.017	.013	.010
2.8	.056	.054	.052	.048	.042	.036	.029	.023	.018	.013	.010
3.2	.048	.046	.044	.041	.037	.032	.028	.023	.018	.014	.010
3.6	.043	.041	.040	.038	.034	.030	.027	.022	.019	.015	.012
4.0	.038	.037	.036	.035	.032	.029	.026	.022	.019	.016	.013
4.4	.033	.033	.032	.031	.029	.027	.024	.020	.018	.015	.013
4.8	.029	.029	.028	.027	.025	.023	.021	.018	.016	.014	.012
5.2	.025	.025	.025	.024	.022	.021	.019	.017	.015	.013	.012
5.6	.022	.022	.022	.021	.020	.018	.017	.016	.014	.012	.011
6.0	.020	.020	.020	.020	.020	.017	.016	.015	.013	.011	.011
6.4	.018	.018	.018	.018	.018	.016	.015	.014	.012	.011	.010
6.8	.016	.016	.016	.016	.016	.014	.014	.013	.012	.010	.010
7.2	.015	.015	.015	.015	.015	.013	.013	.012	.011	.010	.009
7.6	.014	.014	.013	.013	.013	.012	.012	.011	.010	.009	.009
8.0	.013	.013	.012	.012	.012	.011	.011	.010	.010	.009	.008

TABLE 54

PRESSURE COEFFICIENTS FOR A SINGLE LOAD
APPLIED ON SUBGRADE OR FLEXIBLE PAVEMENT

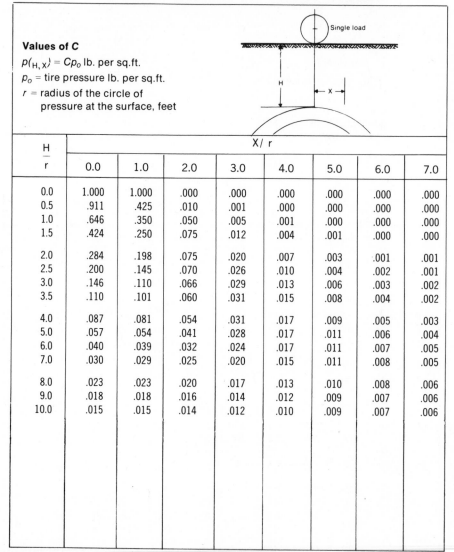

Values of C

$p_{(H, x)} = Cp_o$ lb. per sq.ft.

p_o = tire pressure lb. per sq.ft.

r = radius of the circle of
pressure at the surface, feet

$\dfrac{H}{r}$	X/ r							
	0.0	1.0	2.0	3.0	4.0	5.0	6.0	7.0
0.0	1.000	1.000	.000	.000	.000	.000	.000	.000
0.5	.911	.425	.010	.001	.000	.000	.000	.000
1.0	.646	.350	.050	.005	.001	.000	.000	.000
1.5	.424	.250	.075	.012	.004	.001	.000	.000
2.0	.284	.198	.075	.020	.007	.003	.001	.001
2.5	.200	.145	.070	.026	.010	.004	.002	.001
3.0	.146	.110	.066	.029	.013	.006	.003	.002
3.5	.110	.101	.060	.031	.015	.008	.004	.002
4.0	.087	.081	.054	.031	.017	.009	.005	.003
5.0	.057	.054	.041	.028	.017	.011	.006	.004
6.0	.040	.039	.032	.024	.017	.011	.007	.005
7.0	.030	.029	.025	.020	.015	.011	.008	.005
8.0	.023	.023	.020	.017	.013	.010	.008	.006
9.0	.018	.018	.016	.014	.012	.009	.007	.006
10.0	.015	.015	.014	.012	.010	.009	.007	.006

TABLE 55

VALUES OF RADIUS OF STIFFNESS R_S
IN INCHES FOR RIGID PAVEMENT SLAB

Slab h (in.)	Values of k								
	50	100	150	200	250	300	350	400	500
6	34.84	29.30	26.47	24.63	23.30	22.26	21.42	20.72	19.59
6.5	36.99	31.11	28.11	26.16	24.74	23.64	22.74	22.00	20.80
7	39.11	32.89	29.72	27.65	26.15	24.99	24.04	23.25	21.99
7.5	41.19	34.63	31.29	29.12	27.54	26.32	25.32	24.49	23.16
8	43.23	36.35	32.85	30.57	28.91	27.62	26.58	25.70	24.31
8.5	45.24	38.04	34.37	31.99	30.25	28.91	27.81	26.90	25.44
9	47.22	39.71	35.88	33.39	31.58	30.17	29.03	28.08	26.55
9.5	49.17	41.35	37.36	34.77	32.89	31.42	30.23	29.24	27.65
10	51.10	42.97	38.83	36.14	34.17	32.65	31.42	30.39	28.74
10.5	53.01	44.57	40.28	37.48	35.45	33.87	32.59	31.52	29.81
11	54.89	46.16	41.71	38.81	36.71	35.07	33.75	32.64	30.87
11.5	56.75	47.72	43.12	40.13	37.95	36.26	34.89	33.74	31.91
12	58.59	49.27	44.52	41.43	39.18	37.44	36.02	34.84	32.95
12.5	60.41	50.80	45.90	42.72	40.40	38.60	37.14	35.92	33.97
13	62.22	52.32	47.27	43.99	41.61	39.75	38.25	36.99	34.99
13.5	64.00	53.82	48.63	45.26	42.80	40.89	39.35	38.06	35.99
14	65.77	55.31	49.98	46.51	43.98	42.02	40.44	39.11	36.99
14.5	67.53	56.78	51.31	47.75	45.16	43.15	41.51	40.15	37.97
15	69.27	58.25	52.63	48.98	46.32	44.26	42.58	41.19	38.95
15.5	70.99	59.70	53.94	50.20	47.47	45.36	43.64	42.21	39.92
16	72.70	61.13	55.24	51.41	48.62	46.45	44.70	43.23	40.88
16.5	74.40	62.56	56.53	52.61	49.75	47.54	45.74	44.24	41.84
17	76.08	63.98	57.81	53.80	50.88	48.61	46.77	45.24	42.78
17.5	77.75	65.38	59.08	54.98	52.00	49.68	47.80	46.23	43.72
18	79.41	66.78	60.35	56.16	53.11	50.74	48.82	47.22	44.66
19	82.70	69.54	62.84	58.48	55.31	52.84	50.84	49.17	46.51
20	85.95	72.27	65.30	60.77	57.47	54.92	52.84	51.10	48.33
21	89.15	74.97	67.74	63.04	59.62	56.96	54.81	53.01	50.13
22	92.31	77.63	70.14	65.28	61.73	58.98	56.75	54.89	51.91
23	95.44	80.26	72.52	67.49	63.83	60.98	58.68	56.75	53.67
24	98.54	82.86	74.87	69.68	65.90	62.96	60.58	58.59	55.41

$$R_S = \sqrt[4]{\frac{Eh^3}{12(1-u^2)k}} \quad where \quad \begin{array}{l} E = 4{,}000{,}000 \text{ psi} \\ u = 0.15 \end{array} \quad therefore \quad R_s = 24.1652\sqrt[4]{\frac{h^3}{k}}$$

TABLE 56

AIRCRAFT LOADS ON CIRCULAR PIPE
POUNDS PER LINEAR FOOT

A — RIGID PAVEMENT
HEIGHT OF FILL H ABOVE TOP OF PIPE IN FEET — TO SURFACE OF SUBGRADE

PIPE SIZE D (in.)	1	2	3	4	5	6	7	8	9	10
12	1892	1769	1623	1453	1266	1130	998	877	773	686
15	2304	2154	1975	1779	1542	1377	1216	1069	942	835
18	2714	2537	2327	2084	1817	1622	1433	1260	1111	984
21	3122	2918	2677	2397	2091	1865	1649	1451	1279	1090
24	3527	3297	3025	2709	2363	2110	1863	1640	1447	1280
27	3932	3567	3371	2931	2635	2352	2076	1829	1615	1427
30	4333	4049	3714	3328	2905	2592	2288	2016	1782	1575
33	4732	4421	4055	3636	3175	2832	2498	2203	1949	1722
36	5128	4790	4395	3941	3442	3069	2707	2388	2115	1868
42	5912	5520	5065	4546	3973	3540	3120	2755	2446	2160
48	6682	6237	5725	5142	4496	4003	3528	3118	2774	2449
54	7437	6940	6371	5726	5010	4459	3930	3477	3097	2735
60	8174	7628	7004	6297	5512	4905	4325	3831	3415	3018
66	8892	8298	7621	6855	6002	5341	4714	4180	3729	3297
72	9588	8948	8220	7396	6480	5767	5095	4522	4037	3571
78	10260	9577	8799	7921	6943	6183	5468	4857	4338	3840
84	10900	10180	9358	8427	7392	6587	5831	5184	4632	4105
90	11520	10760	9894	8916	7827	6980	6186	5503	4920	4365
96	12100	11310	10410	9385	8246	7362	6531	5813	5199	4620
102	12660	11840	10900	9837	8615	7732	6867	6116	5471	4870
108	13190	12340	11370	10270	9042	8090	7193	6409	5735	5112
114	13540	12680	11690	10560	9312	8338	7419	6614	5919	5279
120	14010	13120	12110	10960	9676	8674	7727	6892	6170	5507
126	14450	13540	12510	11340	10020	8998	8024	7162	6413	5726
138	15230	14300	13240	12030	10680	9607	8583	7672	6877	6143
144	15580	14640	13560	12340	10980	9889	8842	7910	7095	6342

B — FLEXIBLE PAVEMENT
HEIGHT OF FILL H ABOVE TOP OF PIPE IN FEET — TO SURFACE OF PAVEMENT

PIPE SIZE D (in.)	1	2	3	4	5	6	7	8	9	10
12	14330	6566	4723	3187	2330	1871	1542	1294	1111	1008
15	16460	7783	5668	3853	2881	2276	1878	1576	1353	1229
18	18450	8900	6569	4502	3327	2677	2215	1855	1598	1448
21	20000	9911	7421	5132	3816	3076	2554	2133	1843	1668
24	21210	10820	8228	5745	4300	3474	2891	2410	2084	1887
27	22100	11620	8988	6341	4781	3872	3228	2687	2322	2105
30	22710	12320	9700	6918	5257	4271	3563	2963	2558	2323
33	23190	12940	10360	7479	5731	4673	3902	3241	2793	2541
36	23580	13480	10980	8029	6206	5079	4238	3516	3027	2757
42	24050	14360	12110	9093	7174	5896	4912	4070	3492	3186
48	24270	15060	13180	10180	8177	6717	5579	4616	3949	3609
54	24460	15760	14340	11360	9202	7510	6227	5154	4390	4024
60	24860	16760	15770	12640	10220	8268	6849	5678	4812	4426
66	26140	18390	17540	14040	11190	8997	7444	6178	5212	4803
72	29770	20810	19600	15440	12110	9693	8004	6647	5589	5149
78	36040	23830	21700	16750	12990	10350	8532	7086	5942	5469
84	42690	26610	23540	17880	13800	10980	9028	7495	6278	5778
90	46700	28660	24970	18860	14540	11550	9482	7862	6588	6069
96	48220	29890	25980	19690	15190	12070	9888	8182	6862	6325
102	48670	30550	26820	20430	15790	12550	10270	8489	7125	6570
108	48830	31030	27500	21060	16330	12980	10630	8784	7376	6803
114	48910	31290	27890	21370	16670	13270	10870	8988	7549	6963
120	48970	31550	28350	21930	17110	13650	11200	9264	7786	7176
126	49010	31750	28720	22340	17500	13990	11500	9528	8017	7377
138	49040	32010	29240	22960	18150	14570	12040	10000	8442	7741
144	49050	32100	29420	23190	18410	14820	12270	10200	8626	7905

180,000 Pound Dual-Tandem Gear Assembly. 190 Pounds per Square Inch Tire Pressure. 26-inch c/c Spacing Between Dual Tires. 66-inch c/c Spacing Between Fore and Aft Tandem Tires. k-300 Pounds per Cubic Foot. R_s -37.44 Inches. h-12 Inches. E-4,000,000 Pounds per Square Inch. u-0.15. Interpolate for intermediate fill heights.

TABLE 57

AIRCRAFT LOADS ON HORIZONTAL ELLIPTICAL PIPE
POUNDS PER LINEAR FOOT

RIGID PAVEMENT

HEIGHT OF FILL **H** MEASURED FROM TOP OF PIPE TO SURFACE OF SUBGRADE

A (R X S in inches)	HEIGHT OF FILL **H** ABOVE TOP OF PIPE IN FEET									
	1	2	3	4	5	6	7	8	9	10
14x23	3354	3136	2875	2576	2247	2006	1771	1560	1375	1216
19x30	4276	3996	3664	3285	2867	2559	2258	1989	1759	1554
22x34	4789	4474	4104	3679	3213	2866	2528	2229	1973	1742
24x38	5297	4949	4538	4072	3557	3172	2796	2467	2187	1931
27x42	5745	5365	4922	4417	3860	3440	3032	2677	2376	2097
29x45	6244	5829	5349	4803	4199	3739	3295	2911	2587	2284
32x49	6737	6288	5772	5185	4533	4036	3557	3144	2797	2469
34x53	7223	6741	6188	5561	4864	4329	3816	3375	3005	2654
38x60	8070	7530	6914	6217	5441	4842	4269	3781	3370	2978
43x68	8993	8392	7707	6933	6071	5403	4769	4229	3773	3336
48x76	9879	9221	8471	7623	6680	5947	5256	4667	4167	3687
53x83	10630	9925	9121	8212	7202	6415	5677	5045	4507	3992
58x91	11430	10680	9819	8847	7765	6925	6136	5458	4879	4328
63x98	12100	11310	10410	9385	8246	7362	6531	5813	5199	4620
68x106	12810	11980	11040	9963	8765	7836	6962	6200	5547	4940
72x113	13400	12540	11560	10450	9205	8240	7330	6532	5846	5213
77x121	14010	13120	12110	10690	9676	8674	7727	6892	6170	5507
82x128	14480	13570	12540	11360	10040	9021	8045	7181	6430	5741
87x136	14970	14040	12990	11790	10450	9396	8389	7495	6715	5997
92x143	15390	14450	13380	12160	10810	9730	8696	7875	6971	6229
97x151	15810	14860	13780	12550	11180	10080	9019	8072	7245	6481
106x166	16490	15520	14440	13210	11830	10690	9574	8586	7729	6931
116x180	17000	16030	14960	13740	12350	11180	10040	9092	8145	7323

FLEXIBLE PAVEMENT

HEIGHT OF FILL **H** MEASURED FROM TOP OF PIPE TO SURFACE OF PAVEMENT

B (R X S in inches)	HEIGHT OF FILL **H** ABOVE TOP OF PIPE IN FEET									
	1	2	3	4	5	6	7	8	9	10
14x23	20730	10440	7888	5484	4093	3304	2747	2292	1981	1793
19x30	22630	12220	9601	6832	5189	4214	3515	2924	2524	2292
22x34	23250	13020	10450	7558	5798	4731	3950	3280	2826	2572
24x38	23710	13690	11230	8260	6412	5254	4382	3635	3127	2850
27x42	23980	14190	11880	8863	6965	5721	4768	3952	3393	3095
29x45	24150	14670	12570	9553	7600	6249	5200	4305	3689	3369
32x49	24290	15110	13260	10260	8250	6775	5626	4655	3981	3639
34x53	24400	15550	13990	11010	8909	7287	6044	5001	4266	3907
38x60	24760	16590	15540	12450	10070	8162	6762	5604	4753	4369
43x68	26500	18690	17820	14240	11320	9098	7525	6247	5267	4854
48x76	32140	22040	20510	16020	12490	9981	8234	6839	5742	5288
53x83	40160	25490	22800	17420	13460	10710	8819	7324	6136	5647
58x91	46290	28420	24790	18730	14440	11470	9422	7815	6548	6031
63x98	48220	29890	25980	19690	15190	12070	9888	8182	6862	6325
68x106	48720	30700	27030	20620	15950	13160	10380	8575	7198	6638
72x113	48880	31190	27740	21300	16540	13650	10780	8907	7480	6900
77x121	48970	31550	28350	21930	17110	14010	11200	9264	7786	7176
82x128	49010	31760	28740	22360	17520	14370	11520	9547	8033	7391
87x136	49040	31930	29080	22760	17940	14680	11860	9843	8299	7617
92x143	49040	32050	29320	23060	18270	14990	12140	10090	8523	7813
97x151	49050	32150	29530	23320	18580	15180	12420	10330	8748	8014
106x166	49050	32270	29800	23700	19010	15480	12900	10740	9113	8338
116x180	49050	32350	29970	23930	19270	15770	13230	11040	9361	8574

PIPE SIZE—INSIDE RISE X SPAN **R X S** IN INCHES

180,000 Pound Dual-Tandem Gear Assembly. 190 Pounds per Square Inch Tire Pressure. 26-inch c/c Spacing Between Dual Tires. 66-inch c/c Spacing Between Fore and Aft Tandem Tires. k-300 Pounds per Cubic Foot. R_S -37.44 Inches. h-12 Inches. E-4,000,000 Pounds per Square Inch. u-0.15. Interpolate for intermediate fill heights.

TABLE 58

AIRCRAFT LOADS ON ARCH PIPE

POUNDS PER LINEAR FOOT

RIGID PAVEMENT

A — HEIGHT OF FILL MEASURED FROM TOP OF PIPE TO SURFACE OF SUBGRADE

PIPE SIZE — INSIDE RISE × SPAN **R** × **S** IN INCHES	HEIGHT OF FILL **H** ABOVE TOP OF PIPE IN FEET									
	1	2	3	4	5	6	7	8	9	10
11×18	2656	2483	2277	2039	1778	1588	1403	1234	1087	962
13½×22	3180	2973	2727	2442	2130	1908	1679	1478	1303	1153
15½×26	3701	3460	3173	2843	2481	2214	1955	1722	1519	1343
18×28½	4047	3782	3469	3109	2712	2421	2137	1882	1663	1470
22½×36¼	5043	4698	4322	3876	3385	3019	2662	2348	2104	1836
26⅝×43¾	5954	5559	5136	4610	4030	3590	3164	2794	2482	2191
31 5/16×51⅛	6914	6452	5923	5321	4653	4142	3650	3228	2872	2536
36×58½	7808	7286	6689	6014	5262	4683	4122	3654	3257	2878
40×65	8587	8013	7358	6617	5794	5155	4548	4031	3595	3178
45×73	9490	8857	8135	7320	6412	5707	5041	4474	3993	3532
54×88	11080	10350	9513	8569	7518	6701	5934	5276	4715	4180
62×102	12420	11620	10690	9645	8479	7575	6724	5987	5355	4764
72×115	13470	12610	11620	10510	9258	8289	7374	6573	5882	5246
77¼×122	14010	13120	12110	10960	9676	8674	7727	6892	6170	5507
87⅛×138	15080	14150	13090	11880	10540	9481	8468	7567	6780	6056
96⅞×154	15940	14990	13910	12680	11300	10190	9122	8167	7334	6562
106½×168¾	16440	15480	14390	13170	11780	10640	9535	8551	7695	6899

FLEXIBLE PAVEMENT

B — HEIGHT OF FILL MEASURED FROM TOP OF PIPE TO SURFACE OF PAVEMENT

PIPE SIZE — INSIDE RISE × SPAN **R** × **S** IN INCHES	HEIGHT OF FILL **H** ABOVE TOP OF PIPE IN FEET									
	1	2	3	4	5	6	7	8	9	10
11×18	18190	8745	6442	4410	3257	2620	2167	1815	1563	1417
13½×22	20200	10050	7540	5220	3886	3133	2602	2173	1878	1699
15½×26	21640	11180	8559	6002	4507	3645	3036	2530	2186	1980
18×28½	22280	11820	9197	6508	4917	3986	3323	2764	2390	2167
22½×36¼	23500	13380	10850	7912	6104	4991	4166	3457	2977	2710
26⅝×43¾	24080	14440	12230	9207	7280	5984	4984	4128	3542	3209
31 5/16×51⅛	24320	15260	13510	10530	8487	6962	5778	4781	4084	3736
36×58½	24580	16200	15010	11980	9712	7894	6542	5418	4604	4227
40×65	25410	17600	16740	13430	10780	8688	7193	5967	5043	4645
45×73	29090	20420	19300	15250	11980	9596	7926	6582	5537	5102
54×88	44100	27280	23990	18180	14020	11150	9163	7606	6371	5865
62×102	48570	30300	26480	20130	15540	12340	10110	8359	7014	6466
72×115	48890	31240	27810	21370	16600	13220	10830	8948	7515	6931
77¼×122	48970	31550	28350	21930	17110	13650	11200	9264	7786	7176
87⅛×138	49040	31960	29140	22840	18020	14450	11930	9908	8357	7667
96⅞×154	49050	32170	29590	23400	18670	15090	12510	10410	8818	8077
106½×168¾	49050	32270	29790	23690	18990	15450	12870	10710	9090	8317

180,000 Pound Dual-Tandem Gear Assembly. 190 Pounds per Square Inch Tire Pressure. 26-inch c/c Spacing Between Dual Tires. 66-inch c/c Spacing Between Fore and Aft Tandem Tires. k-300 Pounds per Cubic Foot. R_s-37.44 Inches. h-12 Inches. E-4,000,000 Pounds per Square Inch. u-0.15. Interpolate for intermediate fill heights.

TABLE 59

RAILROAD LOADS ON CIRCULAR PIPE
POUNDS PER LINEAR FOOT

PIPE SIZE—INSIDE DIAMETER **D** IN INCHES

HEIGHT OF FILL **H** ABOVE TOP OF PIPE IN FEET

PIPE SIZE D (in.)	1	2	3	4	5	6	7	8	9	10	12	14	16	18	20	25	30
12	3630	3400	3060	2700	2340	2010	1720	1480	1260	1090	880	720	590	490	420	290	210
15	4430	4140	3720	3300	2860	2450	2100	1800	1540	1330	1070	880	720	600	510	350	250
18	5220	4890	4390	3890	3370	2890	2480	2130	1820	1570	1260	1030	840	710	610	410	300
21	6020	5630	5060	4470	3880	3330	2850	2450	2100	1810	1450	1190	970	810	700	480	340
24	6810	6370	5730	5070	4390	3770	3230	2770	2370	2050	1640	1350	1100	920	790	540	390
27	7610	7120	6400	5660	4900	4210	3610	3100	2650	2290	1830	1500	1230	1030	890	600	430
30	8400	7860	7070	6250	5420	4640	3980	3420	2930	2520	2020	1660	1360	1140	980	670	480
33	9200	8610	7740	6840	5930	5080	4360	3740	3200	2760	2220	1820	1480	1240	1070	730	520
36	10000	9350	8400	7430	6450	5520	4740	4070	3480	3000	2410	1980	1610	1350	1160	790	570
42	11600	10800	9740	8610	7470	6400	5500	4710	4030	3480	2790	2290	1870	1570	1350	920	660
48	13200	12300	11100	9790	8500	7280	6250	5360	4590	3960	3170	2600	2130	1780	1530	1040	750
54	14800	13800	12400	11000	9520	8160	7000	6000	5140	4440	3560	2920	2380	2000	1720	1160	840
60	16400	15300	13800	12200	10500	9040	7750	6650	5690	4910	3940	3230	2640	2210	1900	1290	930
66	17900	16800	15100	13300	11600	9920	8510	7300	6250	5390	4320	3550	2900	2430	2090	1420	1020
72	19500	18300	16400	14500	12600	10800	9260	7950	6800	5870	4710	3860	3150	2640	2270	1540	1110
78	21100	19800	17800	15700	13600	11700	10000	8590	7350	6350	5090	4180	3410	2860	2460	1670	1200
84	22700	21200	19100	16900	14600	12600	10800	9240	7900	6820	5470	4490	3670	3070	2640	1800	1290
90	24300	22700	20400	18100	15700	13400	11500	9890	8460	7300	5860	4800	3920	3290	2820	1920	1380
96	25900	24200	21800	19300	16700	14300	12300	10500	9010	7780	6240	5120	4180	3500	3010	2050	1470
102	27500	25700	23100	20400	17700	15200	13000	11200	9560	8250	6620	5430	4440	3720	3200	2180	1560
108	29100	27200	24500	21600	18800	16100	13800	11800	10100	8740	7010	5750	4690	3940	3380	2300	1650
114	30200	28300	25400	22500	19500	16700	14300	12300	10500	9070	7280	5970	4880	4090	3510	2390	1710
120	31800	29800	26800	23700	20500	17600	15100	12900	11100	9560	7660	6290	5130	4300	3700	2520	1800
126	33400	31200	28100	24800	21500	18500	15800	13600	11600	10000	8040	6600	5390	4520	3880	2640	1890
132	35000	32700	29400	26000	22500	19300	16600	14200	12200	10500	8420	6910	5650	4730	4060	2770	1980
138	36600	34200	30800	27200	23600	20200	17300	14900	12700	11000	8810	7230	5900	4950	4250	2890	2070
144	38200	35700	32100	28400	24600	21100	18100	15500	13300	11500	9190	7540	6160	5160	4430	3020	2160

PIPE SIZE—INSIDE DIAMETER **D** IN INCHES

Cooper E80 design loading consisting of four 80,000-pound axles spaced 5 feet c/c. Locomotive load assumed uniformly distributed over an area 8 feet x 20 feet. Weight of track structure assumed to be 200 pounds per linear foot. Impact included. Height of fill measured from top of pipe to bottom of ties. Interpolate for intermediate pipe sizes and/or fill heights.

TABLE 60

RAILROAD LOADS ON HORIZONTAL ELLIPTICAL PIPE
POUNDS PER LINEAR FOOT

PIPE SIZE — INSIDE RISE X SPAN **R** X **S** IN INCHES

HEIGHT OF FILL **H** ABOVE TOP OF PIPE

PIPE SIZE R X S	1	2	3	4	5	6	7	8	9	10	12	14	16	18	20	25	30
14X23	6470	6060	5440	4810	4170	3580	3070	2630	2250	1940	1560	1280	1040	880	760	510	370
19X30	8290	7760	6970	6170	5350	4580	3930	3370	2890	2490	2000	1640	1340	1120	960	660	470
22X34	9310	8710	7830	6930	6010	5150	4420	3790	3240	2800	2240	1840	1500	1260	1080	740	530
24X38	10300	9670	8690	7690	6670	5710	4900	4200	3600	3110	2490	2040	1670	1400	1200	820	590
27X42	11200	10500	9460	8360	7250	6220	5330	4570	3910	3380	2710	2220	1820	1520	1310	890	640
29X45	12300	11500	10300	9120	7910	6780	5820	4910	4270	3680	3000	2420	1980	1660	1420	970	700
32X49	13300	12400	11200	9880	8570	7340	6300	5410	4630	3990	3200	2630	2140	1800	1540	1050	750
34X53	14300	13400	12000	10600	9230	7910	6780	5820	4980	4300	3450	2830	2310	1940	1660	1130	810
38X60	16100	15100	13600	12000	10400	8910	7650	6560	5610	4850	3890	3190	2600	2180	1870	1280	910
43X68	18200	17000	15300	13500	11700	10000	8620	7390	6330	5460	4380	3590	2930	2460	2110	1440	1030
48X76	20200	18900	17000	15000	13000	11200	9580	8220	7040	6070	4870	4000	3260	2740	2350	1600	1150
53X83	22000	20600	18500	16400	14200	12200	10400	8960	7670	6620	5310	4360	3560	2980	2560	1740	1250
58X91	24100	22500	20200	17900	15500	13300	11400	9790	8380	7230	5800	4760	3890	3260	2800	1900	1360
63X98	25900	24200	21800	19300	16700	14300	12300	10500	9010	7780	6240	5120	4180	3500	3010	2050	1470
68X106	27900	26100	23500	20800	18000	15500	13300	11400	9730	8380	6730	5520	4510	3780	3250	2210	1580
72X113	29800	27800	25000	22100	19200	16500	14100	12100	10400	8940	7170	5880	4800	4030	3460	2350	1690
77X121	31800	29800	26800	23700	20500	17600	15100	12900	11100	9560	7660	6290	5130	4300	3700	2520	1800
82X128	33500	31300	28200	24900	21600	18500	15900	13600	11700	10100	8070	6620	5410	4530	3890	2650	1900
87X136	35400	33200	29800	26300	22900	19600	16800	14400	12300	10600	8540	7010	5720	4800	4120	2800	2010
92X143	37300	34900	31300	27700	24000	20600	17700	15200	13000	11200	8980	7370	6010	5040	4330	2950	2110
97X151	39300	36800	33100	29200	25300	21700	18600	16000	13700	11800	9470	7770	6340	5320	4570	3110	2230
106X166	43100	40400	36300	32100	27800	23800	20500	17600	15000	12300	10400	8530	6970	5840	5010	3410	2440
116X180	46800	43800	39400	34800	30200	25900	22200	19000	16300	14100	11300	9250	7550	6330	5440	3700	2640

PIPE SIZE — INSIDE RISE X SPAN **R** X **S** IN INCHES

Cooper E80 design loading consisting of four 80,000 pound axles spaced 5 feet c/c. Locomotive load assumed uniformly distributed over an area 8 feet x 20 feet. Weight of track structure assumed to be 200 pounds per linear foot. Impact included. Height of fill measured from top of pipe to bottom of ties. Interpolate for intermediate pipe sizes and/or fill heights.

TABLE 61

RAILROAD LOADS ON ARCH PIPE
POUNDS PER LINEAR FOOT

PIPE SIZE — INSIDE RISE X SPAN **R** X **S** IN INCHES

HEIGHT OF FILL H ABOVE TOP OF PIPE IN FEET

PIPE SIZE R X S	30	25	20	18	16	14	12	10	9	8	7	6	5	4	3	2	1
11X18	290	400	600	700	820	1010	1230	1540	1780	2080	2420	2820	3300	3800	4300	4780	5110
13X22	350	480	710	830	990	1210	1480	1840	2140	2500	2910	3390	3960	4560	5160	5740	6130
15X26	410	570	830	970	1160	1410	1720	2150	2490	2910	3390	3960	4610	5320	6020	6690	7150
18X29	440	620	910	1060	1260	1550	1890	2350	2730	3190	3720	4330	5050	5830	6590	7330	7840
22X36	560	780	1140	1330	1590	1940	2370	2950	3420	4000	4660	5430	6340	7300	8260	9190	9820
27X44	670	930	1370	1590	1900	2320	2830	3530	4090	4780	5570	6500	7580	8740	9880	11000	11800
31X51	770	1080	1590	1850	2200	2700	3290	4100	4750	5560	6470	7550	8810	10200	11500	12800	13700
36X58	880	1230	1810	2110	2510	3070	3750	4670	5420	6330	7380	8600	10000	11600	13100	14600	15600
40X65	980	1370	2010	2340	2790	3410	4160	5190	6010	7020	8180	9540	11100	12800	14500	16100	17300
45X73	1100	1520	2240	2610	3120	3820	4650	5800	6720	7850	9150	10700	12400	14400	16200	18100	19300
54X88	1310	1830	2700	3140	3740	4590	5590	6970	8080	9440	11000	12800	15000	17200	19500	21700	23200
62X102	1520	2120	3110	3630	4330	5300	6460	8050	9330	10900	12700	14800	17300	19900	22500	25100	26800
72X115	1700	2370	3480	4060	4840	5930	7220	9010	10400	12200	14200	16600	19300	22300	25200	28000	30000
78X122	1800	2520	3700	4300	5130	6290	7660	9560	11100	12900	15100	17600	20500	23700	26800	29800	31800
88X138	2030	2840	4170	4860	5800	7100	8650	10800	12500	14600	17000	19800	23100	26700	30200	33600	35900
97X154	2270	3160	4650	5410	6450	7910	9630	12000	13900	16300	19000	22100	25800	29700	33600	37400	40000
106X169	2430	3390	4980	5800	6920	8480	10300	12900	14900	17400	20300	23700	27600	31900	36100	40100	42900

Cooper E80 design loading consisting of four 80,000 pound axles spaced 5 feet c/c. Locomotive load assumed uniformly distributed over an area 8 feet x 20 feet. Weight of track structure assumed to be 200 pounds per linear foot. Impact included. Height of fill measured from top of pipe to bottom of ties. Interpolate for intermediate pipe sizes and/or fill heights.

PIPE SIZE — INSIDE RISE X SPAN R X S IN INCHES

TABLE 62.1

BEDDING FACTORS FOR CIRCULAR PIPE
POSITIVE PROJECTING EMBANKMENT INSTALLATIONS

$\dfrac{H}{B_c}$	CLASS A BEDDING					CLASS B BEDDING				
p = 0.9										
	$r_{sd}\,p = 0$	0.1	0.3	0.5	1.0	$r_{sd}\,p = 0$	0.1	0.3	0.5	1.0
0.5	11.26	8.87	8.87	8.87	8.87	4.19	3.82	3.81	3.81	3.81
1.0	6.61	5.37	5.37	5.37	5.37	3.34	3.00	3.00	3.00	3.00
1.5	5.81	4.83	4.47	4.47	4.47	3.13	2.83	2.71	2.71	2.71
2.0	5.48	4.49	4.35	4.19	4.19	3.03	2.77	2.67	2.61	2.61
3.0	5.18	4.50	4.21	4.06	3.88	2.94	2.72	2.62	2.56	2.50
5.0	4.97	4.37	4.11	3.97	3.81	2.88	2.67	2.58	2.52	2.46
10.0	4.82	4.28	4.04	3.90	3.76	2.83	2.64	2.55	2.50	2.44
15.0	4.77	4.25	4.01	3.88	3.74	2.81	2.63	2.54	2.49	2.43
p = 0.7										
	$r_{sd}\,p = 0$	0.1	0.3	0.5	1.0	$r_{sd}\,p = 0$	0.1	0.3	0.5	1.0
0.5	7.52	6.54	6.54	6.54	6.54	3.00	2.88	2.88	2.87	2.87
1.0	5.61	4.79	4.79	4.79	4.79	2.73	2.58	2.58	2.58	2.58
1.5	5.17	4.46	4.19	4.19	4.19	2.65	2.50	2.44	2.44	2.44
2.0	4.98	4.35	4.11	3.99	3.98	2.61	2.48	2.42	2.39	2.39
3.0	4.80	4.25	4.02	3.90	3.75	2.58	2.45	2.40	2.36	2.32
5.0	4.66	4.18	3.95	3.84	3.70	2.55	2.43	2.38	2.35	2.31
10.0	4.57	4.12	3.91	3.79	3.66	2.53	2.42	2.36	2.33	2.30
15.0	4.53	4.09	3.89	3.77	3.65	2.52	2.41	2.36	2.33	2.29
p = 0.5										
	$r_{sd}\,p = 0$	0.1	0.3	0.5	1.0	$r_{sd}\,p = 0$	0.1	0.3	0.5	1.0
0.5	4.84	4.54	4.55	4.55	4.55	2.37	2.33	2.33	2.33	2.33
1.0	4.33	3.97	3.97	3.97	3.97	2.31	2.25	2.25	2.25	2.25
1.5	4.18	3.83	3.68	3.68	3.68	2.28	2.23	2.20	2.20	2.20
2.0	4.11	3.79	3.65	3.58	3.58	2.27	2.22	2.20	2.19	2.18
3.0	4.04	3.75	3.62	3.54	3.45	2.26	2.22	2.19	2.18	2.16
5.0	3.99	3.72	3.58	3.51	3.43	2.26	2.21	2.19	2.17	2.16
10.0	3.95	3.69	3.56	3.49	3.41	2.25	2.20	2.18	2.17	2.15
15.0	3.94	3.68	3.56	3.48	3.40	2.25	2.20	2.18	2.17	2.15
p = 0.3										
	$r_{sd}\,p = 0$	0.1	0.3	0.5	1.0	$r_{sd}\,p = 0$	0.1	0.3	0.5	1.0
0.5	3.49	3.41	3.41	3.41	3.41	2.11	2.10	2.10	2.10	2.10
1.0	3.40	3.28	3.28	3.28	3.28	2.10	2.08	2.08	2.08	2.08
1.5	3.37	3.25	3.20	3.20	3.20	2.09	2.08	2.07	2.07	2.07
2.0	3.35	3.24	3.20	3.16	3.16	2.09	2.08	2.07	2.07	2.07
3.0	3.34	3.23	3.18	3.15	3.11	2.09	2.08	2.07	2.07	2.06
5.0	3.33	3.22	3.17	3.14	3.11	2.09	2.08	2.07	2.07	2.06
10.0	3.32	3.22	3.17	3.14	3.10	2.09	2.08	2.07	2.07	2.06
15.0	3.32	3.22	3.17	3.14	3.10	2.09	2.08	2.07	2.07	2.06
ZERO PROJECTING										
	2.83					2.02				

TABLE 62.2

BEDDING FACTORS FOR CIRCULAR PIPE
POSITIVE PROJECTING EMBANKMENT INSTALLATIONS

$\dfrac{H}{B_c}$	CLASS C BEDDING					CLASS D BEDDING				
p = 0.9										
	$r_{sd}\,p = 0$	0.1	0.3	0.5	1.0	$r_{sd}\,p = 0$	0.1	0.3	0.5	1.0
0.5	3.01	2.82	2.82	2.82	2.82	1.51	1.46	1.46	1.46	1.46
1.0	2.55	2.35	2.35	2.35	2.35	1.39	1.33	1.33	1.33	1.33
1.5	2.42	2.26	2.16	2.16	2.16	1.35	1.29	1.27	1.27	1.27
2.0	2.37	2.20	2.14	2.10	2.10	1.33	1.28	1.26	1.24	1.24
3.0	2.31	2.17	2.10	2.07	2.02	1.31	1.27	1.24	1.23	1.22
5.0	2.27	2.14	2.08	2.04	2.00	1.30	1.26	1.24	1.22	1.21
10.0	2.24	2.12	2.06	2.03	1.99	1.29	1.25	1.23	1.22	1.20
15.0	2.23	2.10	2.05	2.02	1.98	1.29	1.25	1.23	1.21	1.20
p = 0.7										
	$r_{sd}\,p = 0$	0.1	0.3	0.5	1.0	$r_{sd}\,p = 0$	0.1	0.3	0.5	1.0
0.5	2.35	2.27	2.27	2.27	2.27	1.33	1.30	1.30	1.30	1.30
1.0	2.18	2.08	2.08	2.08	2.08	1.27	1.24	1.24	1.24	1.24
1.5	2.13	2.03	1.99	1.99	1.99	1.25	1.22	1.20	1.20	1.20
2.0	2.10	2.01	1.97	1.95	1.95	1.24	1.21	1.20	1.19	1.19
3.0	2.08	2.00	1.96	1.94	1.91	1.24	1.21	1.19	1.18	1.17
5.0	2.06	1.98	1.95	1.93	1.90	1.23	1.20	1.19	1.18	1.17
10.0	2.05	1.98	1.94	1.92	1.89	1.22	1.20	1.18	1.18	1.17
15.0	2.04	1.97	1.94	1.91	1.89	1.22	1.20	1.18	1.18	1.17
p = 0.5										
	$r_{sd}\,p = 0$	0.1	0.3	0.5	1.0	$r_{sd}\,p = 0$	0.1	0.3	0.5	1.0
0.5	1.94	1.92	1.92	1.92	1.92	1.19	1.18	1.18	1.18	1.18
1.0	1.90	1.86	1.86	1.86	1.86	1.17	1.16	1.16	1.16	1.16
1.5	1.88	1.85	1.83	1.83	1.83	1.16	1.15	1.14	1.14	1.14
2.0	1.88	1.84	1.83	1.82	1.82	1.16	1.15	1.14	1.14	1.14
3.0	1.87	1.84	1.82	1.81	1.80	1.16	1.15	1.14	1.14	1.13
5.0	1.86	1.83	1.82	1.81	1.80	1.16	1.14	1.14	1.13	1.13
10.0	1.86	1.83	1.81	1.80	1.79	1.15	1.14	1.14	1.13	1.13
15.0	1.86	1.83	1.81	1.80	1.79	1.15	1.14	1.14	1.13	1.13
p = 0.3										
	$r_{sd}\,p = 0$	0.1	0.3	0.5	1.0	$r_{sd}\,p = 0$	0.1	0.3	0.5	1.0
0.5	1.76	1.76	1.76	1.76	1.76	1.12	1.11	1.11	1.11	1.11
1.0	1.76	1.75	1.75	1.75	1.75	1.11	1.11	1.11	1.11	1.11
1.5	1.75	1.74	1.74	1.74	1.74	1.11	1.11	1.11	1.11	1.11
2.0	1.75	1.74	1.74	1.74	1.74	1.11	1.11	1.11	1.11	1.11
3.0	1.75	1.74	1.74	1.73	1.73	1.11	1.11	1.11	1.11	1.10
5.0	1.75	1.74	1.74	1.73	1.73	1.11	1.11	1.11	1.11	1.10
10.0	1.75	1.74	1.74	1.73	1.73	1.11	1.11	1.11	1.10	1.10
15.0	1.75	1.74	1.74	1.73	1.73	1.11	1.11	1.11	1.10	1.10
ZERO PROJECTING										
	1.70					1.10				

TABLE 63

BEDDING FACTORS FOR VERTICAL ELLIPTICAL PIPE
POSITIVE PROJECTING EMBANKMENT INSTALLATIONS

$\dfrac{H}{B_c}$	CLASS B BEDDING					CLASS C BEDDING					$\dfrac{H}{B_c}$
	P = 0.9										
	$r_{sd}p = 0$	0.1	0.3	0.5	1.0	$r_{sd}p = 0$	0.1	0.3	0.5	1.0	
0.5	–	–	–	–	–	–	–	–	–	–	0.5
1.0	–	6.57	6.57	6.57	6.57	–	4.01	4.01	4.01	4.01	1.0
1.5	–	5.45	5.03	4.70	4.70	5.78	3.57	3.38	3.23	3.23	1.5
2.0	9.20	5.00	4.15	3.88	3.88	4.87	3.36	2.96	2.82	2.82	2.0
3.0	7.08	4.44	3.89	3.54	3.26	4.20	3.10	2.82	2.64	2.48	3.0
5.0	6.00	4.15	3.61	3.37	3.13	3.79	2.96	2.68	2.54	2.40	5.0
10.0	5.36	3.87	3.46	3.27	3.03	3.52	2.82	2.59	2.48	2.34	10.0
15.0	5.18	3.86	3.52	3.21	3.00	3.45	2.81	2.57	2.45	2.32	15.0
	P = 0.7										
	$r_{sd}p = 0$	0.1	0.3	0.5	1.0	$r_{sd}p = 0$	0.1	0.3	0.5	1.0	
0.5	–	–	–	–	–	5.40	4.48	4.48	4.48	4.48	0.5
1.0	5.18	3.54	3.54	3.54	3.54	3.45	2.64	2.64	2.64	2.64	1.0
1.5	4.38	3.36	3.25	3.16	3.16	3.08	2.54	2.47	2.42	.2.42	1.5
2.0	4.07	3.27	3.01	2.91	2.91	2.92	2.48	2.33	2.27	2.27	2.0
3.0	3.80	3.13	2.94	2.80	2.68	2.78	2.40	2.29	2.20	2.13	3.0
5.0	3.61	3.05	2.85	2.74	2.63	2.67	2.36	2.23	2.17	2.10	5.0
10.0	3.48	2.97	2.80	2.71	2.59	2.60	2.31	2.22	2.14	2.07	10.0
15.0	3.43	2.95	2.78	2.68	2.58	2.58	2.30	2.21	2.13	2.06	15.0
	P = 0.5										
	$r_{sd}p = 0$	0.1	0.3	0.5	1.0	$r_{sd}p = 0$	0.1	0.3	0.5	1.0	
0.5	3.10	2.94	2.94	2.94	2.94	2.38	2.29	2.29	2.29	2.29	0.5
1.0	2.77	2.48	2.48	2.48	2.48	2.18	2.00	2.00	2.00	2.00	1.0
1.5	2.67	2.46	2.43	2.40	2.40	2.12	1.98	1.97	1.95	1.95	1.5
2.0	2.63	2.44	2.37	2.34	2.34	2.10	1.97	1.93	1.91	1.91	2.0
3.0	2.59	2.41	2.36	2.31	2.27	2.07	1.96	1.92	1.89	1.86	3.0
5.0	2.55	2.40	2.33	2.30	2.26	2.04	1.95	1.90	1.88	1.85	5.0
10.0	2.53	2.38	2.32	2.29	2.25	2.03	1.94	1.90	1.87	1.84	10.0
15.0	2.52	2.38	2.31	2.28	2.24	2.02	1.93	1.90	1.87	1.84	15.0
	P = 0.3										
	$r_{sd}p = 0$	0.1	0.3	0.5	1.0	$r_{sd}p = 0$	0.1	0.3	0.5	1.0	
0.5	2.18	2.17	2.16	2.16	2.16	1.80	1.79	1.79	1.79	1.79	0.5
1.0	2.15	2.10	2.10	2.10	2.10	1.78	1.74	1.74	1.74	1.74	1.0
1.5	2.14	2.10	2.09	2.08	2.08	1.77	1.74	1.74	1.73	1.73	1.5
2.0	2.13	2.10	2.08	2.07	2.07	1.77	1.74	1.73	1.73	1.73	2.0
3.0	2.13	2.09	2.08	2.07	2.06	1.76	1.74	1.73	1.72	1.72	3.0
5.0	2.12	2.09	2.08	2.07	2.06	1.76	1.74	1.73	1.72	1.71	5.0
10.0	2.12	2.09	2.08	2.06	2.05	1.76	1.74	1.73	1.72	1.71	10.0
15.0	2.12	2.09	2.07	2.06	2.05	1.76	1.74	1.73	1.72	1.71	15.0
	ZERO PROJECTING										
	1.98					1.66					

TABLE 64

BEDDING FACTORS FOR HORIZONTAL ELLIPTICAL PIPE
POSITIVE PROJECTING EMBANKMENT INSTALLATIONS

$\dfrac{H}{B_c}$	CLASS B BEDDING					CLASS C BEDDING					$\dfrac{H}{B_c}$
P = 0.9											
	$r_{sd}p = 0$	0.1	0.3	0.5	1.0	$r_{sd}p = 0$	0.1	0.3	0.5	1.0	
0.5	2.72	2.65	2.65	2.65	2.65	2.14	2.10	2.10	2.10	2.10	0.5
1.0	2.58	2.49	2.49	2.49	2.49	2.05	2.00	2.00	2.00	2.00	1.0
1.5	2.34	2.46	2.42	2.40	2.38	2.03	1.97	1.95	1.94	1.92	1.5
2.0	2.52	2.44	2.41	2.39	2.37	2.01	1.96	1.95	1.93	1.92	2.0
3.0	2.50	2.43	2.40	2.38	2.34	2.00	1.96	1.94	1.92	1.90	3.0
5.0	2.48	2.42	2.39	2.36	2.33	1.99	1.95	1.93	1.91	1.89	5.0
10.0	2.47	2.41	2.37	2.35	2.33	1.98	1.94	1.92	1.91	1.89	10.0
15.0	2.46	2.40	2.36	2.35	2.32	1.98	1.94	1.92	1.91	1.89	15.0
P = 0.7											
	$r_{sd}p = 0$	0.1	0.3	0.5	1.0	$r_{sd}p = 0$	0.1	0.3	0.5	1.0	
0.5	2.46	2.42	2.42	2.42	2.42	1.98	1.95	1.95	1.95	1.95	0.5
1.0	2.40	2.35	2.35	2.35	2.35	1.94	1.90	1.90	1.90	1.90	1.0
1.5	2.38	2.33	2.31	2.30	2.28	1.92	1.89	1.88	1.87	1.86	1.5
2.0	2.37	2.32	2.31	2.29	2.28	1.92	1.89	1.88	1.87	1.86	2.0
3.0	2.36	2.32	2.30	2.29	2.27	1.91	1.88	1.87	1.86	1.85	3.0
5.0	2.35	2.32	2.29	2.28	2.26	1.90	1.88	1.87	1.86	1.84	5.0
10.0	2.34	2.31	2.28	2.27	2.26	1.90	1.88	1.86	1.85	1.84	10.0
15.0	2.34	2.31	2.28	2.27	2.25	1.90	1.88	1.86	1.85	1.84	15.0
P = 0.5											
	$r_{sd}p = 0$	0.1	0.3	0.5	1.0	$r_{sd}p = 0$	0.1	0.3	0.5	1.0	
0.5	2.27	2.25	2.25	2.25	2.25	1.85	1.84	1.84	1.84	1.84	0.5
1.0	2.25	2.23	2.23	2.23	2.23	1.84	1.82	1.82	1.82	1.82	1.0
1.5	2.24	2.22	2.21	2.21	2.20	1.83	1.82	1.81	1.81	1.80	1.5
2.0	2.24	2.22	2.21	2.20	2.20	1.83	1.82	1.81	1.81	1.80	2.0
3.0	2.24	2.22	2.21	2.20	2.19	1.83	1.82	1.81	1.80	1.80	3.0
5.0	2.23	2.22	2.21	2.20	2.19	1.83	1.82	1.81	1.80	1.80	5.0
10.0	2.23	2.22	2.20	2.20	2.19	1.83	1.82	1.81	1.80	1.80	10.0
15.0	2.23	2.21	2.20	2.20	2.19	1.82	1.81	1.81	1.80	1.80	15.0
P = 0.3											
	$r_{sd}p = 0$	0.1	0.3	0.5	1.0	$r_{sd}p = 0$	0.1	0.3	0.5	1.0	
0.5	2.16	2.16	2.16	2.16	2.16	1.78	1.78	1.78	1.78	1.78	0.5
1.0	2.16	2.15	2.15	2.15	2.15	1.78	1.77	1.77	1.77	1.77	1.0
1.5	2.16	2.15	2.15	2.15	2.15	1.78	1.77	1.77	1.77	1.77	1.5
2.0	2.16	2.15	2.15	2.15	2.15	1.78	1.77	1.77	1.77	1.77	2.0
3.0	2.16	2.15	2.15	2.15	2.14	1.78	1.77	1.77	1.77	1.77	3.0
5.0	2.16	2.15	2.15	2.15	2.14	1.78	1.77	1.77	1.77	1.77	5.0
10.0	2.16	2.15	2.15	2.15	2.14	1.78	1.77	1.77	1.77	1.77	10.0
15.0	2.16	2.15	2.15	2.15	2.14	1.78	1.77	1.77	1.77	1.77	15.0
ZERO PROJECTING											
	2.12					1.75					

TABLE 65

BEDDING FACTORS FOR ARCH PIPE
POSITIVE PROJECTING EMBANKMENT INSTALLATIONS

$\dfrac{H}{B_c}$	CLASS B BEDDING					CLASS C BEDDING					$\dfrac{H}{B_c}$
P = 0.9											
	$r_{sd}p = 0$	0.1	0.3	0.5	1.0	$r_{sd}p = 0$	0.1	0.3	0.5	1.0	
0.5	2.72	2.65	2.65	2.65	2.65	2.14	2.10	2.10	2.10	2.10	0.5
1.0	2.58	2.49	2.49	2.49	2.49	2.05	2.00	2.00	2.00	2.00	1.0
1.5	2.34	2.46	2.42	2.40	2.38	2.03	1.97	1.95	1.94	1.92	1.5
2.0	2.52	2.44	2.41	2.39	2.37	2.01	1.96	1.95	1.93	1.92	2.0
3.0	2.50	2.43	2.40	2.38	2.34	2.00	1.96	1.94	1.92	1.90	3.0
5.0	2.48	2.42	2.39	2.36	2.33	1.99	1.95	1.93	1.91	1.89	5.0
10.0	2.47	2.41	2.37	2.35	2.33	1.98	1.94	1.92	1.91	1.89	10.0
15.0	2.46	2.40	2.36	2.35	2.32	1.98	1.94	1.92	1.91	1.89	15.0
P = 0.7											
	$r_{sd}p = 0$	0.1	0.3	0.5	1.0	$r_{sd}p = 0$	0.1	0.3	0.5	1.0	
0.5	2.46	2.42	2.42	2.42	2.42	1.98	1.95	1.95	1.95	1.95	0.5
1.0	2.40	2.35	2.35	2.35	2.35	1.94	1.90	1.90	1.90	1.90	1.0
1.5	2.38	2.33	2.31	2.30	2.28	1.92	1.89	1.88	1.87	1.86	1.5
2.0	2.37	2.32	2.31	2.29	2.28	1.92	1.89	1.88	1.87	1.86	2.0
3.0	2.36	2.32	2.30	2.29	2.27	1.91	1.88	1.87	1.86	1.85	3.0
5.0	2.35	2.32	2.29	2.28	2.26	1.90	1.88	1.87	1.86	1.84	5.0
10.0	2.34	2.31	2.28	2.27	2.26	1.90	1.88	1.86	1.85	1.84	10.0
15.0	2.34	2.31	2.28	2.27	2.25	1.90	1.88	1.86	1.85	1.84	15.0
P = 0.5											
	$r_{sd}p = 0$	0.1	0.3	0.5	1.0	$r_{sd}p = 0$	0.1	0.3	0.5	1.0	
0.5	2.27	2.25	2.25	2.25	2.25	1.85	1.84	1.84	1.84	1.84	0.5
1.0	2.25	2.23	2.23	2.23	2.23	1.84	1.82	1.82	1.82	1.82	1.0
1.5	2.24	2.22	2.21	2.21	2.20	1.83	1.82	1.81	1.81	1.80	1.5
2.0	2.24	2.22	2.21	2.20	2.20	1.83	1.82	1.81	1.81	1.80	2.0
3.0	2.24	2.22	2.21	2.20	2.19	1.83	1.82	1.81	1.81	1.80	3.0
5.0	2.23	2.22	2.21	2.20	2.19	1.83	1.82	1.81	1.80	1.80	5.0
10.0	2.23	2.22	2.20	2.20	2.19	1.83	1.82	1.81	1.80	1.80	10.0
15.0	2.23	2.21	2.20	2.20	2.19	1.82	1.81	1.81	1.80	1.80	15.0
P = 0.3											
	$r_{sd}p = 0$	0.1	0.3	0.5	1.0	$r_{sd}p = 0$	0.1	0.3	0.5	1.0	
0.5	2.16	2.16	2.16	2.16	2.16	1.78	1.78	1.78	1.78	1.78	0.5
1.0	2.16	2.15	2.15	2.15	2.15	1.78	1.77	1.77	1.77	1.77	1.0
1.5	2.16	2.15	2.15	2.15	2.15	1.78	1.77	1.77	1.77	1.77	1.5
2.0	2.16	2.15	2.15	2.15	2.15	1.78	1.77	1.77	1.77	1.77	2.0
3.0	2.16	2.15	2.15	2.15	2.14	1.78	1.77	1.77	1.77	1.77	3.0
5.0	2.16	2.15	2.15	2.15	2.14	1.78	1.77	1.77	1.77	1.77	5.0
10.0	2.16	2.15	2.15	2.15	2.14	1.78	1.77	1.77	1.77	1.77	10.0
15.0	2.16	2.15	2.15	2.15	2.14	1.78	1.77	1.77	1.77	1.77	15.0
ZERO PROJECTING											
			2.12					1.75			

TABLE 66

BEDDING FACTORS FOR CIRCULAR PIPE
INDUCED TRENCH INSTALLATIONS

$\frac{H}{B_c}$	CLASS A BEDDING					CLASS B BEDDING					CLASS C BEDDING					$\frac{H}{B_c}$
P = 0.9																
	$r_{sd}=-0.1$	-0.3	-0.5	-1.0	-2.0	$r_{sd}=-0.1$	-0.3	-0.5	-1.0	-2.0	$r_{sd}=-0.1$	-0.3	-0.5	-1.0	-2.0	
1	7.11	7.11	7.11	7.11	7.11	3.46	3.46	3.46	3.46	3.46	2.62	2.62	2.62	2.62	2.62	1
2	7.12	7.12	7.12	7.12	7.12	3.46	3.46	3.46	3.46	3.46	2.62	2.62	2.62	2.62	2.62	2
3	7.20	8.03	8.41	8.41	8.41	3.50	3.66	3.73	3.73	3.73	2.64	2.64	2.64	2.64	2.64	3
5	7.30	8.21	9.42	12.15	12.92	3.51	3.67	3.91	4.30	4.39	2.64	2.74	2.87	3.07	3.12	5
10	7.32	8.57	9.76	13.60	26.95	3.51	3.76	3.97	4.46	5.29	2.64	2.79	2.90	3.15	3.55	10
15	7.32	8.69	10.04	14.94	35.12	3.51	3.78	4.01	4.59	5.54	2.64	2.80	2.92	3.22	3.66	15
20	7.32	8.71	10.09	15.70	41.89	3.51	3.78	4.02	4.66	5.68	2.64	2.80	2.93	3.25	3.72	20
25	7.32	8.72	10.13	16.20	47.57	3.51	3.79	4.02	4.70	5.77	2.64	2.81	2.93	3.27	3.75	25
P = 0.7																
	$r_{sd}=-0.1$	-0.3	-0.5	-1.0	-2.0	$r_{sd}=-0.1$	-0.3	-0.5	-1.0	-2.0	$r_{sd}=-0.1$	-0.3	-0.5	-1.0	-2.0	
1	5.91	5.91	5.91	5.91	5.91	2.78	2.78	2.78	2.78	2.78	2.21	2.21	2.21	2.21	2.21	1
2	6.15	6.15	6.15	6.15	6.15	2.82	2.82	2.82	2.82	2.82	2.23	2.23	2.23	2.23	2.23	2
3	6.65	6.82	7.06	7.06	7.06	2.88	2.92	2.95	2.95	2.95	2.28	2.29	2.31	2.31	2.31	3
5	6.44	6.98	7.84	9.45	9.87	2.88	2.94	3.04	3.19	3.23	2.26	2.31	2.37	2.46	2.48	5
10	6.47	7.39	8.19	10.47	16.15	2.88	3.00	3.08	3.27	3.56	2.26	2.34	2.39	2.51	2.68	10
15	6.54	7.52	8.42	11.29	18.86	2.88	3.00	3.10	3.33	3.64	2.27	2.35	2.41	2.54	2.72	15
20	6.55	7.53	8.48	11.74	20.71	2.88	3.01	3.11	3.36	3.69	2.27	2.36	2.41	2.56	2.75	20
25	6.56	7.54	8.52	12.04	22.05	2.88	3.02	3.11	3.37	3.72	2.27	2.36	2.41	2.57	2.76	25
P = 0.5																
	$r_{sd}=-0.1$	-0.3	-0.5	-1.0	-2.0	$r_{sd}=-0.1$	-0.3	-0.5	-1.0	-2.0	$r_{sd}=-0.1$	-0.3	-0.5	-1.0	-2.0	
1	4.45	4.45	4.45	4.45	4.45	2.32	2.32	2.32	2.32	2.32	1.91	1.91	1.91	1.91	1.91	1
2	4.84	4.84	4.84	4.84	4.84	2.37	2.37	2.37	2.37	2.37	1.94	1.94	1.94	1.94	1.94	2
3	4.84	4.95	5.04	5.04	5.04	2.38	2.38	2.39	2.39	2.39	1.95	1.95	1.96	1.96	1.96	3
5	4.84	5.06	5.37	5.88	6.00	2.38	2.40	2.43	2.48	2.49	1.95	1.96	1.98	2.00	2.02	5
10	4.88	5.25	5.54	6.22	7.37	2.38	2.42	2.45	2.51	2.59	1.95	1.97	1.99	2.03	2.08	10
15	4.92	5.31	5.63	6.46	7.80	2.38	2.42	2.46	2.52	2.61	1.95	1.98	2.00	2.04	2.10	15
20	4.93	5.31	5.66	6.58	8.04	2.38	2.43	2.46	2.53	2.62	1.95	1.98	2.00	2.05	2.11	20
25	4.94	5.32	5.68	6.66	8.20	2.38	2.43	2.46	2.54	2.63	1.95	1.98	2.00	2.05	2.12	25
P = 0.3																
	$r_{sd}=-0.1$	-0.3	-0.5	-1.0	-2.0	$r_{sd}=-0.1$	-0.3	-0.5	-1.0	-2.0	$r_{sd}=-0.1$	-0.3	-0.5	-1.0	-2.0	
1	3.43	3.43	3.43	3.43	3.43	2.10	2.10	2.10	2.10	2.10	1.76	1.76	1.76	1.76	1.76	1
2	3.57	3.57	3.57	3.57	3.57	2.12	2.12	2.12	2.12	2.12	1.77	1.77	1.77	1.77	1.76	2
3	3.60	3.61	3.64	3.64	3.64	2.12	2.12	2.12	2.12	2.12	1.77	1.77	1.77	1.77	1.77	3
5	3.60	3.65	3.74	3.85	3.88	2.12	2.12	2.13	2.14	2.14	1.77	1.77	1.78	1.79	1.79	5
10	3.62	3.72	3.79	3.94	4.15	2.12	2.13	2.14	2.15	2.17	1.77	1.78	1.78	1.79	1.80	10
15	3.63	3.74	3.81	3.99	4.22	2.12	2.13	2.14	2.16	2.17	1.77	1.78	1.78	1.80	1.81	15
20	3.64	3.74	3.82	4.02	4.26	2.12	2.13	2.14	2.16	2.18	1.77	1.78	1.78	1.80	1.81	20
25	3.64	3.74	3.83	4.04	4.29	2.12	2.13	2.14	2.16	2.18	1.77	1.78	1.78	1.80	1.81	25
ZERO PROJECTING																
	2.83					2.02					1.70						

FIGURES

FIGURE 1

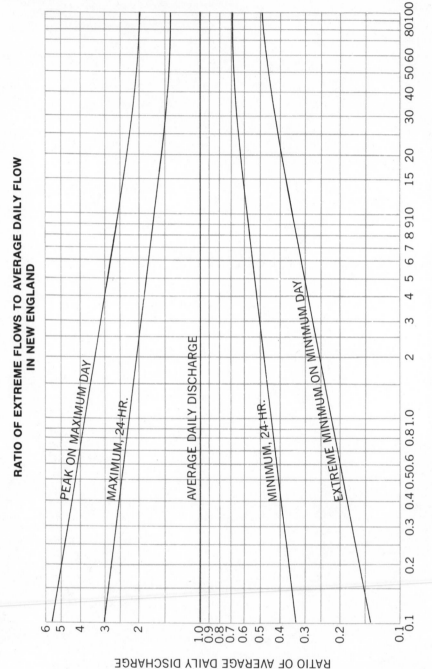

RATIO OF EXTREME FLOWS TO AVERAGE DAILY FLOW
IN NEW ENGLAND

PEAK ON MAXIMUM DAY

MAXIMUM, 24-HR.

AVERAGE DAILY DISCHARGE

MINIMUM, 24-HR.

EXTREME MINIMUM ON MINIMUM DAY

RATIO OF AVERAGE DAILY DISCHARGE

AVERAGE DAILY DISCHARGE OF DOMESTIC SEWAGE IN MGD

FIGURE 2

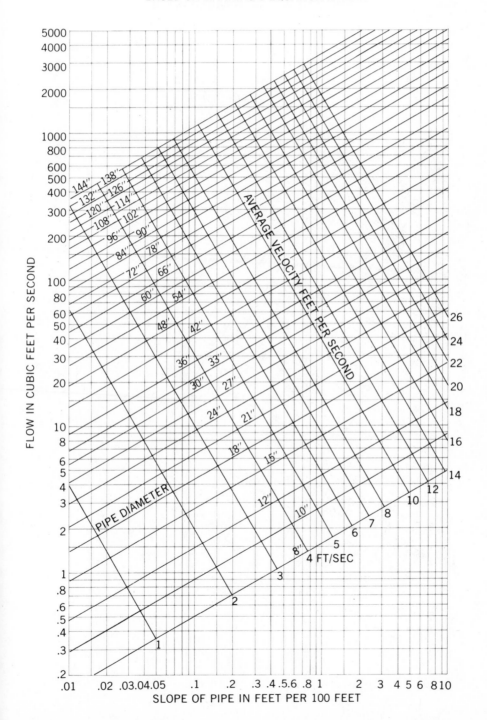

FLOW FOR CIRCULAR PIPE FLOWING FULL
BASED ON MANNING'S EQUATION n=0.010

FIGURE 3

FLOW FOR CIRCULAR PIPE FLOWING FULL
BASED ON MANNING'S EQUATION n=0.011

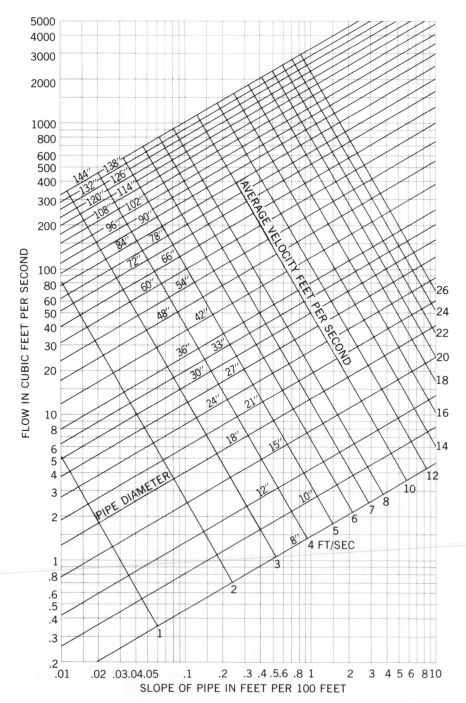

FIGURE 4

FLOW FOR CIRCULAR PIPE FLOWING FULL
BASED ON MANNING'S EQUATION n=0.012

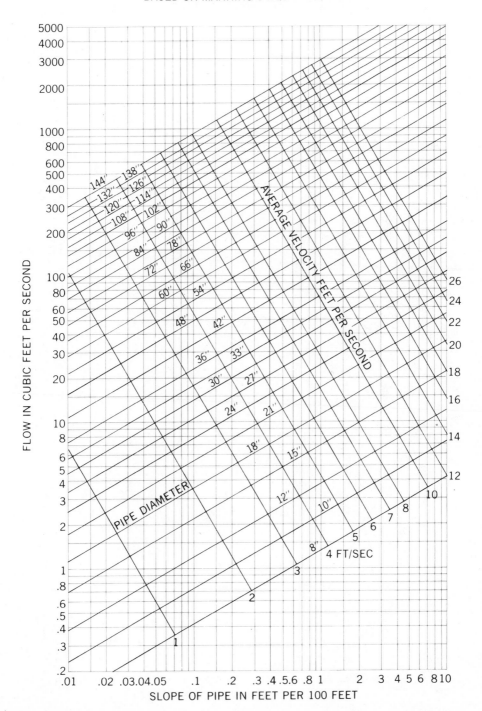

FIGURE 5

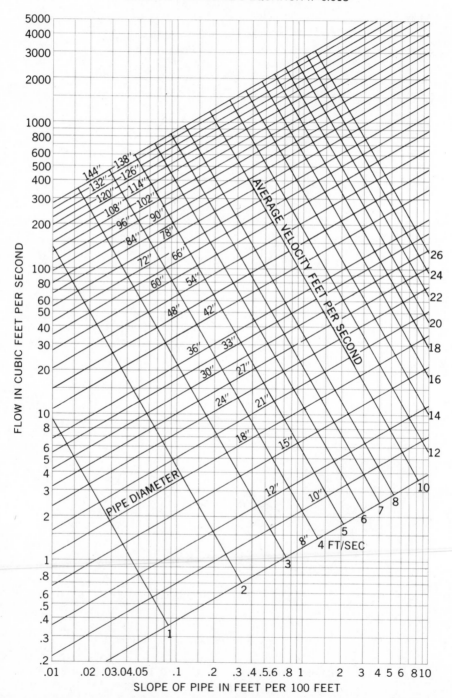

FLOW FOR CIRCULAR PIPE FLOWING FULL
BASED ON MANNING'S EQUATION n=0.013

SLOPE OF PIPE IN FEET PER 100 FEET

FIGURE 6

FLOW FOR HORIZONTAL ELLIPTICAL PIPE FLOWING FULL
BASED ON MANNING'S EQUATION n=0.010

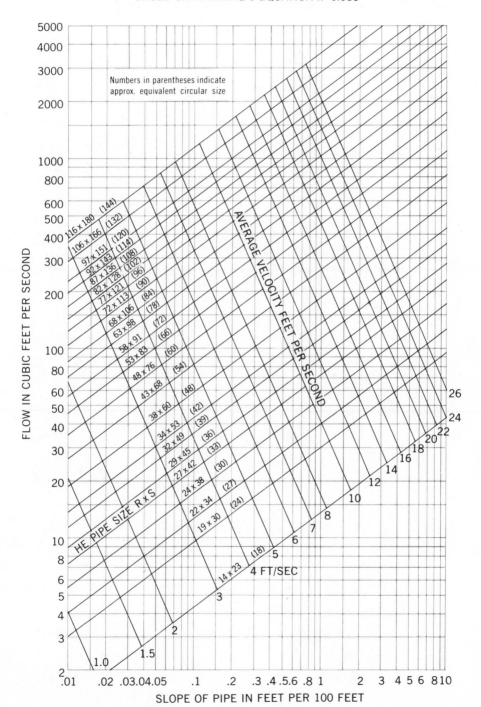

Numbers in parentheses indicate approx. equivalent circular size

FIGURE 7

FLOW FOR HORIZONTAL ELLIPTICAL PIPE FLOWING FULL
BASED ON MANNING'S EQUATION n=0.011

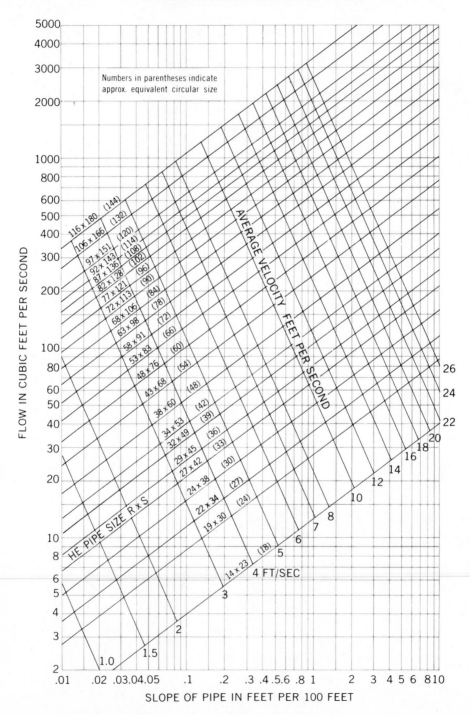

SLOPE OF PIPE IN FEET PER 100 FEET

FIGURE 8

FLOW FOR HORIZONTAL ELLIPTICAL PIPE FLOWING FULL
BASED ON MANNING'S EQUATION n=0.012

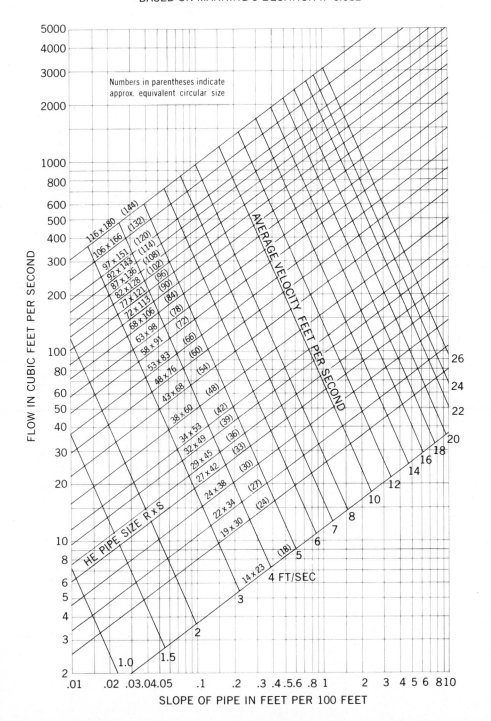

FIGURE 9

FLOW FOR HORIZONTAL ELLIPTICAL PIPE FLOWING FULL
BASED ON MANNING'S EQUATION n=0.013

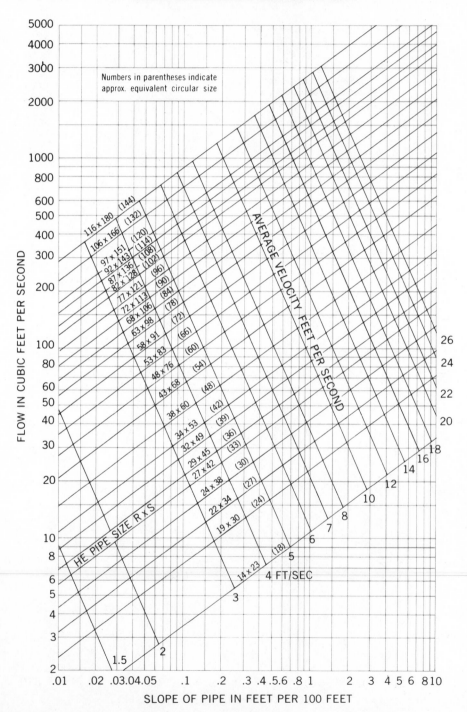

SLOPE OF PIPE IN FEET PER 100 FEET

FIGURE 10

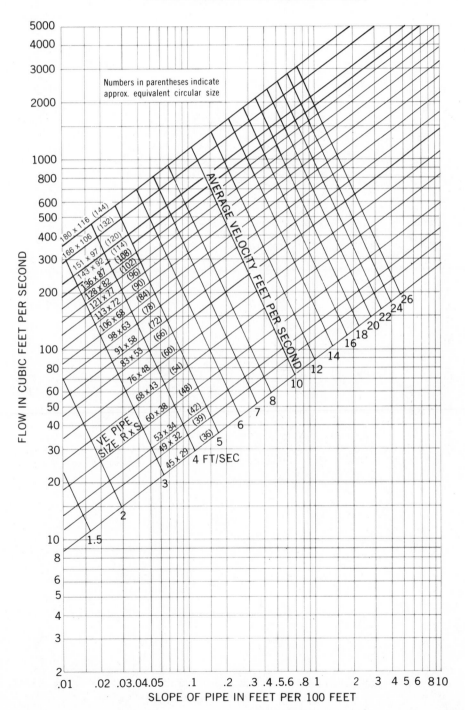

FLOW FOR VERTICAL ELLIPTICAL PIPE FLOWING FULL
BASED ON MANNING'S EQUATION n=0.010

FIGURE 11

FLOW FOR VERTICAL ELLIPTICAL PIPE FLOWING FULL
BASED ON MANNING'S EQUATION n=0.011

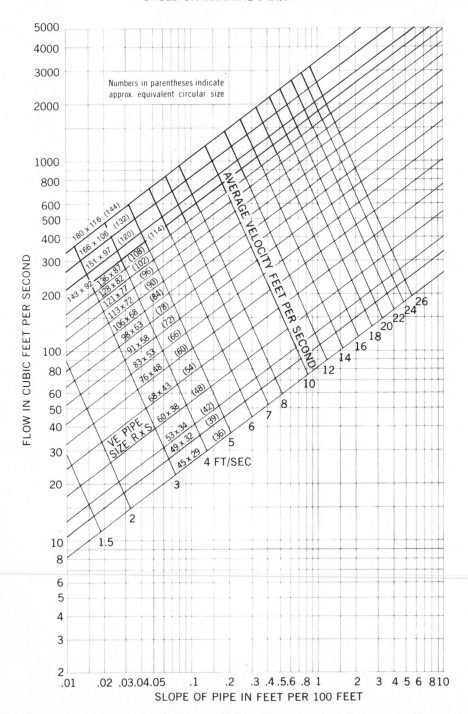

Numbers in parentheses indicate approx. equivalent circular size

SLOPE OF PIPE IN FEET PER 100 FEET

FLOW IN CUBIC FEET PER SECOND

FIGURE 12

FLOW FOR VERTICAL ELLIPTICAL PIPE FLOWING FULL
BASED ON MANNING'S EQUATION n=0.012

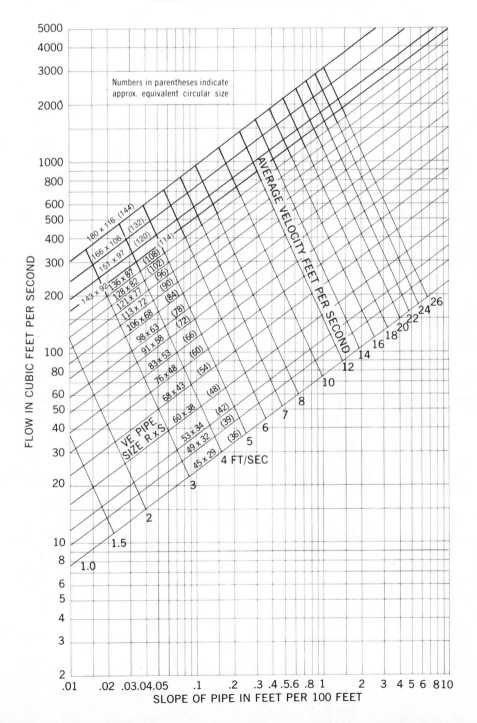

FIGURE 13

FLOW FOR VERTICAL ELLIPTICAL PIPE FLOWING FULL
BASED ON MANNING'S EQUATION n=0.013

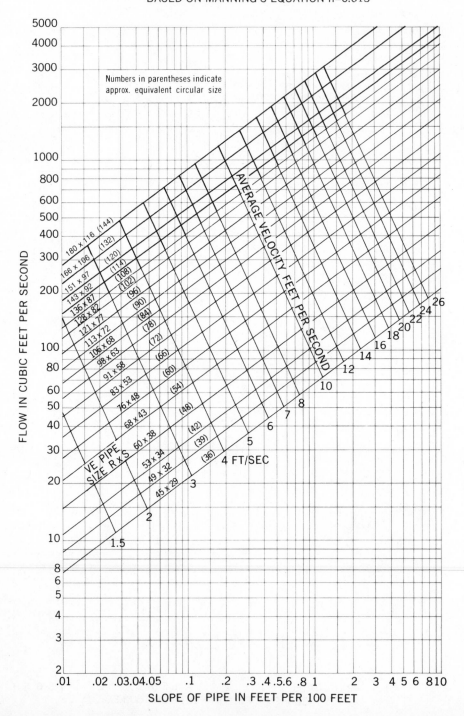

Numbers in parentheses indicate approx. equivalent circular size

FIGURE 14

FLOW FOR ARCH PIPE FLOWING FULL
BASED ON MANNING'S EQUATION n=0.010

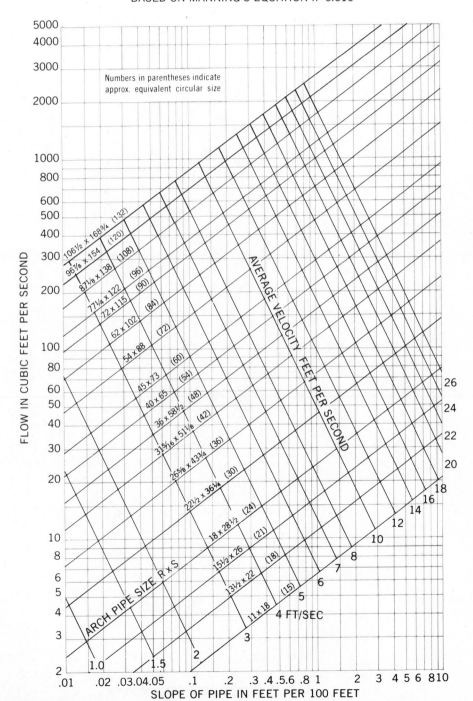

FIGURE 15

FLOW FOR ARCH PIPE FLOWING FULL
BASED ON MANNING'S EQUATION n=0.011

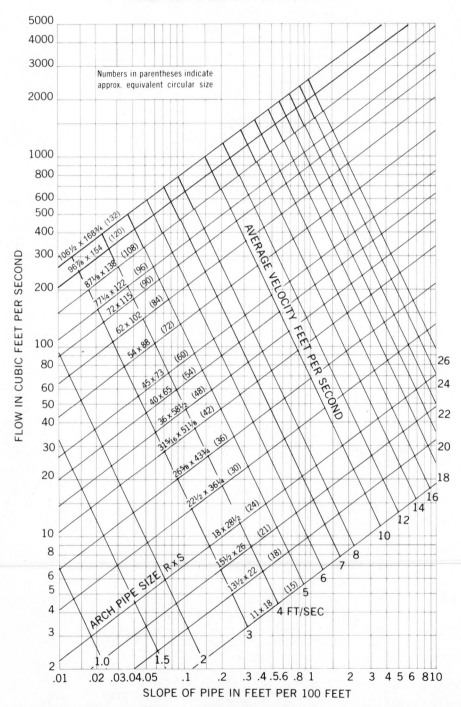

FIGURE 16

FLOW FOR ARCH PIPE FLOWING FULL
BASED ON MANNING'S EQUATION n 0.012

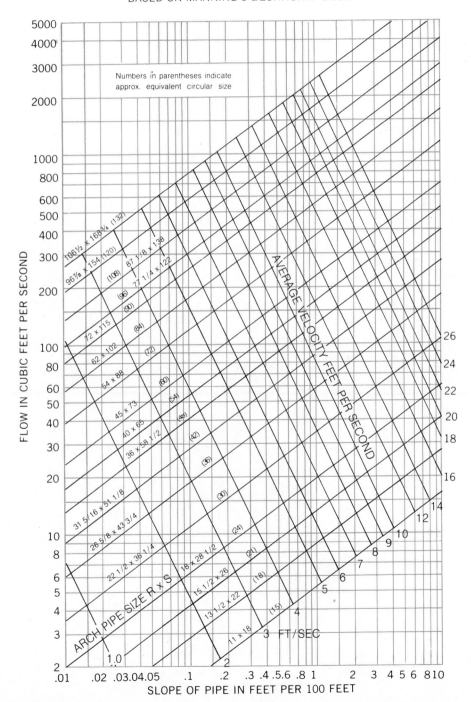

FIGURE 17

FLOW FOR ARCH PIPE FLOWING FULL
BASED ON MANNING'S EQUATION n=0.013

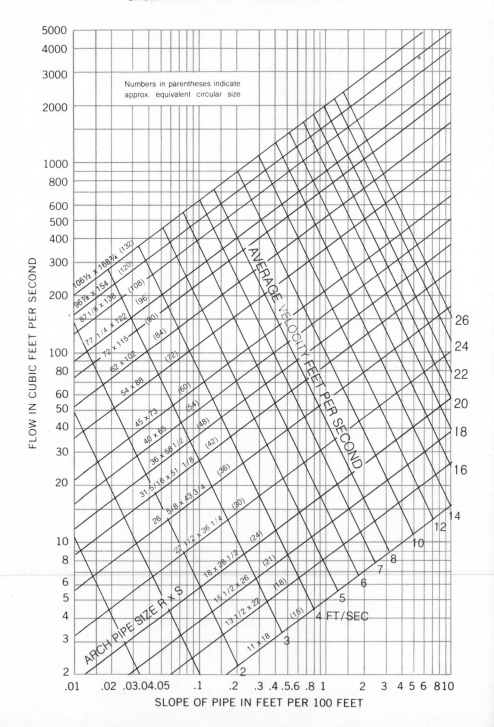

FIGURE 18.1

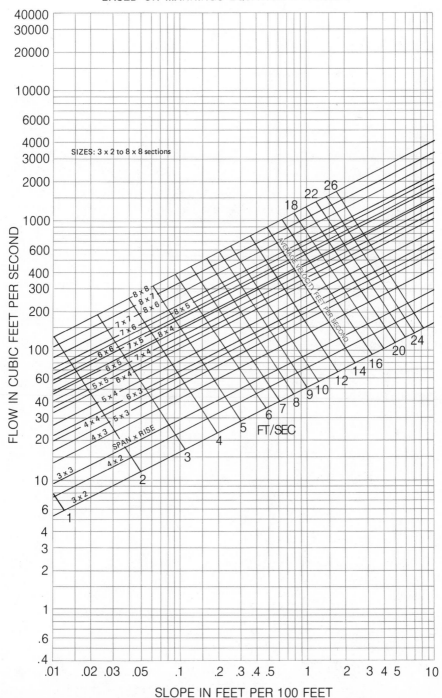

FLOW FOR BOX SECTIONS FLOWING FULL
BASED ON MANNINGS EQUATION n = 0.012

FIGURE 18.2

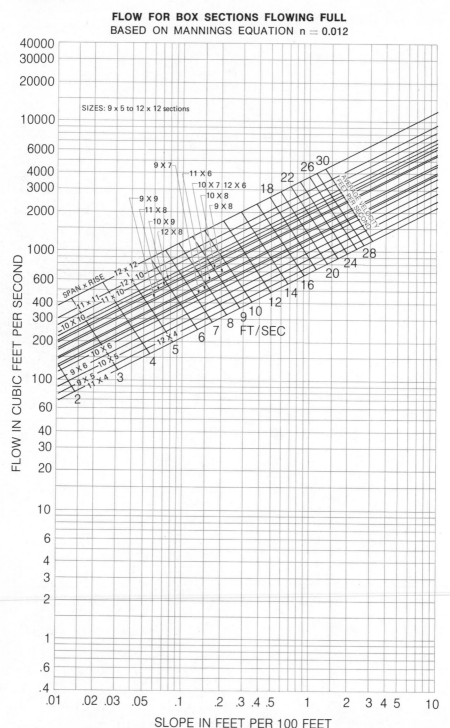

FLOW FOR BOX SECTIONS FLOWING FULL
BASED ON MANNINGS EQUATION n = 0.012

SIZES: 9 x 5 to 12 x 12 sections

FLOW IN CUBIC FEET PER SECOND

SLOPE IN FEET PER 100 FEET

FIGURE 19.1

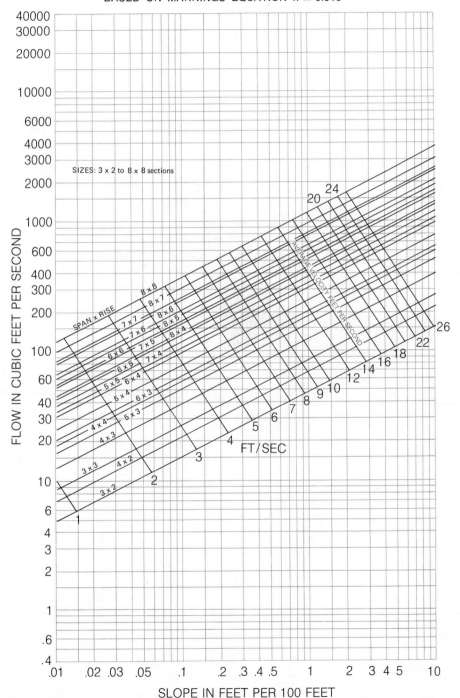

FLOW FOR BOX SECTIONS FLOWING FULL
BASED ON MANNINGS EQUATION n = 0.013

FIGURE 19.2

FLOW FOR BOX SECTIONS FLOWING FULL
BASED ON MANNINGS EQUATION n = 0.013

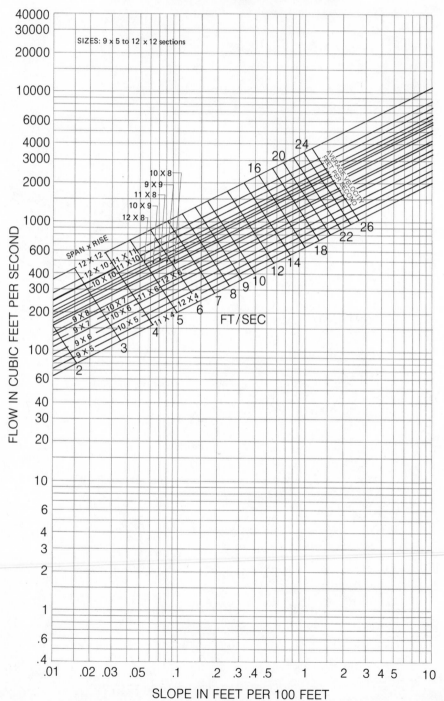

FIGURE 20

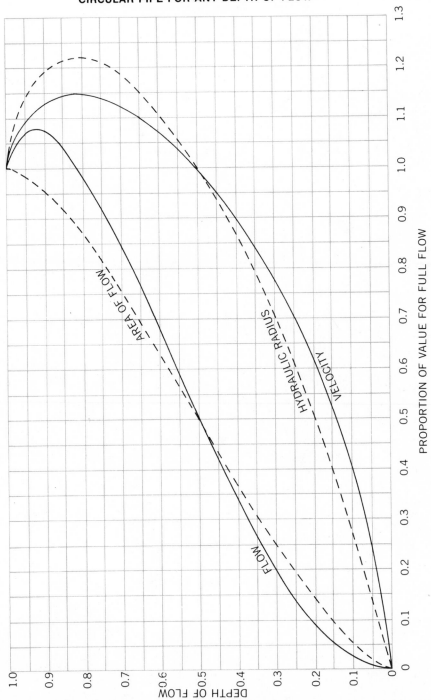

RELATIVE VELOCITY AND FLOW IN
CIRCULAR PIPE FOR ANY DEPTH OF FLOW

FIGURE 21

RELATIVE VELOCITY AND FLOW IN
HORIZONTAL ELLIPTICAL PIPE FOR ANY DEPTH OF FLOW

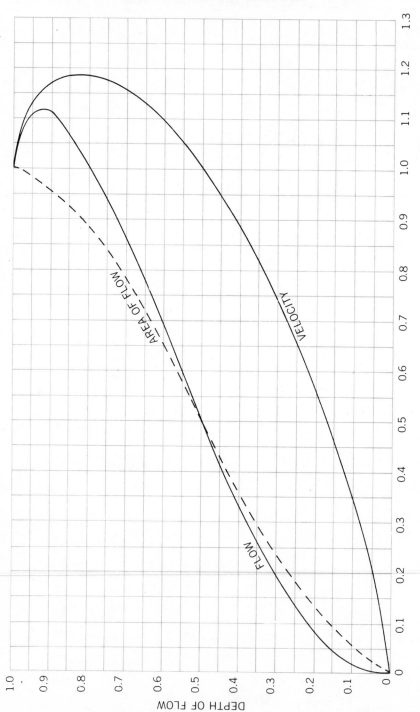

PROPORTION OF VALUE FOR FULL FLOW

DEPTH OF FLOW

FIGURE 22

RELATIVE VELOCITY AND FLOW IN
VERTICAL ELLIPTICAL PIPE FOR ANY DEPTH OF FLOW

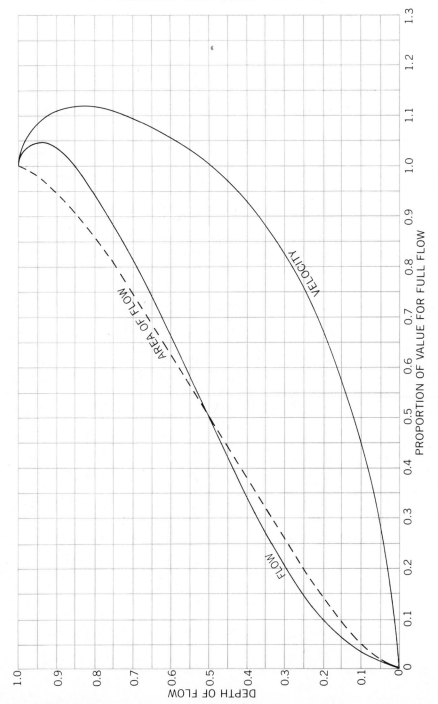

FIGURE 23

RELATIVE VELOCITY AND FLOW IN
ARCH PIPE FOR ANY DEPTH OF FLOW

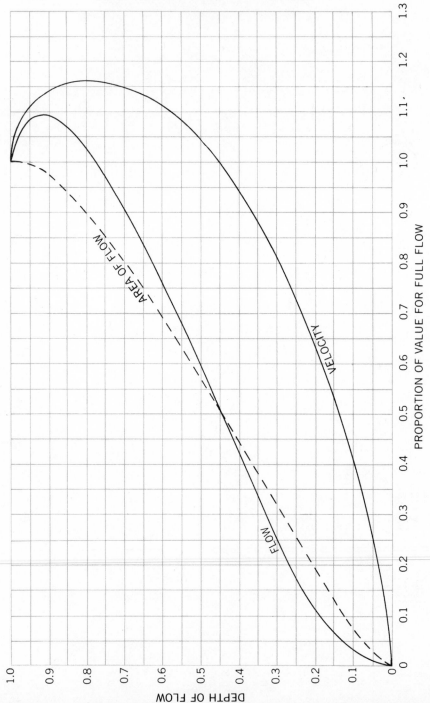

FIGURE 24.1

RELATIVE VELOCITY AND FLOW IN PRECAST BOX
SECTIONS FOR ANY DEPTH OF FLOW

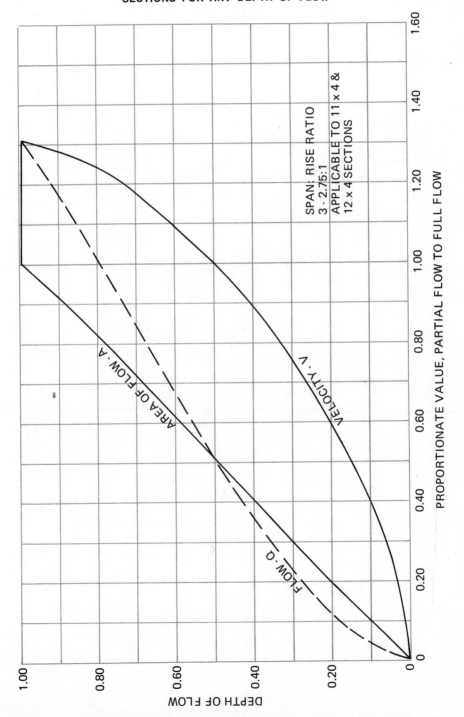

FIGURE 24.2

RELATIVE VELOCITY AND FLOW IN PRECAST BOX
SECTIONS FOR ANY DEPTH OF FLOW

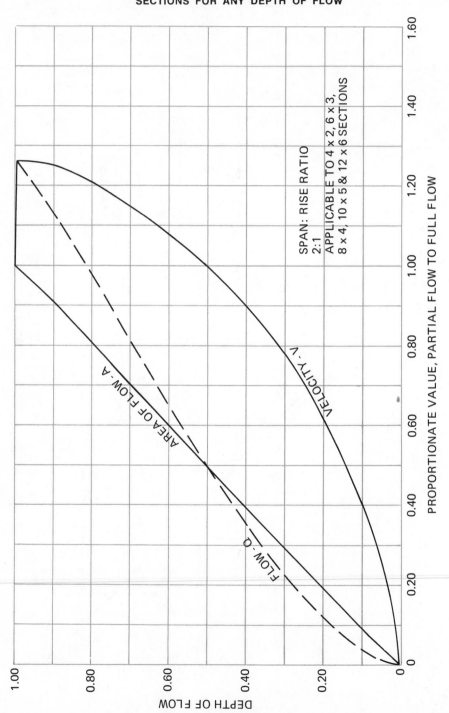

FIGURE 24.3

**RELATIVE VELOCITY AND FLOW IN PRECAST BOX
SECTIONS FOR ANY DEPTH OF FLOW**

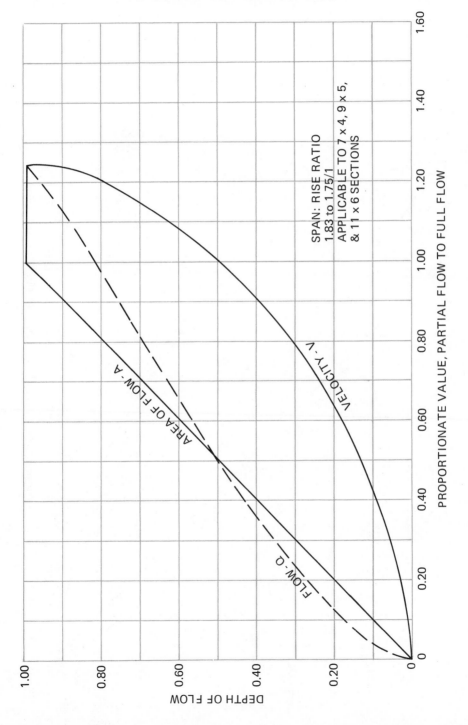

FIGURE 24.4

RELATIVE VELOCITY AND FLOW IN PRECAST BOX
SECTIONS FOR ANY DEPTH OF FLOW

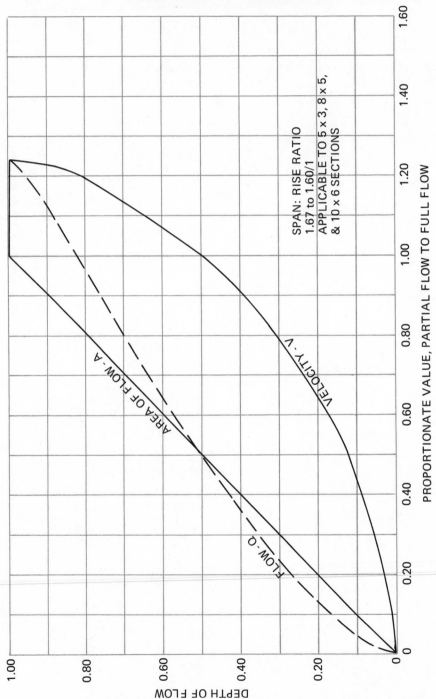

SPAN: RISE RATIO
1.67 to 1.60/1
APPLICABLE TO 5 × 3, 8 × 5,
& 10 × 6 SECTIONS

VELOCITY - V

AREA OF FLOW - A

FLOW - Q

PROPORTIONATE VALUE, PARTIAL FLOW TO FULL FLOW

DEPTH OF FLOW

FIGURE 24.5

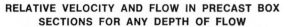

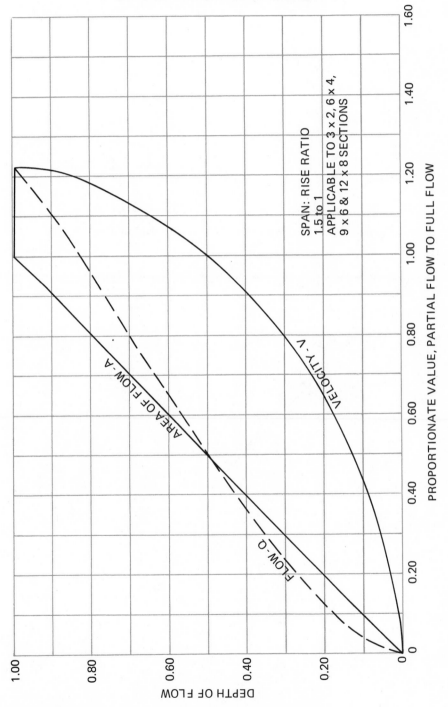

FIGURE 24.6

RELATIVE VELOCITY AND FLOW IN PRECAST BOX
SECTIONS FOR ANY DEPTH OF FLOW

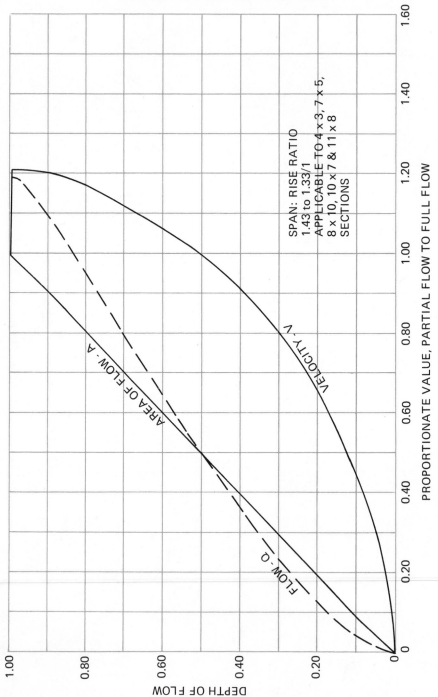

SPAN: RISE RATIO
1.43 to 1.33/1
APPLICABLE TO 4 x 3, 7 x 5,
8 x 10, 10 x 7 & 11 x 8
SECTIONS

VELOCITY - V

AREA OF FLOW - A

FLOW - Q

PROPORTIONATE VALUE, PARTIAL FLOW TO FULL FLOW

DEPTH OF FLOW

FIGURE 24.7

RELATIVE VELOCITY AND FLOW IN PRECAST BOX
SECTIONS FOR ANY DEPTH OF FLOW

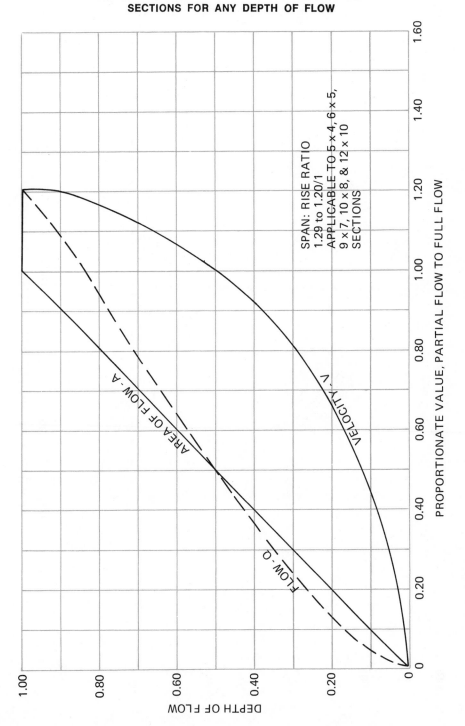

FIGURE 24.8

RELATIVE VELOCITY AND FLOW IN PRECAST BOX
SECTIONS FOR ANY DEPTH OF FLOW

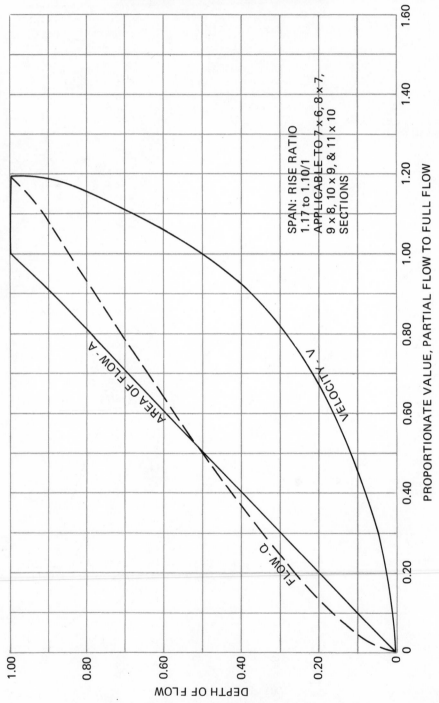

SPAN: RISE RATIO
1.17 to 1.10/1
APPLICABLE TO 7 x 6, 8 x 7,
9 x 8, 10 x 9, & 11 x 10
SECTIONS

PROPORTIONATE VALUE, PARTIAL FLOW TO FULL FLOW

DEPTH OF FLOW

VELOCITY - V

AREA OF FLOW - A

FLOW - Q

FIGURE 24.9

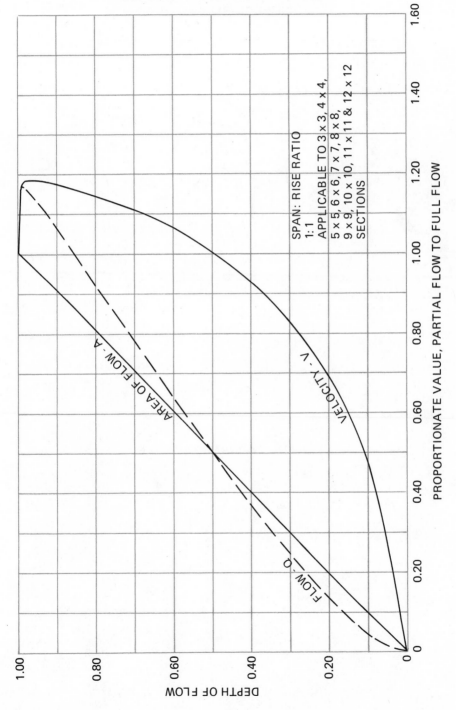

RELATIVE VELOCITY AND FLOW IN PRECAST BOX
SECTIONS FOR ANY DEPTH OF FLOW

FIGURE 25

MAP OF THE UNITED STATES
2-YEAR, 30-MINUTE RAINFALL INTENSITY

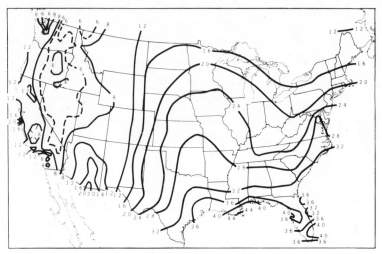

ADAPTED FROM CHART 2, RAINFALL FREQUENCY ATLAS OF THE UNITED STATES,
U.S. DEPARTMENT OF COMMERCE, WEATHER BUREAU, TECHNICAL PAPER NO. 40
MAY 1961

FIGURE 26

INTENSITY-DURATION CURVE

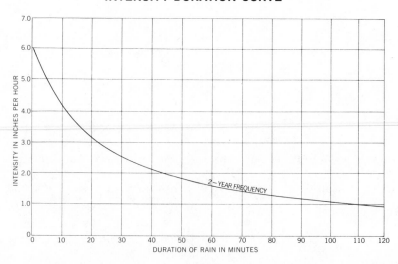

FIGURE 27

CALIFORNIA CHART "A" FOR CALCULATION OF "DESIGN DISCHARGES"

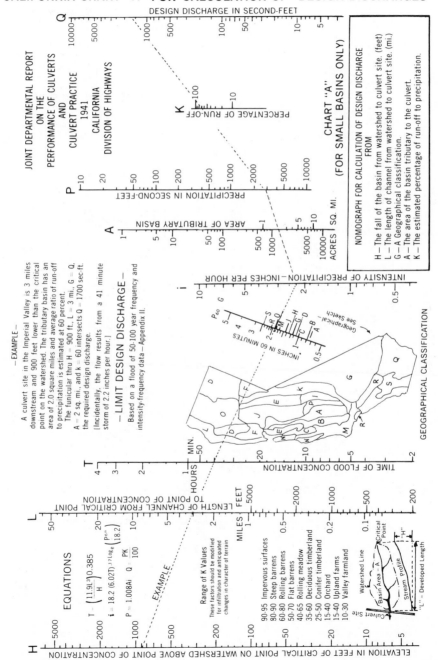

FIGURE 28

CRITICAL DEPTH
CIRCULAR PIPE

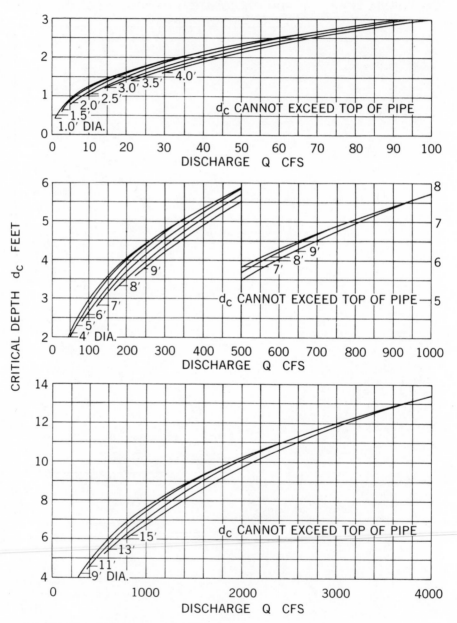

FIGURE 29

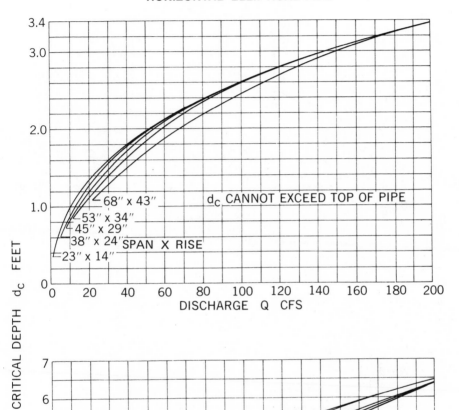

CRITICAL DEPTH
HORIZONTAL ELLIPTICAL PIPE

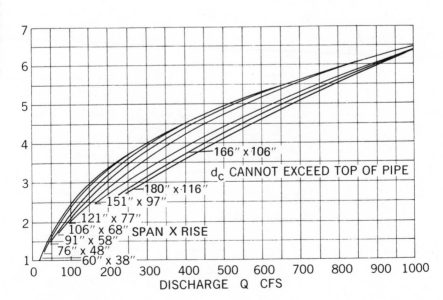

BUREAU OF PUBLIC ROADS JAN. 1964

FIGURE 30

CRITICAL DEPTH
VERTICAL ELLIPTICAL PIPE

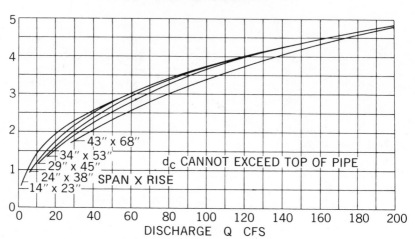

CRITICAL DEPTH d_C FEET

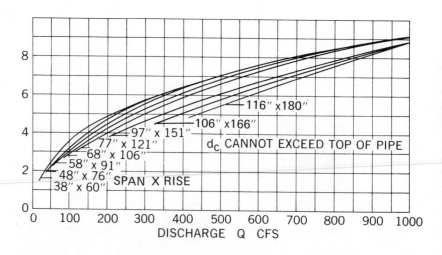

BUREAU OF PUBLIC ROADS JAN. 1964

FIGURE 31.1

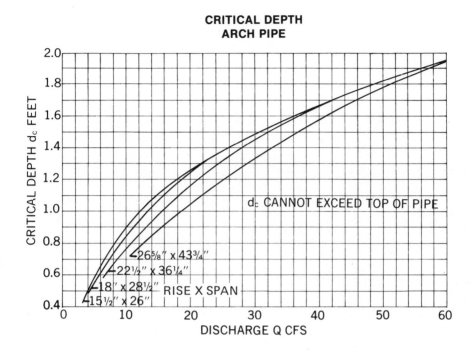

**CRITICAL DEPTH
ARCH PIPE**

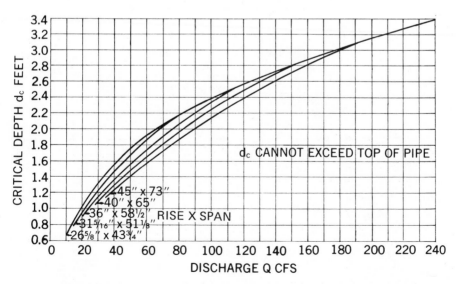

BUREAU OF PUBLIC ROADS, JAN. 1964

FIGURE 31.2

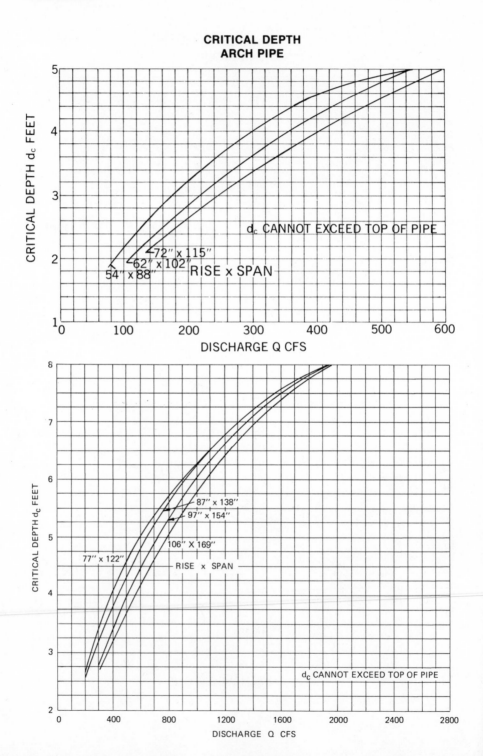

CRITICAL DEPTH
ARCH PIPE

FIGURE 32

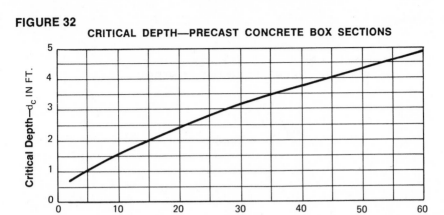

CRITICAL DEPTH—PRECAST CONCRETE BOX SECTIONS

NOTE: d_c CANNOT EXCEED RISE

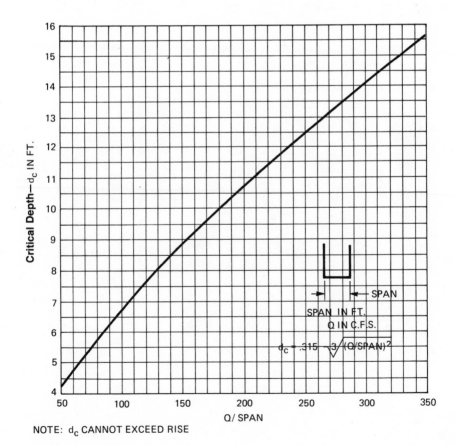

$$d_c = .315 \sqrt[3]{(Q/SPAN)^2}$$

SPAN IN FT.
Q IN C.F.S.

SPAN

NOTE: d_c CANNOT EXCEED RISE

BUREAU OF PUBLIC ROADS - JAN. 1963

FIGURE 33

HEADWATER DEPTH FOR CIRCULAR CONCRETE PIPE CULVERTS WITH INLET CONTROL

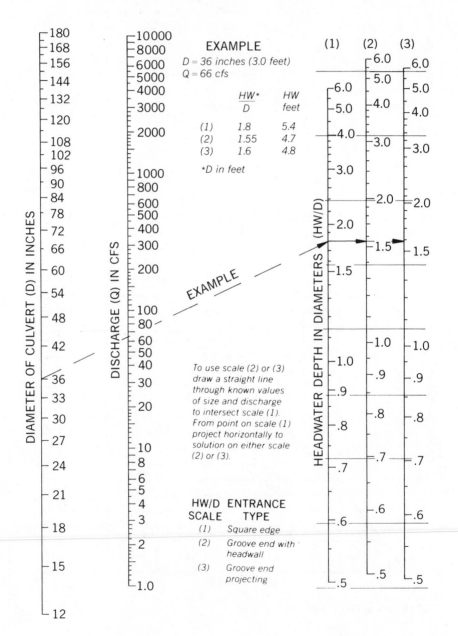

EXAMPLE

$D = 36$ inches (3.0 feet)
$Q = 66$ cfs

	$\dfrac{HW*}{D}$	HW feet
(1)	1.8	5.4
(2)	1.55	4.7
(3)	1.6	4.8

*D in feet

DIAMETER OF CULVERT (D) IN INCHES

DISCHARGE (Q) IN CFS

EXAMPLE

To use scale (2) or (3) draw a straight line through known values of size and discharge to intersect scale (1). From point on scale (1) project horizontally to solution on either scale (2) or (3).

HEADWATER DEPTH IN DIAMETERS (HW/D)

HW/D ENTRANCE
SCALE   TYPE

(1)   Square edge

(2)   Groove end with headwall

(3)   Groove end projecting

BUREAU OF PUBLIC ROADS JAN. 1963

HEADWATER SCALES 2&3
REVISED MAY 1964

FIGURE 34

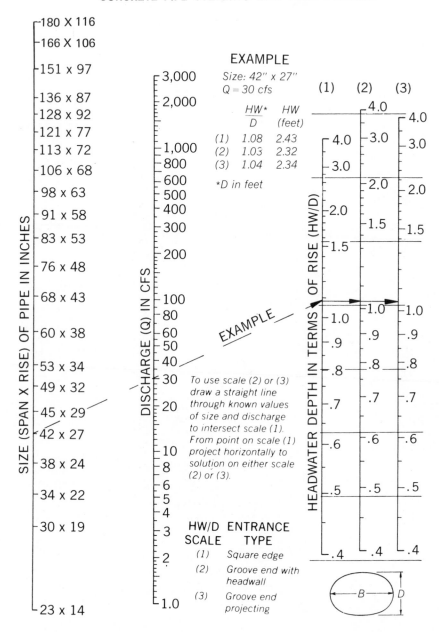

HEADWATER DEPTH FOR HORIZONTAL ELLIPTICAL CONCRETE PIPE CULVERTS WITH INLET CONTROL

EXAMPLE

Size: 42" x 27"
Q = 30 cfs

	$\frac{HW*}{D}$	HW (feet)
(1)	1.08	2.43
(2)	1.03	2.32
(3)	1.04	2.34

*D in feet

To use scale (2) or (3) draw a straight line through known values of size and discharge to intersect scale (1). From point on scale (1) project horizontally to solution on either scale (2) or (3).

HW/D SCALE	ENTRANCE TYPE
(1)	Square edge
(2)	Groove end with headwall
(3)	Groove end projecting

SIZE (SPAN X RISE) OF PIPE IN INCHES

DISCHARGE (Q) IN CFS

HEADWATER DEPTH IN TERMS OF RISE (HW/D)

BUREAU OF PUBLIC ROADS JAN. 1963

FIGURE 35

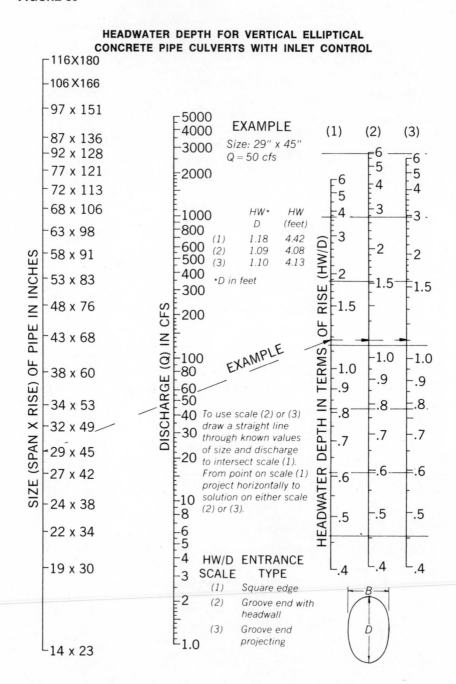

HEADWATER DEPTH FOR VERTICAL ELLIPTICAL CONCRETE PIPE CULVERTS WITH INLET CONTROL

EXAMPLE

Size: 29" x 45"
Q = 50 cfs

	$\frac{HW^*}{D}$	HW (feet)
(1)	1.18	4.42
(2)	1.09	4.08
(3)	1.10	4.13

*D in feet

EXAMPLE

To use scale (2) or (3) draw a straight line through known values of size and discharge to intersect scale (1). From point on scale (1) project horizontally to solution on either scale (2) or (3).

SIZE (SPAN X RISE) OF PIPE IN INCHES

DISCHARGE (Q) IN CFS

HEADWATER DEPTH IN TERMS OF RISE (HW/D)

HW/D SCALE	ENTRANCE TYPE
(1)	Square edge
(2)	Groove end with headwall
(3)	Groove end projecting

FIGURE 36

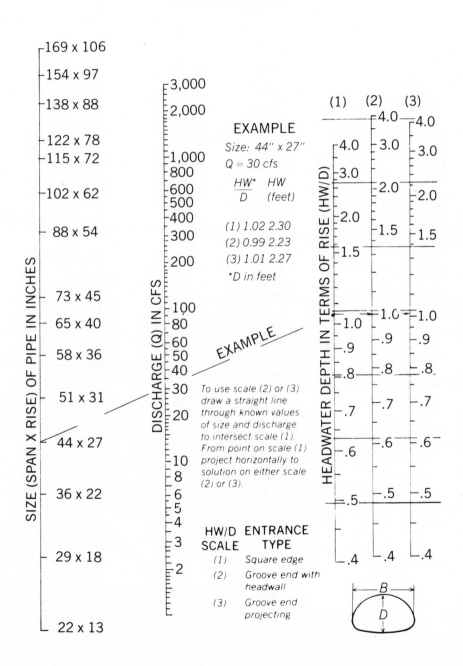

HEADWATER DEPTH FOR CONCRETE ARCH CULVERTS
WITH INLET CONTROL

SIZE (SPAN X RISE) OF PIPE IN INCHES

- 169 x 106
- 154 x 97
- 138 x 88
- 122 x 78
- 115 x 72
- 102 x 62
- 88 x 54
- 73 x 45
- 65 x 40
- 58 x 36
- 51 x 31
- 44 x 27
- 36 x 22
- 29 x 18
- 22 x 13

DISCHARGE (Q) IN CFS

3,000
2,000
1,000
800
600
500
400
300
200
100
80
60
50
40
30
20
10
8
6
5
4
3
2

EXAMPLE

Size: 44" x 27"

Q = 30 cfs

$\dfrac{HW^*}{D}$ HW (feet)

(1) 1.02 2.30
(2) 0.99 2.23
(3) 1.01 2.27

*D in feet

EXAMPLE

To use scale (2) or (3)
draw a straight line
through known values
of size and discharge
to intersect scale (1).
From point on scale (1)
project horizontally to
solution on either scale
(2) or (3).

HEADWATER DEPTH IN TERMS OF RISE (HW/D)

(1)   (2)   (3)

(1)
- 4.0
- 3.0
- 2.0
- 1.5
- 1.0
- .9
- .8
- .7
- .6
- .5
- .4

(2)
- 4.0
- 3.0
- 2.0
- 1.5
- 1.0
- .9
- .8
- .7
- .6
- .5
- .4

(3)
- 4.0
- 3.0
- 2.0
- 1.5
- 1.0
- .9
- .8
- .7
- .6
- .5
- .4

HW/D   ENTRANCE
SCALE   TYPE

(1)   Square edge
(2)   Groove end with headwall
(3)   Groove end projecting

FIGURE 37

HEADWATER DEPTH FOR CONCRETE BOX CULVERTS WITH INLET CONTROL

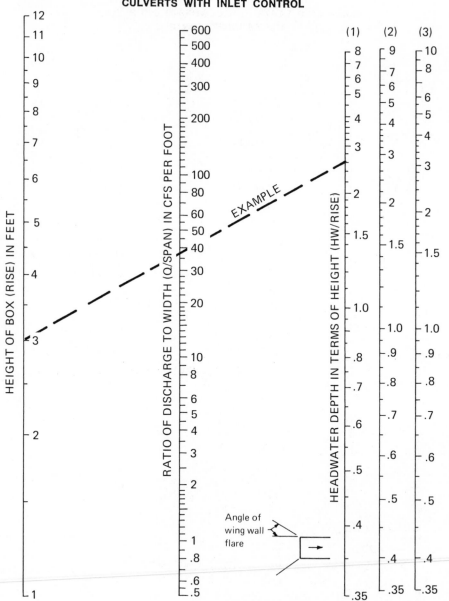

EXAMPLE

$6' \times 3'$ Box Q = 225 cfs
Q/Span = 37.5 cfs/ft

Inlet	$\dfrac{HW}{Rise}$	HW ft
(1)	2.6	7.8

$\dfrac{HW}{Rise}$ SCALE

	WING WALL FLARE
(1)	30° to 75°
(2)	90° and 15°
(3)	0° (extensions of sides)

To use scale (2) or (3) project horizontally to scale (1), then use straight inclined line through rise and Q scales, or reverse as illustrated.

FIGURE 38

HEAD FOR CIRCULAR CONCRETE PIPE
CULVERTS FLOWING FULL
n = 0.012

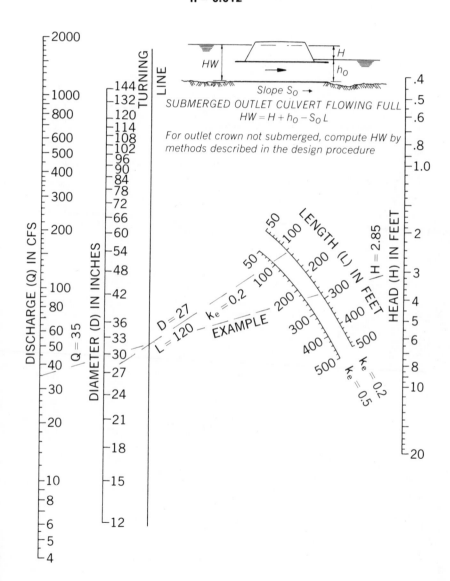

SUBMERGED OUTLET CULVERT FLOWING FULL

$HW = H + h_O - S_O L$

For outlet crown not submerged, compute HW by methods described in the design procedure

FIGURE 39

HEAD FOR ELLIPTICAL CONCRETE PIPE
CULVERTS FLOWING FULL
n = 0.012

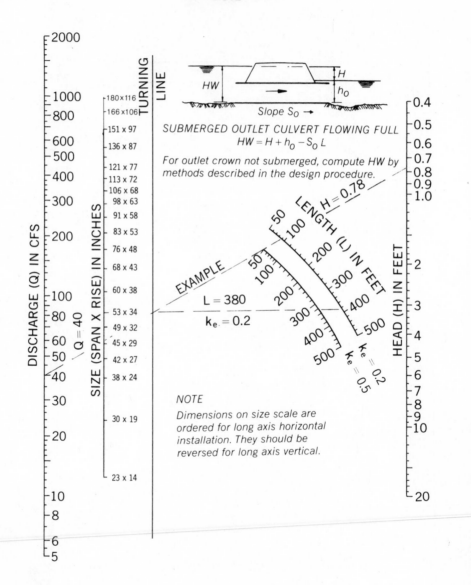

SUBMERGED OUTLET CULVERT FLOWING FULL

$$HW = H + h_O - S_O L$$

For outlet crown not submerged, compute HW by methods described in the design procedure.

EXAMPLE

L = 380

$k_e = 0.2$

H = 0.78

NOTE

Dimensions on size scale are ordered for long axis horizontal installation. They should be reversed for long axis vertical.

BUREAU OF PUBLIC ROADS JAN. 1963

FIGURE 40

HEAD FOR CONCRETE ARCH CULVERTS FLOWING FULL

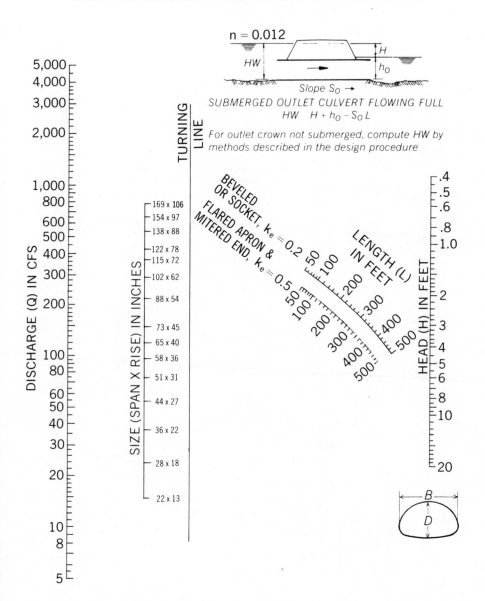

$n = 0.012$

SUBMERGED OUTLET CULVERT FLOWING FULL

$HW \quad H + h_0 - S_0 L$

For outlet crown not submerged, compute HW by methods described in the design procedure

FIGURE 41

HEAD FOR CONCRETE BOX
CULVERTS FLOWING FULL
$n = 0.012$

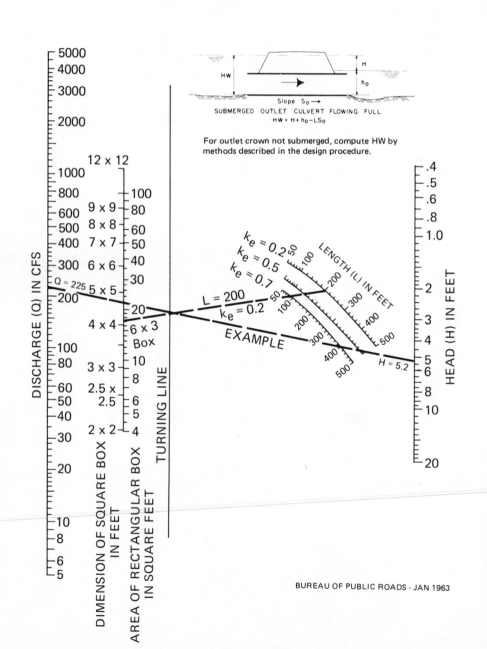

SUBMERGED OUTLET CULVERT FLOWING FULL
$HW = H + h_o - LS_o$

For outlet crown not submerged, compute HW by methods described in the design procedure.

FIGURE 42

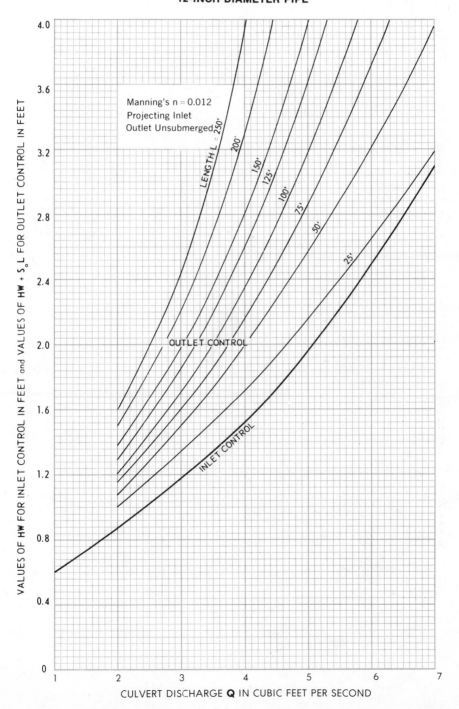

CULVERT CAPACITY
12-INCH DIAMETER PIPE

Manning's n = 0.012
Projecting Inlet
Outlet Unsubmerged

LENGTH L = 250'
200'
150'
125'
100'
75'
50'
25'

OUTLET CONTROL

INLET CONTROL

VALUES OF HW FOR INLET CONTROL IN FEET and VALUES OF HW + S₀L FOR OUTLET CONTROL IN FEET

CULVERT DISCHARGE **Q** IN CUBIC FEET PER SECOND

FIGURE 43

CULVERT CAPACITY
15-INCH DIAMETER PIPE

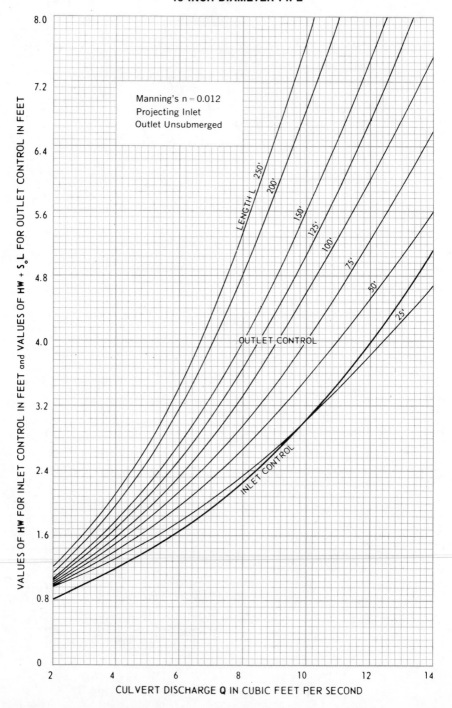

Manning's n = 0.012
Projecting Inlet
Outlet Unsubmerged

LENGTH L   250'   200'   150'   125'   100'   75'   50'   25'

OUTLET CONTROL

INLET CONTROL

VALUES OF **HW** FOR INLET CONTROL IN FEET and VALUES OF **HW** + S$_o$ L FOR OUTLET CONTROL IN FEET

CULVERT DISCHARGE **Q** IN CUBIC FEET PER SECOND

FIGURE 44

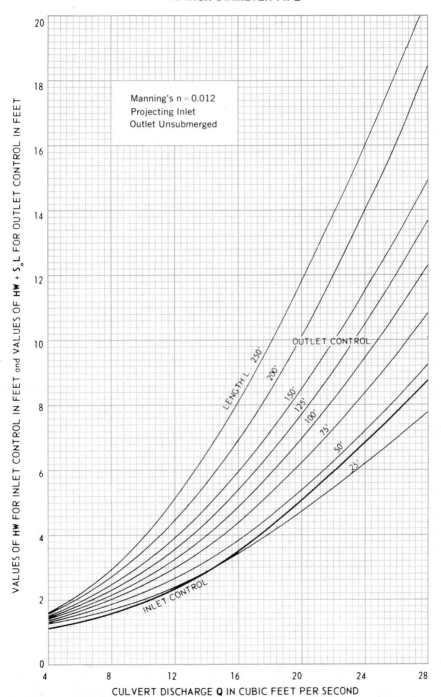

CULVERT CAPACITY
18-INCH DIAMETER PIPE

Manning's n = 0.012
Projecting Inlet
Outlet Unsubmerged

OUTLET CONTROL

LENGTH L   250'   200'   150'   125'   100'   75'   50'   25'

INLET CONTROL

VALUES OF HW FOR INLET CONTROL IN FEET and VALUES OF HW + S_o L FOR OUTLET CONTROL IN FEET

CULVERT DISCHARGE **Q** IN CUBIC FEET PER SECOND

FIGURE 45

CULVERT CAPACITY
21-INCH DIAMETER PIPE

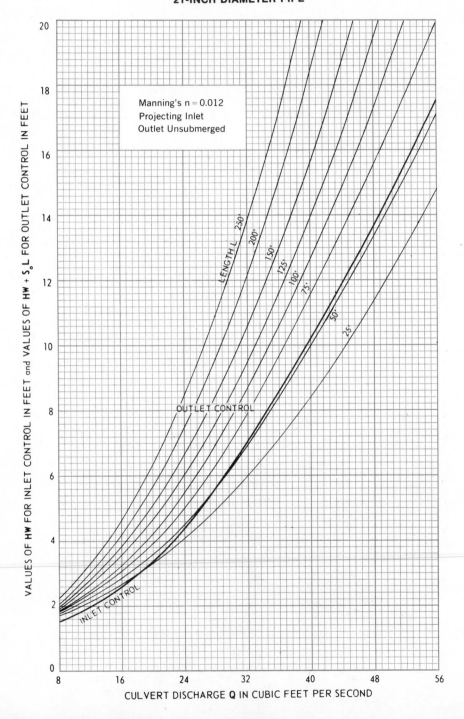

Manning's n = 0.012
Projecting Inlet
Outlet Unsubmerged

VALUES OF **HW** FOR INLET CONTROL IN FEET and VALUES OF **HW** + **S₀L** FOR OUTLET CONTROL IN FEET

CULVERT DISCHARGE **Q** IN CUBIC FEET PER SECOND

FIGURE 46

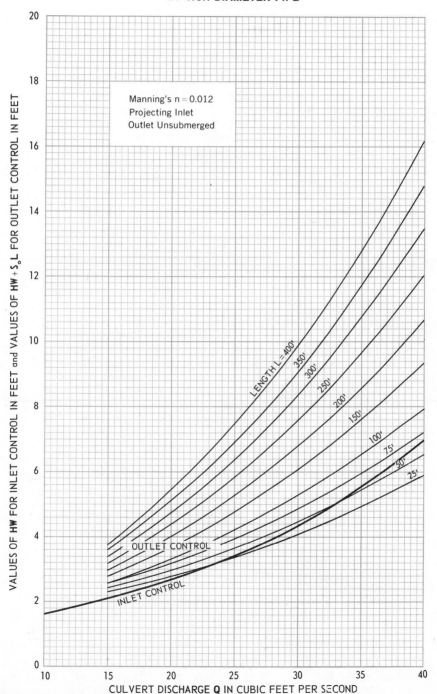

CULVERT CAPACITY
24-INCH DIAMETER PIPE

Manning's n = 0.012
Projecting Inlet
Outlet Unsubmerged

VALUES OF **HW** FOR INLET CONTROL IN FEET and VALUES OF $HW + S_o L$ FOR OUTLET CONTROL IN FEET

LENGTH L = 400'
350'
300'
250'
200'
150'
100'
75'
50'
25'

OUTLET CONTROL

INLET CONTROL

CULVERT DISCHARGE **Q** IN CUBIC FEET PER SECOND

FIGURE 47

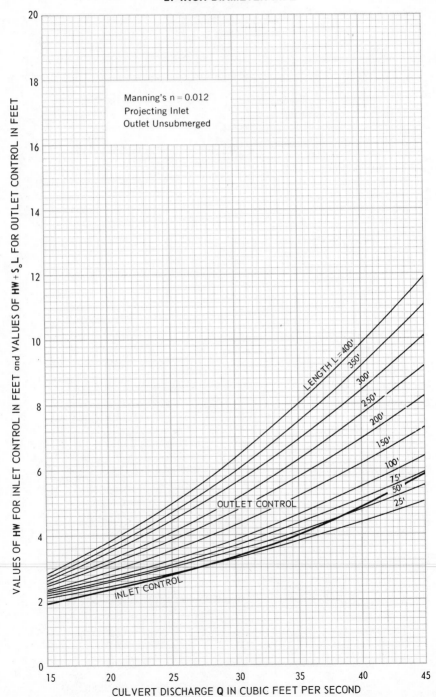

CULVERT CAPACITY
27-INCH DIAMETER PIPE

Manning's n = 0.012
Projecting Inlet
Outlet Unsubmerged

LENGTH L = 400'
350'
300'
250'
200'
150'
100'
75'
50'
25'

OUTLET CONTROL

INLET CONTROL

VALUES OF **HW** FOR INLET CONTROL IN FEET and VALUES OF **HW** + S₀L FOR OUTLET CONTROL IN FEET

CULVERT DISCHARGE **Q** IN CUBIC FEET PER SECOND

FIGURE 48

CULVERT CAPACITY
30-INCH DIAMETER PIPE

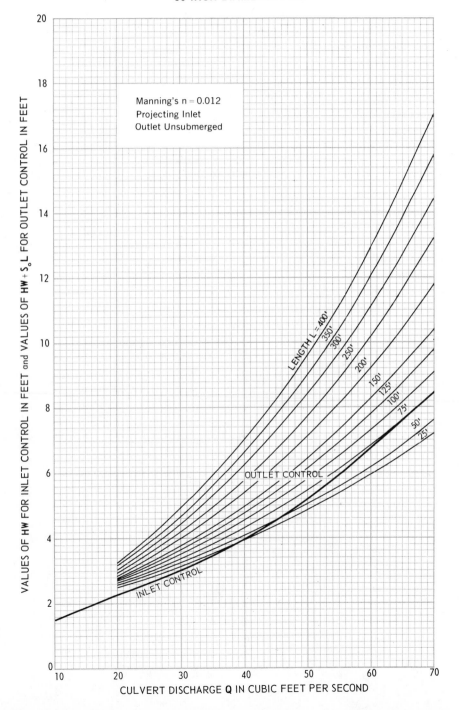

Manning's n = 0.012
Projecting Inlet
Outlet Unsubmerged

VALUES OF HW FOR INLET CONTROL IN FEET and VALUES OF $HW + S_o L$ FOR OUTLET CONTROL IN FEET

LENGTH L = 400'
350'
300'
250'
200'
150'
125'
100'
75'
50'
25'

OUTLET CONTROL

INLET CONTROL

CULVERT DISCHARGE **Q** IN CUBIC FEET PER SECOND

FIGURE 49

CULVERT CAPACITY
33-INCH DIAMETER PIPE

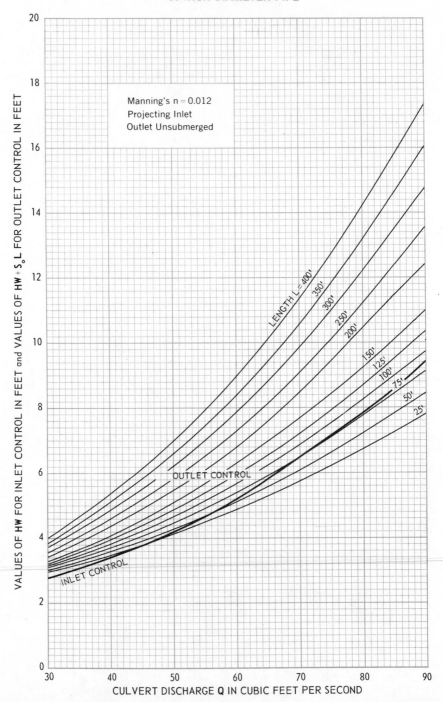

Manning's n = 0.012
Projecting Inlet
Outlet Unsubmerged

LENGTH L = 400'
350'
300'
250'
200'
150'
125'
100'
75'
50'
25'

OUTLET CONTROL

INLET CONTROL

VALUES OF **HW** FOR INLET CONTROL IN FEET and VALUES OF **HW + S$_o$L** FOR OUTLET CONTROL IN FEET

CULVERT DISCHARGE **Q** IN CUBIC FEET PER SECOND

FIGURE 50

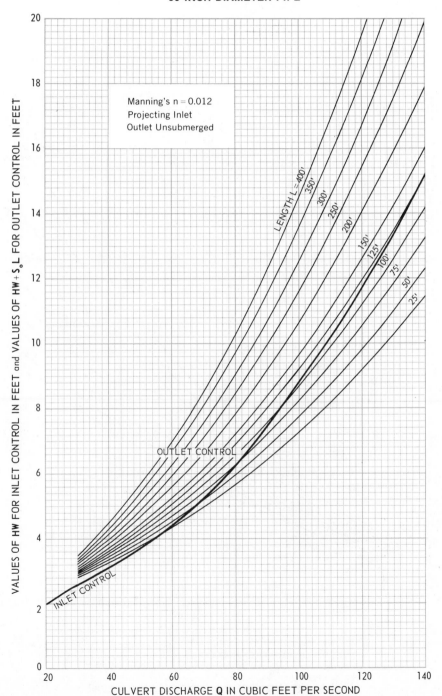

CULVERT CAPACITY
36-INCH DIAMETER PIPE

Manning's n = 0.012
Projecting Inlet
Outlet Unsubmerged

LENGTH L = 400'
350'
300'
250'
200'
150'
125'
100'
75'
50'
25'

OUTLET CONTROL

INLET CONTROL

VALUES OF HW FOR INLET CONTROL IN FEET and VALUES OF $HW + S_oL$ FOR OUTLET CONTROL IN FEET

CULVERT DISCHARGE **Q** IN CUBIC FEET PER SECOND

FIGURE 51

CULVERT CAPACITY
42-INCH DIAMETER PIPE

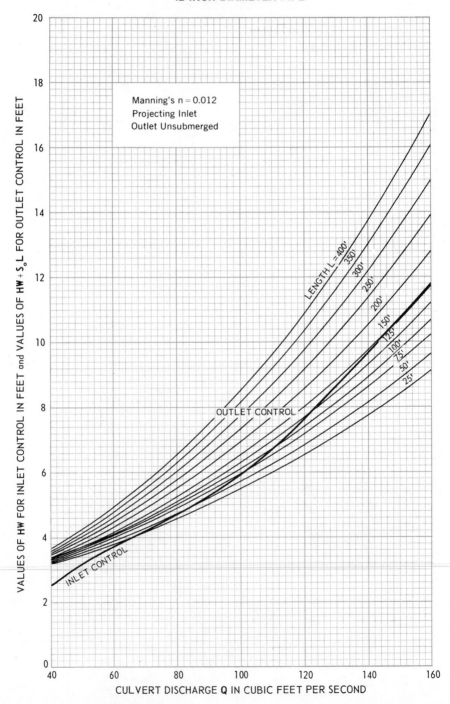

Manning's n = 0.012
Projecting Inlet
Outlet Unsubmerged

LENGTH L = 400'
350'
300'
250'
200'
150'
125'
100'
75'
50'
25'

OUTLET CONTROL

INLET CONTROL

VALUES OF **HW** FOR INLET CONTROL IN FEET and VALUES OF **HW** + S$_o$ **L** FOR OUTLET CONTROL IN FEET

CULVERT DISCHARGE **Q** IN CUBIC FEET PER SECOND

FIGURE 52

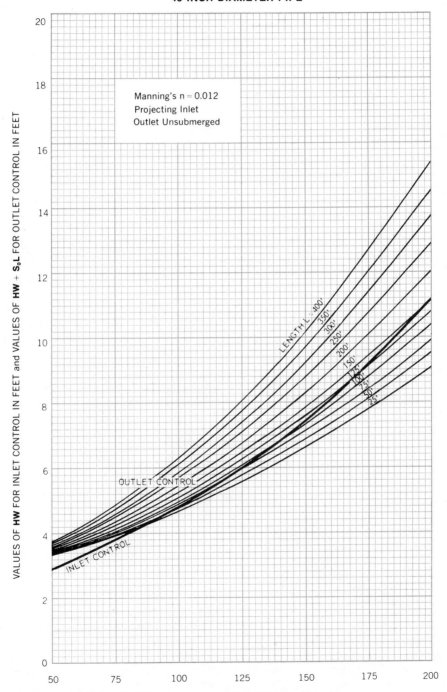

CULVERT CAPACITY
48-INCH DIAMETER PIPE

Manning's n = 0.012
Projecting Inlet
Outlet Unsubmerged

VALUES OF **HW** FOR INLET CONTROL IN FEET and VALUES OF **HW** + **S₀L** FOR OUTLET CONTROL IN FEET

LENGTH L = 400'
350'
300'
250'
200'
150'
125'
100'
75'
50'
25'

OUTLET CONTROL

INLET CONTROL

CULVERT DISCHARGE **Q** IN CUBIC FEET PER SECOND

FIGURE 53

CULVERT CAPACITY
54-INCH DIAMETER PIPE

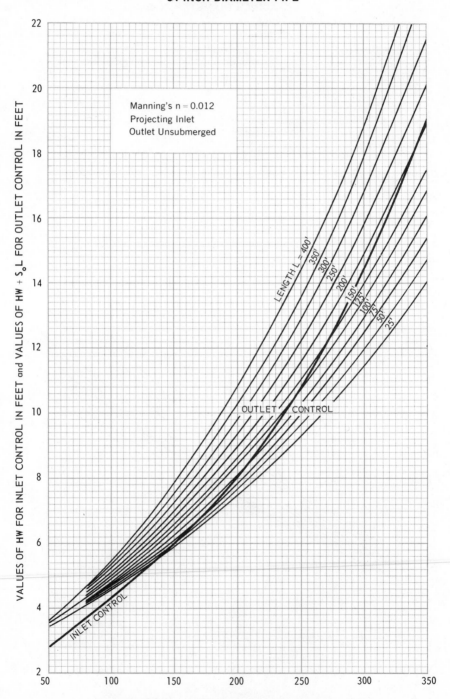

Manning's n = 0.012
Projecting Inlet
Outlet Unsubmerged

VALUES OF HW FOR INLET CONTROL IN FEET and VALUES OF HW + S_oL FOR OUTLET CONTROL IN FEET

LENGTH L = 400'
350'
300'
250'
200'
150'
125'
100'
75'
50'
25'

OUTLET CONTROL

INLET CONTROL

CULVERT DISCHARGE Q IN CUBIC FEET PER SECOND

FIGURE 54

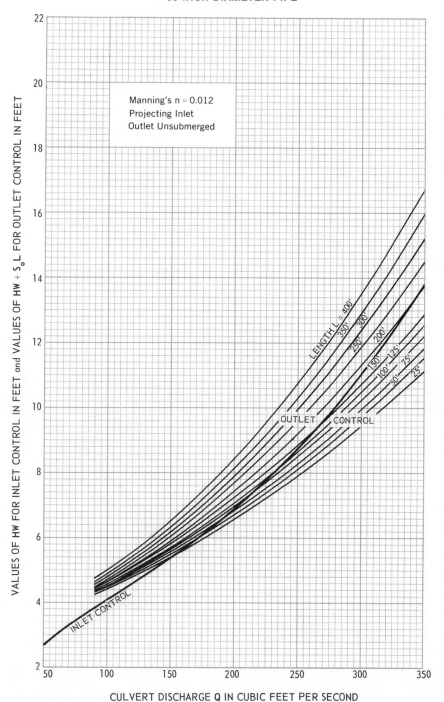

CULVERT CAPACITY
60-INCH DIAMETER PIPE

Manning's n = 0.012
Projecting Inlet
Outlet Unsubmerged

VALUES OF HW FOR INLET CONTROL IN FEET and VALUES OF HW + S_o L FOR OUTLET CONTROL IN FEET

LENGTH L = 400'
350'
300'
250'
200'
150'
125'
100'
75'
50'
25'

OUTLET CONTROL

INLET CONTROL

CULVERT DISCHARGE Q IN CUBIC FEET PER SECOND

FIGURE 55

CULVERT CAPACITY
66-INCH DIAMETER PIPE

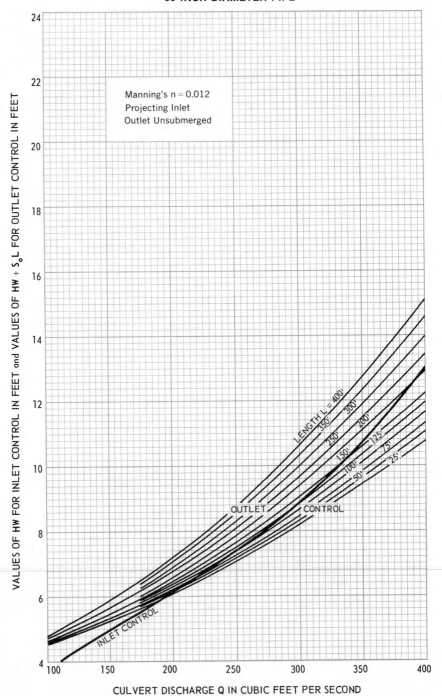

Manning's n = 0.012
Projecting Inlet
Outlet Unsubmerged

VALUES OF HW FOR INLET CONTROL IN FEET and VALUES OF HW + S_oL FOR OUTLET CONTROL IN FEET

LENGTH L = 400'
350'
300'
250'
200'
150'
125'
100'
75'
50'
25'

OUTLET CONTROL

INLET CONTROL

CULVERT DISCHARGE Q IN CUBIC FEET PER SECOND

FIGURE 56

CULVERT CAPACITY
72-INCH DIAMETER PIPE

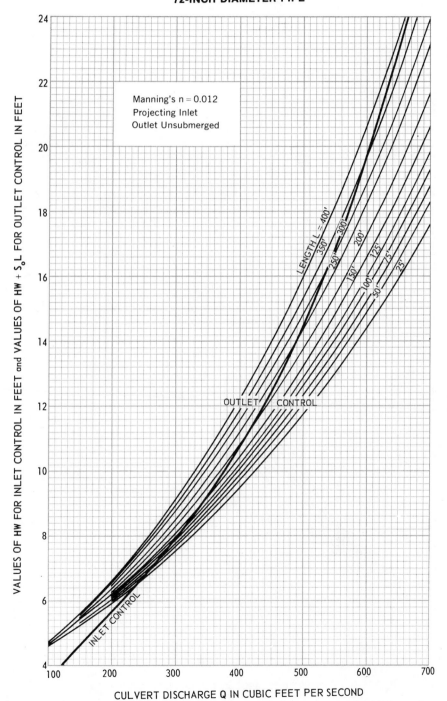

Manning's n = 0.012
Projecting Inlet
Outlet Unsubmerged

VALUES OF HW FOR INLET CONTROL IN FEET and VALUES OF HW + S_oL FOR OUTLET CONTROL IN FEET

LENGTH L = 400'
350'
300'
250'
200'
150'
125'
100'
75'
50'
25'

OUTLET CONTROL

INLET CONTROL

CULVERT DISCHARGE Q IN CUBIC FEET PER SECOND

FIGURE 57

CULVERT CAPACITY
78-INCH DIAMETER PIPE

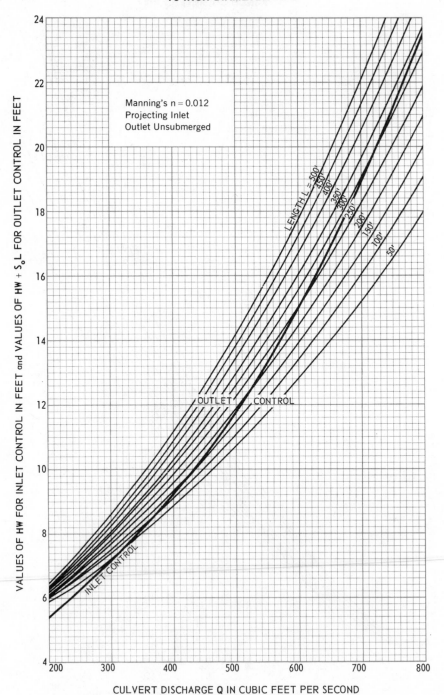

Manning's n = 0.012
Projecting Inlet
Outlet Unsubmerged

VALUES OF HW FOR INLET CONTROL IN FEET and VALUES OF HW + S_oL FOR OUTLET CONTROL IN FEET

CULVERT DISCHARGE Q IN CUBIC FEET PER SECOND

LENGTH L = 500'
450'
400'
350'
300'
250'
200'
150'
100'
50'

OUTLET CONTROL

INLET CONTROL

FIGURE 58

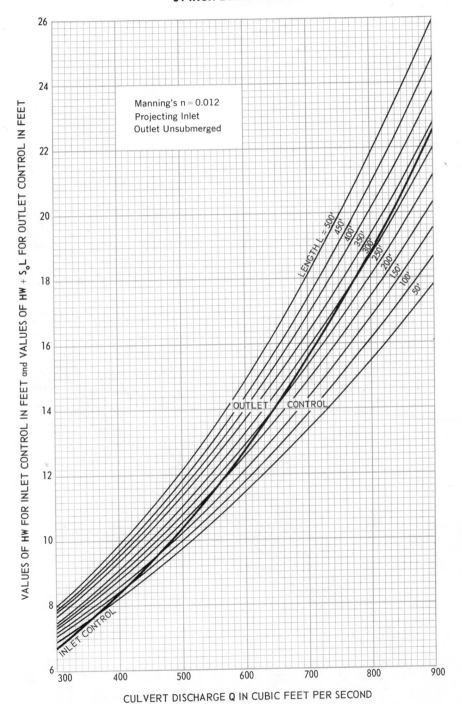

CULVERT CAPACITY
84-INCH DIAMETER PIPE

Manning's n = 0.012
Projecting Inlet
Outlet Unsubmerged

CULVERT DISCHARGE Q IN CUBIC FEET PER SECOND

VALUES OF HW FOR INLET CONTROL IN FEET and VALUES OF HW + S₀L FOR OUTLET CONTROL IN FEET

FIGURE 59

CULVERT CAPACITY
90-INCH DIAMETER PIPE

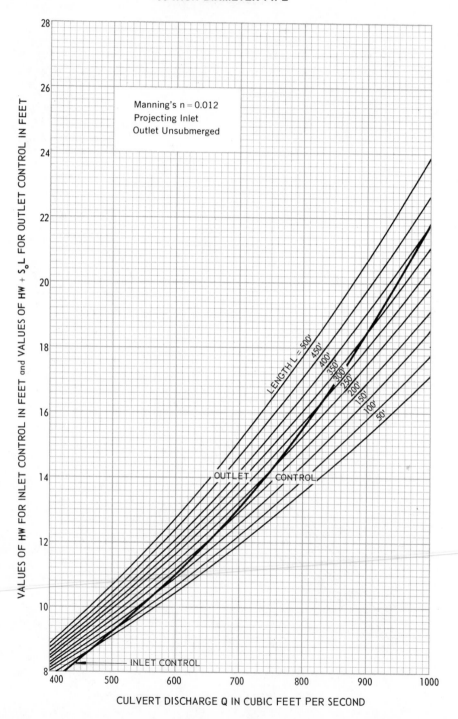

Manning's n = 0.012
Projecting Inlet
Outlet Unsubmerged

VALUES OF HW FOR INLET CONTROL IN FEET and VALUES OF HW + S_oL FOR OUTLET CONTROL IN FEET

LENGTH L = 500'
450'
400'
350'
300'
250'
200'
150'
100'
50'

OUTLET CONTROL

INLET CONTROL

CULVERT DISCHARGE Q IN CUBIC FEET PER SECOND

FIGURE 60

CULVERT CAPACITY
96-INCH DIAMETER PIPE

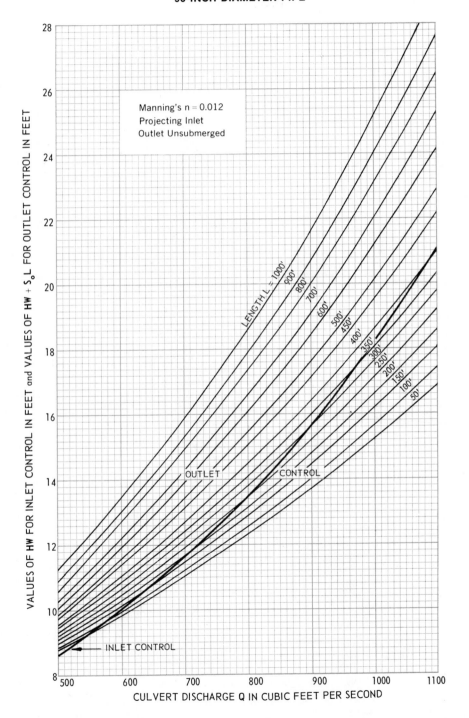

Manning's n = 0.012
Projecting Inlet
Outlet Unsubmerged

VALUES OF HW FOR INLET CONTROL IN FEET and VALUES OF HW + S₀L FOR OUTLET CONTROL IN FEET

LENGTH L = 1000' 900' 800' 700' 600' 500' 450' 400' 350' 300' 250' 200' 150' 100' 50'

OUTLET   CONTROL

INLET CONTROL

CULVERT DISCHARGE Q IN CUBIC FEET PER SECOND

FIGURE 61

CULVERT CAPACITY
102-INCH DIAMETER PIPE

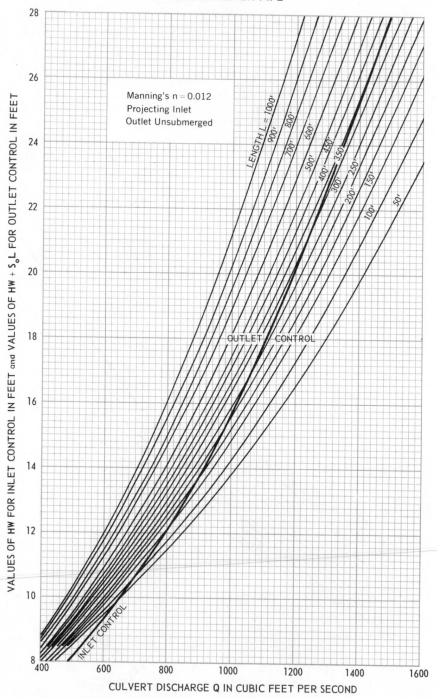

Manning's n = 0.012
Projecting Inlet
Outlet Unsubmerged

VALUES OF HW FOR INLET CONTROL IN FEET and VALUES OF HW + S_oL FOR OUTLET CONTROL IN FEET

LENGTH L = 1000'
900'
800'
700'
600'
500'
450'
400'
350'
300'
250'
200'
150'
100'
50'

OUTLET CONTROL

INLET CONTROL

CULVERT DISCHARGE Q IN CUBIC FEET PER SECOND

FIGURE 62

CULVERT CAPACITY

108-INCH DIAMETER PIPE

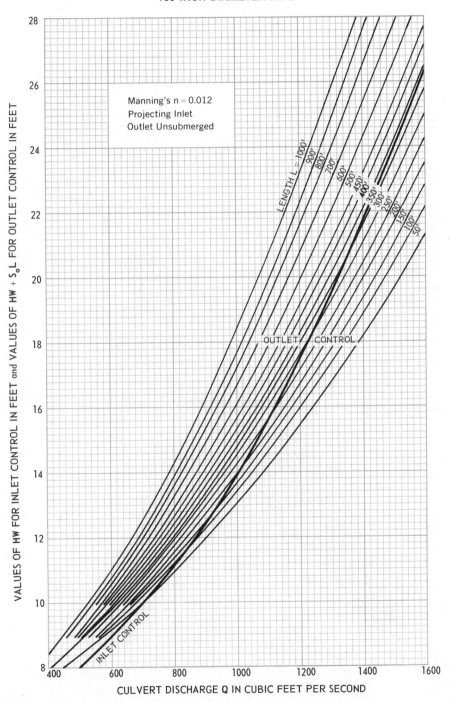

Manning's n = 0.012
Projecting Inlet
Outlet Unsubmerged

FIGURE 63

CULVERT CAPACITY
114-INCH DIAMETER PIPE

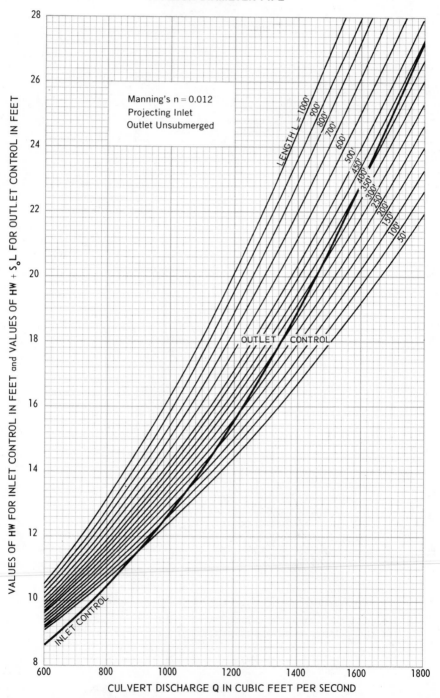

Manning's n = 0.012
Projecting Inlet
Outlet Unsubmerged

VALUES OF HW FOR INLET CONTROL IN FEET and VALUES OF HW + S_oL FOR OUTLET CONTROL IN FEET

CULVERT DISCHARGE Q IN CUBIC FEET PER SECOND

FIGURE 64

CULVERT CAPACITY
120-INCH DIAMETER PIPE

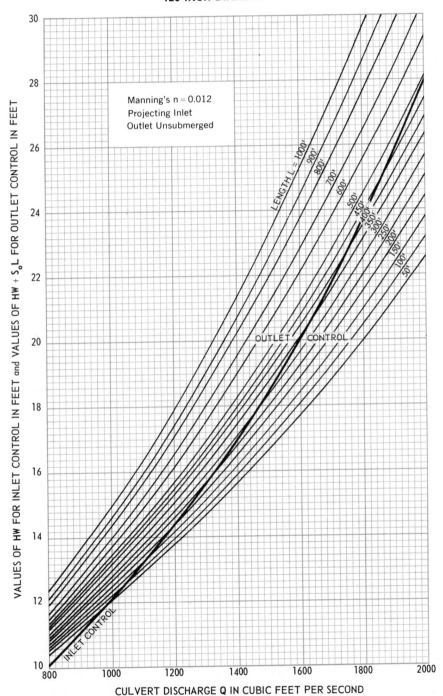

Manning's n = 0.012
Projecting Inlet
Outlet Unsubmerged

VALUES OF HW FOR INLET CONTROL IN FEET and VALUES OF HW + S_oL FOR OUTLET CONTROL IN FEET

LENGTH L = 1000'
900'
800'
700'
600'
500'
450'
400'
350'
300'
250'
200'
150'
100'
50'

OUTLET CONTROL

INLET CONTROL

CULVERT DISCHARGE Q IN CUBIC FEET PER SECOND

FIGURE 65

CULVERT CAPACITY
132-INCH DIAMETER PIPE

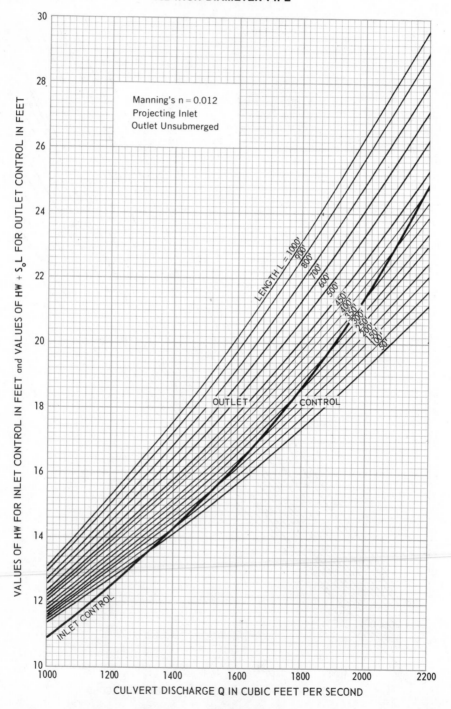

Manning's n = 0.012
Projecting Inlet
Outlet Unsubmerged

VALUES OF HW FOR INLET CONTROL IN FEET and VALUES OF HW + S_oL FOR OUTLET CONTROL IN FEET

LENGTH L = 1000'
900'
800'
700'
600'
500'
450'
400'
350'
300'
250'
200'
150'
100'
50'

OUTLET CONTROL

INLET CONTROL

CULVERT DISCHARGE Q IN CUBIC FEET PER SECOND

FIGURE 66

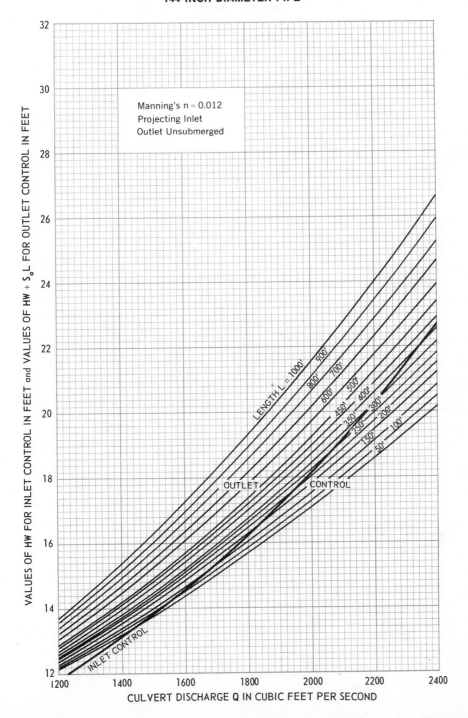

CULVERT CAPACITY
144-INCH DIAMETER PIPE

Manning's n = 0.012
Projecting Inlet
Outlet Unsubmerged

VALUES OF HW FOR INLET CONTROL IN FEET and VALUES OF HW + S_oL FOR OUTLET CONTROL IN FEET

LENGTH L = 1000' 900' 800' 700' 600' 500' 450' 400' 350' 300' 250' 200' 150' 100' 50'

OUTLET CONTROL

INLET CONTROL

CULVERT DISCHARGE Q IN CUBIC FEET PER SECOND

FIGURE 67

CULVERT CAPACITY
14 x 23-INCH (RISE x SPAN) HORIZONTAL ELLIPTICAL
EQUIVALENT 18-INCH CIRCULAR

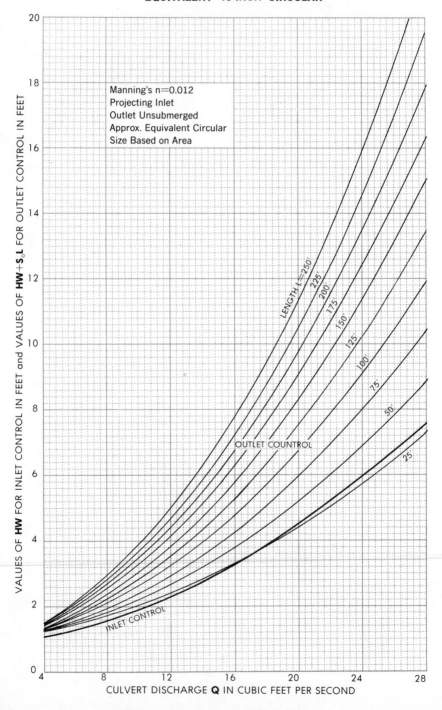

Manning's n=0.012
Projecting Inlet
Outlet Unsubmerged
Approx. Equivalent Circular
Size Based on Area

VALUES OF **HW** FOR INLET CONTROL IN FEET and VALUES OF **HW+S₀L** FOR OUTLET CONTROL IN FEET

CULVERT DISCHARGE **Q** IN CUBIC FEET PER SECOND

FIGURE 68

CULVERT CAPACITY
19 x 30-INCH (RISE x SPAN) HORIZONTAL ELLIPTICAL
EQUIVALENT 24-INCH CIRCULAR

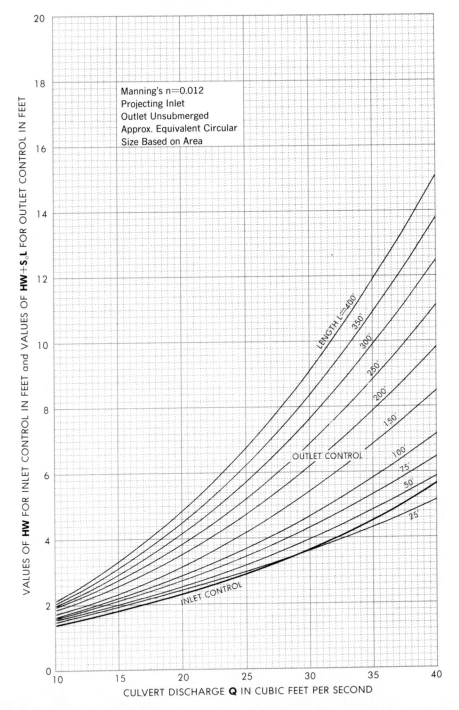

Manning's n=0.012
Projecting Inlet
Outlet Unsubmerged
Approx. Equivalent Circular
Size Based on Area

VALUES OF **HW** FOR INLET CONTROL IN FEET and VALUES OF **HW+S$_o$L** FOR OUTLET CONTROL IN FEET

CULVERT DISCHARGE **Q** IN CUBIC FEET PER SECOND

FIGURE 69

CULVERT CAPACITY
24 x 38-INCH (RISE x SPAN) HORIZONTAL ELLIPTICAL
EQUIVALENT 30-INCH CIRCULAR

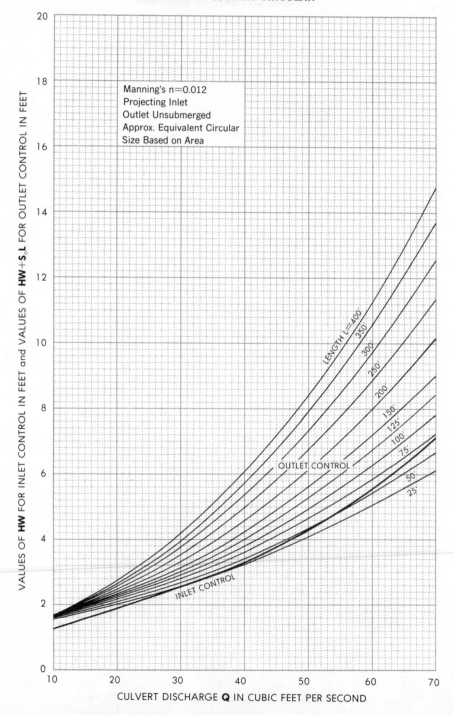

Manning's n=0.012
Projecting Inlet
Outlet Unsubmerged
Approx. Equivalent Circular
Size Based on Area

VALUES OF **HW** FOR INLET CONTROL IN FEET and VALUES OF **HW+S₀L** FOR OUTLET CONTROL IN FEET

LENGTH L=400'
350'
300'
250'
200'
150'
125'
100'
75'
50'
25'

OUTLET CONTROL

INLET CONTROL

CULVERT DISCHARGE **Q** IN CUBIC FEET PER SECOND

FIGURE 70

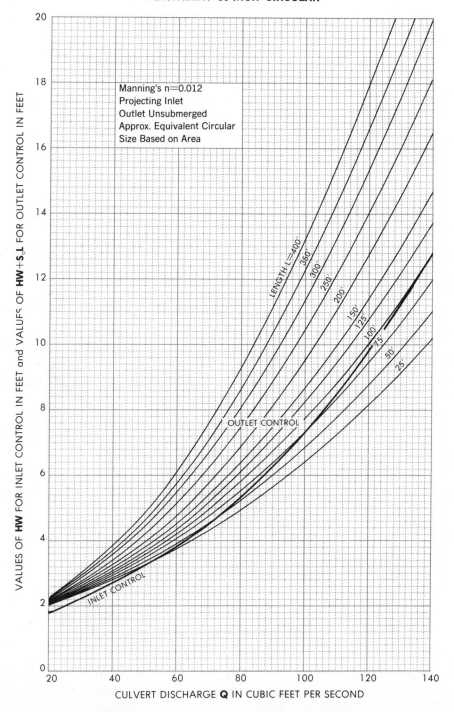

CULVERT CAPACITY
29 x 45-INCH (RISE x SPAN) HORIZONTAL ELLIPTICAL
EQUIVALENT 36-INCH CIRCULAR

Manning's n=0.012
Projecting Inlet
Outlet Unsubmerged
Approx. Equivalent Circular
Size Based on Area

LENGTH L=400'
350'
300'
250'
200'
150'
125'
100'
75'
50'
25'

OUTLET CONTROL

INLET CONTROL

VALUES OF **HW** FOR INLET CONTROL IN FEET and VALUES OF **HW+S₀L** FOR OUTLET CONTROL IN FEET

CULVERT DISCHARGE **Q** IN CUBIC FEET PER SECOND

FIGURE 71

CULVERT CAPACITY
34 x 54-INCH (RISE x SPAN) HORIZONTAL ELLIPTICAL
EQUIVALENT 42-INCH CIRCULAR

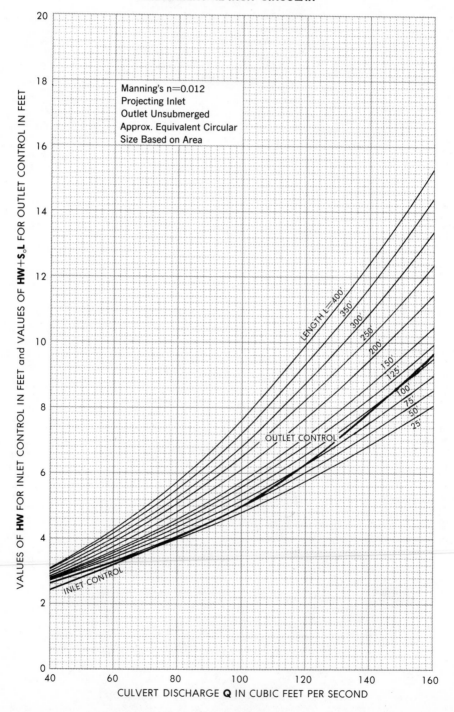

Manning's n=0.012
Projecting Inlet
Outlet Unsubmerged
Approx. Equivalent Circular
Size Based on Area

VALUES OF **HW** FOR INLET CONTROL IN FEET and VALUES OF **HW+S$_o$L** FOR OUTLET CONTROL IN FEET

LENGTH L=400'
350'
300'
250'
200'
150'
125'
100'
75'
50'
25'

OUTLET CONTROL

INLET CONTROL

CULVERT DISCHARGE **Q** IN CUBIC FEET PER SECOND

FIGURE 72

CULVERT CAPACITY
38 x 60-INCH (RISE x SPAN) HORIZONTAL ELLIPTICAL
EQUIVALENT 48-INCH CIRCULAR

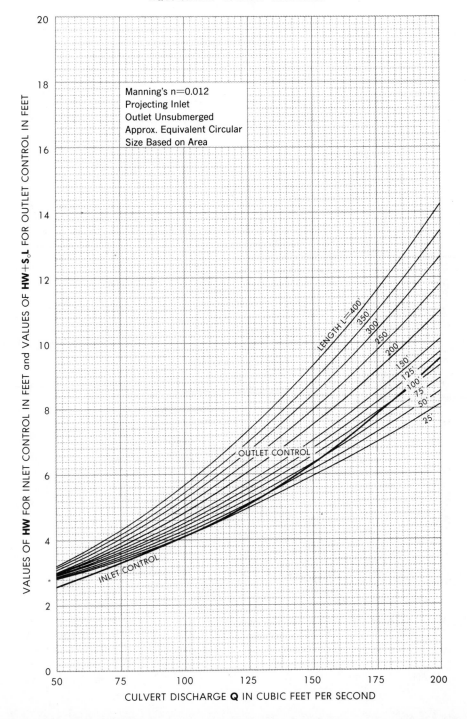

Manning's n=0.012
Projecting Inlet
Outlet Unsubmerged
Approx. Equivalent Circular
Size Based on Area

VALUES OF **HW** FOR INLET CONTROL IN FEET and VALUES OF **HW**+**S₀L** FOR OUTLET CONTROL IN FEET

LENGTH L = 400' 350' 300' 250' 200' 150' 125' 100' 75' 50' 25'

OUTLET CONTROL

INLET CONTROL

CULVERT DISCHARGE **Q** IN CUBIC FEET PER SECOND

FIGURE 73

CULVERT CAPACITY
43 x 68-INCH (RISE x SPAN) HORIZONTAL ELLIPTICAL
EQUIVALENT 54-INCH CIRCULAR

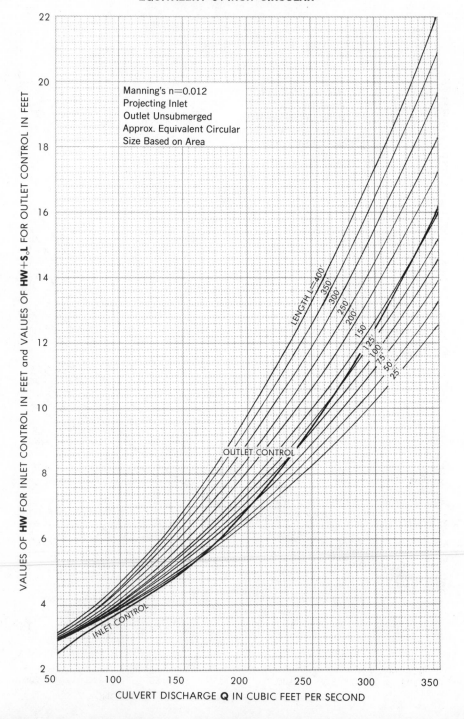

Manning's n=0.012
Projecting Inlet
Outlet Unsubmerged
Approx. Equivalent Circular
Size Based on Area

VALUES OF **HW** FOR INLET CONTROL IN FEET and VALUES OF **HW+S$_o$L** FOR OUTLET CONTROL IN FEET

LENGTH L=400'
350'
300'
250'
200'
150'
125'
100'
75'
50'
25'

OUTLET CONTROL

INLET CONTROL

CULVERT DISCHARGE **Q** IN CUBIC FEET PER SECOND

FIGURE 74

CULVERT CAPACITY
48 x 76-INCH (RISE x SPAN) HORIZONTAL ELLIPTICAL
EQUIVALENT 60-INCH CIRCULAR

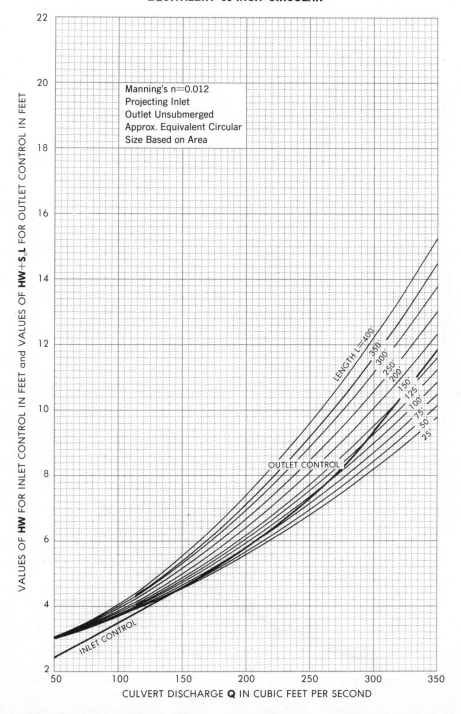

Manning's n=0.012
Projecting Inlet
Outlet Unsubmerged
Approx. Equivalent Circular
Size Based on Area

VALUES OF **HW** FOR INLET CONTROL IN FEET and VALUES OF **HW+S₀L** FOR OUTLET CONTROL IN FEET

LENGTH L=400'
350'
300'
250'
200'
150'
125'
100'
75'
50'
25'

OUTLET CONTROL

INLET CONTROL

CULVERT DISCHARGE **Q** IN CUBIC FEET PER SECOND

FIGURE 75

CULVERT CAPACITY
53 x 83-INCH (RISE x SPAN) HORIZONTAL ELLIPTICAL
EQUIVALENT 66-INCH CIRCULAR

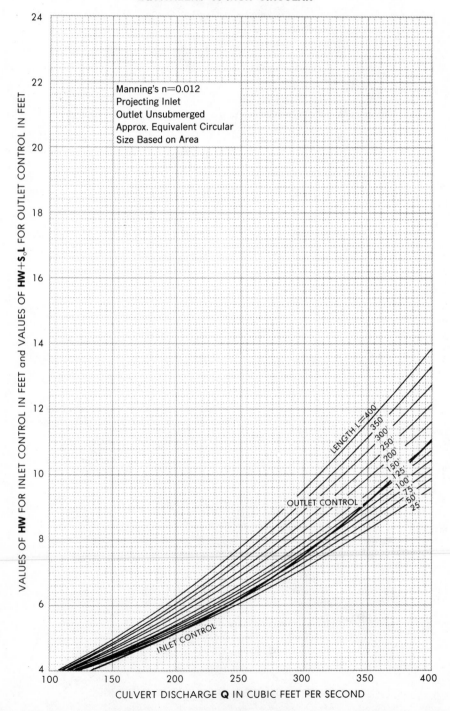

Manning's n=0.012
Projecting Inlet
Outlet Unsubmerged
Approx. Equivalent Circular
Size Based on Area

VALUES OF **HW** FOR INLET CONTROL IN FEET and VALUES OF **HW+S₀L** FOR OUTLET CONTROL IN FEET

LENGTH L=400'
350'
300'
250'
200'
150'
125'
100'
75'
50'
25'

OUTLET CONTROL

INLET CONTROL

CULVERT DISCHARGE **Q** IN CUBIC FEET PER SECOND

FIGURE 76

CULVERT CAPACITY
58 x 91-INCH (RISE x SPAN) HORIZONTAL ELLIPTICAL
EQUIVALENT 72-INCH CIRCULAR

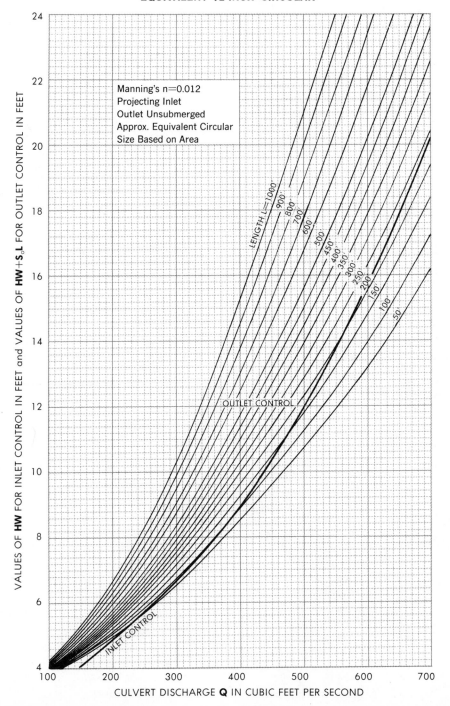

Manning's n=0.012
Projecting Inlet
Outlet Unsubmerged
Approx. Equivalent Circular
Size Based on Area

VALUES OF **HW** FOR INLET CONTROL IN FEET and VALUES OF **HW+S₀L** FOR OUTLET CONTROL IN FEET

CULVERT DISCHARGE **Q** IN CUBIC FEET PER SECOND

FIGURE 77

CULVERT CAPACITY
63 x 98-INCH (RISE x SPAN) HORIZONTAL ELLIPTICAL
EQUIVALENT 78-INCH CIRCULAR

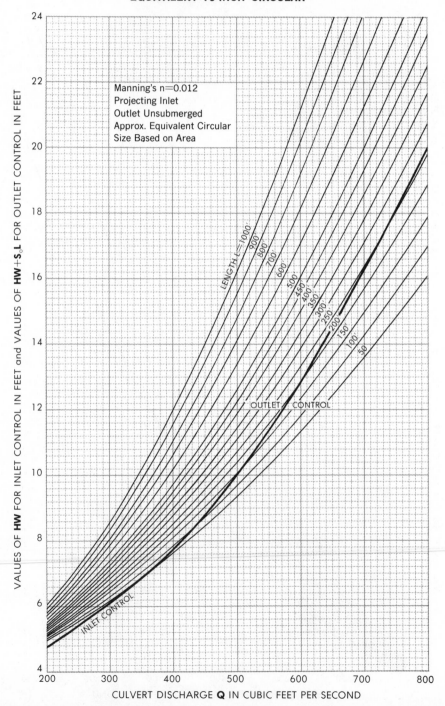

Manning's n=0.012
Projecting Inlet
Outlet Unsubmerged
Approx. Equivalent Circular
Size Based on Area

VALUES OF **HW** FOR INLET CONTROL IN FEET and VALUES OF **HW+S₀L** FOR OUTLET CONTROL IN FEET

CULVERT DISCHARGE **Q** IN CUBIC FEET PER SECOND

FIGURE 78

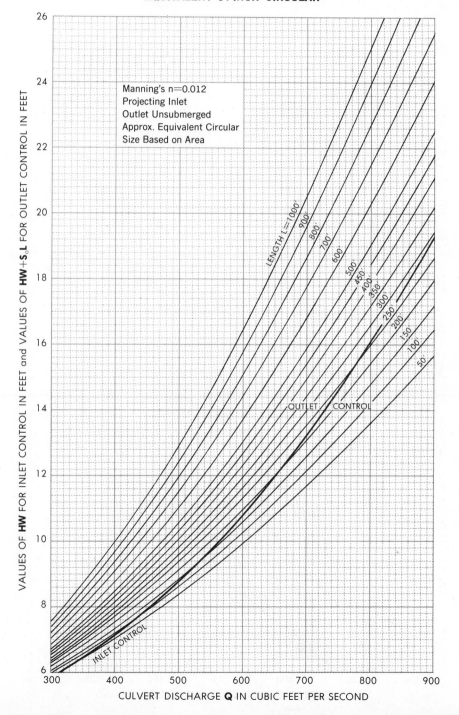

CULVERT CAPACITY
68 x 106-INCH (RISE x SPAN) HORIZONTAL ELLIPTICAL
EQUIVALENT 84-INCH CIRCULAR

Manning's n=0.012
Projecting Inlet
Outlet Unsubmerged
Approx. Equivalent Circular
Size Based on Area

VALUES OF **HW** FOR INLET CONTROL IN FEET and VALUES OF **HW+S₀L** FOR OUTLET CONTROL IN FEET

CULVERT DISCHARGE **Q** IN CUBIC FEET PER SECOND

FIGURE 79

CULVERT CAPACITY
72 x 113-INCH (RISE x SPAN) HORIZONTAL ELLIPTICAL
EQUIVALENT 90-INCH CIRCULAR

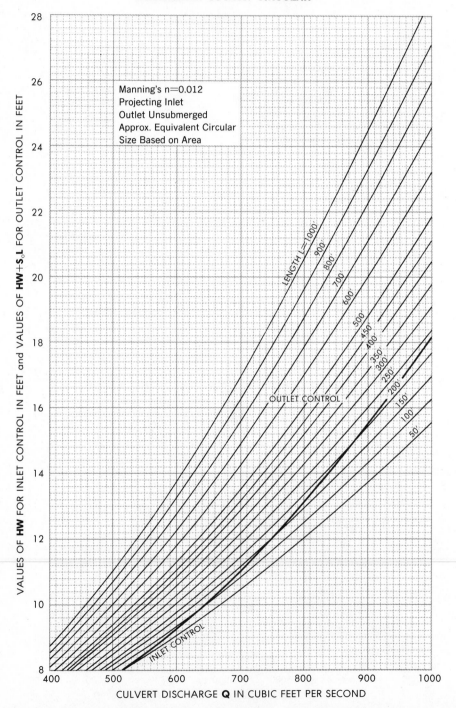

Manning's n=0.012
Projecting Inlet
Outlet Unsubmerged
Approx. Equivalent Circular
Size Based on Area

VALUES OF **HW** FOR INLET CONTROL IN FEET and VALUES OF **HW+S₀L** FOR OUTLET CONTROL IN FEET

CULVERT DISCHARGE **Q** IN CUBIC FEET PER SECOND

FIGURE 80

CULVERT CAPACITY
77 x 121-INCH (RISE x SPAN) HORIZONTAL ELLIPTICAL
EQUIVALENT 96-INCH CIRCULAR

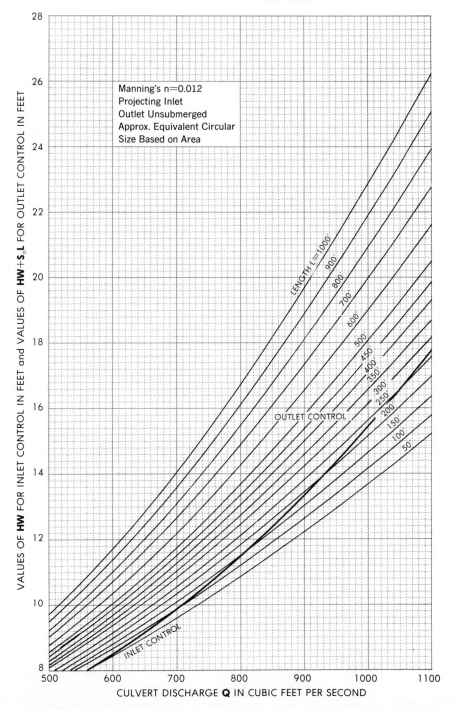

Manning's n=0.012
Projecting Inlet
Outlet Unsubmerged
Approx. Equivalent Circular
Size Based on Area

LENGTH L=1000'
900'
800'
700'
600'
500'
450'
400'
350'
300'
250'
200'
150'
100'
50'

OUTLET CONTROL

INLET CONTROL

VALUES OF **HW** FOR INLET CONTROL IN FEET and VALUES OF **HW+S$_o$L** FOR OUTLET CONTROL IN FEET

CULVERT DISCHARGE **Q** IN CUBIC FEET PER SECOND

FIGURE 81

CULVERT CAPACITY
82 x 128-INCH (RISE x SPAN) HORIZONTAL ELLIPTICAL
EQUIVALENT 102-INCH CIRCULAR

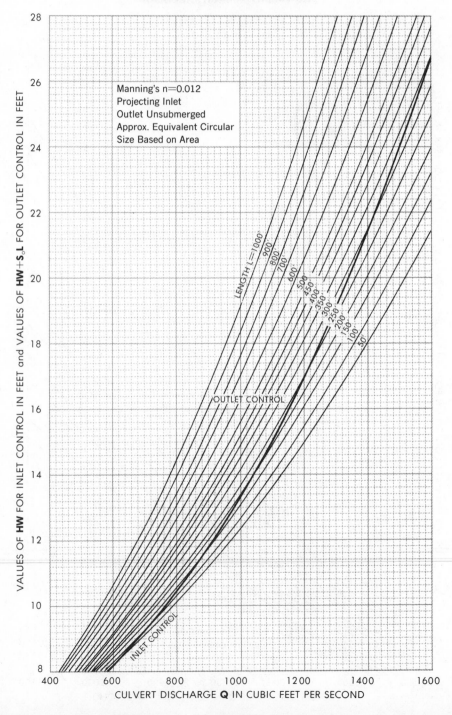

Manning's n=0.012
Projecting Inlet
Outlet Unsubmerged
Approx. Equivalent Circular
Size Based on Area

VALUES OF **HW** FOR INLET CONTROL IN FEET and VALUES OF **HW+S₀L** FOR OUTLET CONTROL IN FEET

LENGTH L=1000', 900', 800', 700', 600', 500', 450', 400', 350', 300', 250', 200', 150', 100', 50'

OUTLET CONTROL

INLET CONTROL

CULVERT DISCHARGE **Q** IN CUBIC FEET PER SECOND

FIGURE 82

CULVERT CAPACITY
87 x 136-INCH (RISE x SPAN) HORIZONTAL ELLIPTICAL
EQUIVALENT 108-INCH CIRCULAR

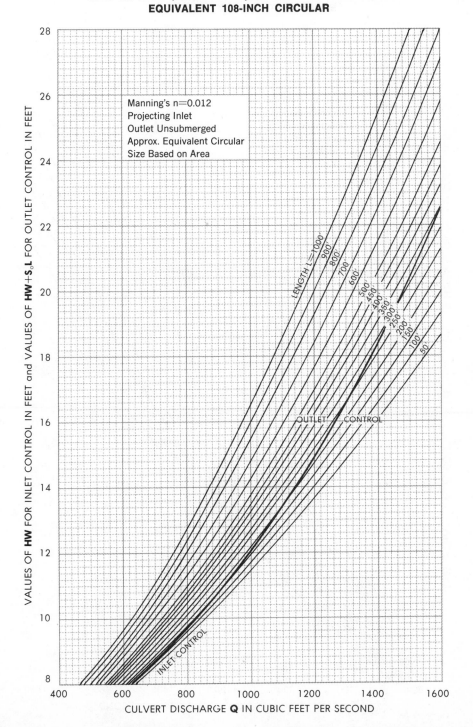

Manning's n=0.012
Projecting Inlet
Outlet Unsubmerged
Approx. Equivalent Circular
Size Based on Area

VALUES OF **HW** FOR INLET CONTROL IN FEET and VALUES OF **HW+S₀L** FOR OUTLET CONTROL IN FEET

CULVERT DISCHARGE **Q** IN CUBIC FEET PER SECOND

FIGURE 83

CULVERT CAPACITY
92 x 143-INCH (RISE x SPAN) HORIZONTAL ELLIPTICAL
EQUIVALENT 114-INCH CIRCULAR

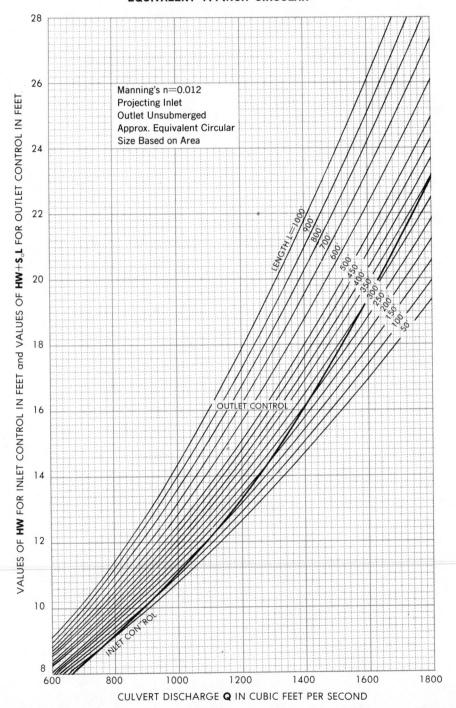

Manning's n=0.012
Projecting Inlet
Outlet Unsubmerged
Approx. Equivalent Circular
Size Based on Area

VALUES OF **HW** FOR INLET CONTROL IN FEET and VALUES OF **HW+S₀L** FOR OUTLET CONTROL IN FEET

CULVERT DISCHARGE **Q** IN CUBIC FEET PER SECOND

FIGURE 84

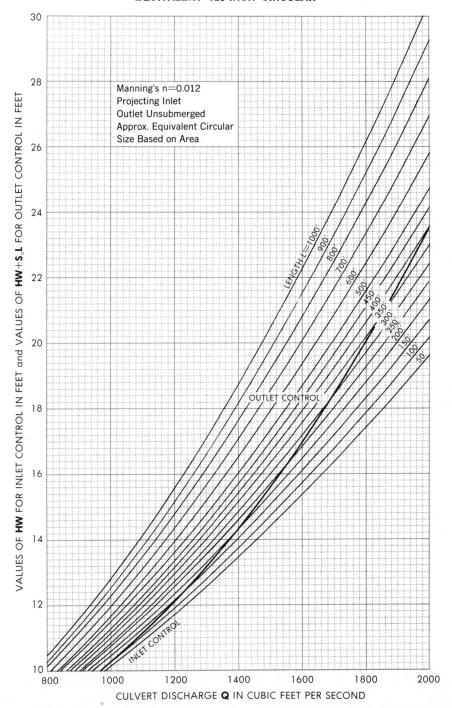

CULVERT CAPACITY
97 x 151-INCH (RISE x SPAN) HORIZONTAL ELLIPTICAL
EQUIVALENT 120-INCH CIRCULAR

Manning's n=0.012
Projecting Inlet
Outlet Unsubmerged
Approx. Equivalent Circular
Size Based on Area

OUTLET CONTROL

INLET CONTROL

LENGTH L=1000' 900' 800' 700' 600' 500' 450' 400' 350' 300' 250' 200' 150' 100' 50'

VALUES OF **HW** FOR INLET CONTROL IN FEET and VALUES OF **HW+S₀L** FOR OUTLET CONTROL IN FEET

CULVERT DISCHARGE **Q** IN CUBIC FEET PER SECOND

FIGURE 85

CULVERT CAPACITY
106 x 166-INCH (RISE x SPAN) HORIZONTAL ELLIPTICAL
EQUIVALENT 132-INCH CIRCULAR

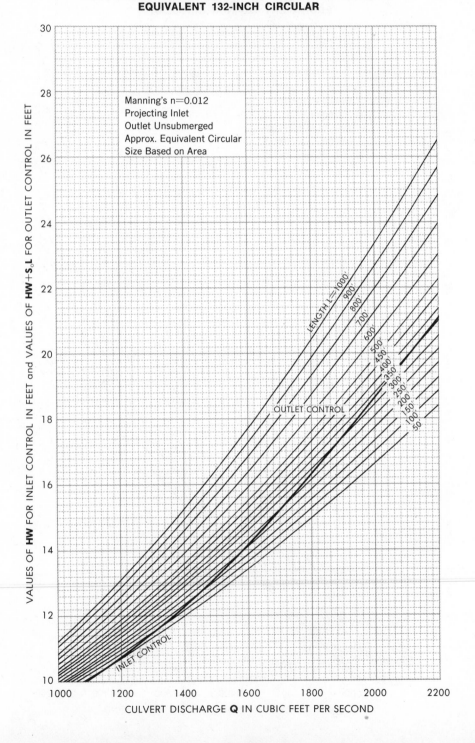

Manning's n=0.012
Projecting Inlet
Outlet Unsubmerged
Approx. Equivalent Circular
Size Based on Area

VALUES OF **HW** FOR INLET CONTROL IN FEET and VALUES OF **HW+S₀L** FOR OUTLET CONTROL IN FEET

LENGTH L = 1000'

OUTLET CONTROL

INLET CONTROL

CULVERT DISCHARGE **Q** IN CUBIC FEET PER SECOND

FIGURE 86

CULVERT CAPACITY
116 x 180-INCH (RISE x SPAN) HORIZONTAL ELLIPTICAL
EQUIVALENT 144-INCH CIRCULAR

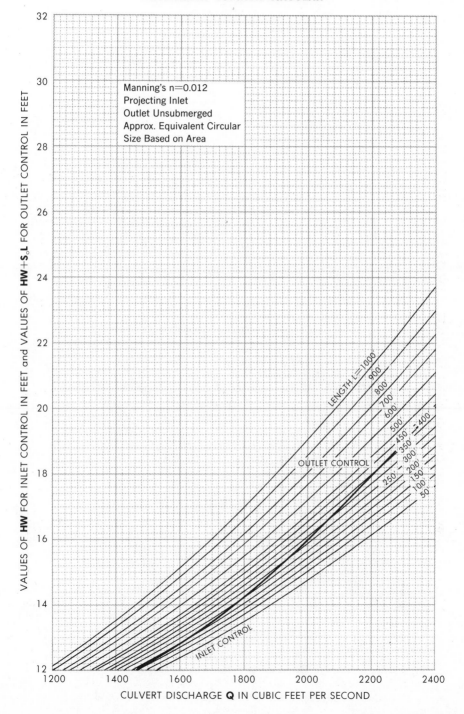

Manning's n=0.012
Projecting Inlet
Outlet Unsubmerged
Approx. Equivalent Circular
Size Based on Area

VALUES OF **HW** FOR INLET CONTROL IN FEET and VALUES OF **HW+S₀L** FOR OUTLET CONTROL IN FEET

CULVERT DISCHARGE **Q** IN CUBIC FEET PER SECOND

FIGURE 87

CULVERT CAPACITY
11 x 18-INCH (RISE x SPAN) ARCH
EQUIVALENT 15-INCH CIRCULAR

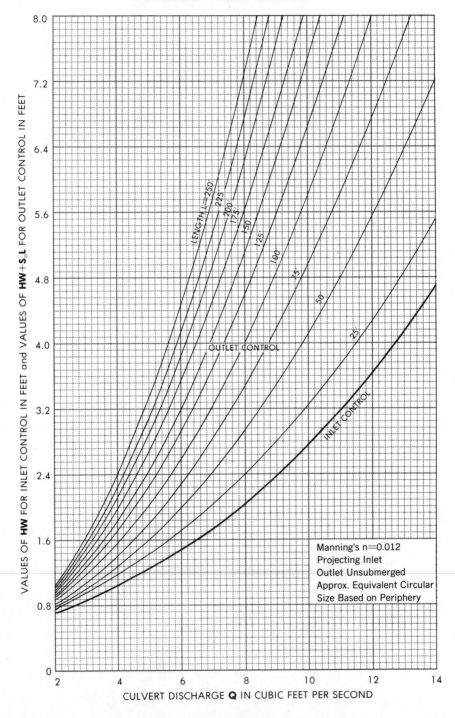

Manning's n=0.012
Projecting Inlet
Outlet Unsubmerged
Approx. Equivalent Circular
Size Based on Periphery

CULVERT DISCHARGE **Q** IN CUBIC FEET PER SECOND

VALUES OF **HW** FOR INLET CONTROL IN FEET and VALUES OF **HW+S₀L** FOR OUTLET CONTROL IN FEET

FIGURE 88

CULVERT CAPACITY
13 x 22-INCH (RISE x SPAN) ARCH
EQUIVALENT 18-INCH CIRCULAR

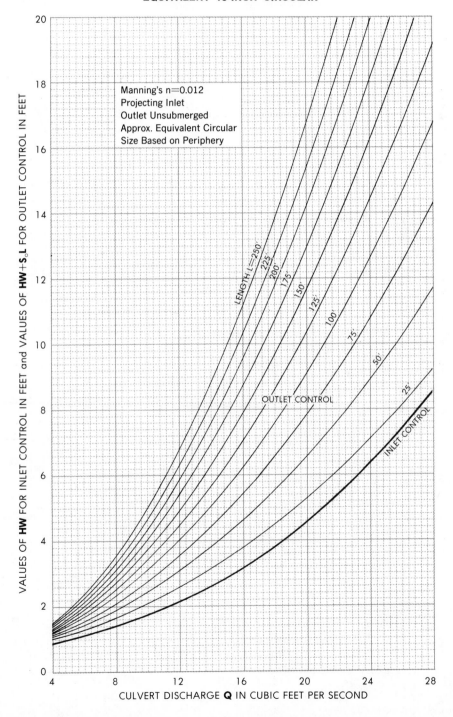

Manning's n=0.012
Projecting Inlet
Outlet Unsubmerged
Approx. Equivalent Circular
Size Based on Periphery

LENGTH L=250'
225'
200'
175'
150'
125'
100'
75'
50'
25'

OUTLET CONTROL

INLET CONTROL

VALUES OF **HW** FOR INLET CONTROL IN FEET and VALUES OF **HW+S₀L** FOR OUTLET CONTROL IN FEET

CULVERT DISCHARGE **Q** IN CUBIC FEET PER SECOND

FIGURE 89

CULVERT CAPACITY
15 x 26-INCH (RISE x SPAN) ARCH
EQUIVALENT 21-INCH CIRCULAR

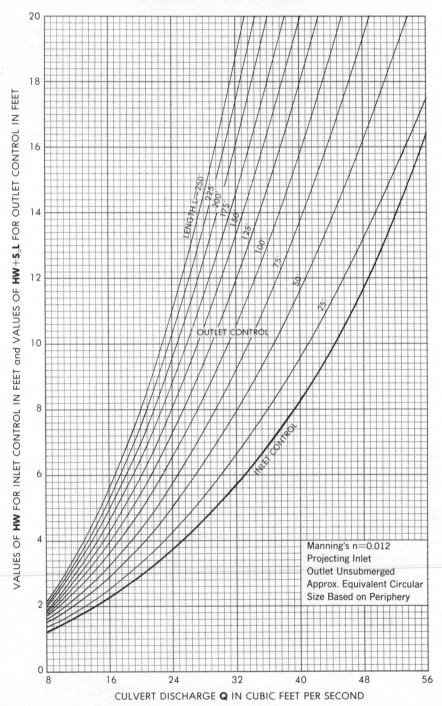

VALUES OF **HW** FOR INLET CONTROL IN FEET and VALUES OF **HW+S$_o$L** FOR OUTLET CONTROL IN FEET

LENGTH L=250' 225' 200' 175' 150' 125' 100' 75' 50' 25'

OUTLET CONTROL

INLET CONTROL

Manning's n=0.012
Projecting Inlet
Outlet Unsubmerged
Approx. Equivalent Circular
Size Based on Periphery

CULVERT DISCHARGE **Q** IN CUBIC FEET PER SECOND

FIGURE 90

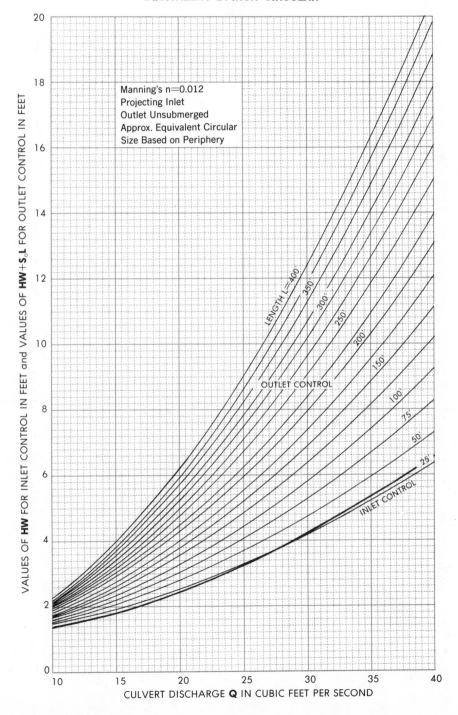

CULVERT CAPACITY
18 x 28-INCH (RISE x SPAN) ARCH
EQUIVALENT 24-INCH CIRCULAR

Manning's n=0.012
Projecting Inlet
Outlet Unsubmerged
Approx. Equivalent Circular
Size Based on Periphery

LENGTH L=400'
350'
300'
250'
200'
150'
100'
75'
50'
25'

OUTLET CONTROL

INLET CONTROL

VALUES OF **HW** FOR INLET CONTROL IN FEET and VALUES OF **HW+S₀L** FOR OUTLET CONTROL IN FEET

CULVERT DISCHARGE **Q** IN CUBIC FEET PER SECOND

FIGURE 91

CULVERT CAPACITY
22 x 36-INCH (RISE x SPAN) ARCH
EQUIVALENT 30-INCH CIRCULAR

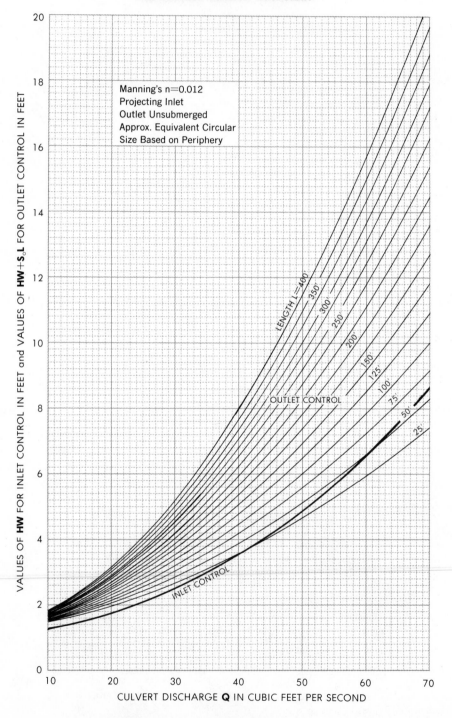

Manning's n=0.012
Projecting Inlet
Outlet Unsubmerged
Approx. Equivalent Circular
Size Based on Periphery

VALUES OF **HW** FOR INLET CONTROL IN FEET and VALUES OF **HW+S₀L** FOR OUTLET CONTROL IN FEET

LENGTH L=400'
350'
300'
250'
200'
150'
125'
100'
75'
50'
25'

OUTLET CONTROL

INLET CONTROL

CULVERT DISCHARGE **Q** IN CUBIC FEET PER SECOND

FIGURE 92

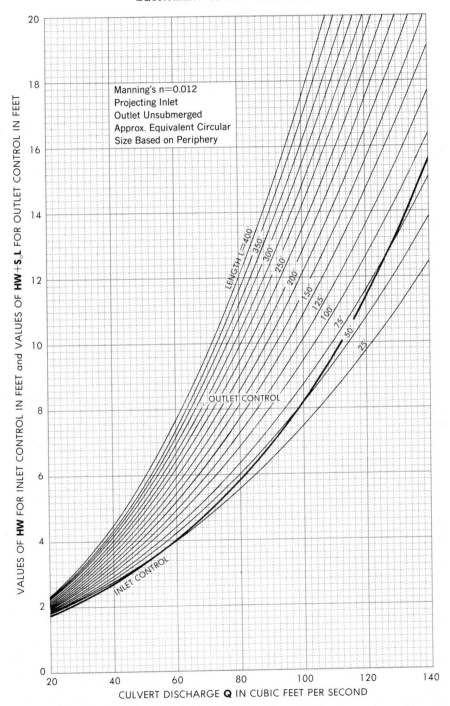

CULVERT CAPACITY
27 x 44-INCH (RISE x SPAN) ARCH
EQUIVALENT 36-INCH CIRCULAR

Manning's n=0.012
Projecting Inlet
Outlet Unsubmerged
Approx. Equivalent Circular
Size Based on Periphery

VALUES OF **HW** FOR INLET CONTROL IN FEET and VALUES OF **HW**+**S**₀**L** FOR OUTLET CONTROL IN FEET

LENGTH L=400'
350'
300'
250'
200'
150'
125'
100'
75'
50'
25'

OUTLET CONTROL

INLET CONTROL

CULVERT DISCHARGE **Q** IN CUBIC FEET PER SECOND

FIGURE 93

CULVERT CAPACITY
31 x 51-INCH (RISE x SPAN) ARCH
EQUIVALENT 42-INCH CIRCULAR

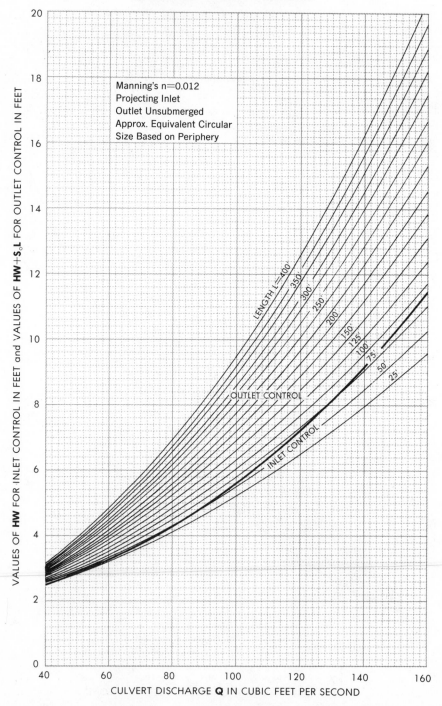

Manning's n=0.012
Projecting Inlet
Outlet Unsubmerged
Approx. Equivalent Circular
Size Based on Periphery

VALUES OF **HW** FOR INLET CONTROL IN FEET and VALUES OF **HW+S₀L** FOR OUTLET CONTROL IN FEET

LENGTH L=400'
350'
300'
250'
200'
150'
125'
100'
75'
50'
25'

OUTLET CONTROL

INLET CONTROL

CULVERT DISCHARGE **Q** IN CUBIC FEET PER SECOND

FIGURE 94

CULVERT CAPACITY
36 x 58-INCH (RISE x SPAN) ARCH
EQUIVALENT 48-INCH CIRCULAR

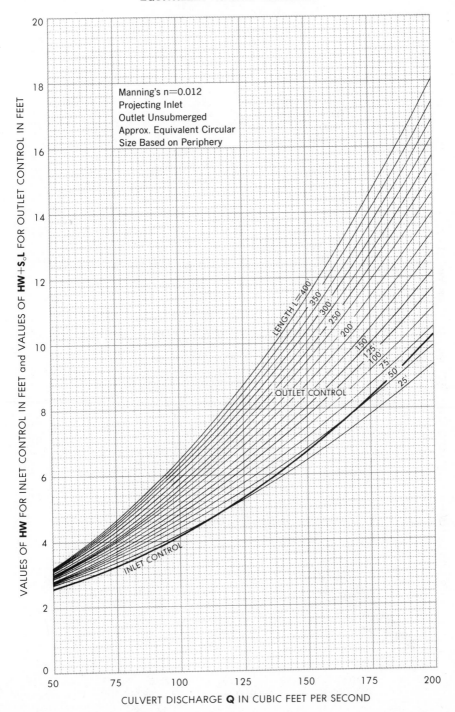

Manning's n=0.012
Projecting Inlet
Outlet Unsubmerged
Approx. Equivalent Circular
Size Based on Periphery

VALUES OF **HW** FOR INLET CONTROL IN FEET and VALUES OF **HW+S₀L** FOR OUTLET CONTROL IN FEET

LENGTH L=400'
350'
300'
250'
200'
150'
125'
100'
75'
50'
25'

OUTLET CONTROL

INLET CONTROL

CULVERT DISCHARGE **Q** IN CUBIC FEET PER SECOND

FIGURE 95

CULVERT CAPACITY
40 x 65-INCH (RISE x SPAN) ARCH
EQUIVALENT 54-INCH CIRCULAR

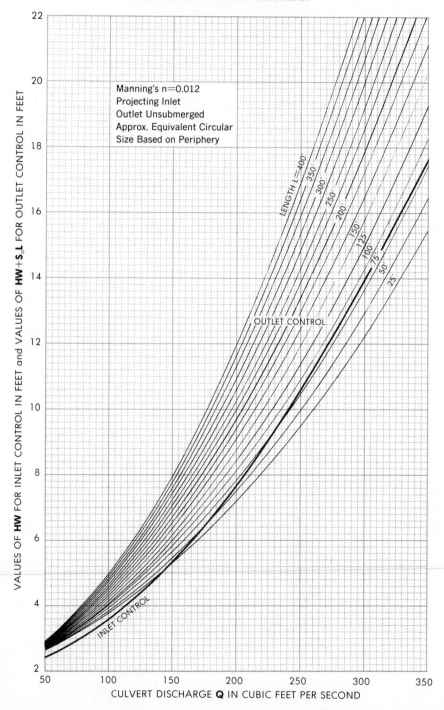

Manning's n=0.012
Projecting Inlet
Outlet Unsubmerged
Approx. Equivalent Circular
Size Based on Periphery

LENGTH L=400'
350'
300'
250'
200'
150'
125'
100'
75'
50'
25'

OUTLET CONTROL

INLET CONTROL

VALUES OF **HW** FOR INLET CONTROL IN FEET and VALUES OF **HW+S**$_o$**L** FOR OUTLET CONTROL IN FEET

CULVERT DISCHARGE **Q** IN CUBIC FEET PER SECOND

FIGURE 96

CULVERT CAPACITY
45 x 73-INCH (RISE x SPAN) ARCH
EQUIVALENT 60-INCH CIRCULAR

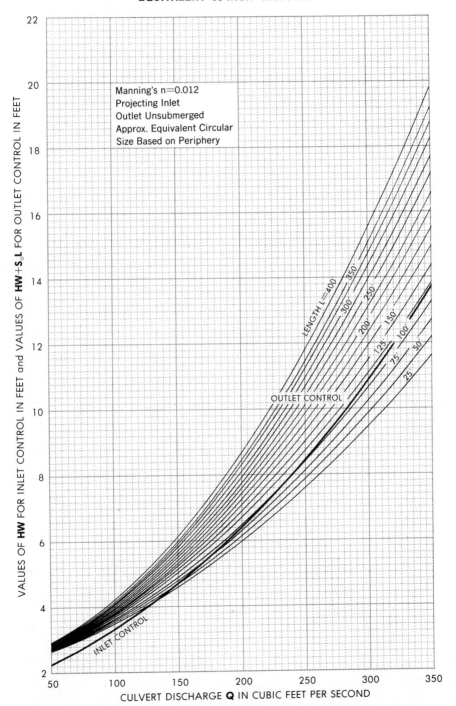

Manning's n=0.012
Projecting Inlet
Outlet Unsubmerged
Approx. Equivalent Circular
Size Based on Periphery

VALUES OF **HW** FOR INLET CONTROL IN FEET and VALUES OF **HW+S₀L** FOR OUTLET CONTROL IN FEET

CULVERT DISCHARGE **Q** IN CUBIC FEET PER SECOND

FIGURE 97

CULVERT CAPACITY
54 x 88-INCH (RISE x SPAN) ARCH
EQUIVALENT 72-INCH CIRCULAR

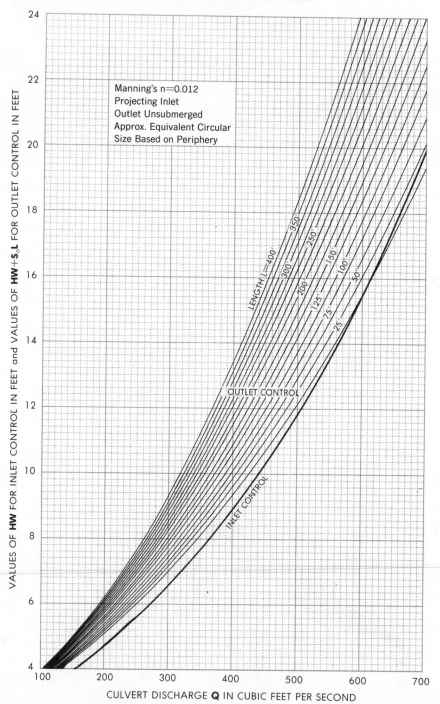

Manning's n=0.012
Projecting Inlet
Outlet Unsubmerged
Approx. Equivalent Circular
Size Based on Periphery

VALUES OF **HW** FOR INLET CONTROL IN FEET and VALUES OF **HW+S₀L** FOR OUTLET CONTROL IN FEET

LENGTH L=400' 350' 300' 250' 200' 150' 125' 100' 75' 50' 25'

OUTLET CONTROL

INLET CONTROL

CULVERT DISCHARGE **Q** IN CUBIC FEET PER SECOND

FIGURE 98

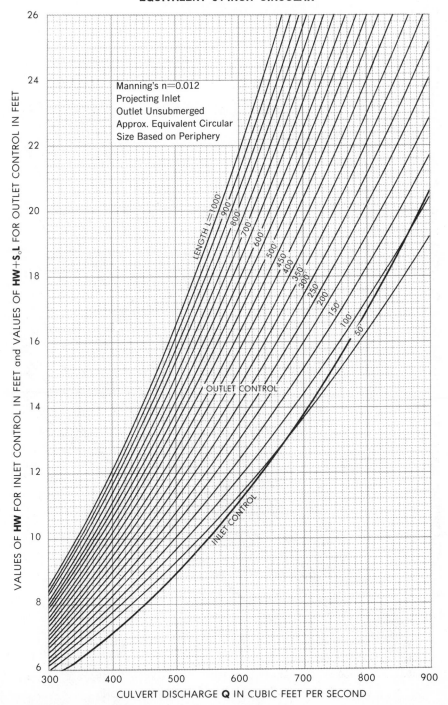

CULVERT CAPACITY
62 x 102-INCH (RISE x SPAN) ARCH
EQUIVALENT 84-INCH CIRCULAR

Manning's n=0.012
Projecting Inlet
Outlet Unsubmerged
Approx. Equivalent Circular
Size Based on Periphery

LENGTH L = 1000'
900'
800'
700'
600'
500'
450'
400'
350'
300'
250'
200'
150'
100'
50'

OUTLET CONTROL

INLET CONTROL

VALUES OF **HW** FOR INLET CONTROL IN FEET and VALUES OF **HW+S₀L** FOR OUTLET CONTROL IN FEET

CULVERT DISCHARGE **Q** IN CUBIC FEET PER SECOND

FIGURE 99

CULVERT CAPACITY
72 x 115-INCH (RISE x SPAN) ARCH
EQUIVALENT 90-INCH CIRCULAR

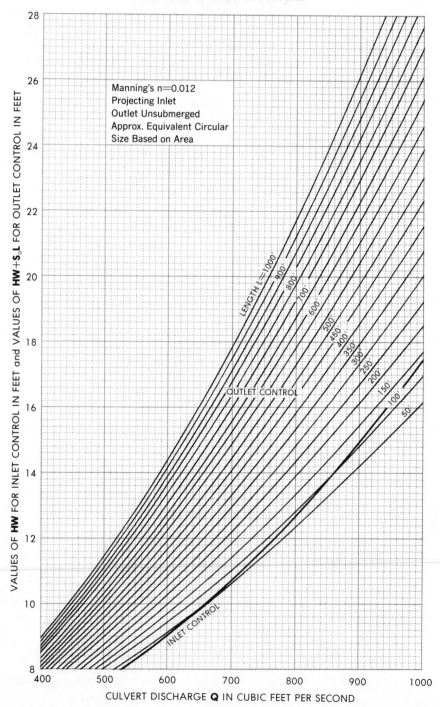

Manning's n=0.012
Projecting Inlet
Outlet Unsubmerged
Approx. Equivalent Circular
Size Based on Area

VALUES OF **HW** FOR INLET CONTROL IN FEET and VALUES OF **HW+S₀L** FOR OUTLET CONTROL IN FEET

OUTLET CONTROL

INLET CONTROL

LENGTH L=1000' 900' 800' 700' 600' 500' 450' 400' 350' 300' 250' 200' 150' 100' 50'

CULVERT DISCHARGE **Q** IN CUBIC FEET PER SECOND

FIGURE 100

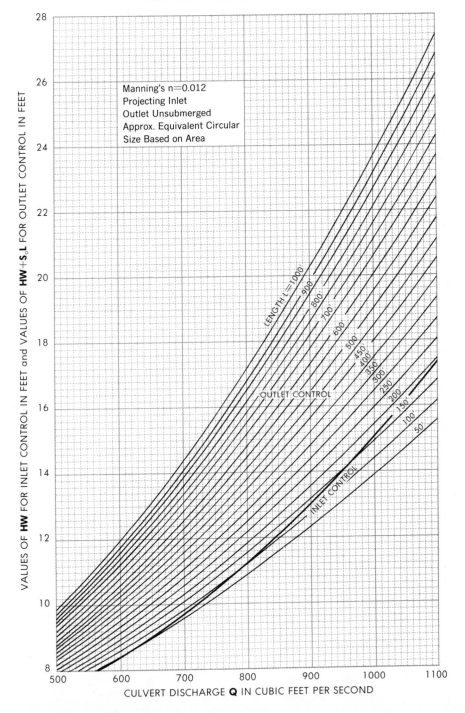

CULVERT CAPACITY
77 x 122-INCH (RISE x SPAN) ARCH
EQUIVALENT 96-INCH CIRCULAR

Manning's n=0.012
Projecting Inlet
Outlet Unsubmerged
Approx. Equivalent Circular
Size Based on Area

VALUES OF **HW** FOR INLET CONTROL IN FEET and VALUES OF **HW+S₀L** FOR OUTLET CONTROL IN FEET

LENGTH L=1000'
900'
800'
700'
600'
500'
450'
400'
350'
300'
250'
200'
150'
100'
50'

OUTLET CONTROL

INLET CONTROL

CULVERT DISCHARGE **Q** IN CUBIC FEET PER SECOND

FIGURE 101

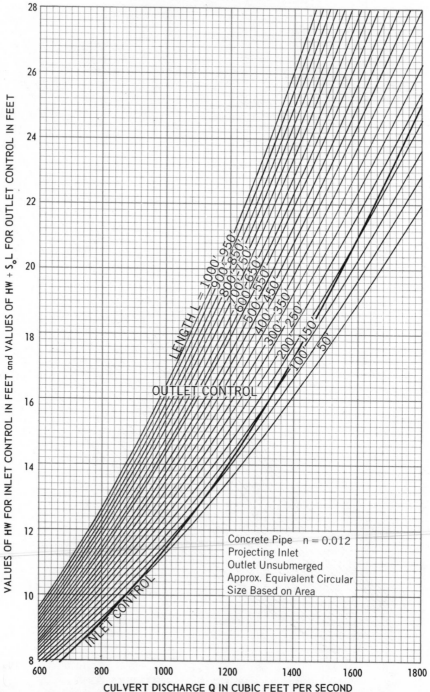

CULVERT CAPACITY
87 x 138-INCH (RISE x SPAN) ARCH
EQUIVALENT 108-INCH CIRCULAR

FIGURE 102

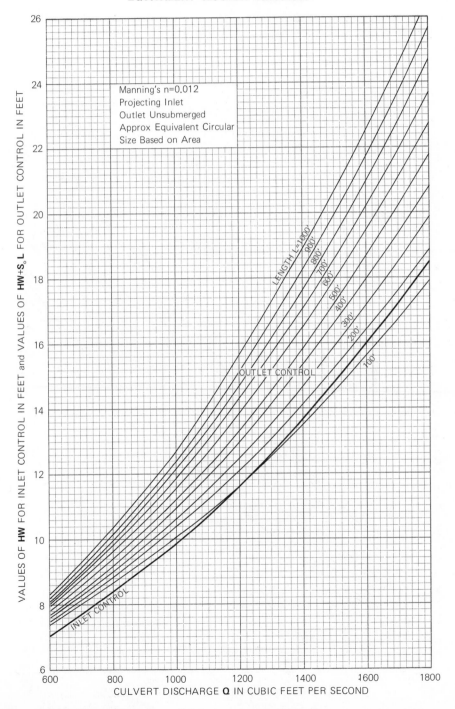

CULVERT CAPACITY
97 x 154-INCH (RISE x SPAN) ARCH
EQUIVALENT 120-INCH CIRCULAR

Manning's n=0.012
Projecting Inlet
Outlet Unsubmerged
Approx Equivalent Circular
Size Based on Area

LENGTH L=1000'
900'
800'
700'
600'
500'
400'
300'
200'
100'

OUTLET CONTROL

INLET CONTROL

VALUES OF **HW** FOR INLET CONTROL IN FEET and VALUES OF **HW+S₀L** FOR OUTLET CONTROL IN FEET

CULVERT DISCHARGE **Q** IN CUBIC FEET PER SECOND

FIGURE 103

CULVERT CAPACITY
106 x 169-INCH (RISE x SPAN) ARCH
EQUIVALENT 132-INCH CIRCULAR

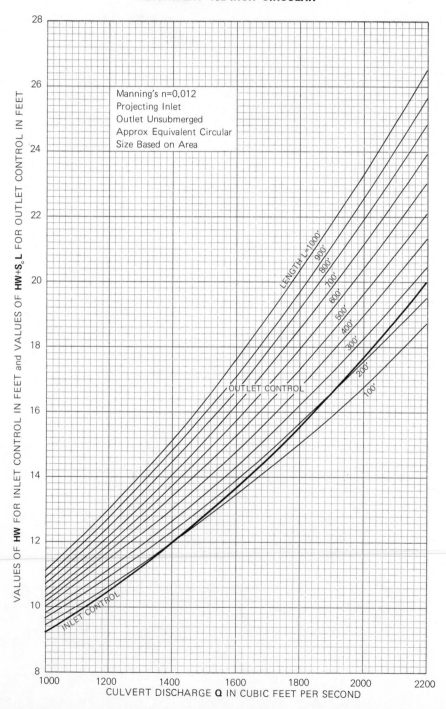

Manning's n=0.012
Projecting Inlet
Outlet Unsubmerged
Approx Equivalent Circular
Size Based on Area

LENGTH L=1000'
900'
800'
700'
600'
500'
400'
300'
200'
100'

OUTLET CONTROL

INLET CONTROL

VALUES OF **HW** FOR INLET CONTROL IN FEET and VALUES OF **HW+S₀L** FOR OUTLET CONTROL IN FEET

CULVERT DISCHARGE **Q** IN CUBIC FEET PER SECOND

FIGURE 104

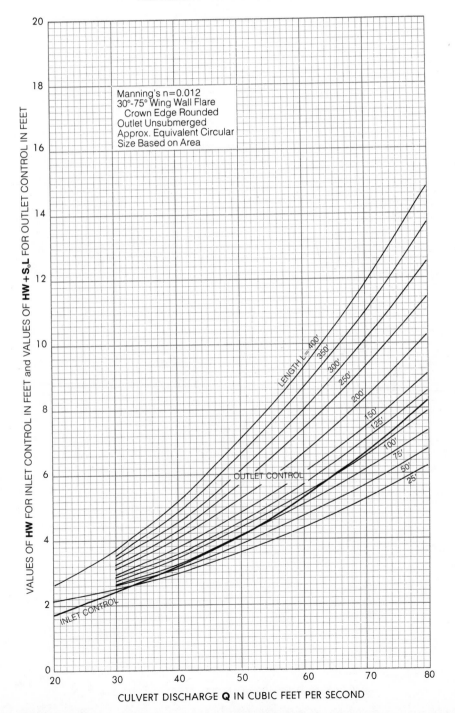

CULVERT CAPACITY
3 x 2-FOOT (SPAN x RISE) BOX SECTION
EQUIVALENT 33-INCH CIRCULAR

Manning's n=0.012
30°-75° Wing Wall Flare
Crown Edge Rounded
Outlet Unsubmerged
Approx. Equivalent Circular
Size Based on Area

VALUES OF **HW** FOR INLET CONTROL IN FEET and VALUES OF **HW + S₀L** FOR OUTLET CONTROL IN FEET

LENGTH L = 400'
350'
300'
250'
200'
150'
125'
100'
75'
50'
25'

OUTLET CONTROL

INLET CONTROL

CULVERT DISCHARGE **Q** IN CUBIC FEET PER SECOND

FIGURE 105

CULVERT CAPACITY
3 x 3-FOOT (SPAN x RISE) BOX SECTION
EQUIVALENT 39-INCH CIRCULAR

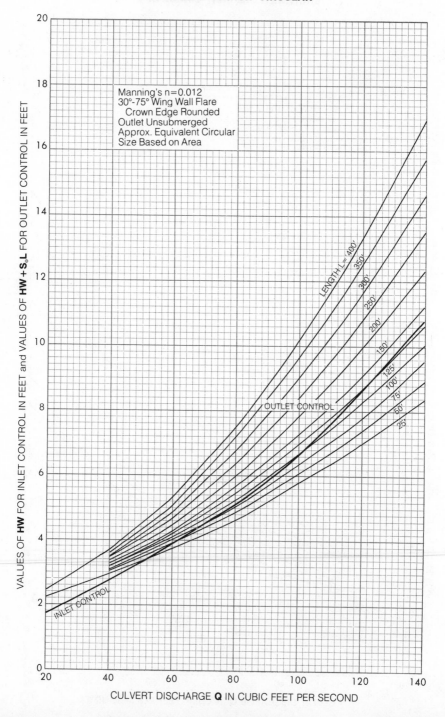

Manning's n=0.012
30°-75° Wing Wall Flare
  Crown Edge Rounded
Outlet Unsubmerged
Approx. Equivalent Circular
Size Based on Area

VALUES OF **HW** FOR INLET CONTROL IN FEET and VALUES OF **HW + S₀L** FOR OUTLET CONTROL IN FEET

CULVERT DISCHARGE **Q** IN CUBIC FEET PER SECOND

FIGURE 106

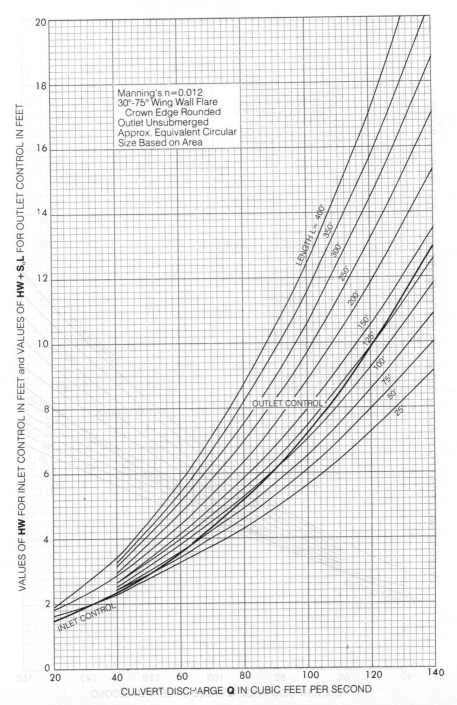

**CULVERT CAPACITY
4 x 2-FOOT (SPAN x RISE) BOX SECTION
EQUIVALENT 36-INCH CIRCULAR**

Manning's n=0.012
30°-75° Wing Wall Flare
Crown Edge Rounded
Outlet Unsubmerged
Approx. Equivalent Circular
Size Based on Area

VALUES OF **HW** FOR INLET CONTROL IN FEET and VALUES OF **HW + S₀L** FOR OUTLET CONTROL IN FEET

CULVERT DISCHARGE **Q** IN CUBIC FEET PER SECOND

LENGTH L = 400'
350'
300'
250'
200'
150'
125'
100'
75'
50'
25'

OUTLET CONTROL

INLET CONTROL

FIGURE 107

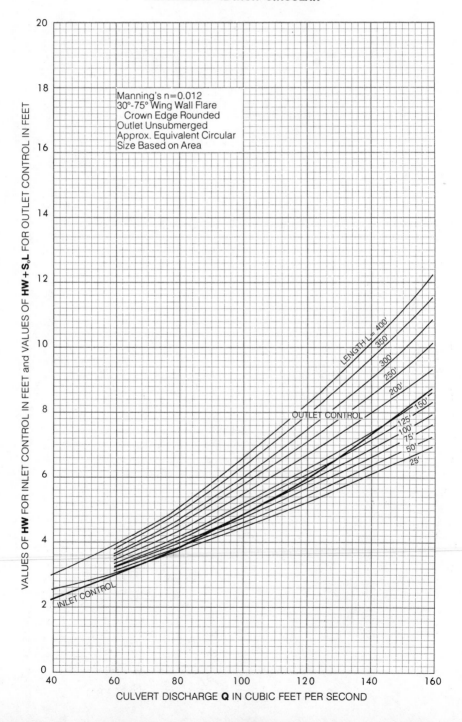

CULVERT CAPACITY
4 x 3-FOOT (SPAN x RISE) BOX SECTION
EQUIVALENT 42-INCH CIRCULAR

Manning's n=0.012
30°-75° Wing Wall Flare
  Crown Edge Rounded
Outlet Unsubmerged
Approx. Equivalent Circular
Size Based on Area

VALUES OF **HW** FOR INLET CONTROL IN FEET and VALUES OF **HW + S₀L** FOR OUTLET CONTROL IN FEET

LENGTH L= 400'
350'
300'
250'
200'
150'
125'
100'
75'
50'
25'

OUTLET CONTROL

INLET CONTROL

CULVERT DISCHARGE **Q** IN CUBIC FEET PER SECOND

FIGURE 108

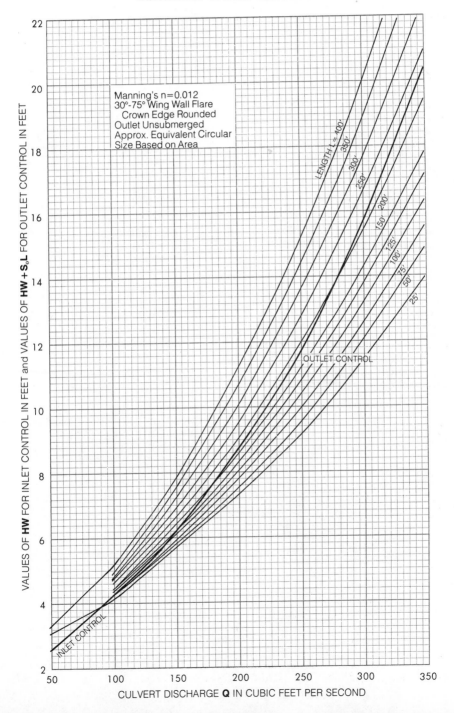

CULVERT CAPACITY
4 x 4-FOOT (SPAN x RISE) BOX SECTION
EQUIVALENT 54-INCH CIRCULAR

Manning's n=0.012
30°-75° Wing Wall Flare
  Crown Edge Rounded
Outlet Unsubmerged
Approx. Equivalent Circular
Size Based on Area

LENGTH L = 400'
350'
300'
250'
200'
150'
125'
100'
75'
50'
25'

OUTLET CONTROL

INLET CONTROL

VALUES OF **HW** FOR INLET CONTROL IN FEET and VALUES OF **HW+S$_o$L** FOR OUTLET CONTROL IN FEET

CULVERT DISCHARGE **Q** IN CUBIC FEET PER SECOND

FIGURE 109

CULVERT CAPACITY
5 x 3-FOOT (SPAN x RISE) BOX SECTION
EQUIVALENT 48-INCH CIRCULAR

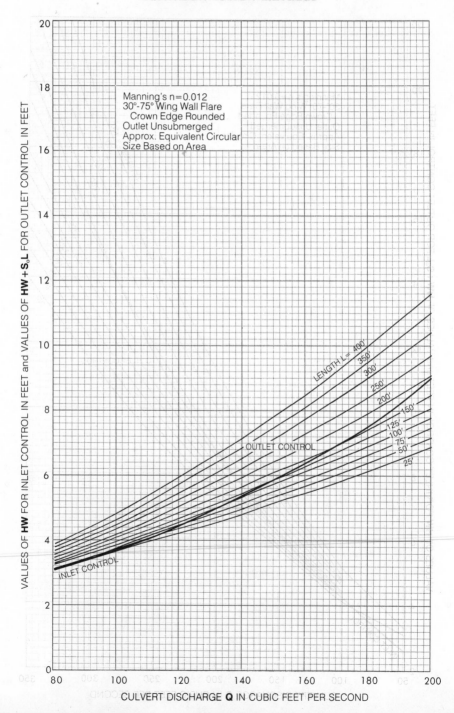

Manning's n=0.012
30°-75° Wing Wall Flare
Crown Edge Rounded
Outlet Unsubmerged
Approx. Equivalent Circular
Size Based on Area

VALUES OF **HW** FOR INLET CONTROL IN FEET and VALUES OF **HW+S₀L** FOR OUTLET CONTROL IN FEET

LENGTH L = 400'
350'
300'
250'
200'
150'
125'
100'
75'
50'
25'

OUTLET CONTROL

INLET CONTROL

CULVERT DISCHARGE **Q** IN CUBIC FEET PER SECOND

FIGURE 110

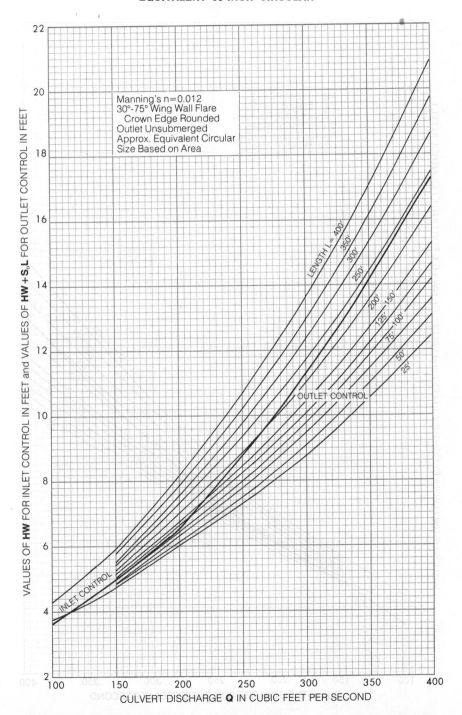

CULVERT CAPACITY
5 x 4-FOOT (SPAN x RISE) BOX SECTION
EQUIVALENT 60-INCH CIRCULAR

Manning's n=0.012
30°-75° Wing Wall Flare
Crown Edge Rounded
Outlet Unsubmerged
Approx. Equivalent Circular
Size Based on Area

VALUES OF **HW** FOR INLET CONTROL IN FEET and VALUES OF **HW+S₀L** FOR OUTLET CONTROL IN FEET

LENGTH L = 400'
350'
300'
250'
200'
125'-150'
75'-100'
50'
25'

OUTLET CONTROL

INLET CONTROL

CULVERT DISCHARGE **Q** IN CUBIC FEET PER SECOND

FIGURE 111

CULVERT CAPACITY
5 x 5-FOOT (SPAN x RISE) BOX SECTION
EQUIVALENT 66-INCH CIRCULAR

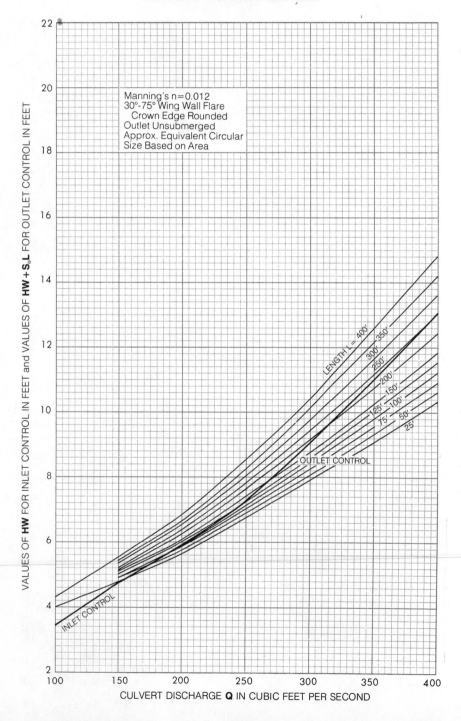

Manning's n=0.012
30°-75° Wing Wall Flare
  Crown Edge Rounded
Outlet Unsubmerged
Approx. Equivalent Circular
Size Based on Area

VALUES OF **HW** FOR INLET CONTROL IN FEET and VALUES OF **HW+S₀L** FOR OUTLET CONTROL IN FEET

LENGTH L = 400'
350'
300'
250'
200'
150'
125'
100'
75'
50'
25'

OUTLET CONTROL

INLET CONTROL

CULVERT DISCHARGE **Q** IN CUBIC FEET PER SECOND

FIGURE 112

CULVERT CAPACITY
6 x 3-FOOT (SPAN x RISE) BOX SECTION
EQUIVALENT 57-INCH CIRCULAR

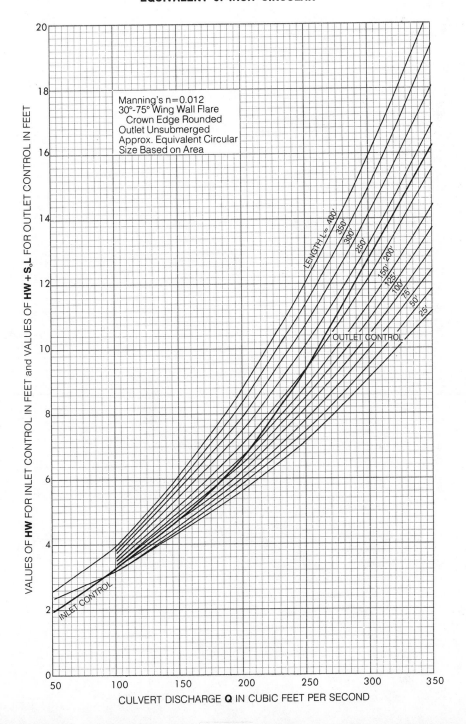

Manning's n=0.012
30°-75° Wing Wall Flare
　Crown Edge Rounded
Outlet Unsubmerged
Approx. Equivalent Circular
Size Based on Area

VALUES OF **HW** FOR INLET CONTROL IN FEET and VALUES OF **HW+S₀L** FOR OUTLET CONTROL IN FEET

LENGTH L = 400'
350'
300'
250'
150'-200'
125'
100'
75'
50'
25'

OUTLET CONTROL

INLET CONTROL

CULVERT DISCHARGE **Q** IN CUBIC FEET PER SECOND

FIGURE 113

CULVERT CAPACITY
6 x 4-FOOT (SPAN x RISE) BOX SECTION
EQUIVALENT 66-INCH CIRCULAR

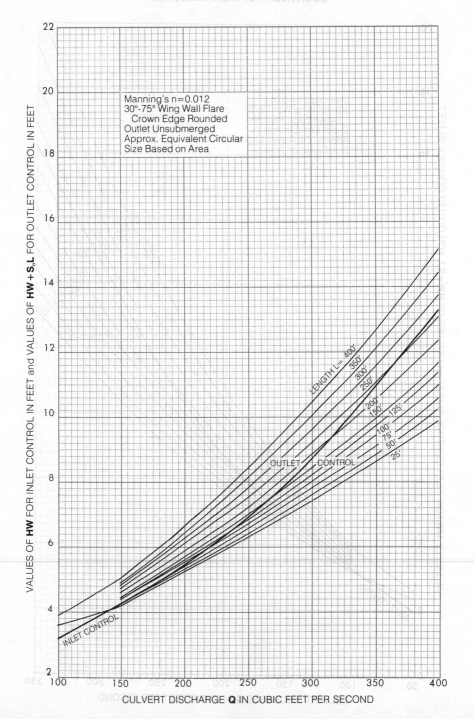

Manning's n=0.012
30°-75° Wing Wall Flare
 Crown Edge Rounded
Outlet Unsubmerged
Approx. Equivalent Circular
Size Based on Area

LENGTH L = 400'
350'
300'
250'
200'
150'
125'
100'
75'
50'
25'

OUTLET CONTROL

INLET CONTROL

VALUES OF **HW** FOR INLET CONTROL IN FEET and VALUES OF **HW + S₀L** FOR OUTLET CONTROL IN FEET

CULVERT DISCHARGE **Q** IN CUBIC FEET PER SECOND

FIGURE 114

CULVERT CAPACITY
6 x 5-FOOT (SPAN x RISE) BOX SECTION
EQUIVALENT 75-INCH CIRCULAR

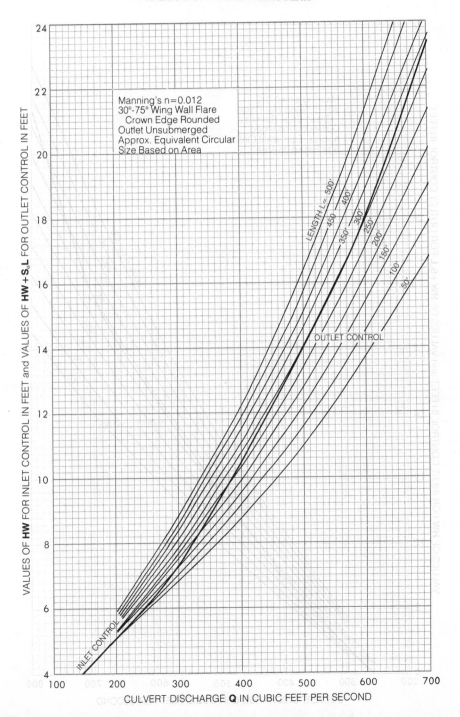

Manning's n=0.012
30°-75° Wing Wall Flare
  Crown Edge Rounded
Outlet Unsubmerged
Approx. Equivalent Circular
Size Based on Area

VALUES OF **HW** FOR INLET CONTROL IN FEET and VALUES OF $HW+S_oL$ FOR OUTLET CONTROL IN FEET

LENGTH L= 500'

OUTLET CONTROL

INLET CONTROL

CULVERT DISCHARGE **Q** IN CUBIC FEET PER SECOND

FIGURE 115

CULVERT CAPACITY
6 x 6-FOOT (SPAN x RISE) BOX SECTION
EQUIVALENT 81-INCH CIRCULAR

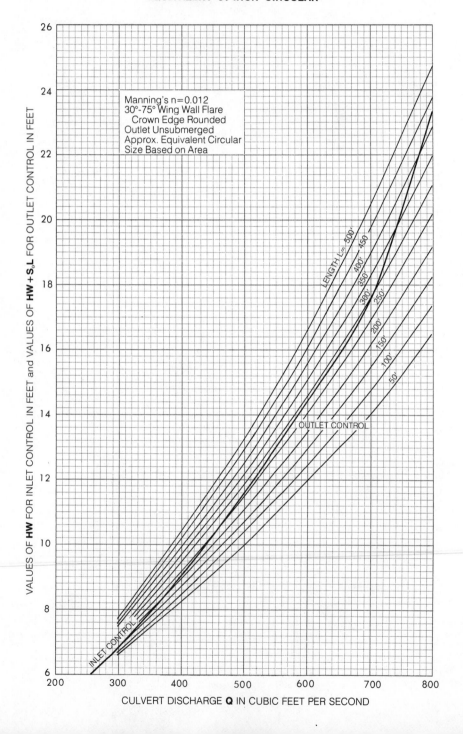

Manning's n=0.012
30°-75° Wing Wall Flare
   Crown Edge Rounded
Outlet Unsubmerged
Approx. Equivalent Circular
Size Based on Area

VALUES OF **HW** FOR INLET CONTROL IN FEET and VALUES OF **HW + S₀L** FOR OUTLET CONTROL IN FEET

CULVERT DISCHARGE **Q** IN CUBIC FEET PER SECOND

FIGURE 116

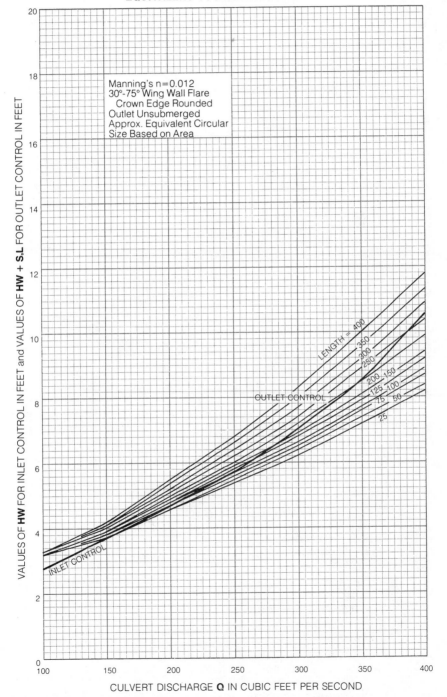

CULVERT CAPACITY
7 x 4-FOOT (SPAN x RISE) BOX SECTION
EQUIVALENT 71-INCH CIRCULAR

Manning's n=0.012
30°-75° Wing Wall Flare
Crown Edge Rounded
Outlet Unsubmerged
Approx. Equivalent Circular
Size Based on Area

VALUES OF **HW** FOR INLET CONTROL IN FEET and VALUES OF **HW + S.L** FOR OUTLET CONTROL IN FEET

INLET CONTROL

OUTLET CONTROL

LENGTH = 400
350
300
250
200 150
125 100
75 50
25

CULVERT DISCHARGE **Q** IN CUBIC FEET PER SECOND

FIGURE 117

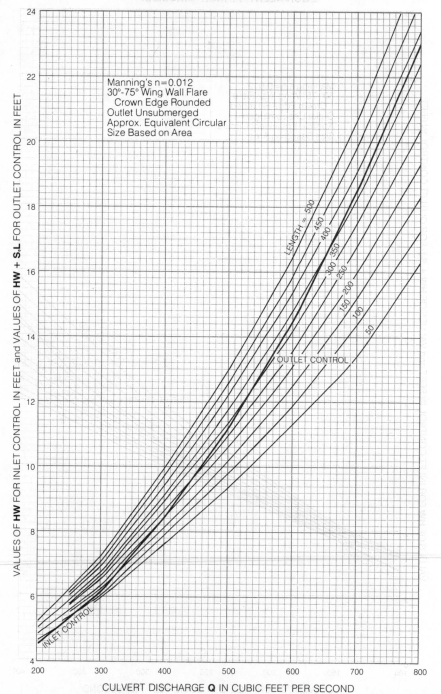

CULVERT CAPACITY
7 x 5-FOOT (SPAN x RISE) BOX SECTION
EQUIVALENT 79-INCH CIRCULAR

Manning's n=0.012
30°-75° Wing Wall Flare
  Crown Edge Rounded
Outlet Unsubmerged
Approx. Equivalent Circular
Size Based on Area

LENGTH = 500
450
400
300 350
250
200
150
100
50

OUTLET CONTROL

INLET CONTROL

VALUES OF **HW** FOR INLET CONTROL IN FEET and VALUES OF **HW + S₀L** FOR OUTLET CONTROL IN FEET

CULVERT DISCHARGE **Q** IN CUBIC FEET PER SECOND

FIGURE 118

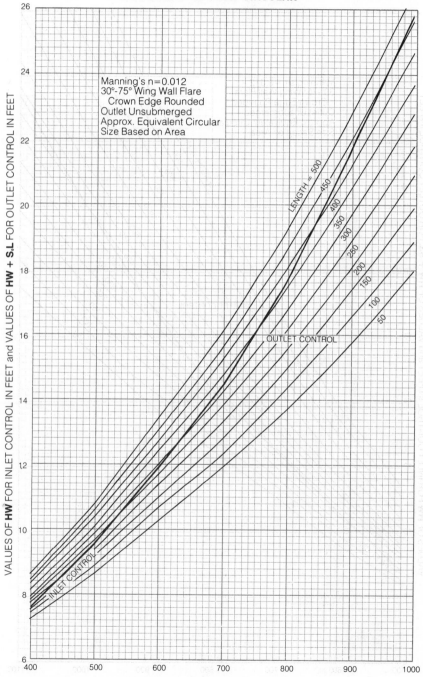

CULVERT CAPACITY
7 x 6-FOOT (SPAN x RISE) BOX SECTION
EQUIVALENT 87-INCH CIRCULAR

Manning's n=0.012
30°-75° Wing Wall Flare
Crown Edge Rounded
Outlet Unsubmerged
Approx. Equivalent Circular
Size Based on Area

LENGTH = 500
450
400
350
300
250
200
150
100
50

OUTLET CONTROL

INLET CONTROL

VALUES OF **HW** FOR INLET CONTROL IN FEET and VALUES OF **HW + S.L** FOR OUTLET CONTROL IN FEET

CULVERT DISCHARGE **Q** IN CUBIC FEET PER SECOND

FIGURE 119

CULVERT CAPACITY
7 x 7-FOOT (SPAN x RISE) BOX SECTION
EQUIVALENT 94-INCH CIRCULAR

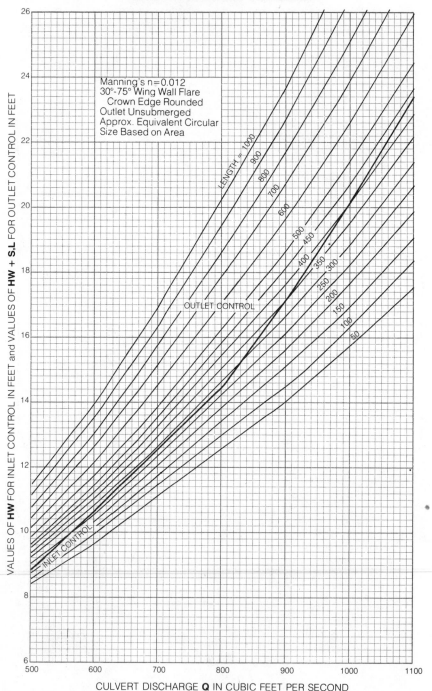

Manning's n=0.012
30°-75° Wing Wall Flare
    Crown Edge Rounded
Outlet Unsubmerged
Approx. Equivalent Circular
Size Based on Area

LENGTH = 1000
900
800
700
600
500
450
400
350
300
250
200
150
100
50

OUTLET CONTROL

INLET CONTROL

VALUES OF **HW** FOR INLET CONTROL IN FEET and VALUES OF **HW + S.L** FOR OUTLET CONTROL IN FEET

CULVERT DISCHARGE **Q** IN CUBIC FEET PER SECOND

FIGURE 120

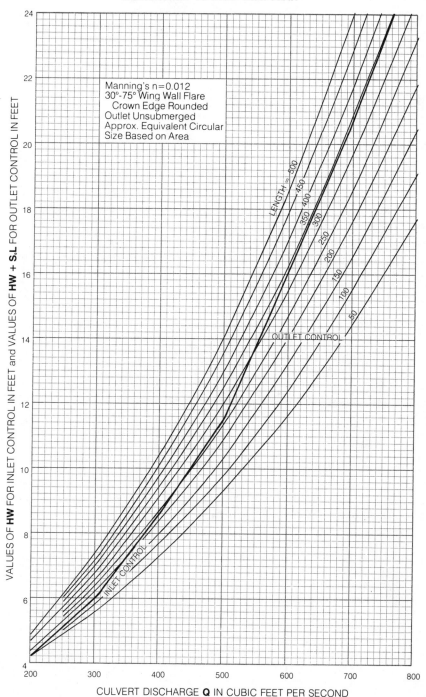

CULVERT CAPACITY
8 x 4-FOOT (SPAN x RISE) BOX SECTION
EQUIVALENT 76-INCH CIRCULAR

Manning's n=0.012
30°-75° Wing Wall Flare
  Crown Edge Rounded
Outlet Unsubmerged
Approx. Equivalent Circular
Size Based on Area

LENGTH = 500
450
400
350
300
250
200
150
100
50

OUTLET CONTROL

INLET CONTROL

VALUES OF **HW** FOR INLET CONTROL IN FEET and VALUES OF **HW + S₀L** FOR OUTLET CONTROL IN FEET

CULVERT DISCHARGE **Q** IN CUBIC FEET PER SECOND

FIGURE 121

CULVERT CAPACITY
8 x 5-FOOT (SPAN x RISE) BOX SECTION
EQUIVALENT 85-INCH CIRCULAR

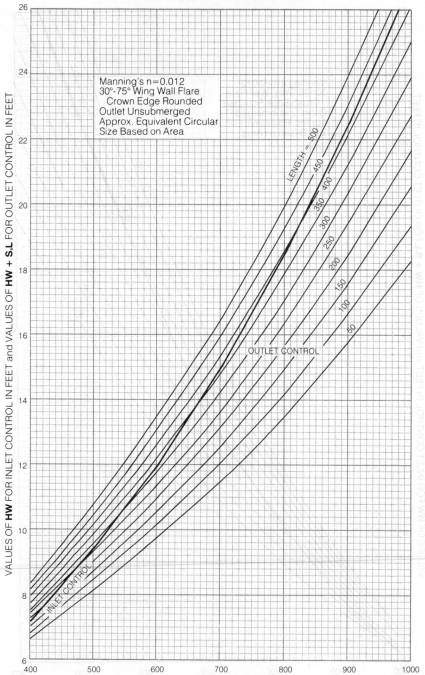

Manning's n=0.012
30°-75° Wing Wall Flare
　Crown Edge Rounded
Outlet Unsubmerged
Approx. Equivalent Circular
Size Based on Area

VALUES OF **HW** FOR INLET CONTROL IN FEET and VALUES OF **HW + S₋L** FOR OUTLET CONTROL IN FEET

CULVERT DISCHARGE **Q** IN CUBIC FEET PER SECOND

LENGTH = 500
450
400
350
300
250
200
150
100
50

OUTLET CONTROL

INLET CONTROL

FIGURE 122

CULVERT CAPACITY
8 x 6-FOOT (SPAN x RISE) BOX SECTION
EQUIVALENT 93-INCH CIRCULAR

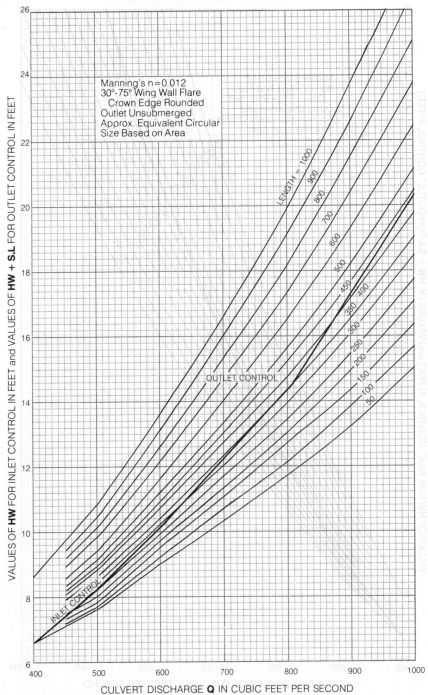

Manning's n=0.012
30°-75° Wing Wall Flare
  Crown Edge Rounded
Outlet Unsubmerged
Approx. Equivalent Circular
Size Based on Area

LENGTH = 1000
900
800
700
600
500
450
400
350
300
250
200
150
100
50

OUTLET CONTROL

INLET CONTROL

VALUES OF **HW** FOR INLET CONTROL IN FEET and VALUES OF **HW + S₀L** FOR OUTLET CONTROL IN FEET

CULVERT DISCHARGE **Q** IN CUBIC FEET PER SECOND

FIGURE 123

CULVERT CAPACITY
8 x 7-FOOT (SPAN x RISE) BOX SECTION
EQUIVALENT 101-INCH CIRCULAR

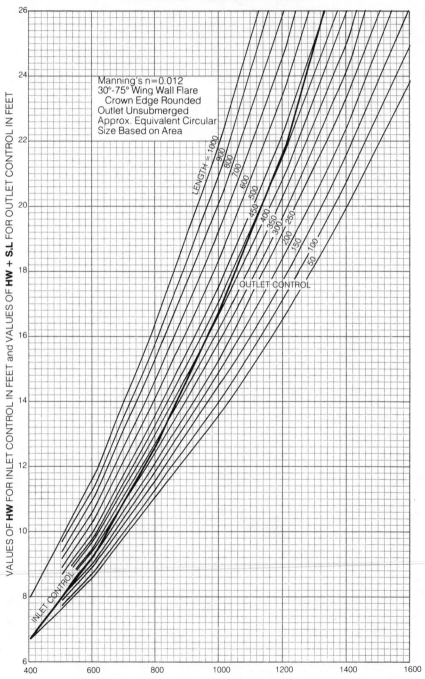

Manning's n=0.012
30°-75° Wing Wall Flare
    Crown Edge Rounded
Outlet Unsubmerged
Approx. Equivalent Circular
Size Based on Area

VALUES OF **HW** FOR INLET CONTROL IN FEET and VALUES OF **HW + S.L** FOR OUTLET CONTROL IN FEET

CULVERT DISCHARGE **Q** IN CUBIC FEET PER SECOND

FIGURE 124

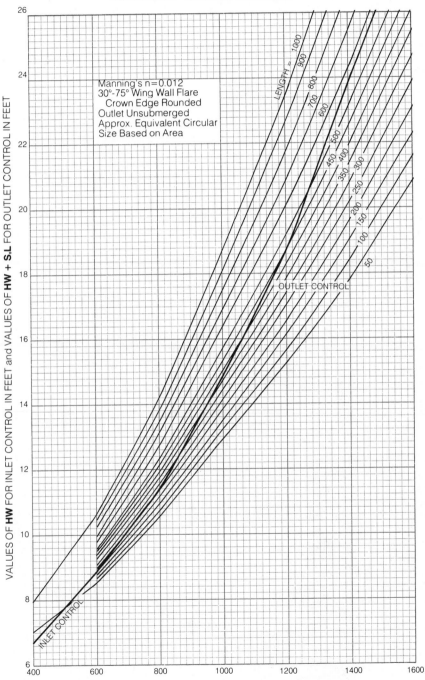

CULVERT CAPACITY
8 x 8-FOOT   (SPAN x RISE) BOX SECTION
EQUIVALENT 108-INCH CIRCULAR

Manning's n=0.012
30°-75° Wing Wall Flare
   Crown Edge Rounded
Outlet Unsubmerged
Approx. Equivalent Circular
Size Based on Area

LENGTH = 1000
900
800
700
600
500
450
400
350
300
250
200
150
100
50

OUTLET CONTROL

INLET CONTROL

VALUES OF **HW** FOR INLET CONTROL IN FEET and VALUES OF **HW + S.L** FOR OUTLET CONTROL IN FEET

CULVERT DISCHARGE **Q** IN CUBIC FEET PER SECOND

FIGURE 125

CULVERT CAPACITY
9 x 5-FOOT (SPAN x RISE) BOX SECTION
EQUIVALENT 90-INCH CIRCULAR

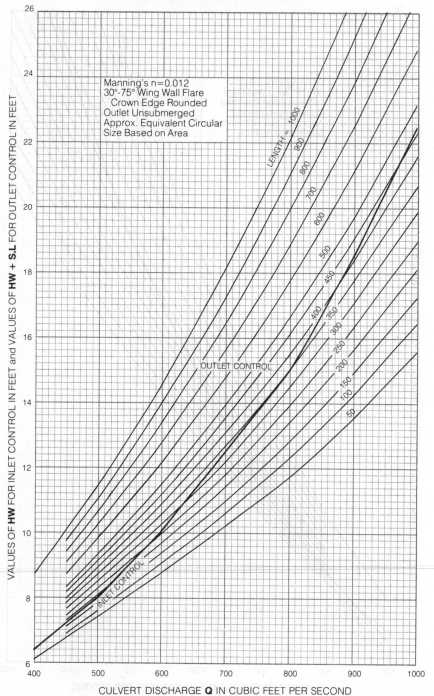

Manning's n=0.012
30°-75° Wing Wall Flare
 Crown Edge Rounded
Outlet Unsubmerged
Approx. Equivalent Circular
Size Based on Area

VALUES OF **HW** FOR INLET CONTROL IN FEET and VALUES OF **HW + S_L** FOR OUTLET CONTROL IN FEET

LENGTH = 1000, 900, 800, 700, 600, 500, 450, 400, 350, 300, 250, 200, 150, 100, 50

OUTLET CONTROL

INLET CONTROL

CULVERT DISCHARGE **Q** IN CUBIC FEET PER SECOND

FIGURE 126

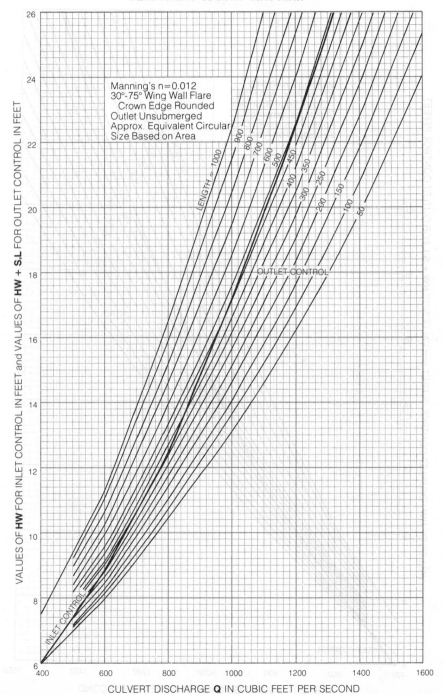

CULVERT CAPACITY
9 x 6-FOOT (SPAN x RISE) BOX SECTION
EQUIVALENT 99-INCH CIRCULAR

Manning's n=0.012
30°-75° Wing Wall Flare
    Crown Edge Rounded
Outlet Unsubmerged
Approx. Equivalent Circular
Size Based on Area

LENGTH = 1000
900
800
700
600
500
450
400
350
300
250
200
150
100
50

OUTLET CONTROL

INLET CONTROL

VALUES OF **HW** FOR INLET CONTROL IN FEET and VALUES OF **HW + S.L** FOR OUTLET CONTROL IN FEET

CULVERT DISCHARGE **Q** IN CUBIC FEET PER SECOND

FIGURE 127

CULVERT CAPACITY
9 x 7-FOOT (SPAN x RISE) BOX SECTION
EQUIVALENT 107-INCH CIRCULAR

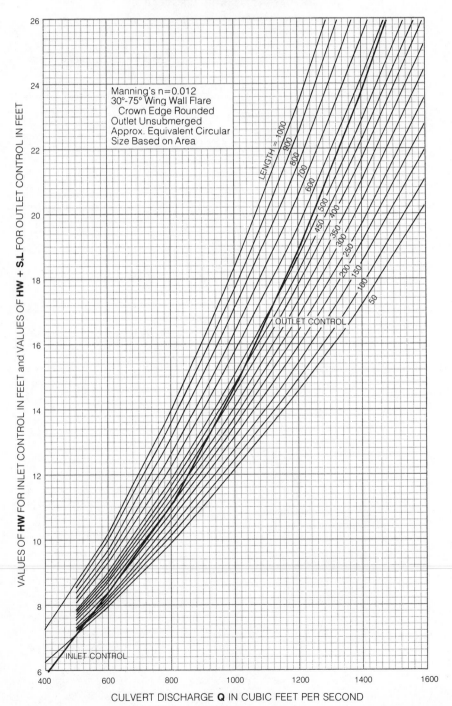

Manning's n=0.012
30°-75° Wing Wall Flare
 Crown Edge Rounded
Outlet Unsubmerged
Approx. Equivalent Circular
Size Based on Area

LENGTH = 1000, 900, 800, 700, 600, 500, 450, 400, 350, 300, 250, 200, 150, 100, 50

OUTLET CONTROL

INLET CONTROL

VALUES OF **HW** FOR INLET CONTROL IN FEET and VALUES OF **HW + S.L** FOR OUTLET CONTROL IN FEET

CULVERT DISCHARGE **Q** IN CUBIC FEET PER SECOND

FIGURE 128

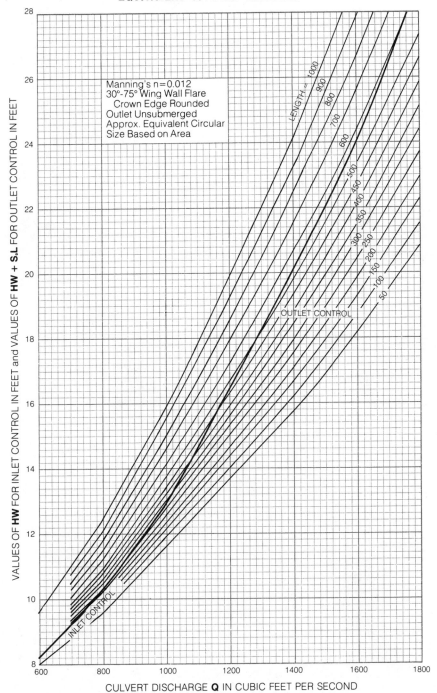

CULVERT CAPACITY
9 x 8-FOOT (SPAN x RISE) BOX SECTION
EQUIVALENT 114-INCH CIRCULAR

Manning's n=0.012
30°-75° Wing Wall Flare
  Crown Edge Rounded
Outlet Unsubmerged
Approx. Equivalent Circular
Size Based on Area

OUTLET CONTROL

INLET CONTROL

LENGTH = 1000 900 800 700 600 500 450 400 350 300 250 200 150 100 50

VALUES OF **HW** FOR INLET CONTROL IN FEET and VALUES OF **HW + S,L** FOR OUTLET CONTROL IN FEET

CULVERT DISCHARGE **Q** IN CUBIC FEET PER SECOND

FIGURE 129

CULVERT CAPACITY
9 x 9-FOOT (SPAN x RISE) BOX SECTION
EQUIVALENT 121-INCH CIRCULAR

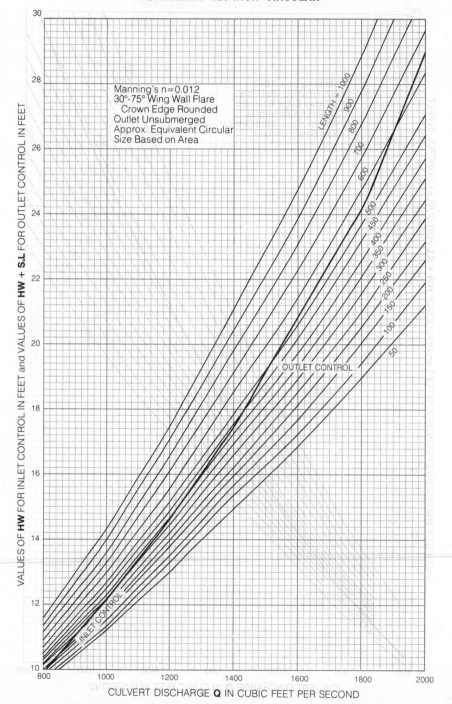

Manning's n=0.012
30°-75° Wing Wall Flare
  Crown Edge Rounded
Outlet Unsubmerged
Approx. Equivalent Circular
Size Based on Area

LENGTH = 1000
900
800
700
600
500
450
400
350
300
250
200
150
100
50

OUTLET CONTROL

INLET CONTROL

VALUES OF **HW** FOR INLET CONTROL IN FEET and VALUES OF **HW + S.L.** FOR OUTLET CONTROL IN FEET

CULVERT DISCHARGE **Q** IN CUBIC FEET PER SECOND

FIGURE 130

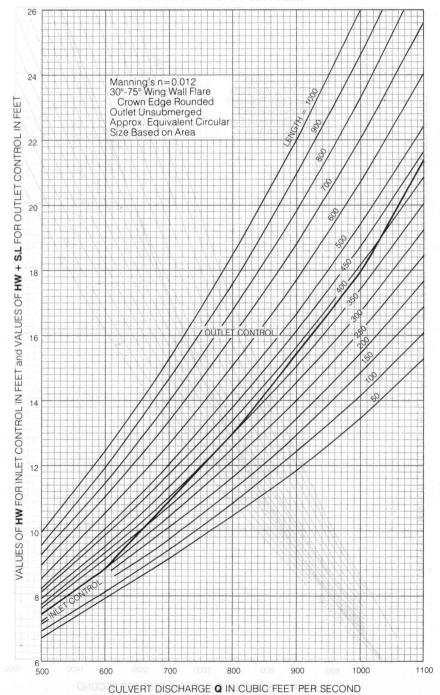

CULVERT CAPACITY
10 x 5-FOOT (SPAN x RISE) BOX SECTION
EQUIVALENT 94-INCH CIRCULAR

Manning's n=0.012
30°-75° Wing Wall Flare
   Crown Edge Rounded
Outlet Unsubmerged
Approx. Equivalent Circular
Size Based on Area

VALUES OF **HW** FOR INLET CONTROL IN FEET and VALUES OF **HW + S.L** FOR OUTLET CONTROL IN FEET

LENGTH = 1000, 900, 800, 700, 600, 500, 450, 400, 350, 300, 250, 200, 150, 100, 50

OUTLET CONTROL

INLET CONTROL

CULVERT DISCHARGE **Q** IN CUBIC FEET PER SECOND

FIGURE 131

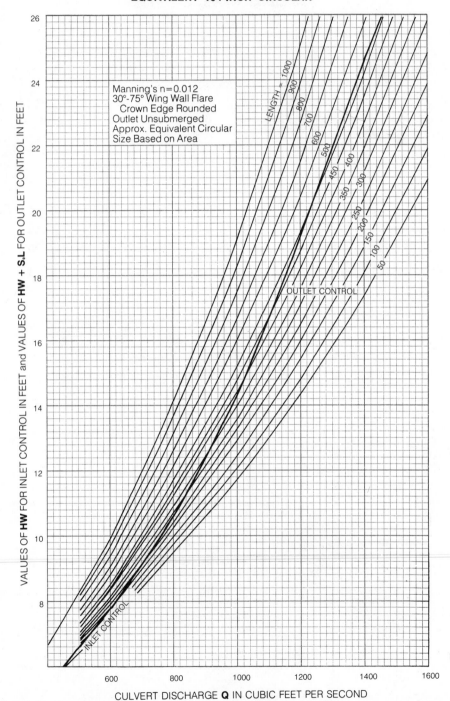

CULVERT CAPACITY
10 x 6-FOOT (SPAN x RISE) BOX SECTION
EQUIVALENT 104-INCH CIRCULAR

Manning's n=0.012
30°-75° Wing Wall Flare
 Crown Edge Rounded
Outlet Unsubmerged
Approx. Equivalent Circular
Size Based on Area

LENGTH = 1000, 900, 800, 700, 600, 500, 450, 400, 350, 300, 250, 200, 150, 100, 50

OUTLET CONTROL

INLET CONTROL

VALUES OF **HW** FOR INLET CONTROL IN FEET and VALUES OF **HW + S₀L** FOR OUTLET CONTROL IN FEET

CULVERT DISCHARGE **Q** IN CUBIC FEET PER SECOND

FIGURE 132

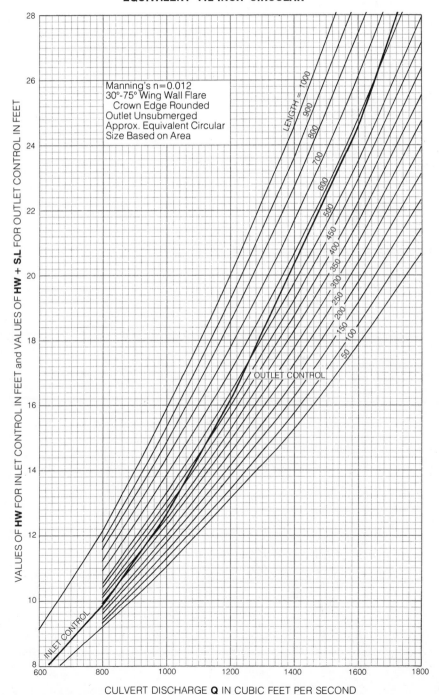

CULVERT CAPACITY
10 x 7-FOOT (SPAN x RISE) BOX SECTION
EQUIVALENT 112-INCH CIRCULAR

Manning's n=0.012
30°-75° Wing Wall Flare
  Crown Edge Rounded
Outlet Unsubmerged
Approx. Equivalent Circular
Size Based on Area

LENGTH = 1000, 900, 800, 700, 600, 500, 450, 400, 350, 300, 250, 200, 150, 100, 50

OUTLET CONTROL

INLET CONTROL

VALUES OF **HW** FOR INLET CONTROL IN FEET and VALUES OF **HW + S.L** FOR OUTLET CONTROL IN FEET

CULVERT DISCHARGE **Q** IN CUBIC FEET PER SECOND

FIGURE 133

CULVERT CAPACITY
10 x 8-FOOT (SPAN x RISE) BOX SECTION
EQUIVALENT 120-INCH CIRCULAR

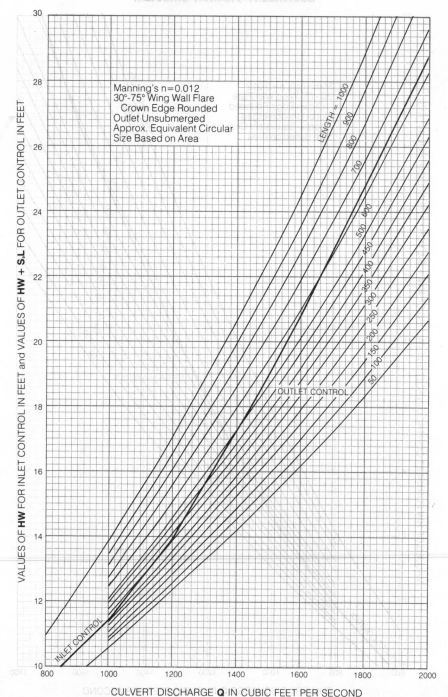

Manning's n=0.012
30°-75° Wing Wall Flare
  Crown Edge Rounded
Outlet Unsubmerged
Approx. Equivalent Circular
Size Based on Area

LENGTH = 1000
900
800
700
600
500
450
400
350
300
250
200
150
100
50

OUTLET CONTROL

INLET CONTROL

VALUES OF **HW** FOR INLET CONTROL IN FEET and VALUES OF **HW + S.L** FOR OUTLET CONTROL IN FEET

CULVERT DISCHARGE **Q** IN CUBIC FEET PER SECOND

FIGURE 134

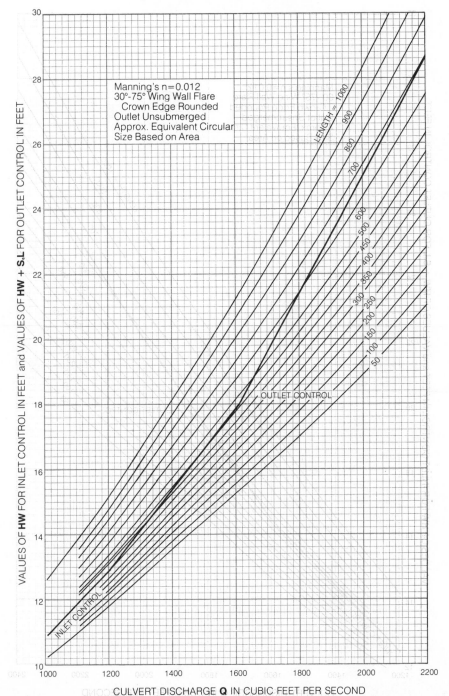

CULVERT CAPACITY
10 x 9-FOOT (SPAN x RISE) BOX SECTION
EQUIVALENT 128-INCH CIRCULAR

Manning's n=0.012
30°-75° Wing Wall Flare
Crown Edge Rounded
Outlet Unsubmerged
Approx. Equivalent Circular
Size Based on Area

VALUES OF **HW** FOR INLET CONTROL IN FEET and VALUES OF **HW + S₀L** FOR OUTLET CONTROL IN FEET

INLET CONTROL

OUTLET CONTROL

LENGTH = 1000, 900, 800, 700, 600, 500, 450, 400, 350, 300, 250, 200, 150, 100, 50

CULVERT DISCHARGE **Q** IN CUBIC FEET PER SECOND

FIGURE 135

CULVERT CAPACITY
10 x 10-FOOT (SPAN x RISE) BOX SECTION
EQUIVALENT 135-INCH CIRCULAR

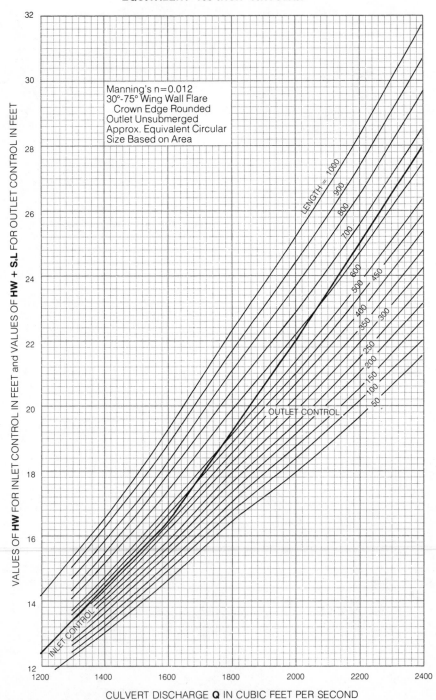

Manning's n=0.012
30°-75° Wing Wall Flare
  Crown Edge Rounded
Outlet Unsubmerged
Approx. Equivalent Circular
Size Based on Area

LENGTH = 1000, 900, 800, 700, 600, 500, 450, 400, 350, 300, 250, 200, 150, 100, 50

OUTLET CONTROL

INLET CONTROL

VALUES OF **HW** FOR INLET CONTROL IN FEET and VALUES OF **HW + S.L** FOR OUTLET CONTROL IN FEET

CULVERT DISCHARGE **Q** IN CUBIC FEET PER SECOND

FIGURE 136

CULVERT CAPACITY
11 x 4-FOOT (SPAN x RISE) BOX SECTION
EQUIVALENT 88-INCH CIRCULAR

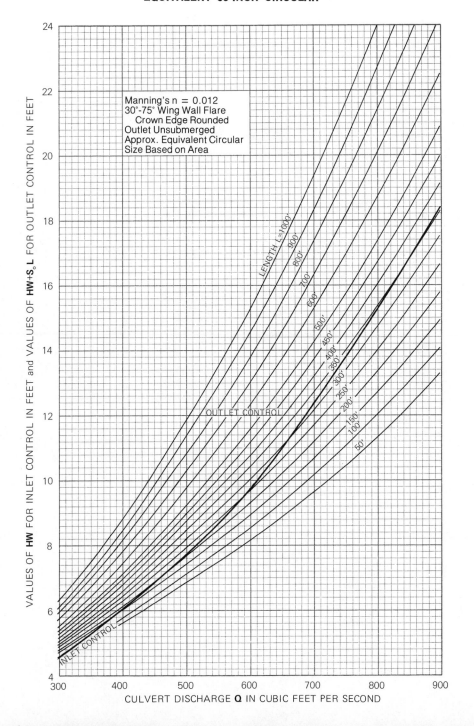

Manning's n = 0.012
30°-75° Wing Wall Flare
 Crown Edge Rounded
Outlet Unsubmerged
Approx. Equivalent Circular
Size Based on Area

VALUES OF **HW** FOR INLET CONTROL IN FEET and VALUES OF **HW+S₀L** FOR OUTLET CONTROL IN FEET

CULVERT DISCHARGE **Q** IN CUBIC FEET PER SECOND

FIGURE 137

CULVERT CAPACITY
11 x 6-FOOT (SPAN x RISE) BOX SECTION
EQUIVALENT 109-INCH CIRCULAR

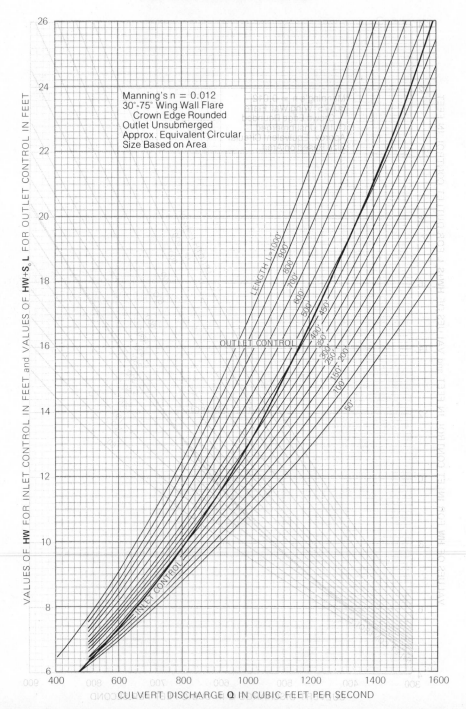

Manning's n = 0.012
30°-75° Wing Wall Flare
    Crown Edge Rounded
Outlet Unsubmerged
Approx. Equivalent Circular
Size Based on Area

VALUES OF **HW** FOR INLET CONTROL IN FEET and VALUES OF **HW+S₀L** FOR OUTLET CONTROL IN FEET

CULVERT DISCHARGE **Q** IN CUBIC FEET PER SECOND

FIGURE 138

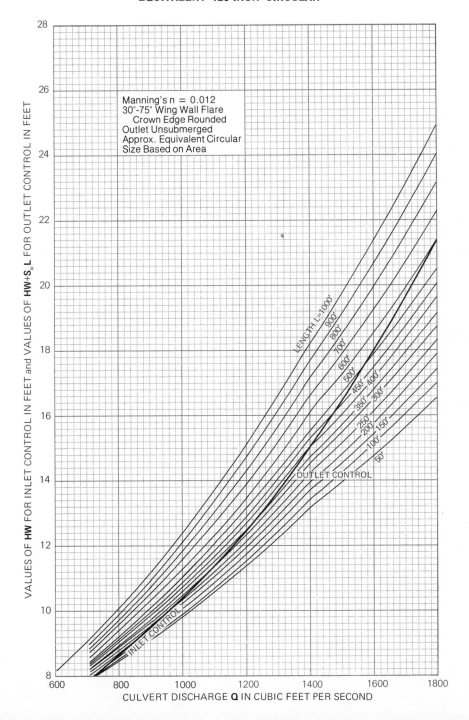

CULVERT CAPACITY
11 x 8-FOOT (SPAN x RISE) BOX SECTION
EQUIVALENT 126-INCH CIRCULAR

Manning's n = 0.012
30°-75° Wing Wall Flare
  Crown Edge Rounded
Outlet Unsubmerged
Approx. Equivalent Circular
Size Based on Area

VALUES OF **HW** FOR INLET CONTROL IN FEET and VALUES OF **HW+S₀ L** FOR OUTLET CONTROL IN FEET

CULVERT DISCHARGE **Q** IN CUBIC FEET PER SECOND

FIGURE 139

CULVERT CAPACITY
11 x 10-FOOT (SPAN x RISE) BOX SECTION
EQUIVALENT 141-INCH CIRCULAR

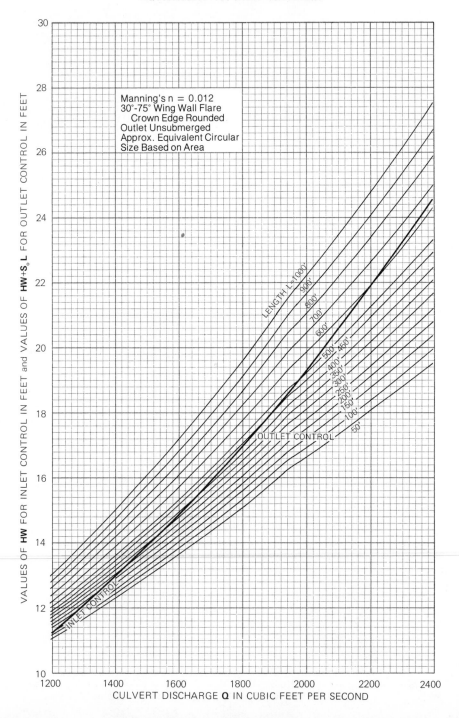

Manning's n = 0.012
30°-75° Wing Wall Flare
 Crown Edge Rounded
Outlet Unsubmerged
Approx. Equivalent Circular
Size Based on Area

VALUES OF **HW** FOR INLET CONTROL IN FEET and VALUES OF $HW + S_o L$ FOR OUTLET CONTROL IN FEET

LENGTH L=1000'
900'
800'
700'
600'
500'
450'
400'
350'
300'
250'
200'
150'
100'
50'

OUTLET CONTROL

INLET CONTROL

CULVERT DISCHARGE **Q** IN CUBIC FEET PER SECOND

FIGURE 140

CULVERT CAPACITY
11 x 11-FOOT (SPAN x RISE) BOX SECTION
EQUIVALENT 148-INCH CIRCULAR

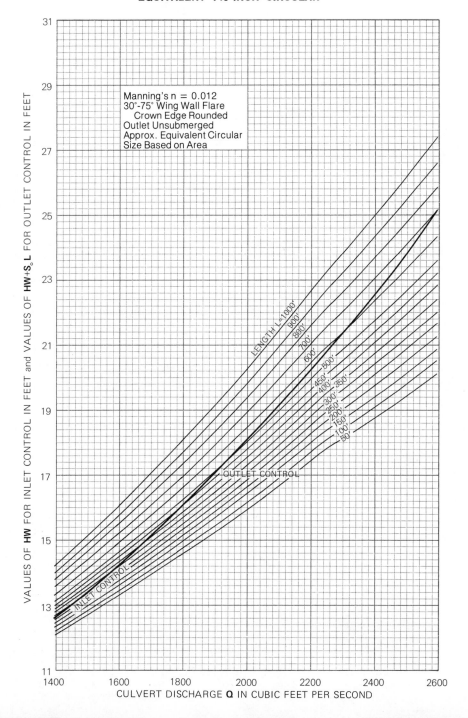

Manning's n = 0.012
30°-75° Wing Wall Flare
   Crown Edge Rounded
Outlet Unsubmerged
Approx. Equivalent Circular
Size Based on Area

CULVERT DISCHARGE Q IN CUBIC FEET PER SECOND

VALUES OF HW FOR INLET CONTROL IN FEET and VALUES OF HW+S_oL FOR OUTLET CONTROL IN FEET

FIGURE 141

CULVERT CAPACITY
12 x 4-FOOT (SPAN x RISE) BOX SECTION
EQUIVALENT 92-INCH CIRCULAR

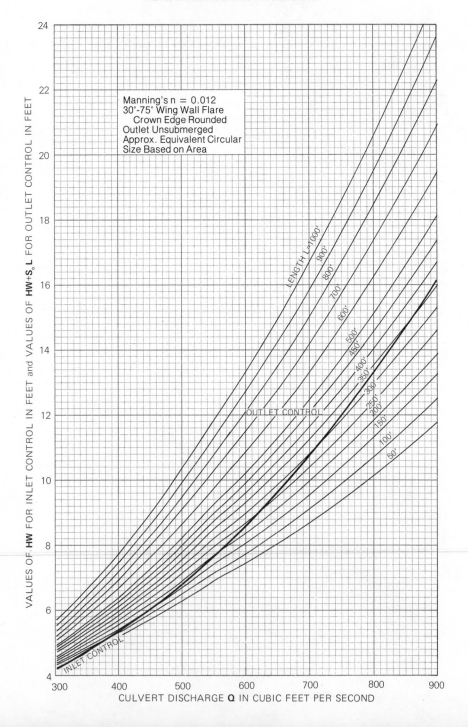

Manning's n = 0.012
30°-75° Wing Wall Flare
  Crown Edge Rounded
Outlet Unsubmerged
Approx. Equivalent Circular
Size Based on Area

VALUES OF **HW** FOR INLET CONTROL IN FEET and VALUES OF **HW+S₀L** FOR OUTLET CONTROL IN FEET

LENGTH L=1000'
900'
800'
700'
600'
500'
450'
400'
350'
300'
250'
200'
150'
100'
50'

OUTLET CONTROL

INLET CONTROL

CULVERT DISCHARGE **Q** IN CUBIC FEET PER SECOND

FIGURE 142

CULVERT CAPACITY
12 x 6-FOOT (SPAN x RISE) BOX SECTION
EQUIVALENT 113-INCH CIRCULAR

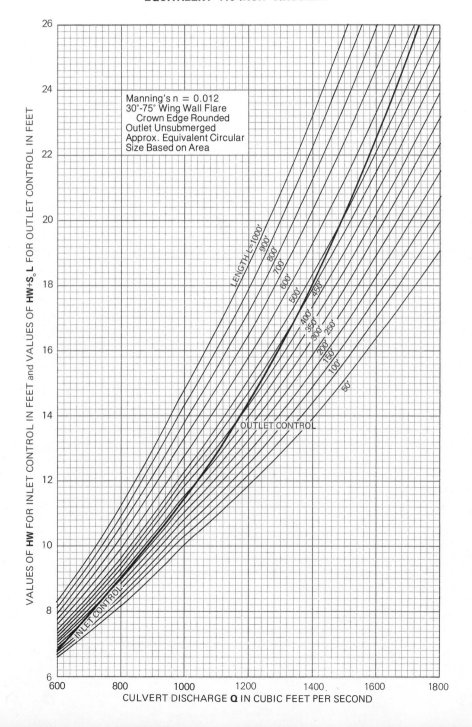

Manning's n = 0.012
30°-75° Wing Wall Flare
Crown Edge Rounded
Outlet Unsubmerged
Approx. Equivalent Circular
Size Based on Area

FIGURE 143

CULVERT CAPACITY
12 x 8-FOOT (SPAN x RISE) BOX SECTION
EQUIVALENT 131-INCH CIRCULAR

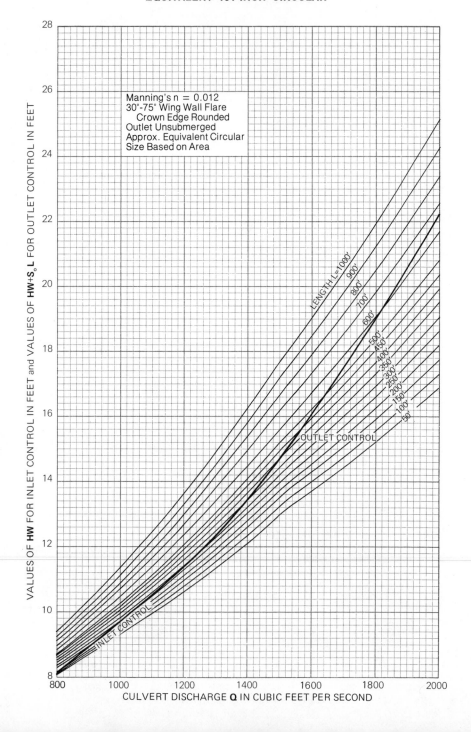

Manning's n = 0.012
30°-75° Wing Wall Flare
   Crown Edge Rounded
Outlet Unsubmerged
Approx. Equivalent Circular
Size Based on Area

VALUES OF **HW** FOR INLET CONTROL IN FEET and VALUES OF **HW+S₀ L** FOR OUTLET CONTROL IN FEET

CULVERT DISCHARGE **Q** IN CUBIC FEET PER SECOND

FIGURE 144

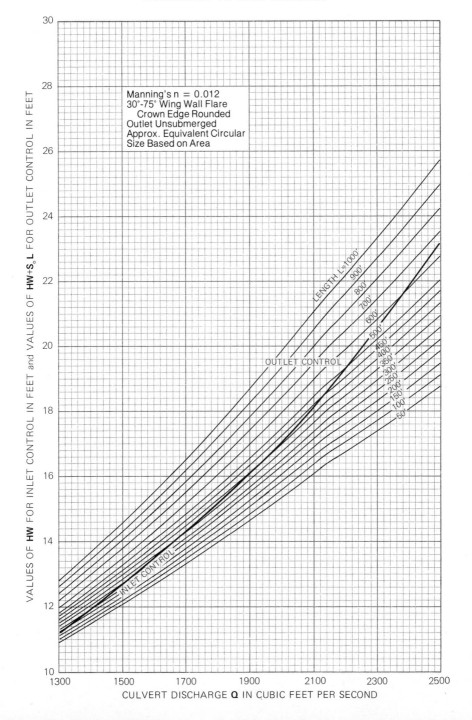

CULVERT CAPACITY
12 x 10-FOOT (SPAN x RISE) BOX CIRCULAR
EQUIVALENT 147-INCH CIRCULAR

Manning's n = 0.012
30°-75° Wing Wall Flare
   Crown Edge Rounded
Outlet Unsubmerged
Approx. Equivalent Circular
Size Based on Area

VALUES OF **HW** FOR INLET CONTROL IN FEET and VALUES OF **HW+S₀L** FOR OUTLET CONTROL IN FEET

CULVERT DISCHARGE **Q** IN CUBIC FEET PER SECOND

LENGTH L=1000'
900'
800'
700'
600'
500'
450'
400'
350'
300'
250'
200'
150'
100'
50'

OUTLET CONTROL

INLET CONTROL

FIGURE 145

CULVERT CAPACITY
12 x 12-FOOT (SPAN x RISE) BOX SECTION
EQUIVALENT 161-INCH CIRCULAR

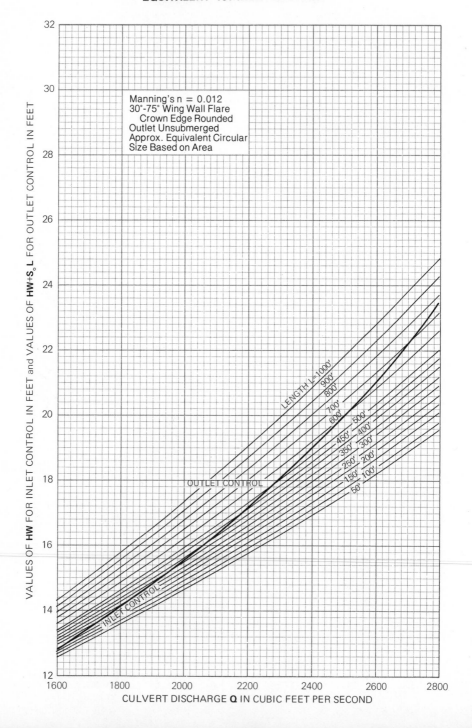

Manning's n = 0.012
30°-75° Wing Wall Flare
   Crown Edge Rounded
Outlet Unsubmerged
Approx. Equivalent Circular
Size Based on Area

VALUES OF **HW** FOR INLET CONTROL IN FEET and VALUES OF $\mathbf{HW+S_o\,L}$ FOR OUTLET CONTROL IN FEET

LENGTH L=1000'
900'
800'
700'
600'
500'
450' 400'
350' 300'
250' 200'
150' 100'
50'

OUTLET CONTROL

INLET CONTROL

CULVERT DISCHARGE **Q** IN CUBIC FEET PER SECOND

FIGURE 146

ESSENTIAL FEATURES OF TYPES OF INSTALLATIONS

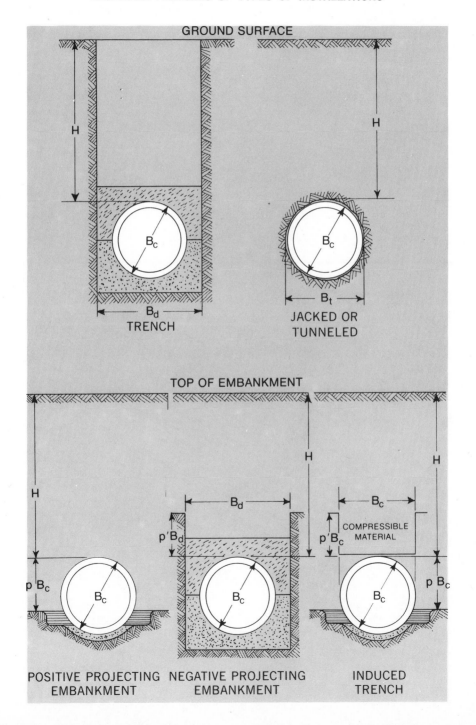

FIGURE 147.1

TRENCH BACKFILL LOADS ON CIRCULAR PIPE
100 POUNDS PER CUBIC FOOT BACKFILL MATERIAL
SAND AND GRAVEL Kμ' = 0.165

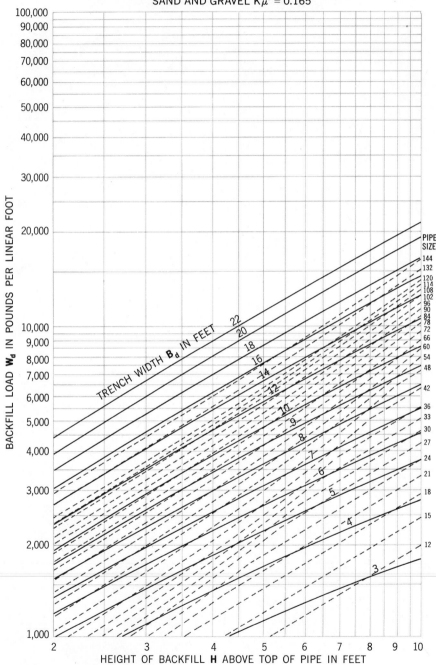

For backfill weighing 110 pounds per cubic foot, increase loads 10%; for 120 pounds per cubic foot, increase 20%; etc.
Transition loads and widths based on Kμ = 0.19, r_{sd} = 0.7 and p = 0.7 in the embankment equation

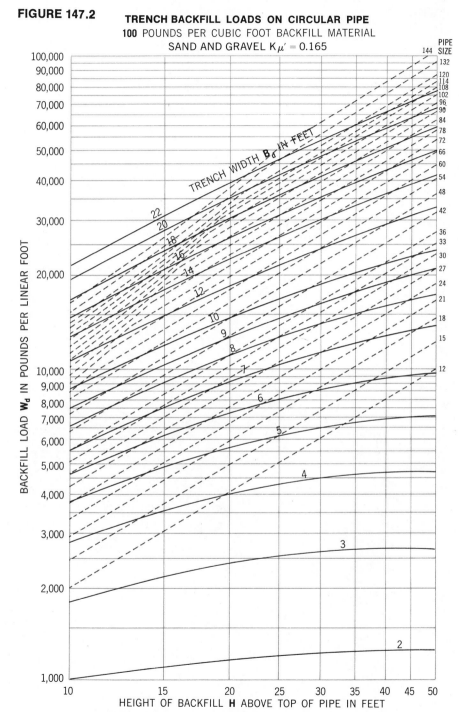

FIGURE 147.2   **TRENCH BACKFILL LOADS ON CIRCULAR PIPE**
100 POUNDS PER CUBIC FOOT BACKFILL MATERIAL
SAND AND GRAVEL K μ' = 0.165

For backfill weighing 110 pounds per cubic foot, increase loads 10%; for 120 pounds per cubic foot, increase 20%; etc.
Transition loads and widths based on $K\mu = 0.19$, $r_{sd} = 0.7$ and $p = 0.7$ in the embankment equation

FIGURE 148.1

TRENCH BACKFILL LOADS ON CIRCULAR PIPE
100 POUNDS PER CUBIC FOOT BACKFILL MATERIAL
SATURATED TOP SOIL $K\mu' = 0.150$

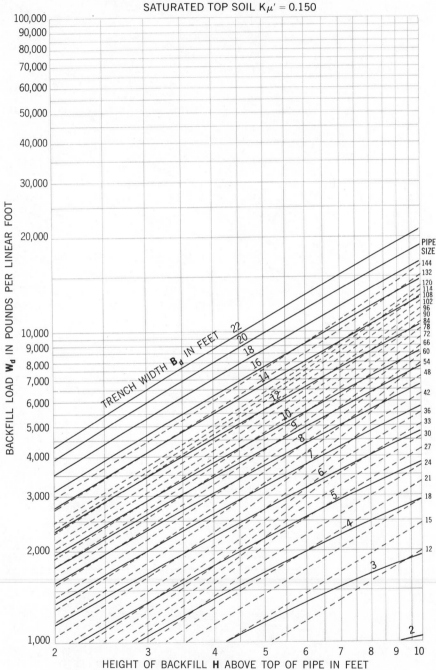

For backfill weighing 110 pounds per cubic foot, increase loads 10%; for 120 pounds per cubic foot, increase 20%; etc.
Transition loads and widths based on $K\mu = 0.19$, $r_{sd} = 0.7$ and $p = 0.7$ in the embankment equation

FIGURE 148.2

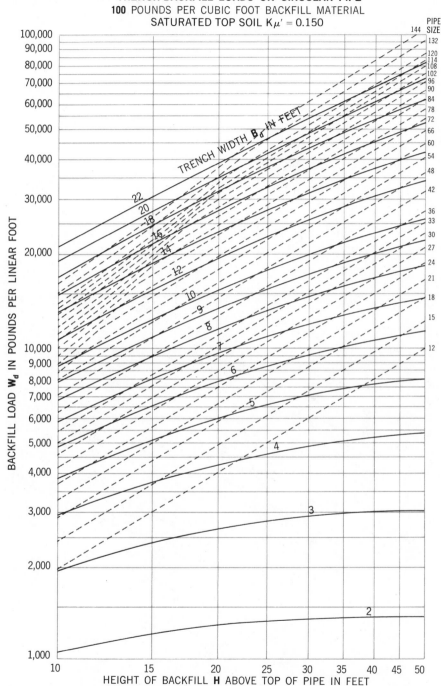

TRENCH BACKFILL LOADS ON CIRCULAR PIPE
100 POUNDS PER CUBIC FOOT BACKFILL MATERIAL
SATURATED TOP SOIL $K\mu' = 0.150$

For backfill weighing 110 pounds per cubic foot, increase loads 10%; for 120 pounds per cubic foot, increase 20%; etc.
Transition loads and widths based on $K\mu = 0.19$, $r_{sd} = 0.7$ and $p = 0.7$ in the embankment equation

FIGURE 149.1

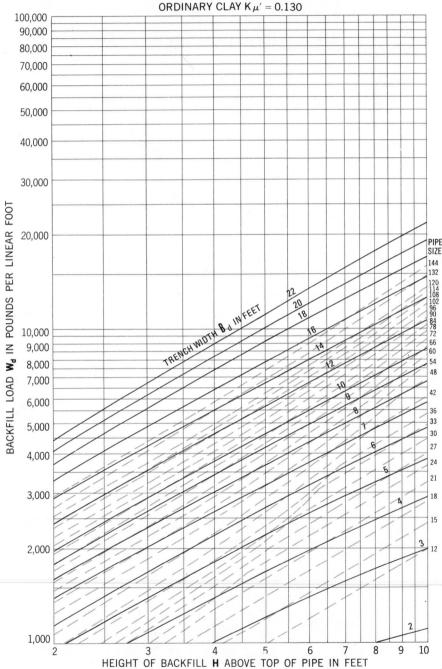

TRENCH BACKFILL LOADS ON CIRCULAR PIPE
100 POUNDS PER CUBIC FOOT BACKFILL MATERIAL
ORDINARY CLAY Kμ' = 0.130

For backfill weighing 110 pounds per cubic foot, increase loads 10%; for 120 pounds per cubic foot, increase 20%; etc.

Transition loads and widths based on Kμ = 0.19, r_{sd} = 0.7 and p = 0.7 in the embankment equation

FIGURE 149.2

TRENCH BACKFILL LOADS ON CIRCULAR PIPE
100 POUNDS PER CUBIC FOOT BACKFILL MATERIAL
ORDINARY CLAY $K\mu' = 0.130$

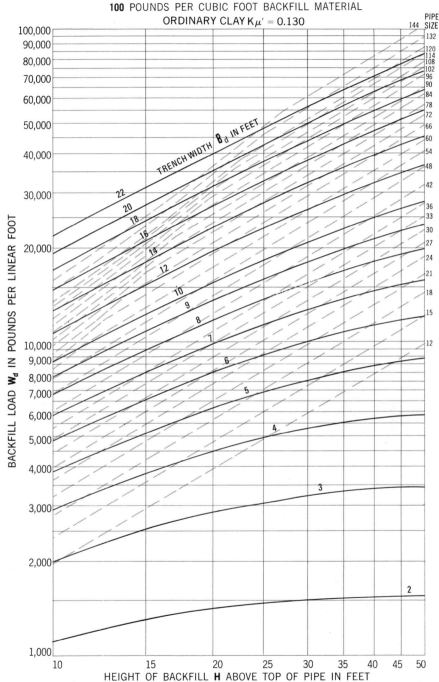

For backfill weighing 110 pounds per cubic foot, increase loads 10%; for 120 pounds per cubic foot, increase 20%; etc.

Transition loads and widths based on $K\mu = 0.19$, $r_{sd} = 0.7$ and $p = 0.7$ in the embankment equation

FIGURE 150.1

TRENCH BACKFILL LOADS ON CIRCULAR PIPE
100 POUNDS PER CUBIC FOOT BACKFILL MATERIAL
SATURATED CLAY Kμ' = 0.110

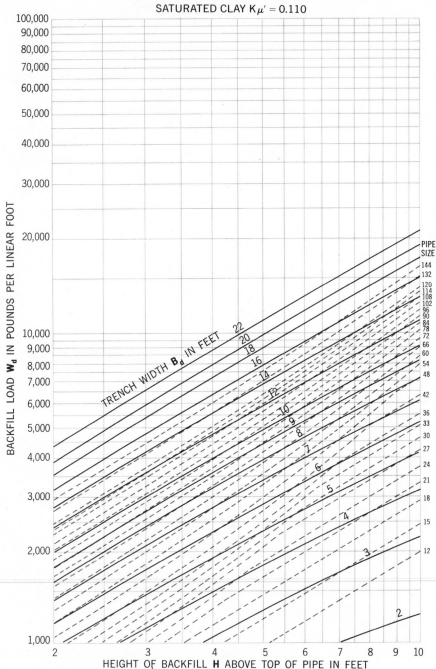

For backfill weighing 110 pounds per cubic foot, increase loads 10%; for 120 pounds per cubic foot, increase 20%; etc.
Transition loads and widths based on Kμ = 0.19, r_{sa} = 0.7 and p = 0.7 in the embankment equation

FIGURE 150.2

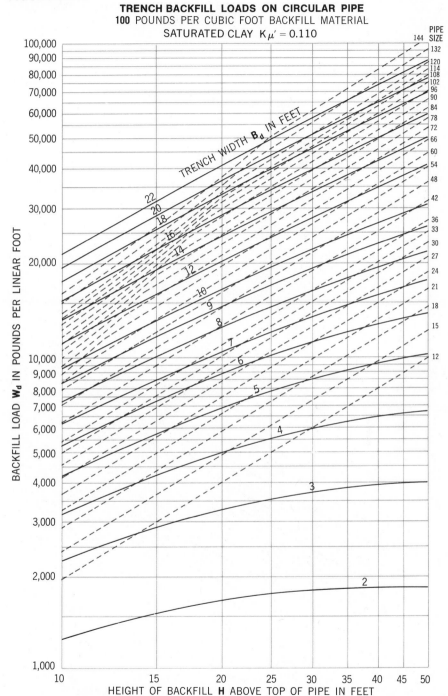

TRENCH BACKFILL LOADS ON CIRCULAR PIPE
100 POUNDS PER CUBIC FOOT BACKFILL MATERIAL
SATURATED CLAY $K\mu' = 0.110$

For backfill weighing 110 pounds per cubic foot, increase loads 10%; for 120 pounds per cubic foot, increase loads 20%; etc.

Transition loads and widths based on $K\mu = 0.19$, $r_{sd} = 0.7$ and $\rho = 0.7$ in the embankment equation

FIGURE 151.1

TRENCH BACKFILL LOADS ON VERTICAL ELLIPTICAL PIPE
100 POUNDS PER CUBIC FOOT BACKFILL MATERIAL
SAND AND GRAVEL $K\mu' = 0.165$

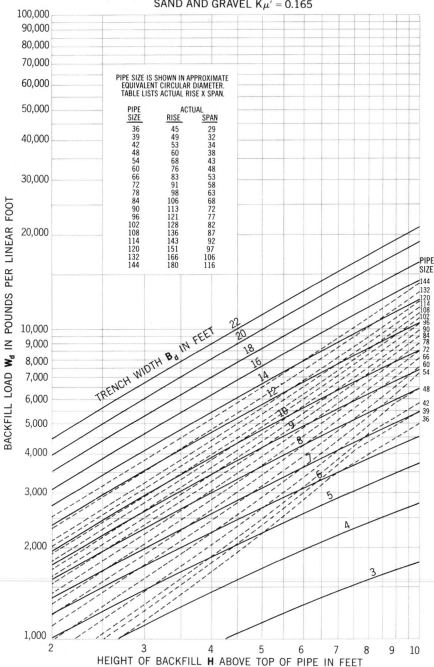

PIPE SIZE IS SHOWN IN APPROXIMATE
EQUIVALENT CIRCULAR DIAMETER.
TABLE LISTS ACTUAL RISE X SPAN.

PIPE SIZE	ACTUAL RISE	SPAN
36	45	29
39	49	32
42	53	34
48	60	38
54	68	43
60	76	48
66	83	53
72	91	58
78	98	63
84	106	68
90	113	72
96	121	77
102	128	82
108	136	87
114	143	92
120	151	97
132	166	106
144	180	116

BACKFILL LOAD W_d IN POUNDS PER LINEAR FOOT

HEIGHT OF BACKFILL **H** ABOVE TOP OF PIPE IN FEET

For backfill weighing 110 pounds per cubic foot, increase loads 10%; for 120 pounds per cubic foot, increase 20%; etc.
Transition loads and widths based on $K\mu = 0.19$, $r_{sd} = 0.7$ and $p = 0.7$ in the embankment equation

FIGURE 151.2

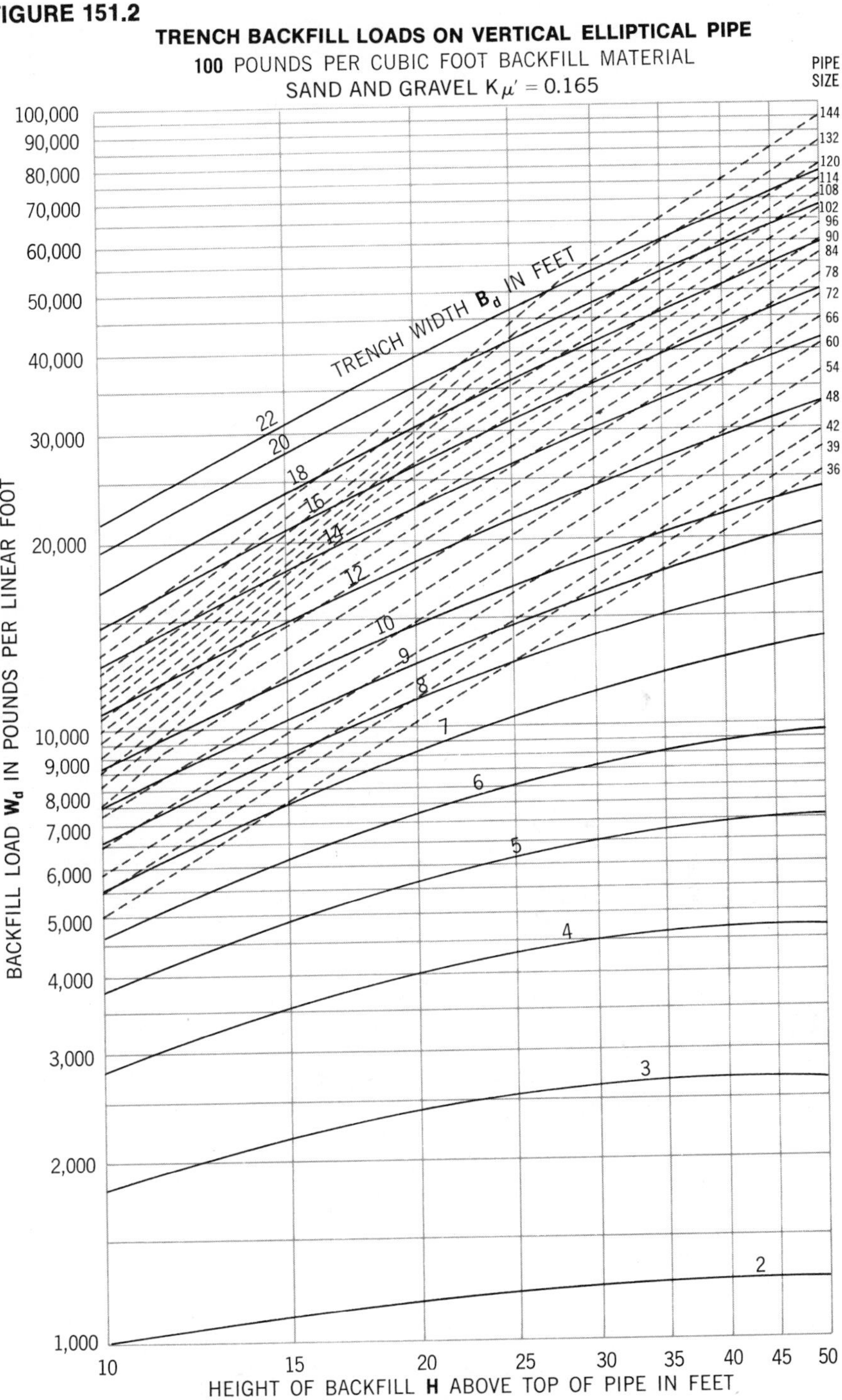

TRENCH BACKFILL LOADS ON VERTICAL ELLIPTICAL PIPE
100 POUNDS PER CUBIC FOOT BACKFILL MATERIAL
SAND AND GRAVEL K μ' = 0.165

For backfill weighing 110 pounds per cubic foot, increase loads 10%; for 120 pounds per cubic foot, increase 20%; etc.
Transition loads and widths based on $K\mu = 0.19$, $r_{sd} = 0.7$ and $p = 0.7$ in the embankment equation

FIGURE 152.1

TRENCH BACKFILL LOADS ON VERTICAL ELLIPTICAL PIPE
100 POUNDS PER CUBIC FOOT BACKFILL MATERIAL
SATURATED TOP SOIL $K\mu' = 0.150$

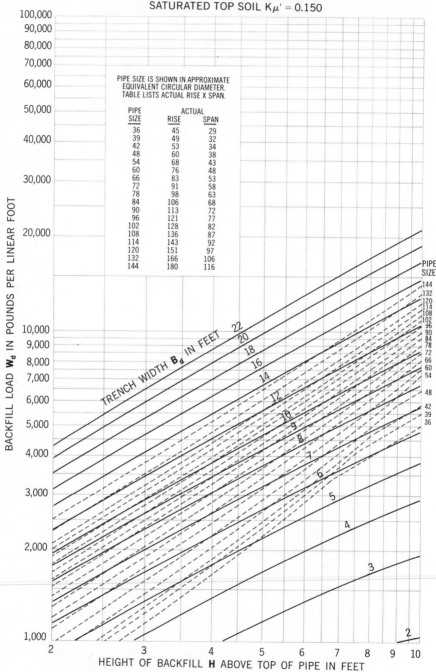

PIPE SIZE IS SHOWN IN APPROXIMATE
EQUIVALENT CIRCULAR DIAMETER.
TABLE LISTS ACTUAL RISE X SPAN.

PIPE SIZE	ACTUAL RISE	SPAN
36	45	29
39	49	32
42	53	34
48	60	38
54	68	43
60	76	48
66	83	53
72	91	58
78	98	63
84	106	68
90	113	72
96	121	77
102	128	82
108	136	87
114	143	92
120	151	97
132	166	106
144	180	116

For backfill weighing 110 pounds per cubic foot, increase loads 10%; for 120 pounds per cubic foot, increase 20%; etc.

Transition loads and widths based on $K\mu = 0.19$, $r_{sd} = 0.7$ and $p = 0.7$ in the embankment equation

FIGURE 152.2

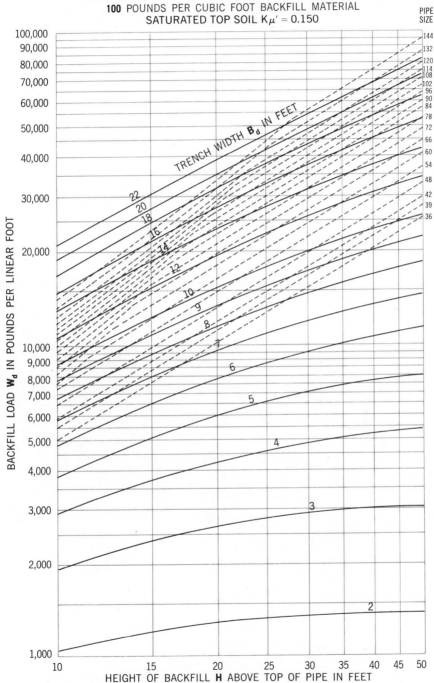

TRENCH BACKFILL LOADS ON VERTICAL ELLIPTICAL PIPE
100 POUNDS PER CUBIC FOOT BACKFILL MATERIAL
SATURATED TOP SOIL $K\mu' = 0.150$

PIPE SIZE

For backfill weighing 110 pounds per cubic foot, increase loads 10%; for 120 pounds per cubic foot, increase 20%; etc.
Transition loads and widths based on $K_\mu = 0.19$, $r_{sd} = 0.7$ and $p = 0.7$ in the embankment equation

FIGURE 153.1

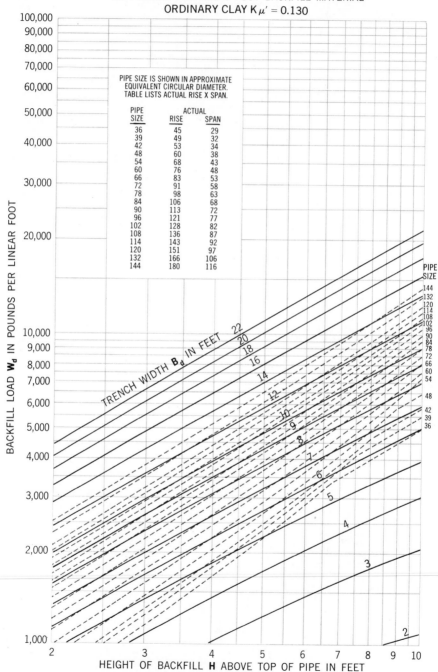

TRENCH BACKFILL LOADS ON VERTICAL ELLIPTICAL PIPE
100 POUNDS PER CUBIC FOOT BACKFILL MATERIAL
ORDINARY CLAY Kμ' = 0.130

PIPE SIZE IS SHOWN IN APPROXIMATE
EQUIVALENT CIRCULAR DIAMETER.
TABLE LISTS ACTUAL RISE X SPAN.

PIPE SIZE	ACTUAL RISE	SPAN
36	45	29
39	49	32
42	53	34
48	60	38
54	68	43
60	76	48
66	83	53
72	91	58
78	98	63
84	106	68
90	113	72
96	121	77
102	128	82
108	136	87
114	143	92
120	151	97
132	166	106
144	180	116

BACKFILL LOAD W_d IN POUNDS PER LINEAR FOOT

TRENCH WIDTH B_d IN FEET

HEIGHT OF BACKFILL **H** ABOVE TOP OF PIPE IN FEET

For backfill weighing 110 pounds per cubic foot, increase loads 10%; for 120 pounds per cubic foot, increase 20%; etc.
Transition loads and widths based on Kμ = 0.19, r_{sd} = 0.7 and p = 0.7 in the embankment equation

FIGURE 153.2

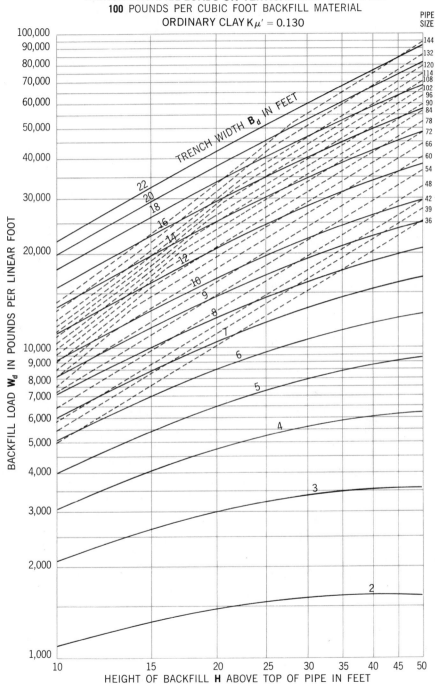

TRENCH BACKFILL LOADS ON VERTICAL ELLIPTICAL PIPE
100 POUNDS PER CUBIC FOOT BACKFILL MATERIAL
ORDINARY CLAY $K\mu' = 0.130$

For backfill weighing 110 pounds per cubic foot, increase loads 10%; for 120 pounds per cubic foot, increase 20%; etc.
Transition loads and widths based on $K\mu = 0.19$, $r_{sd} = 0.7$ and $p = 0.7$ in the embankment equation

FIGURE 154-1

TRENCH BACKFILL LOADS ON VERTICAL ELLIPTICAL PIPE
100 POUNDS PER CUBIC FOOT BACKFILL MATERIAL
SATURATED CLAY $K\mu' = 0.110$

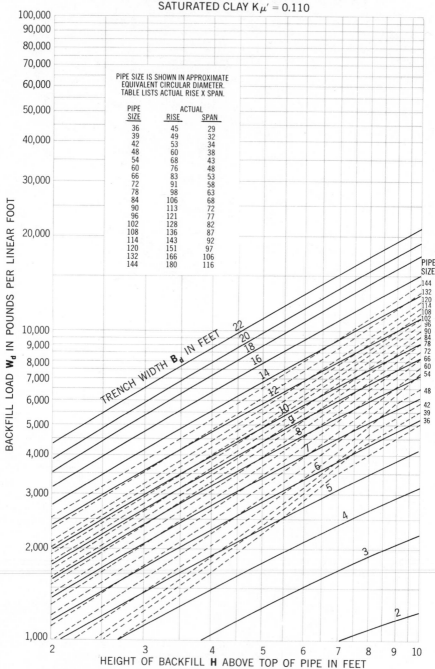

PIPE SIZE IS SHOWN IN APPROXIMATE
EQUIVALENT CIRCULAR DIAMETER.
TABLE LISTS ACTUAL RISE X SPAN.

PIPE SIZE	ACTUAL RISE	SPAN
36	45	29
39	49	32
42	53	34
48	60	38
54	68	43
60	76	48
66	83	53
72	91	58
78	98	63
84	106	68
90	113	72
96	121	77
102	128	82
108	136	87
114	143	92
120	151	97
132	166	106
144	180	116

BACKFILL LOAD W_d IN POUNDS PER LINEAR FOOT

TRENCH WIDTH B_d IN FEET

HEIGHT OF BACKFILL **H** ABOVE TOP OF PIPE IN FEET

For backfill weighing 110 pounds per cubic foot, increase loads 10%; for 120 pounds per cubic foot, increase 20%; etc.
Transition loads and widths based on $K\mu = 0.19$, $r_{sd} = 0.7$ and $p = 0.7$ in the embankment equation

FIGURE 154.2

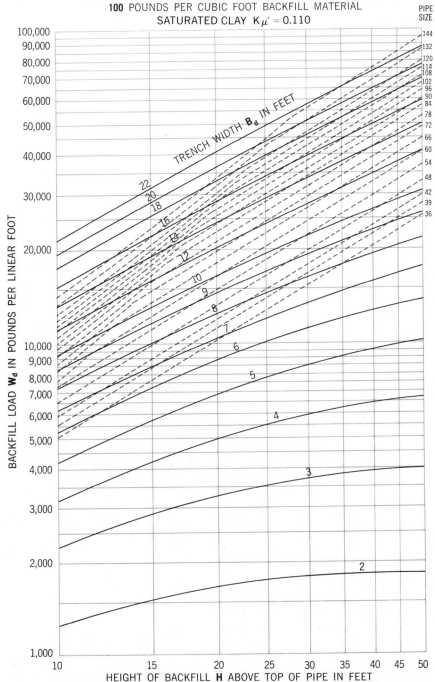

TRENCH BACKFILL LOADS ON VERTICAL ELLIPTICAL PIPE
100 POUNDS PER CUBIC FOOT BACKFILL MATERIAL
SATURATED CLAY $K\mu' = 0.110$

PIPE SIZE

For backfill weighing 110 pounds per cubic foot, increase loads 10%; for 120 pounds per cubic foot, increase 20%; etc.
Transition loads and widths based on $K\mu = 0.19$, $r_{sd} = 0.7$ and $p = 0.7$ in the embankment equation

FIGURE 155.1

TRENCH BACKFILL LOADS ON HORIZONTAL ELLIPTICAL PIPE

100 POUNDS PER CUBIC FOOT BACKFILL MATERIAL
SAND AND GRAVEL Kμ' = 0.165

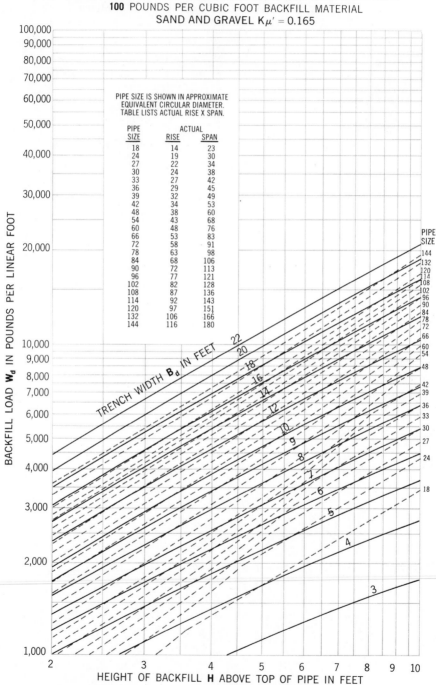

PIPE SIZE IS SHOWN IN APPROXIMATE
EQUIVALENT CIRCULAR DIAMETER.
TABLE LISTS ACTUAL RISE X SPAN.

PIPE SIZE	ACTUAL RISE	ACTUAL SPAN
18	14	23
24	19	30
27	22	34
30	24	38
33	27	42
36	29	45
39	32	49
42	34	53
48	38	60
54	43	68
60	48	76
66	53	83
72	58	91
78	63	98
84	68	106
90	72	113
96	77	121
102	82	128
108	87	136
114	92	143
120	97	151
132	106	166
144	116	180

For backfill weighing 110 pounds per cubic foot, increase loads 10%; for 120 pounds per cubic foot, increase 20%; etc.

Transition loads and widths based on Kμ = 0.19, r_{sd} = 0.7 and p = 0.7 in the embankment equation

FIGURE 155.2

TRENCH BACKFILL LOADS ON HORIZONTAL ELLIPTICAL PIPE
100 POUNDS PER CUBIC FOOT BACKFILL MATERIAL
SAND AND GRAVEL Kμ' = 0.165

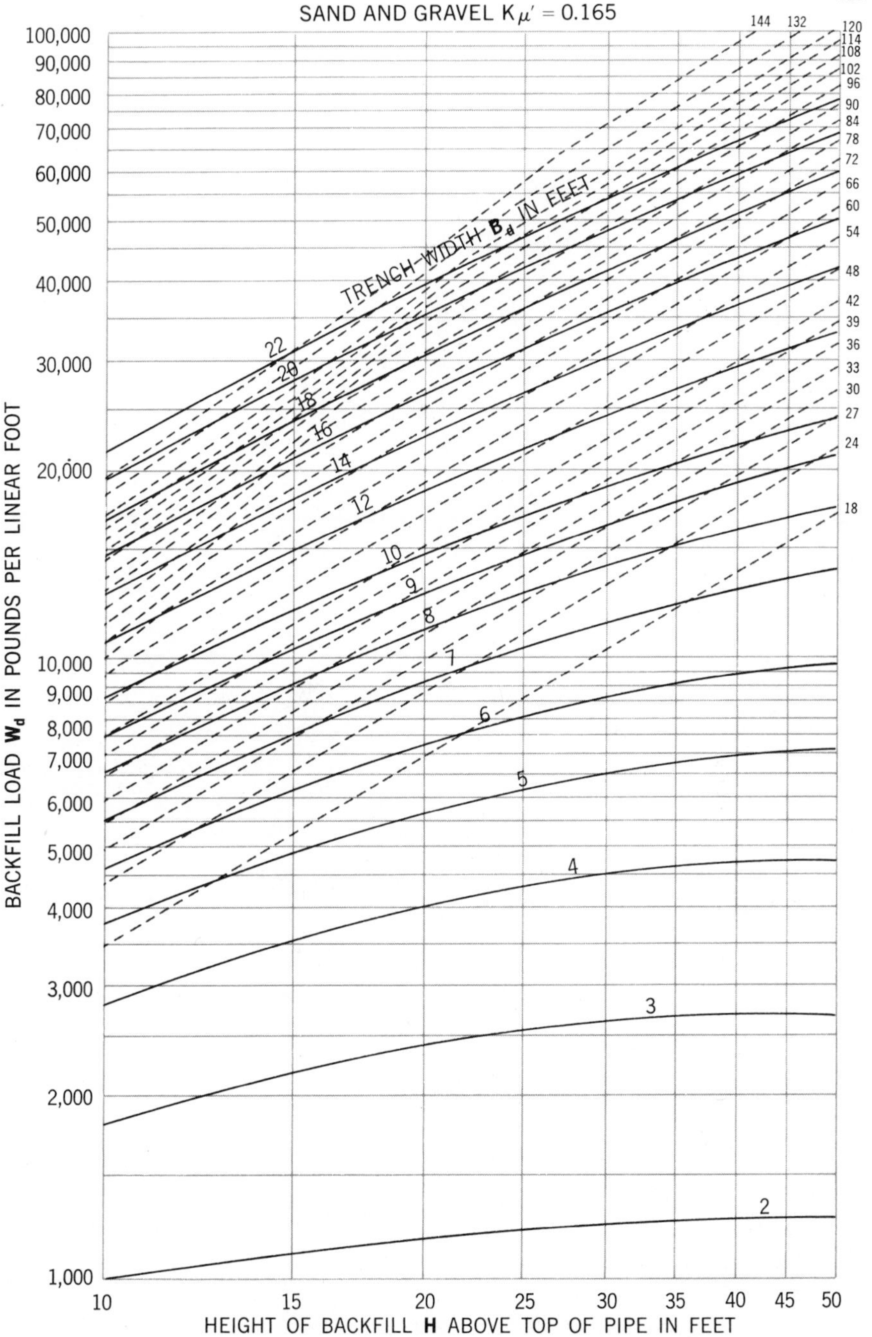

For backfill weighing 110 pounds per cubic foot, increase loads 10%; for 120 pounds per cubic foot, increase 20%; etc.
Transition loads and widths based on Kμ = 0.19, r_{sd} = 0.7 and p = 0.7 in the embankment equation

FIGURE 156.1

TRENCH BACKFILL LOADS ON HORIZONTAL ELLIPTICAL PIPE
100 POUNDS PER CUBIC FOOT BACKFILL MATERIAL
SATURATED TOP SOIL $K\mu' = 0.150$

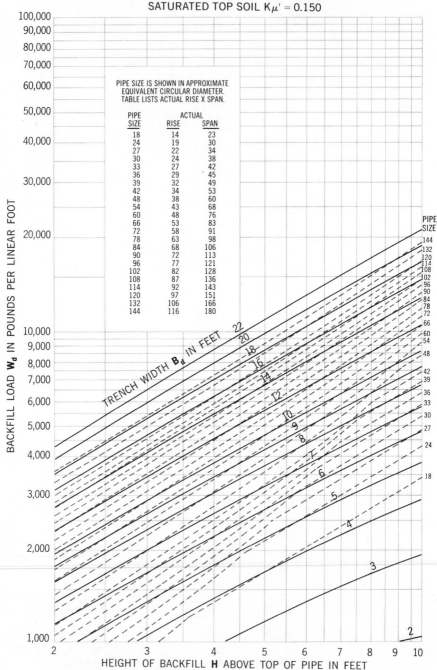

PIPE SIZE IS SHOWN IN APPROXIMATE
EQUIVALENT CIRCULAR DIAMETER.
TABLE LISTS ACTUAL RISE X SPAN.

PIPE SIZE	ACTUAL RISE	SPAN
18	14	23
24	19	30
27	22	34
30	24	38
33	27	42
36	29	45
39	32	49
42	34	53
48	38	60
54	43	68
60	48	76
66	53	83
72	58	91
78	63	98
84	68	106
90	72	113
96	77	121
102	82	128
108	87	136
114	92	143
120	97	151
132	106	166
144	116	180

For backfill weighing 110 pounds per cubic foot, increase loads 10%; for 120 pounds per cubic foot, increase 20%; etc.

Transition loads and widths based on $K\mu = 0.19$, $r_{sd} = 0.7$ and $p = 0.7$ in the embankment equation

FIGURE 156.2

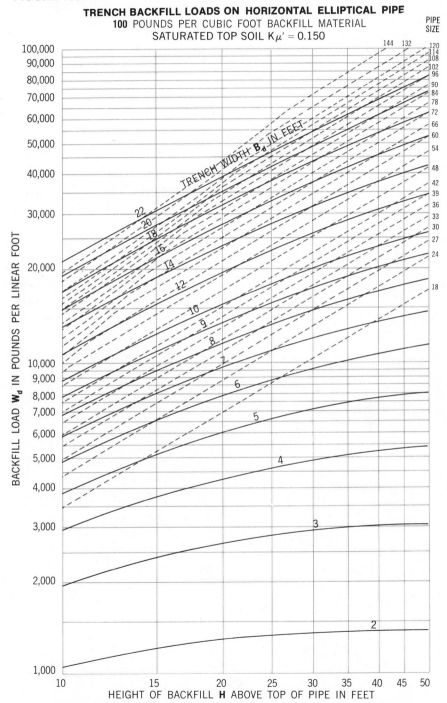

TRENCH BACKFILL LOADS ON HORIZONTAL ELLIPTICAL PIPE
100 POUNDS PER CUBIC FOOT BACKFILL MATERIAL
SATURATED TOP SOIL Kμ' = 0.150

For backfill weighing 110 pounds per cubic foot, increase loads 10%; for 120 pounds per cubic foot, increase 20%; etc.
Transition loads and widths based on Kμ = 0.19, r_{sd} = 0.7 and p = 0.7 in the embankment equation

FIGURE 157.1

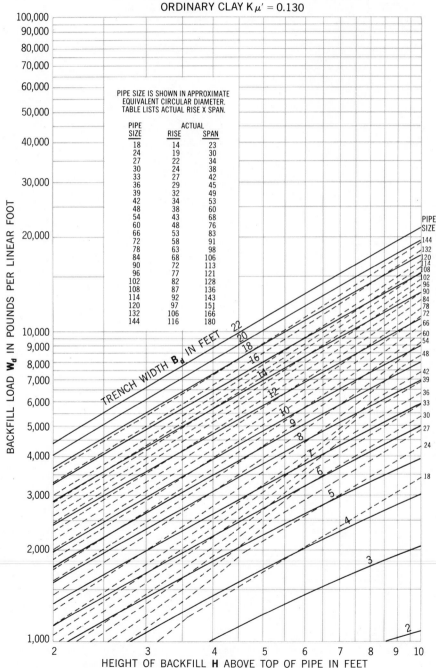

TRENCH BACKFILL LOADS ON HORIZONTAL ELLIPTICAL PIPE
100 POUNDS PER CUBIC FOOT BACKFILL MATERIAL
ORDINARY CLAY K μ' = 0.130

PIPE SIZE IS SHOWN IN APPROXIMATE
EQUIVALENT CIRCULAR DIAMETER.
TABLE LISTS ACTUAL RISE X SPAN.

PIPE SIZE	ACTUAL RISE	SPAN
18	14	23
24	19	30
27	22	34
30	24	38
33	27	42
36	29	45
39	32	49
42	34	53
48	38	60
54	43	68
60	48	76
66	53	83
72	58	91
78	63	98
84	68	106
90	72	113
96	77	121
102	82	128
108	87	136
114	92	143
120	97	151
132	106	166
144	116	180

BACKFILL LOAD W_d IN POUNDS PER LINEAR FOOT

TRENCH WIDTH B_d IN FEET

HEIGHT OF BACKFILL **H** ABOVE TOP OF PIPE IN FEET

For backfill weighing 110 pounds per cubic foot, increase loads 10%; for 120 pounds per cubic foot, increase 20%; etc.
Transition loads and widths based on Kμ = 0.19, r_{sd} = 0.7 and p = 0.7 in the embankment equation

FIGURE 157.2

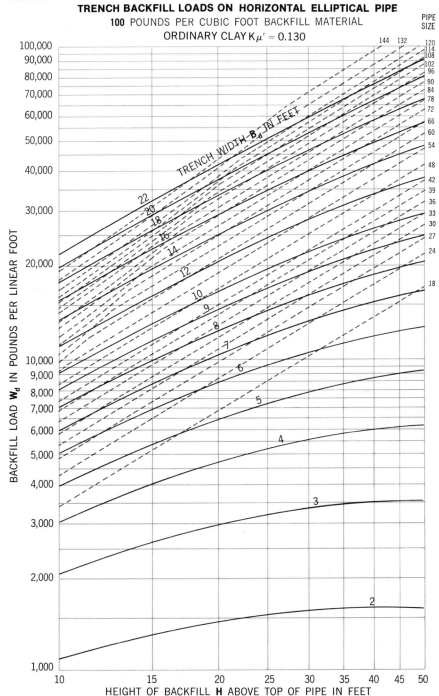

TRENCH BACKFILL LOADS ON HORIZONTAL ELLIPTICAL PIPE
100 POUNDS PER CUBIC FOOT BACKFILL MATERIAL
ORDINARY CLAY $K\mu' = 0.130$

For backfill weighing 110 pounds per cubic foot, increase loads 10%; for 120 pounds per cubic foot, increase 20%; etc.
Transition loads and widths based on $K\mu = 0.19$, $r_{sd} = 0.7$ and $p = 0.7$ in the embankment equation

FIGURE 158.1

TRENCH BACKFILL LOADS ON HORIZONTAL ELLIPTICAL PIPE
100 POUNDS PER CUBIC FOOT BACKFILL MATERIAL
SATURATED CLAY $K\mu' = 0.110$

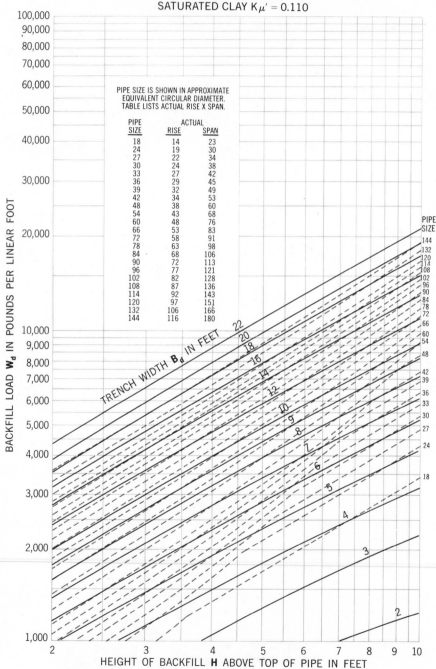

PIPE SIZE IS SHOWN IN APPROXIMATE
EQUIVALENT CIRCULAR DIAMETER.
TABLE LISTS ACTUAL RISE X SPAN.

PIPE SIZE	ACTUAL RISE	SPAN
18	14	23
24	19	30
27	22	34
30	24	38
33	27	42
36	29	45
39	32	49
42	34	53
48	38	60
54	43	68
60	48	76
66	53	83
72	58	91
78	63	98
84	68	106
90	72	113
96	77	121
102	82	128
108	87	136
114	92	143
120	97	151
132	106	166
144	116	180

BACKFILL LOAD W_d IN POUNDS PER LINEAR FOOT

TRENCH WIDTH B_d IN FEET

HEIGHT OF BACKFILL **H** ABOVE TOP OF PIPE IN FEET

For backfill weighing 110 pounds per cubic foot, increase loads 10%; for 120 pounds per cubic foot, increase 20%; etc.
Transition loads and widths based on $K\mu = 0.19$, $r_{sd} = 0.7$ and $p = 0.7$ in the embankment equation

FIGURE 158.2

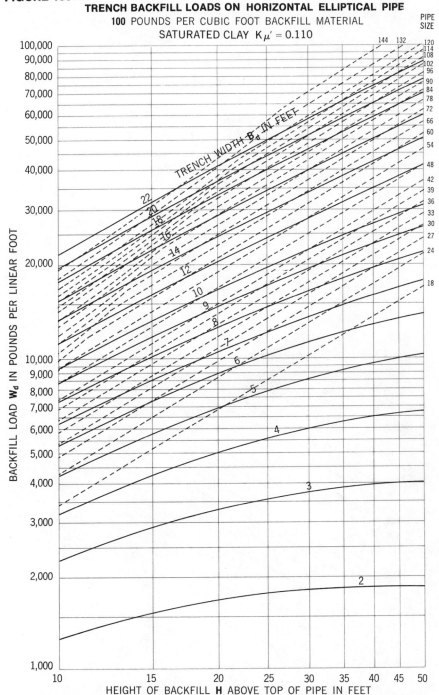

TRENCH BACKFILL LOADS ON HORIZONTAL ELLIPTICAL PIPE
100 POUNDS PER CUBIC FOOT BACKFILL MATERIAL
SATURATED CLAY $K\mu' = 0.110$

For backfill weighing 110 pounds per cubic foot, increase loads 10%; for 120 pounds per cubic foot, increase 20%; etc.
Transition loads and widths based on $K_\mu = 0.19$, $r_{sd} = 0.7$ and $p = 0.7$ in the embankment equation

FIGURE 159.1

TRENCH BACKFILL LOADS ON ARCH PIPE
100 POUNDS PER CUBIC FOOT BACKFILL MATERIAL
SAND AND GRAVEL $K\mu' = 0.165$

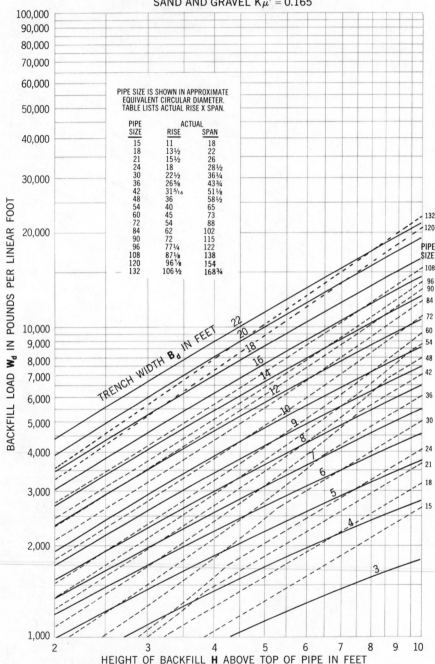

PIPE SIZE IS SHOWN IN APPROXIMATE
EQUIVALENT CIRCULAR DIAMETER.
TABLE LISTS ACTUAL RISE X SPAN.

PIPE SIZE	ACTUAL RISE	SPAN
15	11	18
18	13½	22
21	15½	26
24	18	28½
30	22½	36¼
36	26⅝	43¾
42	31⁵⁄₁₆	51⅛
48	36	58½
54	40	65
60	45	73
72	54	88
84	62	102
90	72	115
96	77¼	122
108	87⅛	138
120	96⅞	154
132	106½	168¾

BACKFILL LOAD **W**$_d$ IN POUNDS PER LINEAR FOOT

HEIGHT OF BACKFILL **H** ABOVE TOP OF PIPE IN FEET

For backfill weighing 110 pounds per cubic foot, increase loads 10%; for 120 pounds per cubic foot, increase 20%; etc.
Transition loads and widths based on $K\mu = 0.19$, $r_{sd} = 0.7$ and $p = 0.7$ in the embankment equation

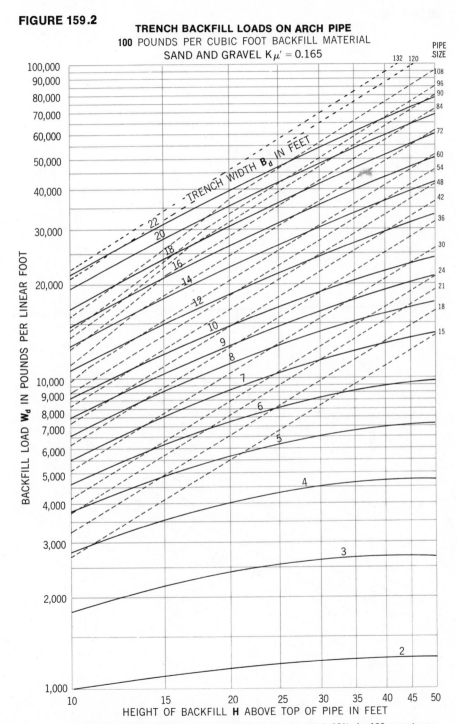

FIGURE 159.2

TRENCH BACKFILL LOADS ON ARCH PIPE
100 POUNDS PER CUBIC FOOT BACKFILL MATERIAL
SAND AND GRAVEL $K\mu' = 0.165$

For backfill weighing 110 pounds per cubic foot, increase loads 10%; for 120 pounds per cubic foot, increase 20%; etc.
Transition loads and widths based on $K\mu = 0.19$, $r_{sd} = 0.7$ and $p = 0.7$ in the embankment equation

FIGURE 160.1

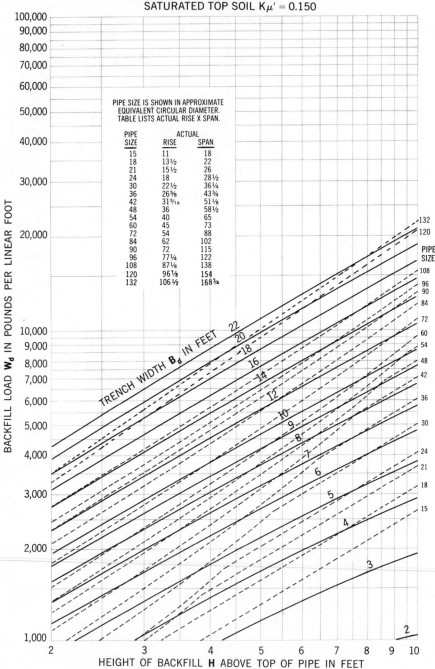

TRENCH BACKFILL LOADS ON ARCH PIPE
100 POUNDS PER CUBIC FOOT BACKFILL MATERIAL
SATURATED TOP SOIL $K\mu' = 0.150$

PIPE SIZE IS SHOWN IN APPROXIMATE
EQUIVALENT CIRCULAR DIAMETER.
TABLE LISTS ACTUAL RISE X SPAN.

PIPE SIZE	ACTUAL RISE	SPAN
15	11	18
18	13½	22
21	15½	26
24	18	28½
30	22½	36¼
36	26⅝	43¾
42	31⁵⁄₁₆	51⅛
48	36	58½
54	40	65
60	45	73
72	54	88
84	62	102
90	72	115
96	77¼	122
108	87⅛	138
120	96⅛	154
132	106½	168¾

Y-axis: BACKFILL LOAD W_d IN POUNDS PER LINEAR FOOT

X-axis: HEIGHT OF BACKFILL **H** ABOVE TOP OF PIPE IN FEET

For backfill weighing 110 pounds per cubic foot, increase loads 10%; for 120 pounds per cubic foot, increase 20%; etc.
Transition loads and widths based on $K\mu = 0.19$, $r_{sd} = 0.7$ and $p = 0.7$ in the embankment equation

FIGURE 160.2

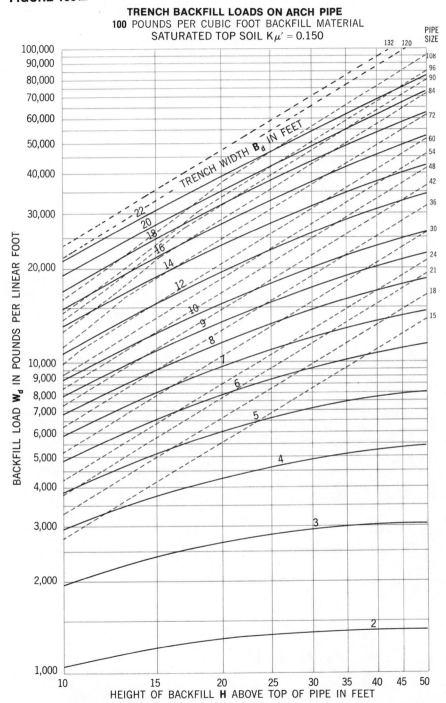

TRENCH BACKFILL LOADS ON ARCH PIPE
100 POUNDS PER CUBIC FOOT BACKFILL MATERIAL
SATURATED TOP SOIL $K\mu' = 0.150$

For backfill weighing 110 pounds per cubic foot, increase loads 10%; for 120 pounds per cubic foot, increase 20%; etc.
Transition loads and widths based on $K\mu = 0.19$, $r_{sd} = 0.7$ and $p = 0.7$ in the embankment equation

FIGURE 161.1

TRENCH BACKFILL LOADS ON ARCH PIPE
100 POUNDS PER CUBIC FOOT BACKFILL MATERIAL
ORDINARY CLAY K μ' = 0.130

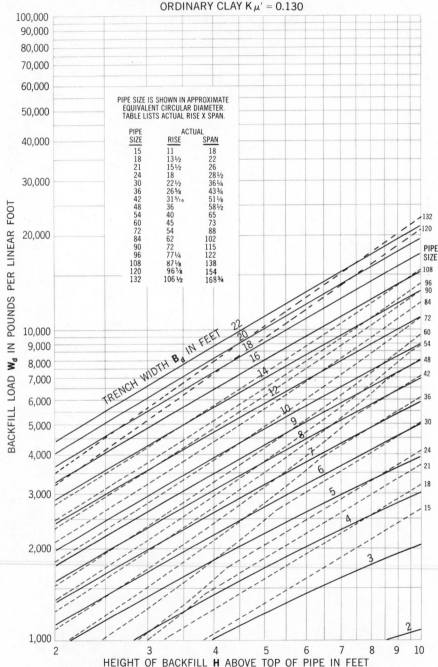

PIPE SIZE IS SHOWN IN APPROXIMATE EQUIVALENT CIRCULAR DIAMETER. TABLE LISTS ACTUAL RISE X SPAN.

PIPE SIZE	ACTUAL RISE	SPAN
15	11	18
18	13½	22
21	15½	26
24	18	28½
30	22½	36¼
36	26⅝	43¾
42	31⁵⁄₁₆	51⅛
48	36	58½
54	40	65
60	45	73
72	54	88
84	62	102
90	72	115
96	77¼	122
108	87⅛	138
120	96⅛	154
132	106½	168¾

For backfill weighing 110 pounds per cubic foot, increase loads 10%; for 120 pounds per cubic foot, increase 20%; etc.

Transition loads and widths based on Kμ = 0.19, r_{sd} = 0.7 and p = 0.7 in the embankment equation

FIGURE 161.2

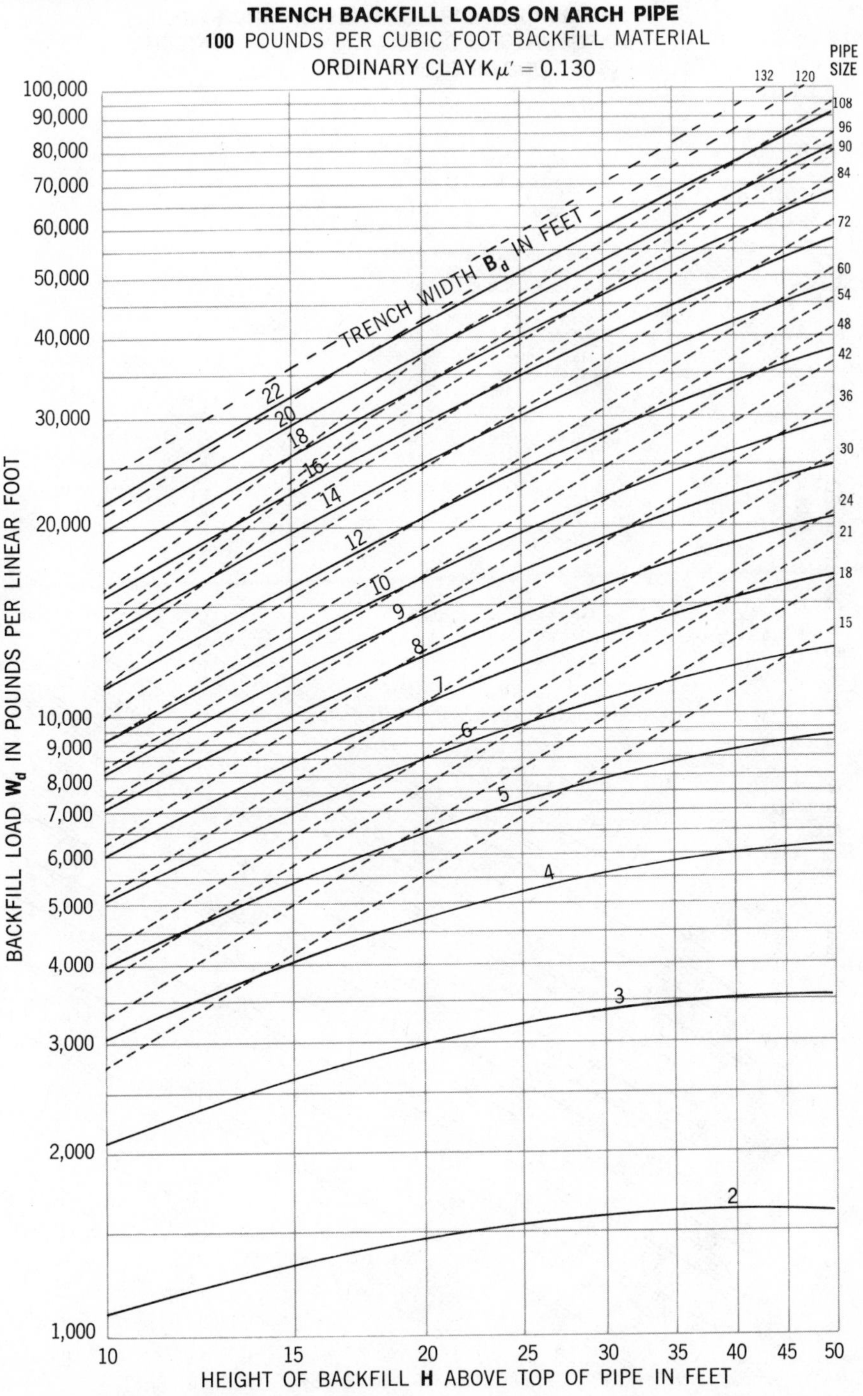

TRENCH BACKFILL LOADS ON ARCH PIPE
100 POUNDS PER CUBIC FOOT BACKFILL MATERIAL
ORDINARY CLAY $K\mu' = 0.130$

For backfill weighing 110 pounds per cubic foot, increase loads 10%; for 120 pounds per cubic foot, increase 20%; etc.
Transition loads and widths based on $K\mu = 0.19$, $r_{sd} = 0.7$ and $p = 0.7$ in the embankment equation

FIGURE 162.1

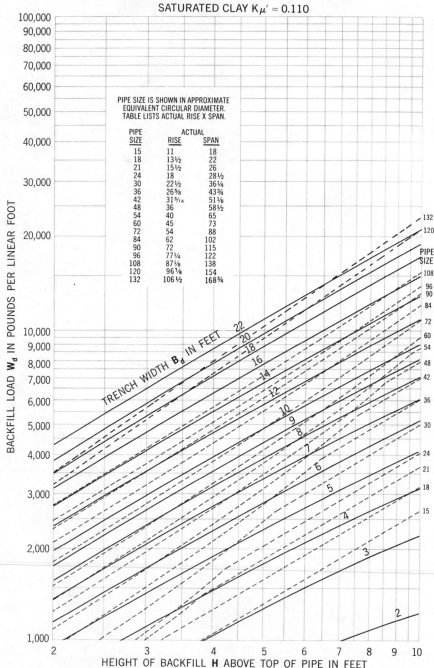

TRENCH BACKFILL LOADS ON ARCH PIPE
100 POUNDS PER CUBIC FOOT BACKFILL MATERIAL
SATURATED CLAY $K\mu' = 0.110$

PIPE SIZE IS SHOWN IN APPROXIMATE
EQUIVALENT CIRCULAR DIAMETER.
TABLE LISTS ACTUAL RISE X SPAN.

PIPE SIZE	ACTUAL RISE	SPAN
15	11	18
18	13½	22
21	15½	26
24	18	28½
30	22½	36¼
36	26⅝	43¾
42	31⁵⁄₁₆	51⅛
48	36	58½
54	40	65
60	45	73
72	54	88
84	62	102
90	72	115
96	77¼	122
108	87⅛	138
120	96⅛	154
132	106½	168¾

BACKFILL LOAD W_d IN POUNDS PER LINEAR FOOT

TRENCH WIDTH B_d IN FEET

HEIGHT OF BACKFILL **H** ABOVE TOP OF PIPE IN FEET

For backfill weighing 110 pounds per cubic foot, increase loads 10%; for 120 pounds per cubic foot, increase 20%; etc.
Transition loads and widths based on $K\mu = 0.19$, $r_{sd} = 0.7$ and $p = 0.7$ in the embankment equation

FIGURE 162 .2

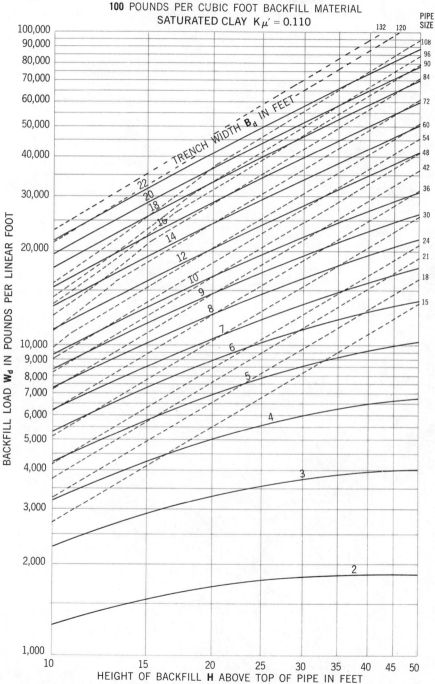

TRENCH BACKFILL LOADS ON ARCH PIPE
100 POUNDS PER CUBIC FOOT BACKFILL MATERIAL
SATURATED CLAY Kμ' = 0.110

For backfill weighing 110 pounds per cubic foot, increase loads 10%; for 120 pounds per cubic foot, increase 20%; etc.

Transition loads and widths based on K μ = 0.19, r_{sd} = 0.7 and ρ = 0.7 in the embankment equation

FIGURE 163

EMBANKMENT FILL LOADS ON CIRCULAR PIPE
POSITIVE PROJECTING $r_{sd} p = 0$ **100** POUNDS PER CUBIC FOOT FILL

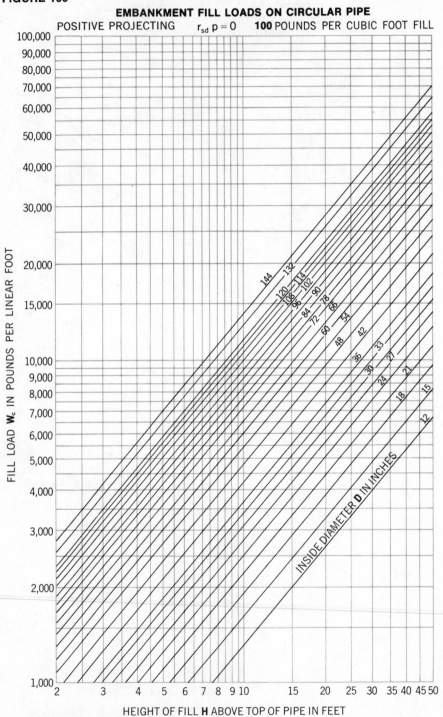

FILL LOAD W_c IN POUNDS PER LINEAR FOOT

HEIGHT OF FILL **H** ABOVE TOP OF PIPE IN FEET

For fill weighing 110 pounds per cubic foot, increase loads 10%; for 120 pounds increase 20%, etc. Interpolate for intermediate pipe sizes.

FIGURE 164

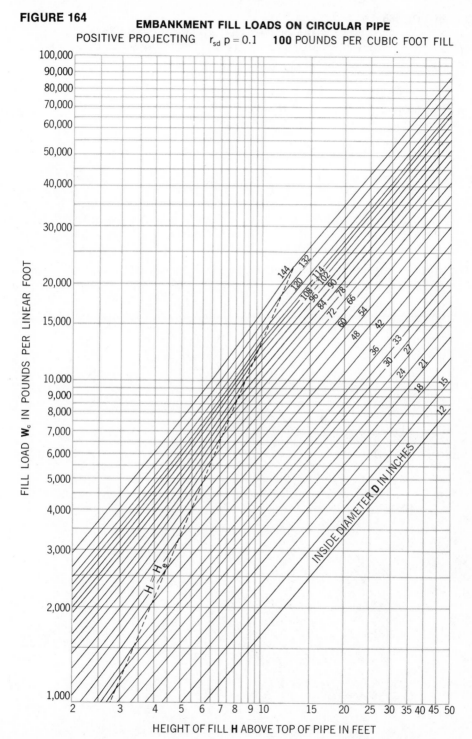

EMBANKMENT FILL LOADS ON CIRCULAR PIPE

POSITIVE PROJECTING $r_{sd} p = 0.1$ **100** POUNDS PER CUBIC FOOT FILL

HEIGHT OF FILL **H** ABOVE TOP OF PIPE IN FEET

For fill weighing 110 pounds per cubic foot, increase loads 10%; for 120 pounds increase 20%, etc. Interpolate for intermediate pipe sizes.

FIGURE 165

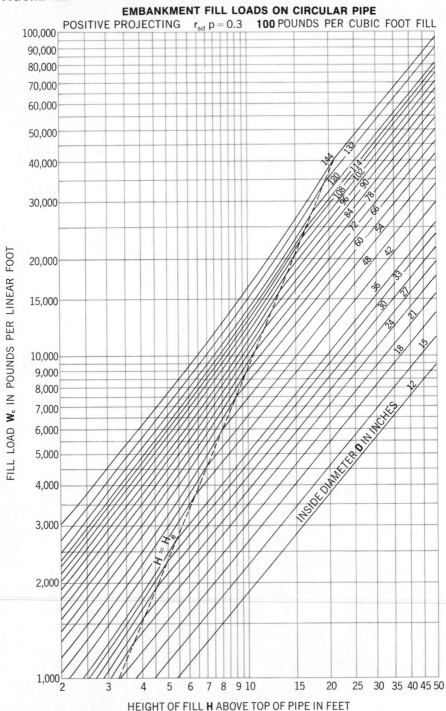

EMBANKMENT FILL LOADS ON CIRCULAR PIPE
POSITIVE PROJECTING r_{sd} p = 0.3   **100** POUNDS PER CUBIC FOOT FILL

HEIGHT OF FILL **H** ABOVE TOP OF PIPE IN FEET

FILL LOAD **W**$_c$ IN POUNDS PER LINEAR FOOT

For fill weighing 110 pounds per cubic foot, increase loads 10%; for 120 pounds increase 20%, etc. Interpolate for intermediate pipe sizes.

FIGURE 166

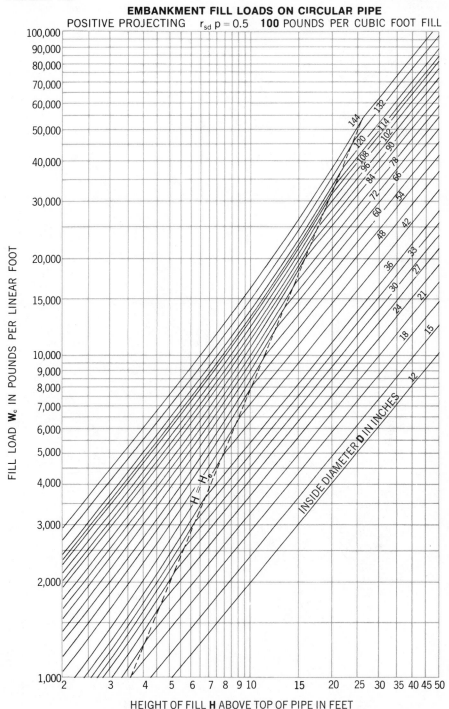

EMBANKMENT FILL LOADS ON CIRCULAR PIPE

POSITIVE PROJECTING $r_{sd}\,p = 0.5$ **100** POUNDS PER CUBIC FOOT FILL

FILL LOAD **W$_c$** IN POUNDS PER LINEAR FOOT

HEIGHT OF FILL **H** ABOVE TOP OF PIPE IN FEET

For fill weighing 110 pounds per cubic foot, increase loads 10%; for 120 pounds increase 20%, etc. Interpolate for intermediate pipe sizes.

FIGURE 167

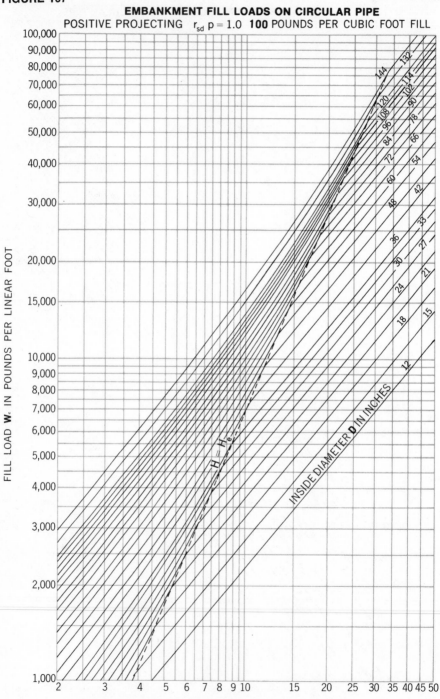

EMBANKMENT FILL LOADS ON CIRCULAR PIPE
POSITIVE PROJECTING $r_{sd}\,p = 1.0$ **100** POUNDS PER CUBIC FOOT FILL

FILL LOAD W_e IN POUNDS PER LINEAR FOOT

HEIGHT OF FILL **H** ABOVE TOP OF PIPE IN FEET

For fill weighing 110 pounds per cubic foot, increase loads 10%; for 120 pounds increase 20%, etc. Interpolate for intermediate pipe sizes.

FIGURE 168   **EMBANKMENT FILL LOADS ON VERTICAL ELLIPTICAL PIPE**

POSITIVE PROJECTING $r_{sd}\, p = 0$ **100** POUNDS PER CUBIC FOOT FILL

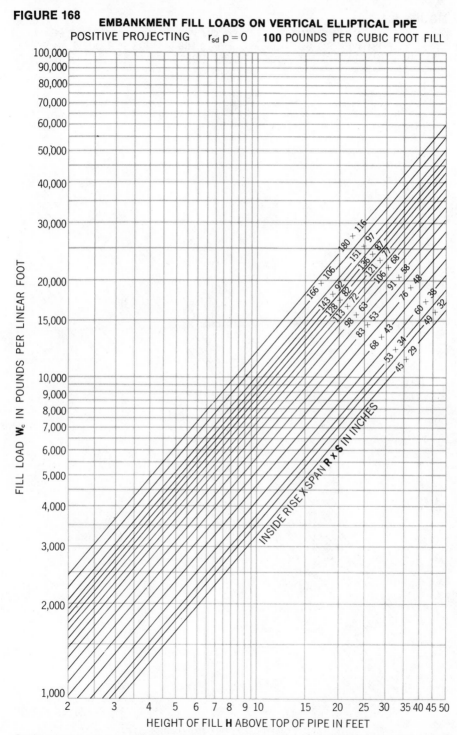

For fill weighing 110 pounds per cubic foot, increase loads 10%; for 120 pounds increase 20%, etc. Interpolate for intermediate pipe sizes.

FIGURE 169

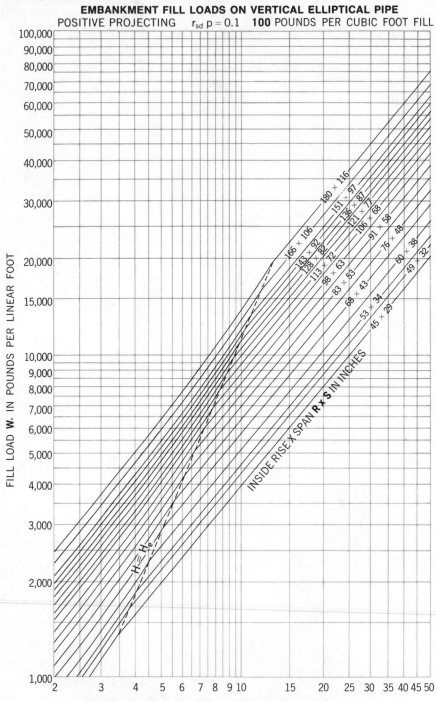

EMBANKMENT FILL LOADS ON VERTICAL ELLIPTICAL PIPE
POSITIVE PROJECTING $r_{sd} p = 0.1$ **100** POUNDS PER CUBIC FOOT FILL

HEIGHT OF FILL **H** ABOVE TOP OF PIPE IN FEET

For fill weighing 110 pounds per cubic foot, increase loads 10%; for 120 pounds increase 20%, etc. Interpolate for intermediate pipe sizes.

FIGURE 170

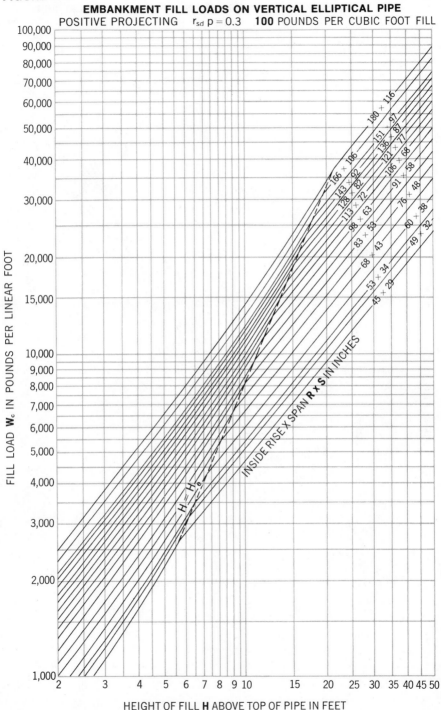

EMBANKMENT FILL LOADS ON VERTICAL ELLIPTICAL PIPE
POSITIVE PROJECTING $r_{sd}\,p = 0.3$ **100** POUNDS PER CUBIC FOOT FILL

HEIGHT OF FILL **H** ABOVE TOP OF PIPE IN FEET

For fill weighing 110 pounds per cubic foot, increase loads 10%; for 120 pounds increase 20%, etc. Interpolate for intermediate pipe sizes.

FIGURE 171

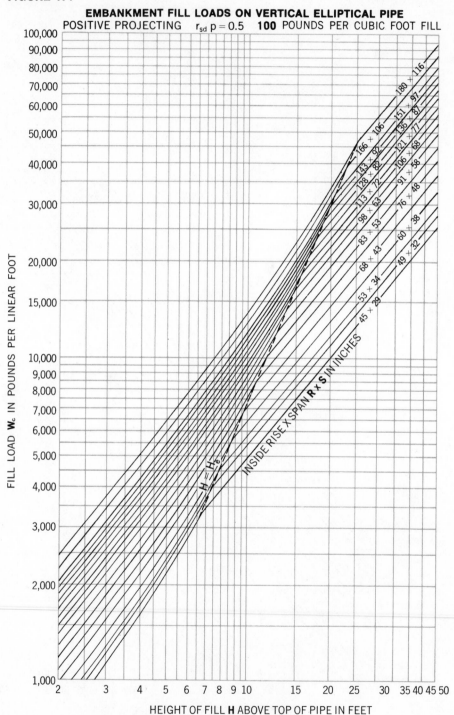

EMBANKMENT FILL LOADS ON VERTICAL ELLIPTICAL PIPE

POSITIVE PROJECTING $r_{sd}\,p = 0.5$ **100** POUNDS PER CUBIC FOOT FILL

HEIGHT OF FILL **H** ABOVE TOP OF PIPE IN FEET

FILL LOAD **W$_c$** IN POUNDS PER LINEAR FOOT

For fill weighing 110 pounds per cubic foot, increase loads 10%; for 120 pounds increase 20%, etc. Interpolate for intermediate pipe sizes.

FIGURE 172

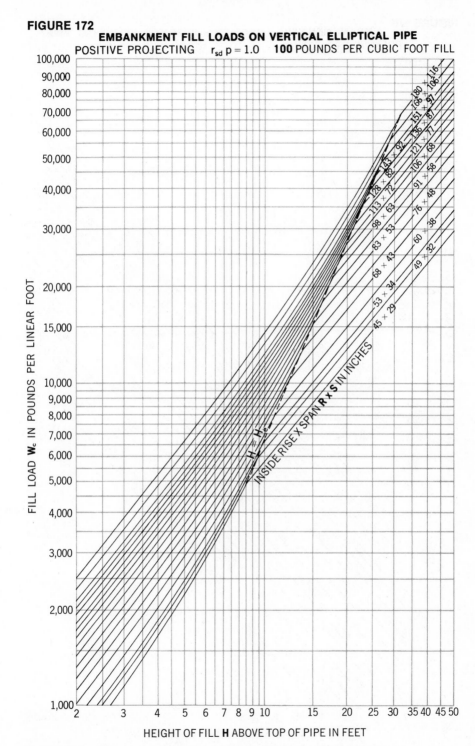

EMBANKMENT FILL LOADS ON VERTICAL ELLIPTICAL PIPE

POSITIVE PROJECTING $r_{sd}\, p = 1.0$ **100** POUNDS PER CUBIC FOOT FILL

HEIGHT OF FILL **H** ABOVE TOP OF PIPE IN FEET

FILL LOAD **W$_c$** IN POUNDS PER LINEAR FOOT

For fill weighing 110 pounds per cubic foot, increase loads 10%; for 120 pounds increase
Interpolate for intermediate pipe sizes.

FIGURE 173

EMBANKMENT FILL LOADS ON HORIZONTAL ELLIPTICAL PIPE

POSITIVE PROJECTING $r_{sd} p = 0$ **100** POUNDS PER CUBIC FOOT FILL

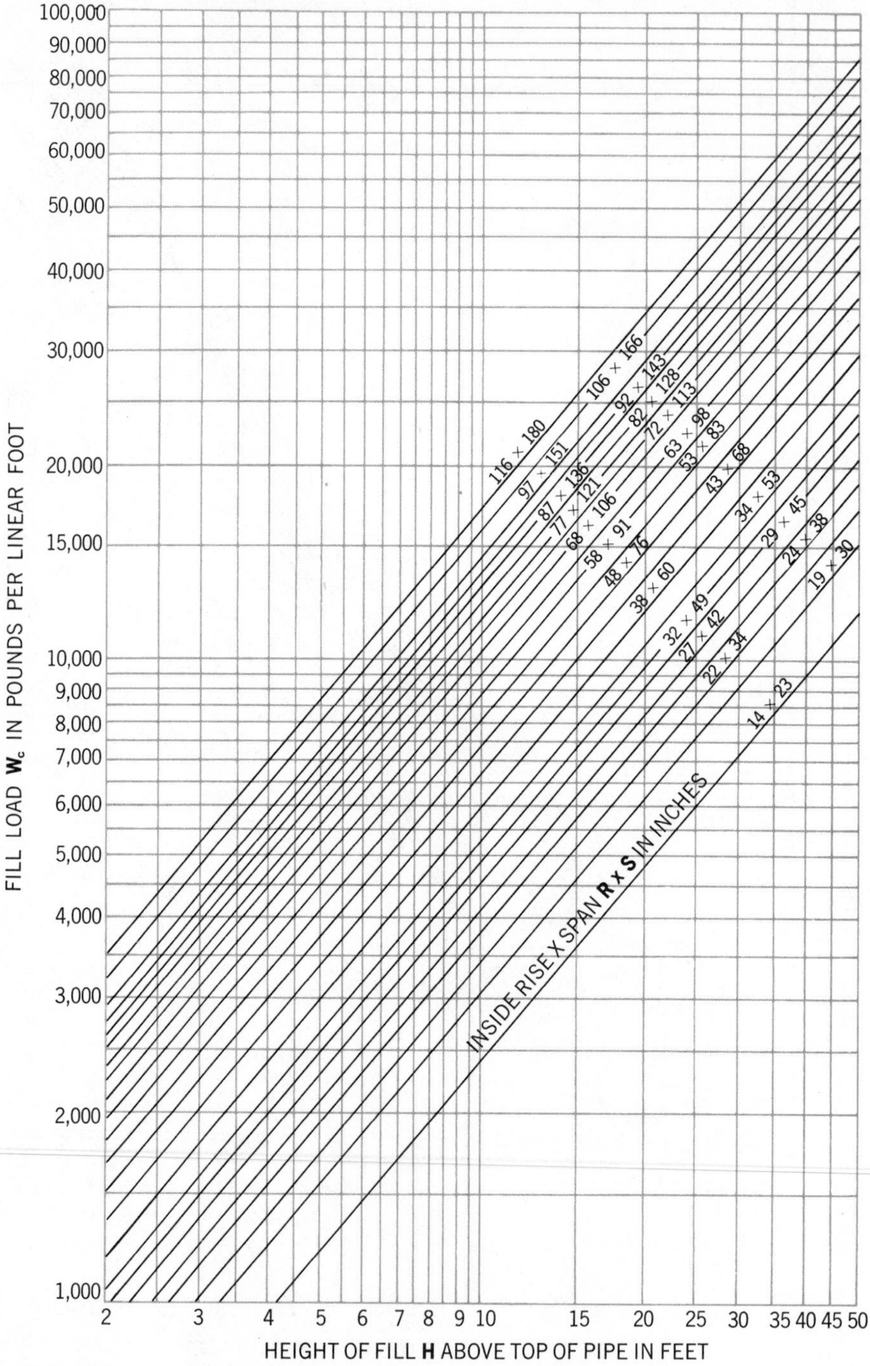

FILL LOAD W_c IN POUNDS PER LINEAR FOOT

HEIGHT OF FILL **H** ABOVE TOP OF PIPE IN FEET

INSIDE RISE × SPAN **R** × **S** IN INCHES

For fill weighing 110 pounds per cubic foot, increase loads 10%; for 120 pounds increase 20%, etc. Interpolate for intermediate pipe sizes.

FIGURE 174

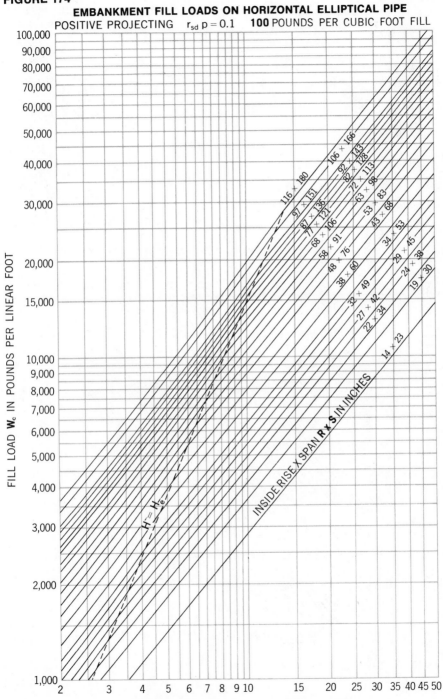

EMBANKMENT FILL LOADS ON HORIZONTAL ELLIPTICAL PIPE
POSITIVE PROJECTING $r_{sd}\, p = 0.1$ **100** POUNDS PER CUBIC FOOT FILL

FILL LOAD W_c IN POUNDS PER LINEAR FOOT

HEIGHT OF FILL **H** ABOVE TOP OF PIPE IN FEET

*For fill weighing 110 pounds per cubic foot, increase loads 10%; for 120 pounds increase 20%, etc.
Interpolate for intermediate pipe sizes.*

FIGURE 175

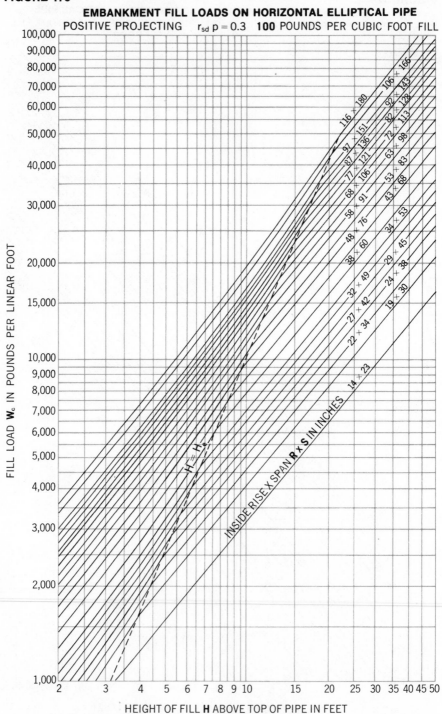

EMBANKMENT FILL LOADS ON HORIZONTAL ELLIPTICAL PIPE

POSITIVE PROJECTING $r_{sd}\, p = 0.3$ **100** POUNDS PER CUBIC FOOT FILL

FILL LOAD W_c IN POUNDS PER LINEAR FOOT

HEIGHT OF FILL **H** ABOVE TOP OF PIPE IN FEET

For fill weighing 110 pounds per cubic foot, increase loads 10%; for 120 pounds increase 20%, etc. Interpolate for intermediate pipe sizes.

FIGURE 176

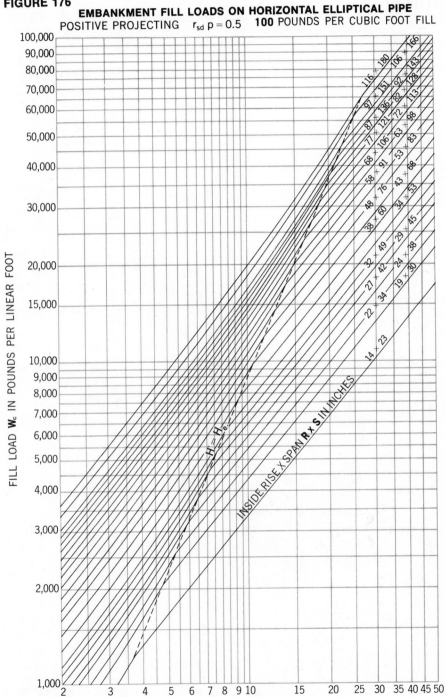

EMBANKMENT FILL LOADS ON HORIZONTAL ELLIPTICAL PIPE
POSITIVE PROJECTING $r_{sd}\, p = 0.5$ **100** POUNDS PER CUBIC FOOT FILL

FILL LOAD W_c IN POUNDS PER LINEAR FOOT

HEIGHT OF FILL **H** ABOVE TOP OF PIPE IN FEET

$H = H_e$

INSIDE RISE X SPAN **R x S** IN INCHES

For fill weighing 110 pounds per cubic foot, increase loads 10%; for 120 pounds increase 20%, etc. Interpolate for intermediate pipe sizes.

FIGURE 177

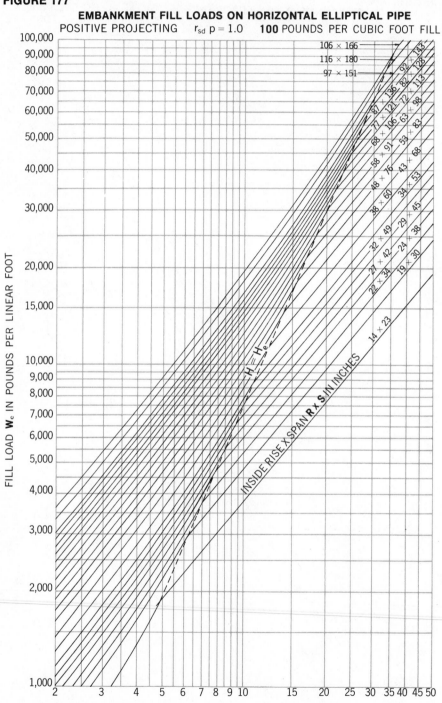

EMBANKMENT FILL LOADS ON HORIZONTAL ELLIPTICAL PIPE
POSITIVE PROJECTING $r_{sd}\,p = 1.0$ **100** POUNDS PER CUBIC FOOT FILL

FILL LOAD W_c IN POUNDS PER LINEAR FOOT

HEIGHT OF FILL **H** ABOVE TOP OF PIPE IN FEET

For fill weighing 110 pounds per cubic foot, increase loads 10%; for 120 pounds increase 20%, etc. Interpolate for intermediate pipe sizes.

FIGURE 178

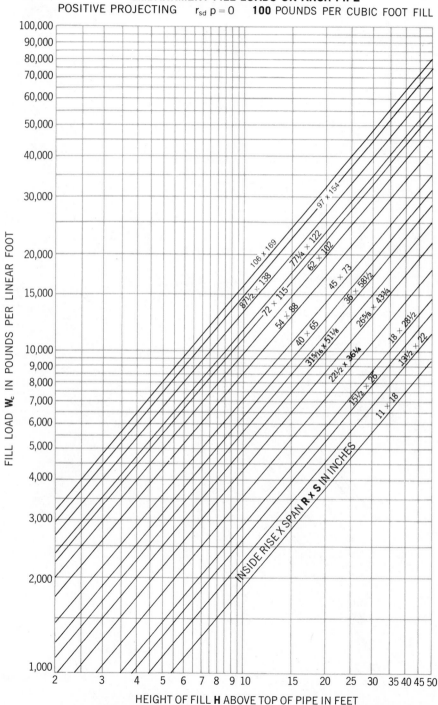

EMBANKMENT FILL LOADS ON ARCH PIPE

POSITIVE PROJECTING $r_{sd}\, p = 0$ **100** POUNDS PER CUBIC FOOT FILL

*For fill weighing 110 pounds per cubic foot, increase loads 10%; for 120 pounds increase 20%, etc.
Interpolate for intermediate pipe sizes.*

FIGURE 179

EMBANKMENT FILL LOADS ON ARCH PIPE

POSITIVE PROJECTING $r_{sd}\,p = 0.1$ **100** POUNDS PER CUBIC FOOT FILL

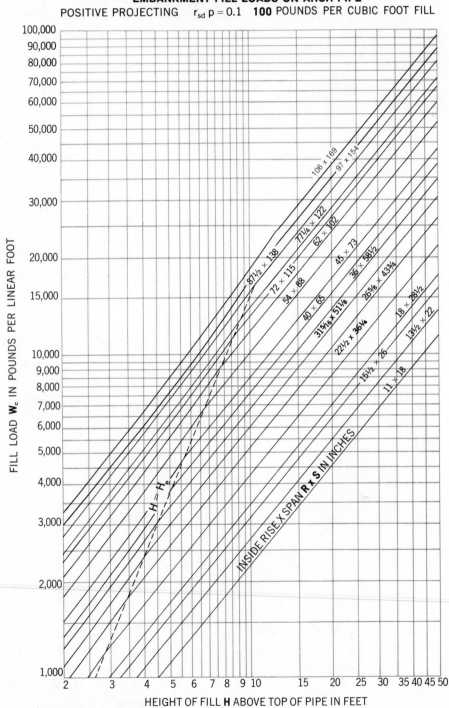

FILL LOAD W_c IN POUNDS PER LINEAR FOOT

HEIGHT OF FILL **H** ABOVE TOP OF PIPE IN FEET

For fill weighing 110 pounds per cubic foot, increase loads 10%; for 120 pounds increase 20%, etc. Interpolate for intermediate pipe sizes.

FIGURE 180

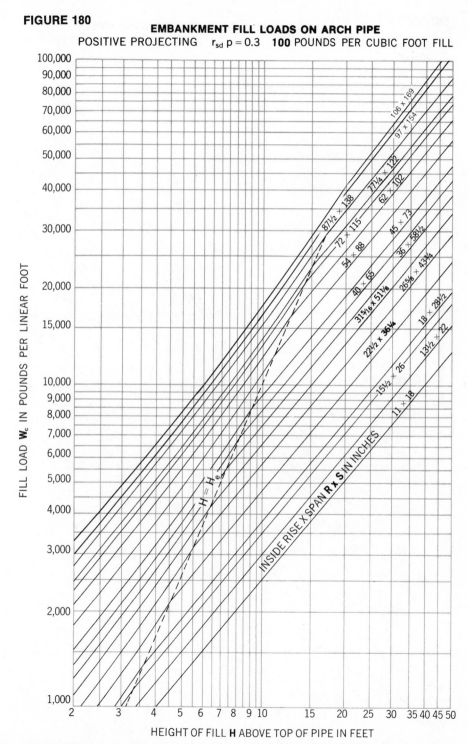

EMBANKMENT FILL LOADS ON ARCH PIPE

POSITIVE PROJECTING $r_{sd}\,p = 0.3$ **100** POUNDS PER CUBIC FOOT FILL

FILL LOAD W_c IN POUNDS PER LINEAR FOOT

HEIGHT OF FILL **H** ABOVE TOP OF PIPE IN FEET

For fill weighing 110 pounds per cubic foot, increase loads 10%; for 120 pounds increase 20%, etc. Interpolate for intermediate pipe sizes.

FIGURE 181

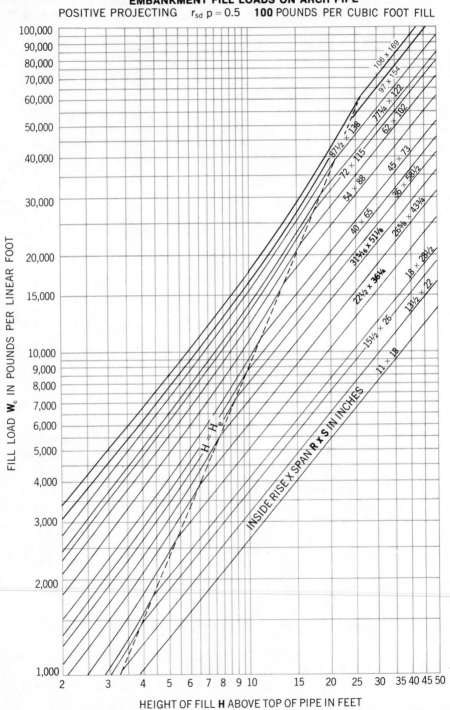

EMBANKMENT FILL LOADS ON ARCH PIPE

POSITIVE PROJECTING $r_{sd}\,p = 0.5$ **100** POUNDS PER CUBIC FOOT FILL

HEIGHT OF FILL **H** ABOVE TOP OF PIPE IN FEET

For fill weighing 110 pounds per cubic foot, increase loads 10%; for 120 pounds increase 20%, etc.
Interpolate for intermediate pipe sizes.

FIGURE 182

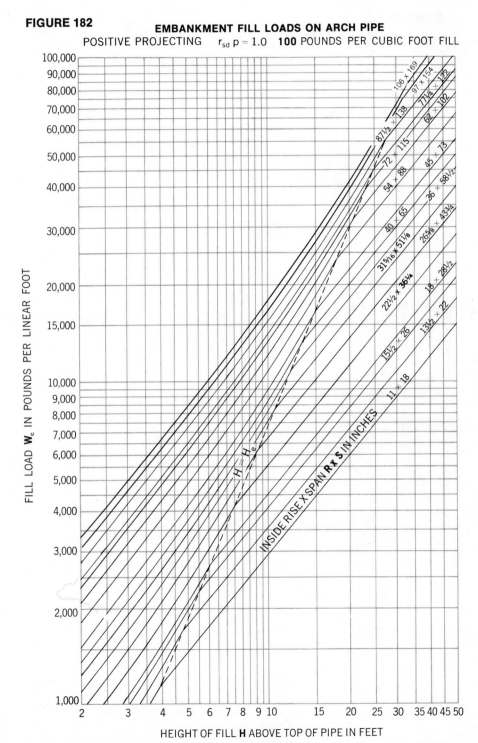

EMBANKMENT FILL LOADS ON ARCH PIPE

POSITIVE PROJECTING $r_{sd}\,p = 1.0$ **100** POUNDS PER CUBIC FOOT FILL

FILL LOAD W_c IN POUNDS PER LINEAR FOOT

HEIGHT OF FILL **H** ABOVE TOP OF PIPE IN FEET

For fill weighing 110 pounds per cubic foot, increase loads 10%; for 120 pounds increase 20%, etc. Interpolate for intermediate pipe sizes.

FIGURE 183

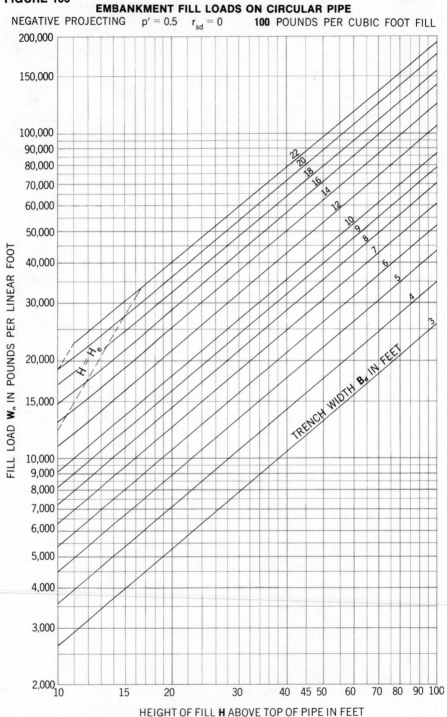

EMBANKMENT FILL LOADS ON CIRCULAR PIPE
NEGATIVE PROJECTING $p' = 0.5$ $r_{sd} = 0$ **100** POUNDS PER CUBIC FOOT FILL

HEIGHT OF FILL **H** ABOVE TOP OF PIPE IN FEET

For fill weighing 110 pounds per cubic foot, increase loads 10%; for 120 pounds increase 20%, etc.
Interpolate for intermediate trench widths.

FIGURE 184

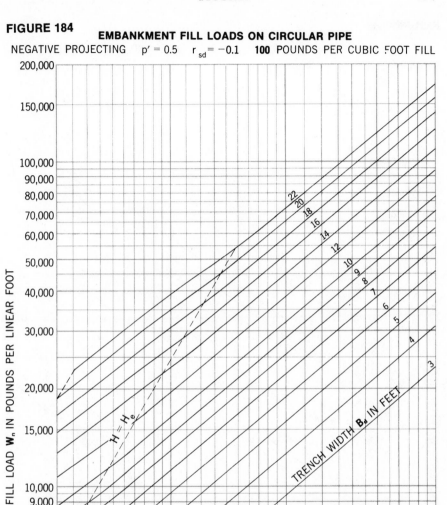

EMBANKMENT FILL LOADS ON CIRCULAR PIPE

NEGATIVE PROJECTING $p' = 0.5$ $r_{sd} = -0.1$ **100** POUNDS PER CUBIC FOOT FILL

HEIGHT OF FILL **H** ABOVE TOP OF PIPE IN FEET

For fill weighing 110 pounds per cubic foot, increase loads 10%; for 120 pounds increase 20%, etc.
Interpolate for intermediate trench widths.

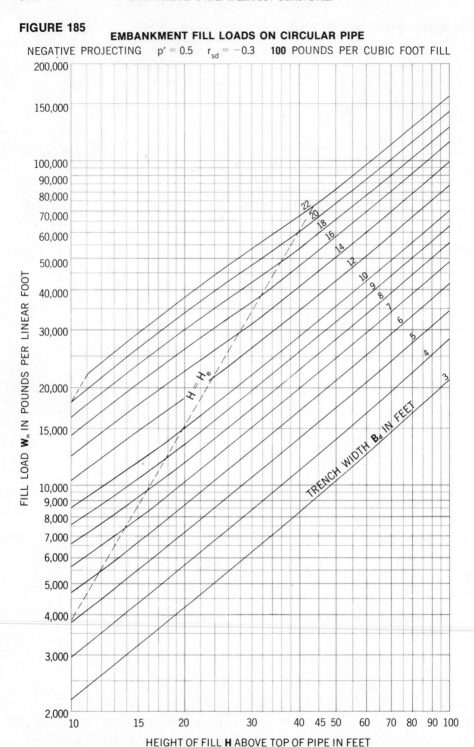

FIGURE 185

EMBANKMENT FILL LOADS ON CIRCULAR PIPE

NEGATIVE PROJECTING $p' = 0.5$ $r_{sd} = -0.3$ **100** POUNDS PER CUBIC FOOT FILL

HEIGHT OF FILL **H** ABOVE TOP OF PIPE IN FEET

For fill weighing 110 pounds per cubic foot, increase loads 10%; for 120 pounds increase 20%, etc.
Interpolate for intermediate trench widths.

FIGURE 186

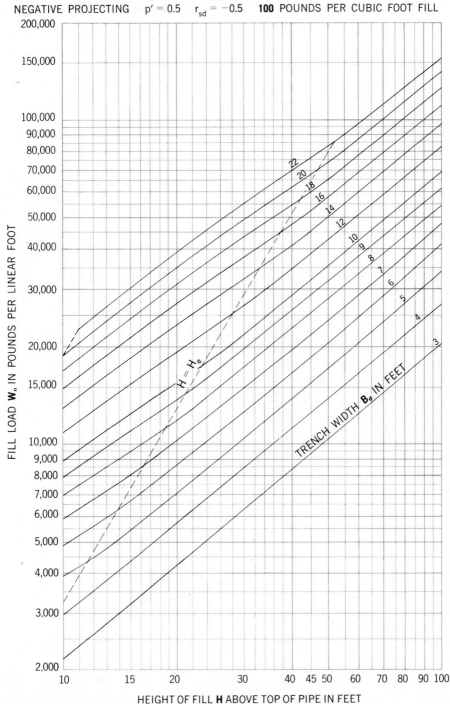

EMBANKMENT FILL LOADS ON CIRCULAR PIPE

NEGATIVE PROJECTING $p' = 0.5$ $r_{sd} = -0.5$ **100** POUNDS PER CUBIC FOOT FILL

FILL LOAD **W**$_n$ IN POUNDS PER LINEAR FOOT

HEIGHT OF FILL **H** ABOVE TOP OF PIPE IN FEET

For fill weighing 110 pounds per cubic foot, increase loads 10%; for 120 pounds increase 20%, etc. Interpolate for intermediate trench widths.

FIGURE 187

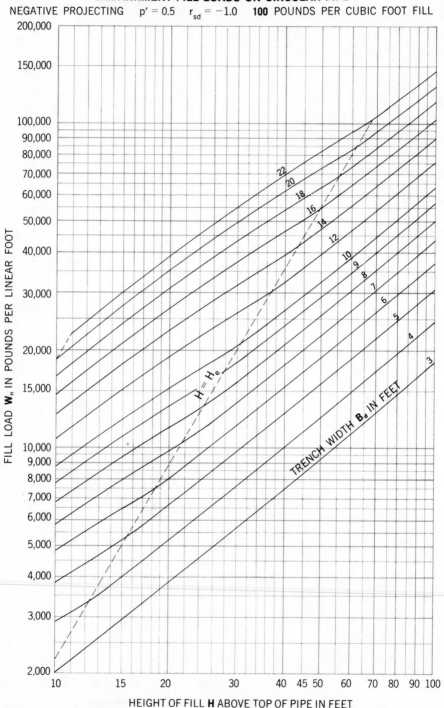

EMBANKMENT FILL LOADS ON CIRCULAR PIPE

NEGATIVE PROJECTING $p' = 0.5$ $r_{sd} = -1.0$ **100** POUNDS PER CUBIC FOOT FILL

FILL LOAD W_n IN POUNDS PER LINEAR FOOT

HEIGHT OF FILL **H** ABOVE TOP OF PIPE IN FEET

For fill weighing 110 pounds per cubic foot, increase loads 10%; for 120 pounds increase 20%, etc.
Interpolate for intermediate trench widths.

FIGURE 188

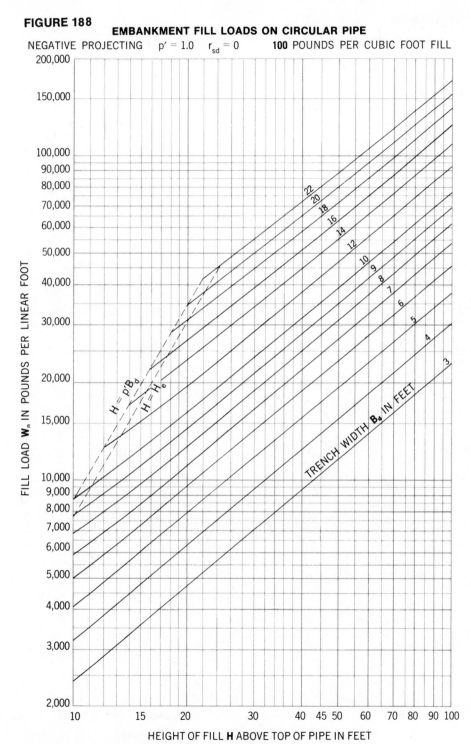

EMBANKMENT FILL LOADS ON CIRCULAR PIPE

NEGATIVE PROJECTING $p' = 1.0$ $r_{sd} = 0$ **100** POUNDS PER CUBIC FOOT FILL

FILL LOAD **Wn** IN POUNDS PER LINEAR FOOT

$H = p'B_d$

$H = H_e$

TRENCH WIDTH **B_d** IN FEET

HEIGHT OF FILL **H** ABOVE TOP OF PIPE IN FEET

For fill weighing 110 pounds per cubic foot, increase loads 10%; for 120 pounds increase 20%, etc.
Interpolate for intermediate trench widths.

FIGURE 189

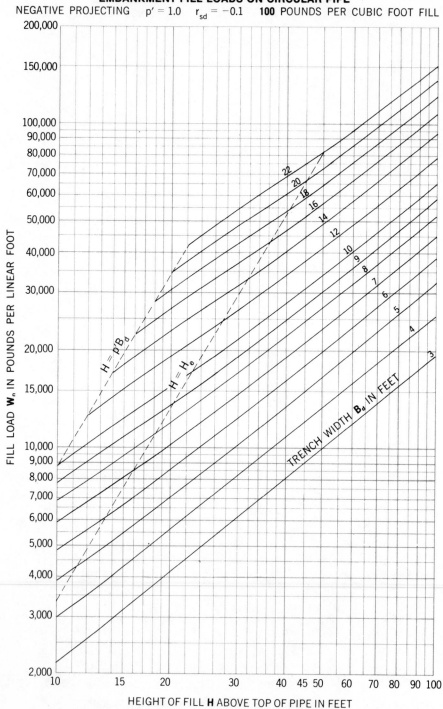

EMBANKMENT FILL LOADS ON CIRCULAR PIPE

NEGATIVE PROJECTING $p' = 1.0$ $r_{sd} = -0.1$ **100** POUNDS PER CUBIC FOOT FILL

For fill weighing 110 pounds per cubic foot, increase loads 10%; for 120 pounds increase 20%, etc. Interpolate for intermediate trench widths.

FIGURE 190

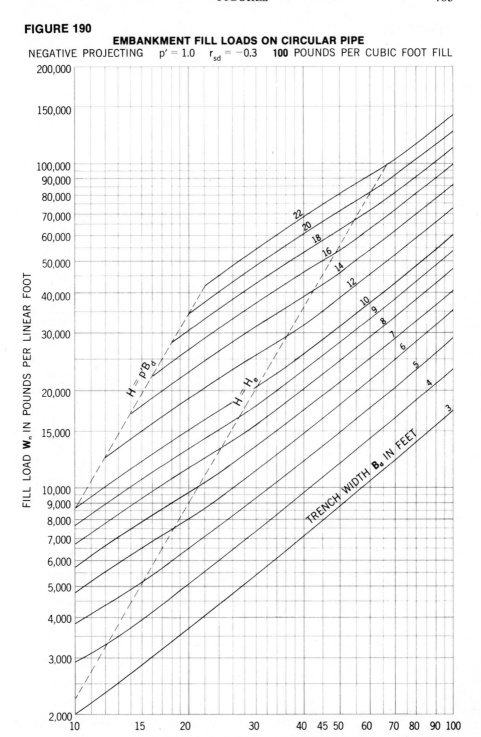

EMBANKMENT FILL LOADS ON CIRCULAR PIPE

NEGATIVE PROJECTING $p' = 1.0$ $r_{sd} = -0.3$ **100** POUNDS PER CUBIC FOOT FILL

HEIGHT OF FILL **H** ABOVE TOP OF PIPE IN FEET

For fill weighing 110 pounds per cubic foot, increase loads 10%; for 120 pounds increase 20%, etc.
Interpolate for intermediate trench widths.

FIGURE 191

EMBANKMENT FILL LOADS ON CIRCULAR PIPE

NEGATIVE PROJECTING $p' = 1.0$ $r_{sd} = -0.5$ **100** POUNDS PER CUBIC FOOT FILL

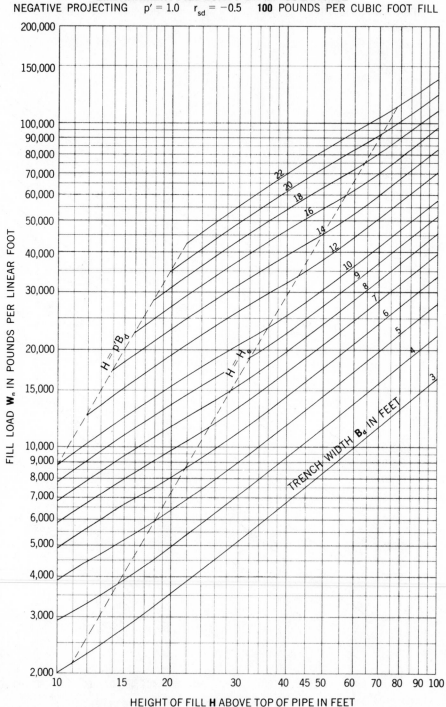

For fill weighing 110 pounds per cubic foot, increase loads 10%; for 120 pounds increase 20%, etc. Interpolate for intermediate trench widths.

FIGURE 192

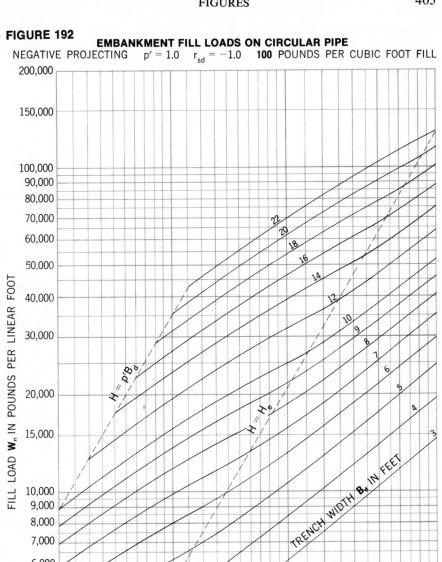

EMBANKMENT FILL LOADS ON CIRCULAR PIPE

NEGATIVE PROJECTING   p' = 1.0 r_{sd} = −1.0   **100** POUNDS PER CUBIC FOOT FILL

FILL LOAD W_n IN POUNDS PER LINEAR FOOT

HEIGHT OF FILL **H** ABOVE TOP OF PIPE IN FEET

For fill weighing 110 pounds per cubic foot, increase loads 10%; for 120 pounds increase 20%, etc.
Interpolate for intermediate trench widths.

FIGURE 193

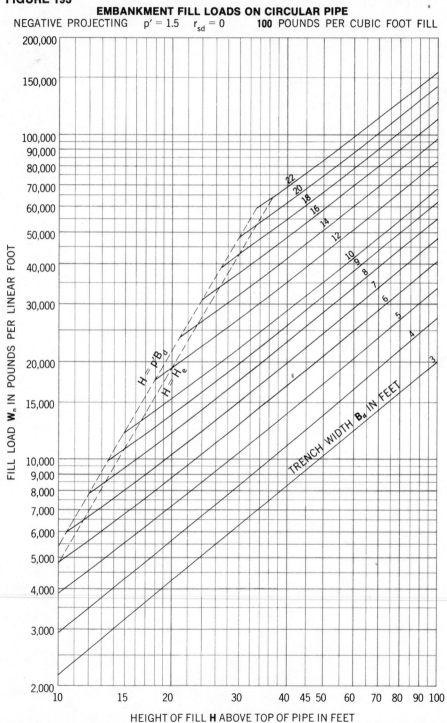

EMBANKMENT FILL LOADS ON CIRCULAR PIPE

NEGATIVE PROJECTING $p' = 1.5$ $r_{sd} = 0$ **100** POUNDS PER CUBIC FOOT FILL

HEIGHT OF FILL **H** ABOVE TOP OF PIPE IN FEET

For fill weighing 110 pounds per cubic foot, increase loads 10%; for 120 pounds increase 20%, etc.
Interpolate for intermediate trench widths.

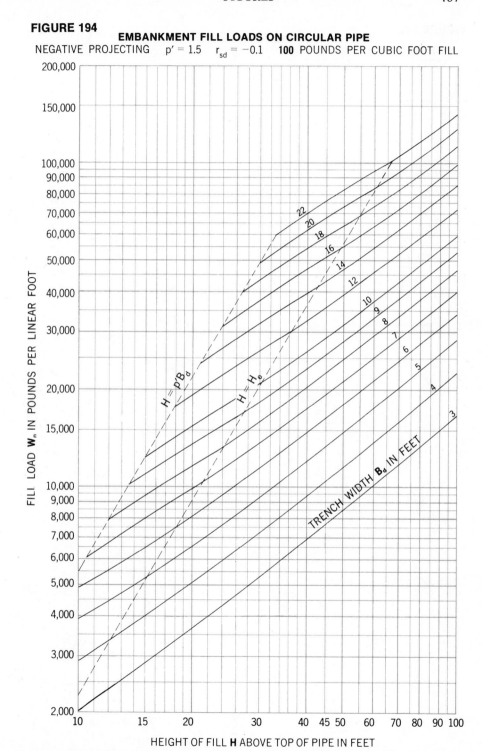

FIGURE 194

EMBANKMENT FILL LOADS ON CIRCULAR PIPE

NEGATIVE PROJECTING   p' = 1.5   r$_{sd}$ = −0.1   **100** POUNDS PER CUBIC FOOT FILL

FILL LOAD **W**$_n$ IN POUNDS PER LINEAR FOOT

HEIGHT OF FILL **H** ABOVE TOP OF PIPE IN FEET

For fill weighing 110 pounds per cubic foot, increase loads 10%; for 120 pounds increase 20%, etc.
Interpolate for intermediate trench widths.

FIGURE 195

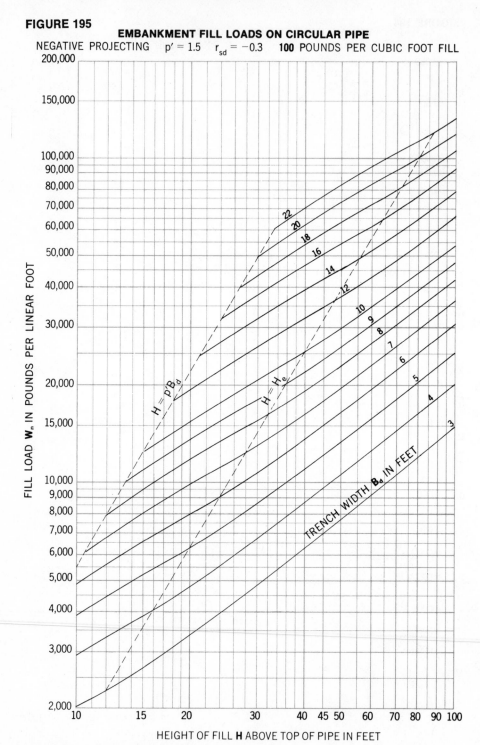

EMBANKMENT FILL LOADS ON CIRCULAR PIPE

NEGATIVE PROJECTING $p' = 1.5$ $r_{sd} = -0.3$ **100** POUNDS PER CUBIC FOOT FILL

FILL LOAD $\mathbf{W_n}$ IN POUNDS PER LINEAR FOOT

HEIGHT OF FILL **H** ABOVE TOP OF PIPE IN FEET

For fill weighing 110 pounds per cubic foot, increase loads 10%; for 120 pounds increase 20%, etc.
Interpolate for intermediate trench widths.

FIGURE 196

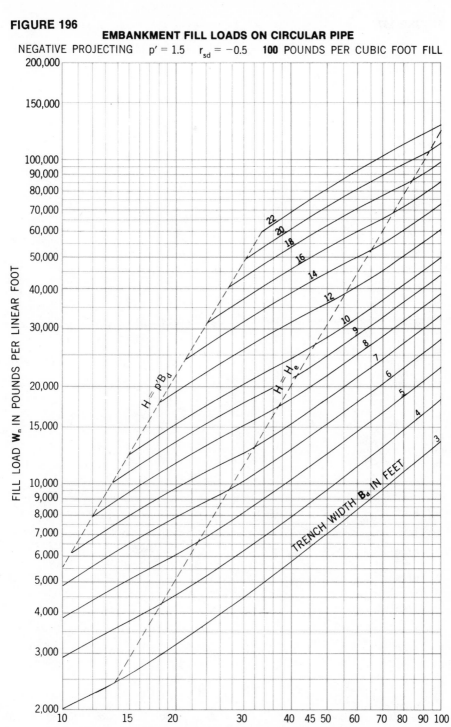

EMBANKMENT FILL LOADS ON CIRCULAR PIPE

NEGATIVE PROJECTING $p' = 1.5$ $r_{sd} = -0.5$ **100** POUNDS PER CUBIC FOOT FILL

FILL LOAD $\mathbf{W_n}$ IN POUNDS PER LINEAR FOOT

$H = p'B_d$

$H = H_e$

TRENCH WIDTH $\mathbf{B_d}$ IN FEET

HEIGHT OF FILL **H** ABOVE TOP OF PIPE IN FEET

For fill weighing 110 pounds per cubic foot, increase loads 10%; for 120 pounds increase 20%, etc. Interpolate for intermediate trench widths.

FIGURE 197

EMBANKMENT FILL LOADS ON CIRCULAR PIPE

NEGATIVE PROJECTING $p' = 1.5$ $r_{sd} = -1.0$ **100** POUNDS PER CUBIC FOOT FILL

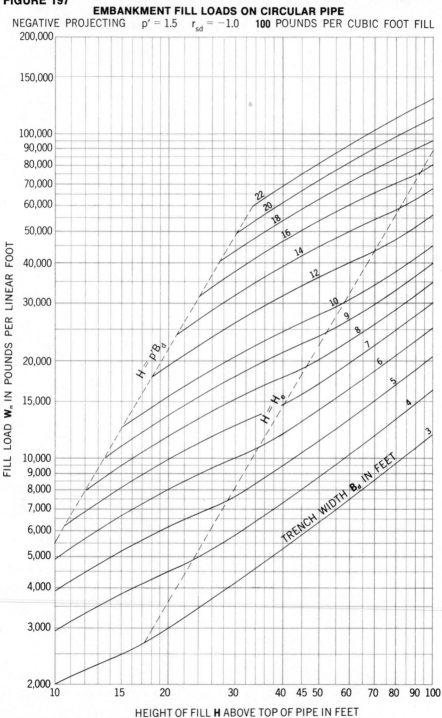

HEIGHT OF FILL **H** ABOVE TOP OF PIPE IN FEET

For fill weighing 110 pounds per cubic foot, increase loads 10%; for 120 pounds increase 20%, etc.
Interpolate for intermediate trench widths.

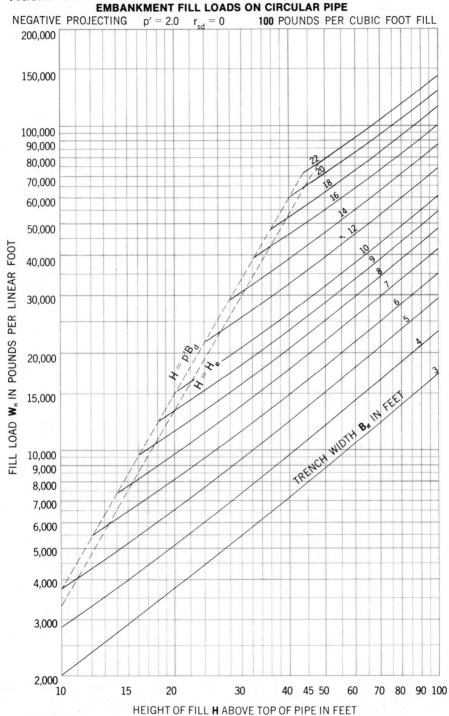

FIGURE 198

EMBANKMENT FILL LOADS ON CIRCULAR PIPE
NEGATIVE PROJECTING $p' = 2.0$ $r_{sd} = 0$ **100** POUNDS PER CUBIC FOOT FILL

For fill weighing 110 pounds per cubic foot, increase loads 10%; for 120 pounds increase 20%, etc.
Interpolate for intermediate trench widths.

FIGURE 199

EMBANKMENT FILL LOADS ON CIRCULAR PIPE

NEGATIVE PROJECTING $p' = 2.0$ $r_{sd} = -0.1$ **100** POUNDS PER CUBIC FOOT FILL

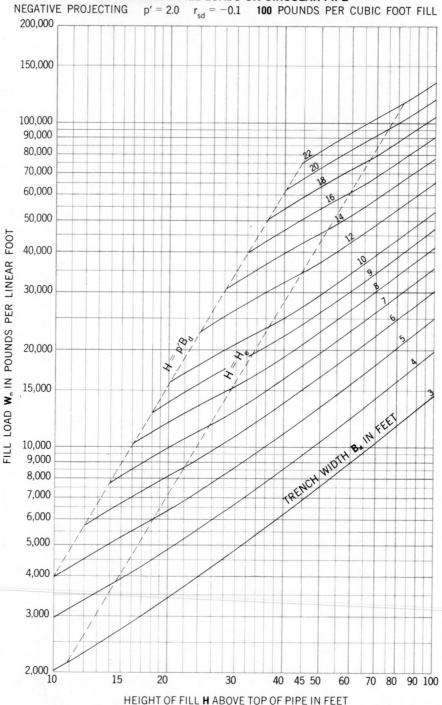

HEIGHT OF FILL **H** ABOVE TOP OF PIPE IN FEET

For fill weighing 110 pounds per cubic foot, increase loads 10%; for 120 pounds increase 20%, etc.
Interpolate for intermediate trench widths.

FIGURE 200   EMBANKMENT FILL LOADS ON CIRCULAR PIPE

NEGATIVE PROJECTING $p' = 2.0$ $r_{sd} = -0.3$ **100** POUNDS PER CUBIC FOOT FILL

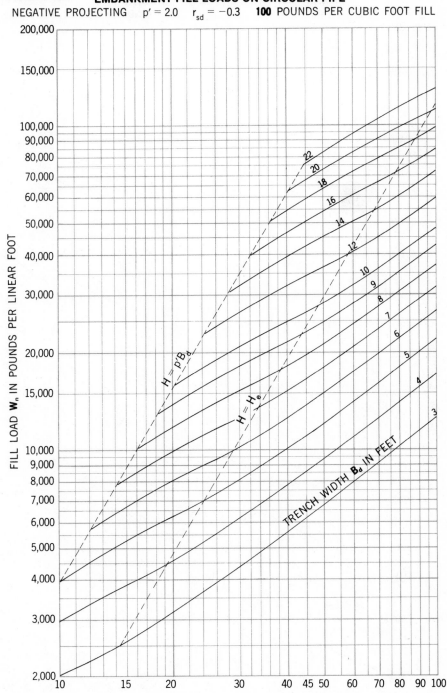

For fill weighing 110 pounds per cubic foot, increase loads 10%; for 120 pounds increase 20%, etc.
Interpolate for intermediate trench widths.

FIGURE 201   **EMBANKMENT FILL LOADS ON CIRCULAR PIPE**

NEGATIVE PROJECTING $p' = 2.0$ $r_{sd} = -0.5$ **100** POUNDS PER CUBIC FOOT FILL

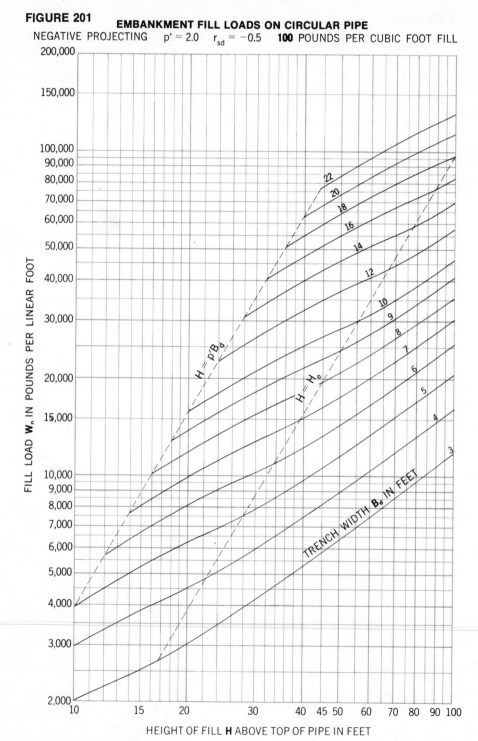

FILL LOAD W_n IN POUNDS PER LINEAR FOOT

HEIGHT OF FILL **H** ABOVE TOP OF PIPE IN FEET

For fill weighing 110 pounds per cubic foot, increase loads 10%; for 120 pounds increase 20%, etc. Interpolate for intermediate trench widths.

FIGURE 202   EMBANKMENT FILL LOADS ON CIRCULAR PIPE

NEGATIVE PROJECTING $p' = 2.0$ $r_{sd} = -1.0$ **100** POUNDS PER CUBIC FOOT FILL

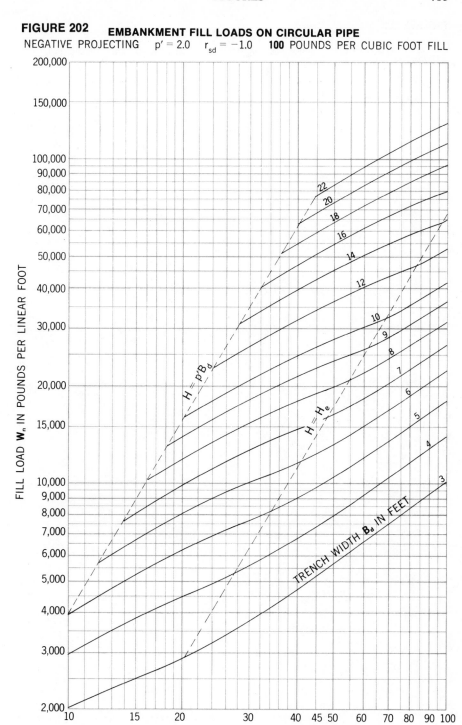

For fill weighing 110 pounds per cubic foot, increase loads 10%; for 120 pounds increase 20%, etc. Interpolate for intermediate trench widths.

FIGURE 203

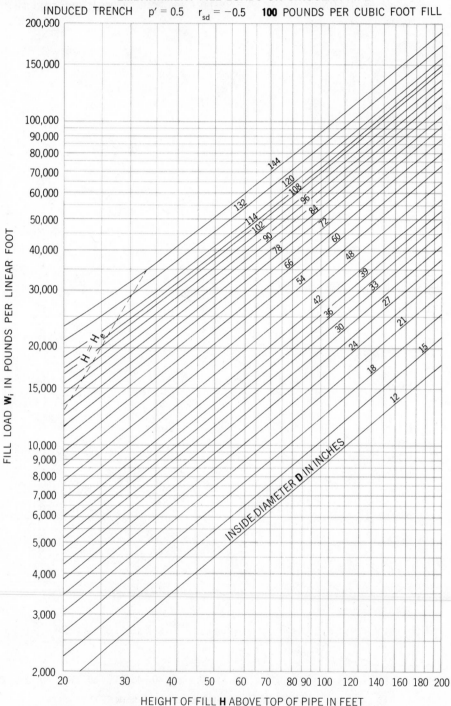

For fill weighing 110 pounds per cubic foot, increase loads 10%; for 120 pounds increase 20%, etc.
Interpolate for intermediate pipe sizes.

FIGURE 204

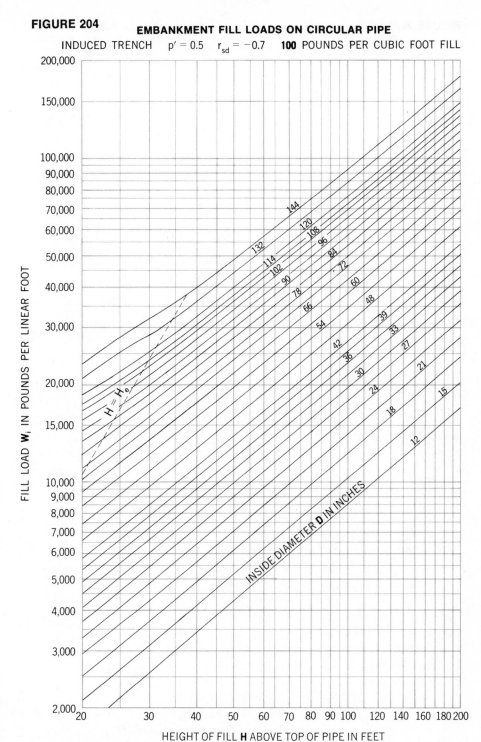

EMBANKMENT FILL LOADS ON CIRCULAR PIPE

INDUCED TRENCH $p' = 0.5$ $r_{sd} = -0.7$ **100** POUNDS PER CUBIC FOOT FILL

FILL LOAD W_i IN POUNDS PER LINEAR FOOT

$H = H_e$

INSIDE DIAMETER **D** IN INCHES

HEIGHT OF FILL **H** ABOVE TOP OF PIPE IN FEET

For fill weighing 110 pounds per cubic foot, increase loads 10%; for 120 pounds increase 20%, etc.
Interpolate for intermediate pipe sizes.

FIGURE 205   **EMBANKMENT FILL LOADS ON CIRCULAR PIPE**

INDUCED TRENCH $p' = 0.5$ $r_{sd} = -1.0$ **100** POUNDS PER CUBIC FOOT FILL

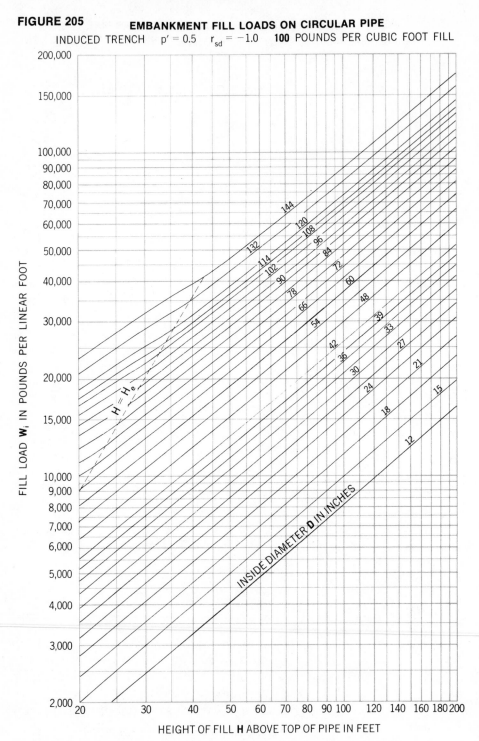

FILL LOAD W_i IN POUNDS PER LINEAR FOOT

HEIGHT OF FILL **H** ABOVE TOP OF PIPE IN FEET

For fill weighing 110 pounds per cubic foot, increase loads 10%; for 120 pounds increase 20%, etc.
Interpolate for infermediate pipe sizes.

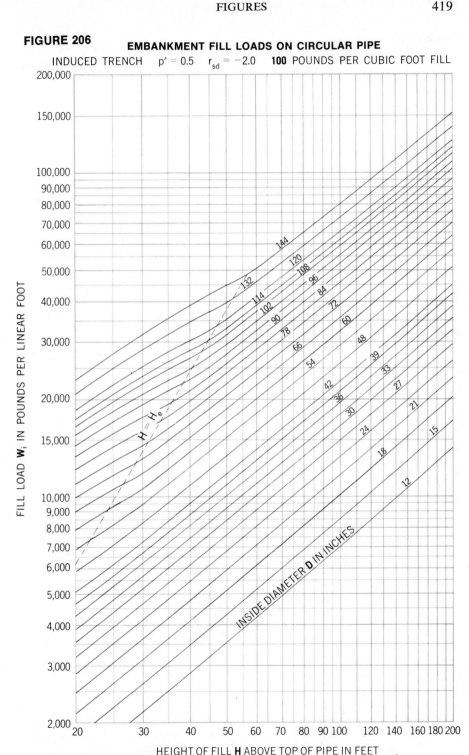

FIGURE 206 **EMBANKMENT FILL LOADS ON CIRCULAR PIPE**

INDUCED TRENCH $p' = 0.5$ $r_{sd} = -2.0$ **100** POUNDS PER CUBIC FOOT FILL

FILL LOAD W_i IN POUNDS PER LINEAR FOOT

$H = H_e$

INSIDE DIAMETER **D** IN INCHES

HEIGHT OF FILL **H** ABOVE TOP OF PIPE IN FEET

For fill weighing 110 pounds per cubic foot, increase loads 10%; for 120 pounds increase 20%, etc.
Interpolate for intermediate pipe sizes.

FIGURE 207   **EMBANKMENT FILL LOADS ON CIRCULAR PIPE**

INDUCED TRENCH $p' = 1.0$ $r_{sd} = -0.5$ **100** POUNDS PER CUBIC FOOT FILL

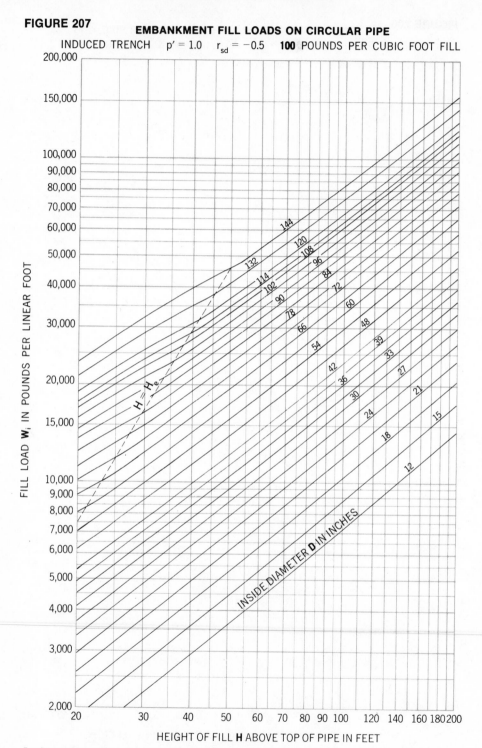

HEIGHT OF FILL **H** ABOVE TOP OF PIPE IN FEET

For fill weighing 110 pounds per cubic foot, increase loads 10%; for 120 pounds increase 20%, etc.
Interpolate for intermediate pipe sizes.

FIGURE 208

EMBANKMENT FILL LOADS ON CIRCULAR PIPE

INDUCED TRENCH $p' = 1.0$ $r_{sd} = -0.7$ **100** POUNDS PER CUBIC FOOT FILL

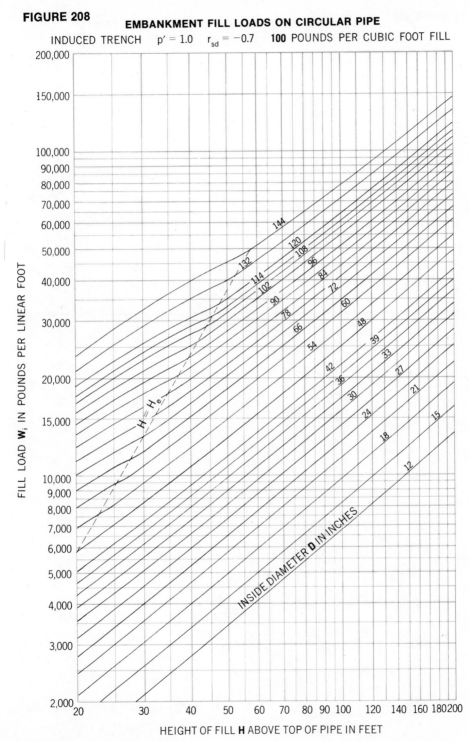

FILL LOAD W_i IN POUNDS PER LINEAR FOOT

HEIGHT OF FILL **H** ABOVE TOP OF PIPE IN FEET

For fill weighing 110 pounds per cubic foot, increase loads 10%; for 120 pounds increase 20%, etc.
Interpolate for intermediate pipe sizes.

FIGURE 209

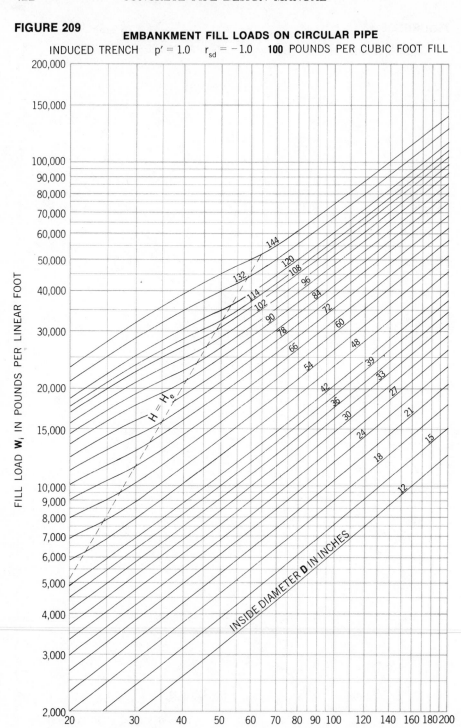

EMBANKMENT FILL LOADS ON CIRCULAR PIPE

INDUCED TRENCH $p' = 1.0$ $r_{sd} = -1.0$ **100** POUNDS PER CUBIC FOOT FILL

HEIGHT OF FILL **H** ABOVE TOP OF PIPE IN FEET

FILL LOAD W_i IN POUNDS PER LINEAR FOOT

INSIDE DIAMETER **D** IN INCHES

$H = H_e$

For fill weighing 110 pounds per cubic foot, increase loads 10%; for 120 pounds increase 20%, etc.

Interpolate for intermediate pipe sizes.

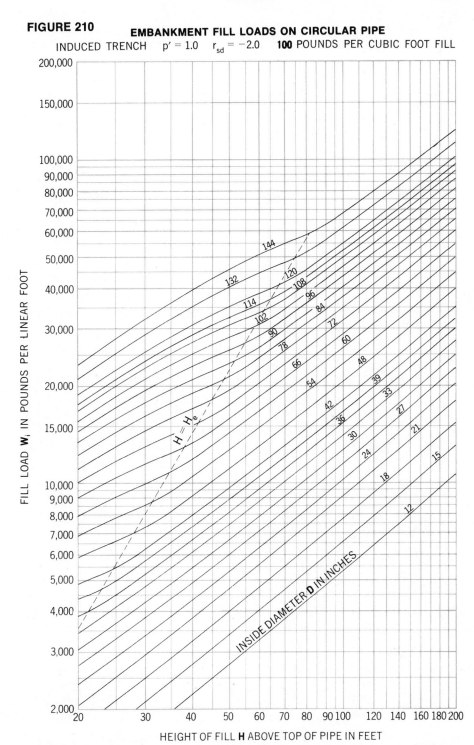

FIGURE 210   **EMBANKMENT FILL LOADS ON CIRCULAR PIPE**

INDUCED TRENCH $p' = 1.0$ $r_{sd} = -2.0$ **100** POUNDS PER CUBIC FOOT FILL

FILL LOAD W_i IN POUNDS PER LINEAR FOOT

$H = H_e$

INSIDE DIAMETER **D** IN INCHES

HEIGHT OF FILL **H** ABOVE TOP OF PIPE IN FEET

For fill weighing 110 pounds per cubic foot, increase loads 10%; for 120 pounds increase 20%, etc. Interpolate for intermediate pipe sizes.

FIGURE 211

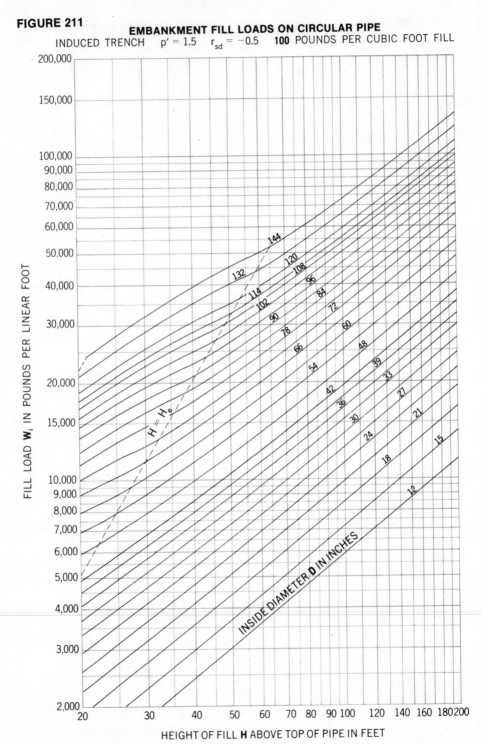

EMBANKMENT FILL LOADS ON CIRCULAR PIPE

INDUCED TRENCH $p' = 1.5$ $r_{sd} = -0.5$ **100** POUNDS PER CUBIC FOOT FILL

For fill weighing 110 pounds per cubic foot, increase loads 10%; for 120 pounds increase 20%, etc.

Interpolate for intermediate pipe sizes.

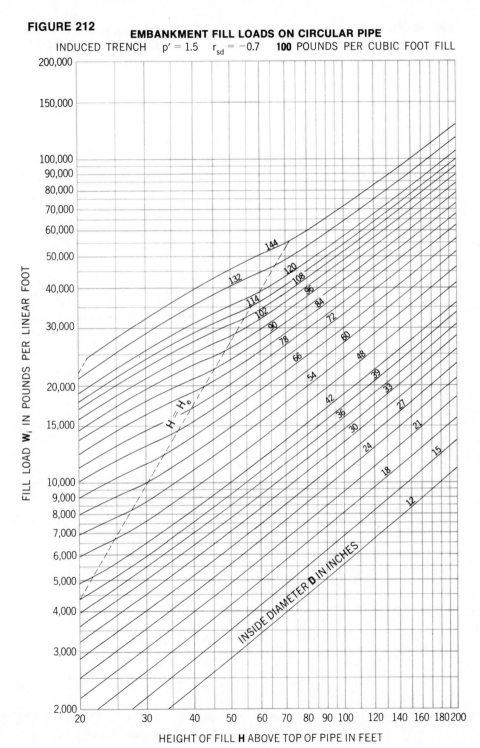

FIGURE 212 **EMBANKMENT FILL LOADS ON CIRCULAR PIPE**

INDUCED TRENCH $p' = 1.5$ $r_{sd} = -0.7$ **100** POUNDS PER CUBIC FOOT FILL

FILL LOAD W_i IN POUNDS PER LINEAR FOOT

HEIGHT OF FILL **H** ABOVE TOP OF PIPE IN FEET

INSIDE DIAMETER **D** IN INCHES

$H = H_e$

For fill weighing 110 pounds per cubic foot, increase loads 10%; for 120 pounds increase 20%, etc.
Interpolate for intermediate pipe sizes.

FIGURE 213

EMBANKMENT FILL LOADS ON CIRCULAR PIPE

INDUCED TRENCH $p' = 1.5$ $r_{sd} = -1.0$ **100** POUNDS PER CUBIC FOOT FILL

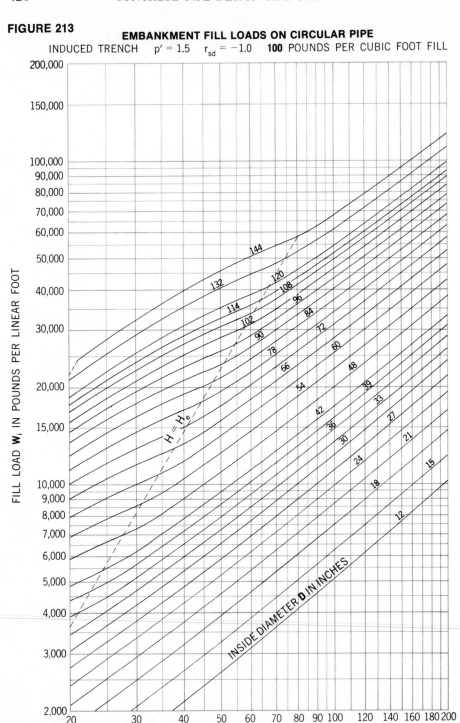

For fill weighing 110 pounds per cubic foot, increase loads 10%; for 120 pounds increase 20%, etc.

Interpolate for intermediate pipe sizes.

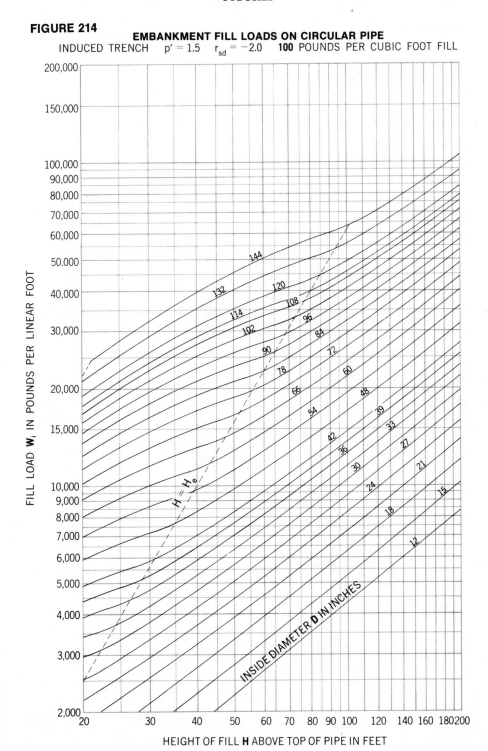

FIGURE 214
EMBANKMENT FILL LOADS ON CIRCULAR PIPE
INDUCED TRENCH $p' = 1.5$ $r_{sd} = -2.0$ **100** POUNDS PER CUBIC FOOT FILL

FILL LOAD W_i IN POUNDS PER LINEAR FOOT

HEIGHT OF FILL **H** ABOVE TOP OF PIPE IN FEET

INSIDE DIAMETER **D** IN INCHES

$H = H_e$

For fill weighing 110 pounds per cubic foot, increase loads 10%; for 120 pounds increase 20%, etc.
Interpolate for intermediate pipe sizes.

FIGURE 215

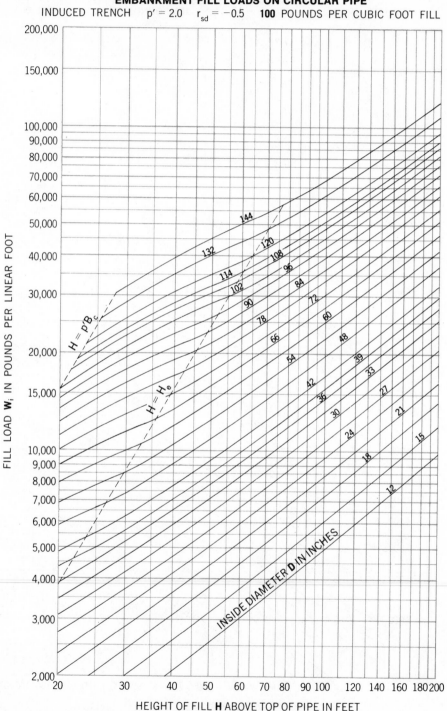

EMBANKMENT FILL LOADS ON CIRCULAR PIPE

INDUCED TRENCH $p' = 2.0$ $r_{sd} = -0.5$ **100** POUNDS PER CUBIC FOOT FILL

FILL LOAD W_i IN POUNDS PER LINEAR FOOT

HEIGHT OF FILL **H** ABOVE TOP OF PIPE IN FEET

For fill weighing 110 pounds per cubic foot, increase loads 10%; for 120 pounds increase 20%, etc. Interpolate for intermediate pipe sizes.

FIGURE 216

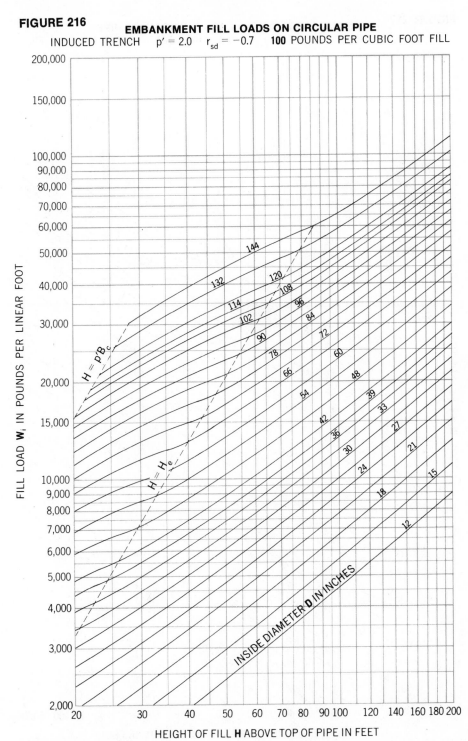

EMBANKMENT FILL LOADS ON CIRCULAR PIPE

INDUCED TRENCH $p' = 2.0$ $r_{sd} = -0.7$ **100** POUNDS PER CUBIC FOOT FILL

FILL LOAD **W$_i$** IN POUNDS PER LINEAR FOOT

HEIGHT OF FILL **H** ABOVE TOP OF PIPE IN FEET

INSIDE DIAMETER **D** IN INCHES

$H = p'B_c$

$H = H_e$

For fill weighing 110 pounds per cubic foot, increase loads 10%; for 120 pounds increase 20%, etc.

Interpolate for intermediate pipe sizes

FIGURE 217

EMBANKMENT FILL LOADS ON CIRCULAR PIPE

INDUCED TRENCH $p' = 2.0$ $r_{sd} = -1.0$ **100** POUNDS PER CUBIC FOOT FILL

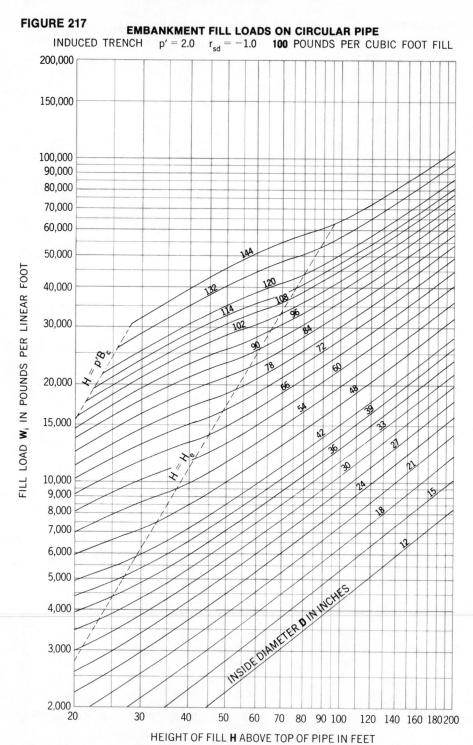

FILL LOAD W_i IN POUNDS PER LINEAR FOOT

HEIGHT OF FILL **H** ABOVE TOP OF PIPE IN FEET

For fill weighing 110 pounds per cubic foot, increase loads 10%; for 120 pounds increase 20%, etc.
Interpolate for intermediate pipe sizes.

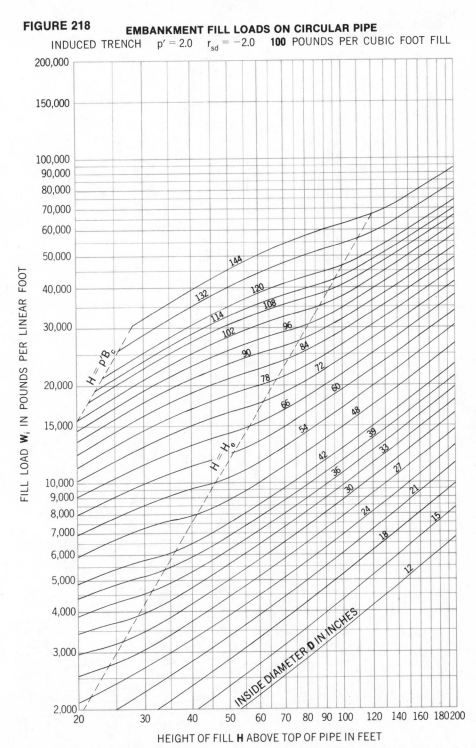

FIGURE 218   **EMBANKMENT FILL LOADS ON CIRCULAR PIPE**

INDUCED TRENCH $p' = 2.0$ $r_{sd} = -2.0$ **100** POUNDS PER CUBIC FOOT FILL

FILL LOAD W_i IN POUNDS PER LINEAR FOOT

HEIGHT OF FILL H ABOVE TOP OF PIPE IN FEET

INSIDE DIAMETER **D** IN INCHES

For fill weighing 110 pounds per cubic foot, increase loads 10%; for 120 pounds increase 20%, etc.

Interpolate for intermediate pipe sizes.

FIGURE 219

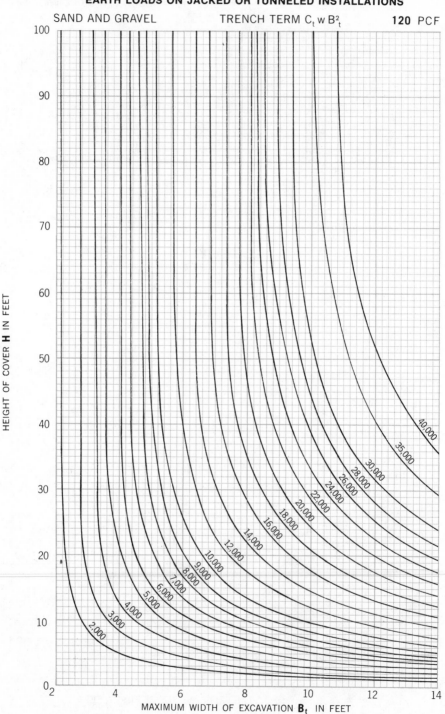

EARTH LOADS ON JACKED OR TUNNELED INSTALLATIONS

SAND AND GRAVEL   TRENCH TERM $C_t\, w\, B_t^2$ **120** PCF

HEIGHT OF COVER **H** IN FEET

MAXIMUM WIDTH OF EXCAVATION **B$_t$** IN FEET

For earth weighing other than 120 pounds per cubic foot, multiply loads by w/120.

FIGURE 220

EARTH LOADS ON JACKED OR TUNNELED INSTALLATIONS

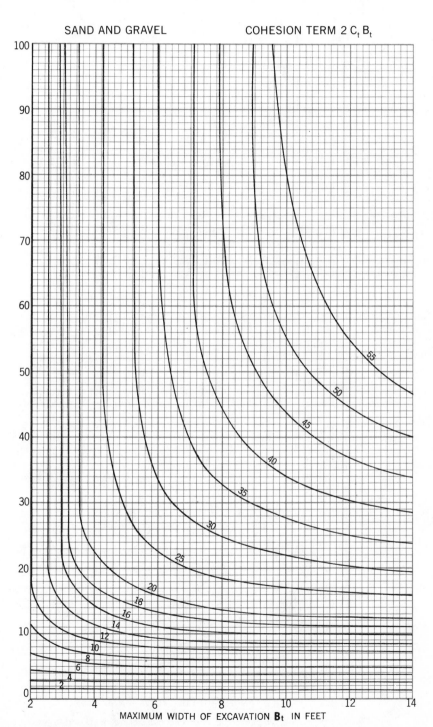

SAND AND GRAVEL   COHESION TERM 2 $C_t B_t$

FIGURE 221

EARTH LOADS ON JACKED OR TUNNELED INSTALLATIONS

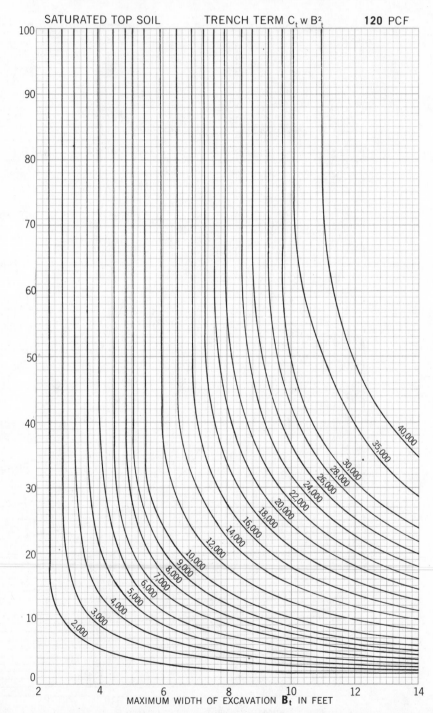

SATURATED TOP SOIL   TRENCH TERM $C_t\,w\,B_t^2$ **120** PCF

HEIGHT OF COVER **H** IN FEET

MAXIMUM WIDTH OF EXCAVATION B_t IN FEET

For earth weighing other than 120 pounds per cubic foot, multiply loads by w/120.

FIGURE 222

EARTH LOADS ON JACKED OR TUNNELED INSTALLATIONS

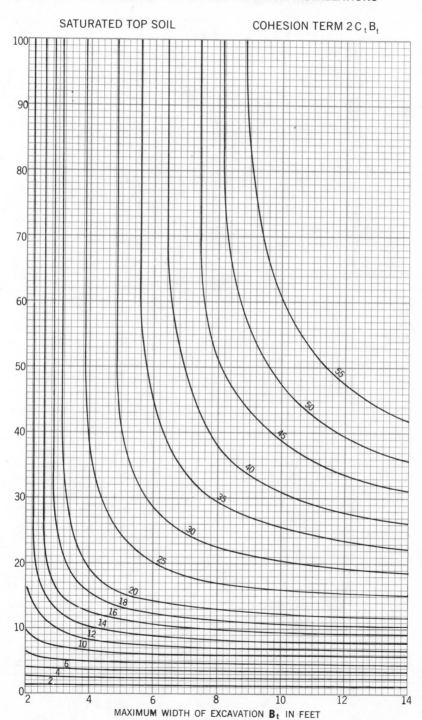

SATURATED TOP SOIL   COHESION TERM $2\,C_t\,B_t$

HEIGHT OF COVER **H** IN FEET

MAXIMUM WIDTH OF EXCAVATION **B$_t$** IN FEET

FIGURE 223

EARTH LOAD ON JACKED OR TUNNELED INSTALLATIONS

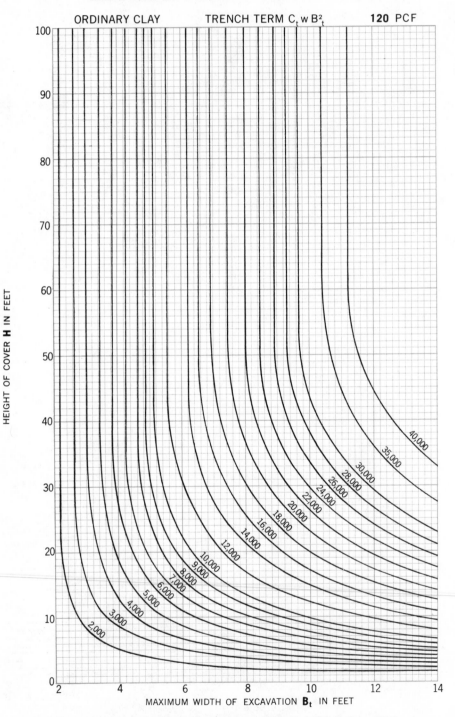

ORDINARY CLAY   TRENCH TERM $C_t w B_t^2$ **120** PCF

HEIGHT OF COVER **H** IN FEET

MAXIMUM WIDTH OF EXCAVATION **B$_t$** IN FEET

For earth weighing other than 120 pounds per cubic foot, multiply loads by w/120.

FIGURE 224

EARTH LOADS ON JACKED OR TUNNELED INSTALLATIONS

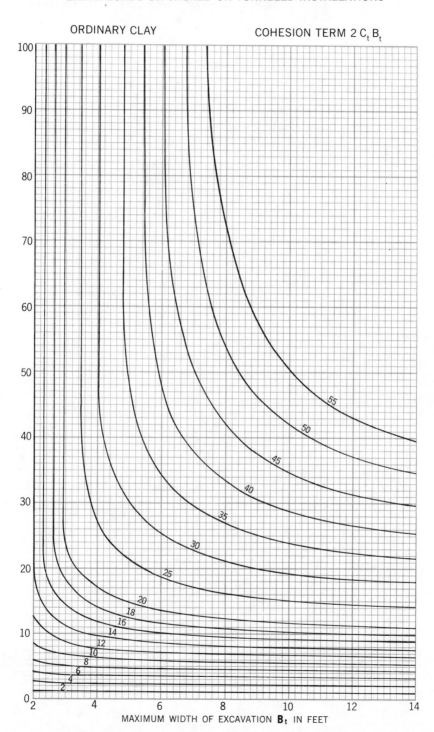

ORDINARY CLAY COHESION TERM $2\,C_t\,B_t$

HEIGHT OF COVER **H** IN FEET

MAXIMUM WIDTH OF EXCAVATION **B**$_t$ IN FEET

FIGURE 225

EARTH LOADS JACKED OR TUNNELED INSTALLATIONS

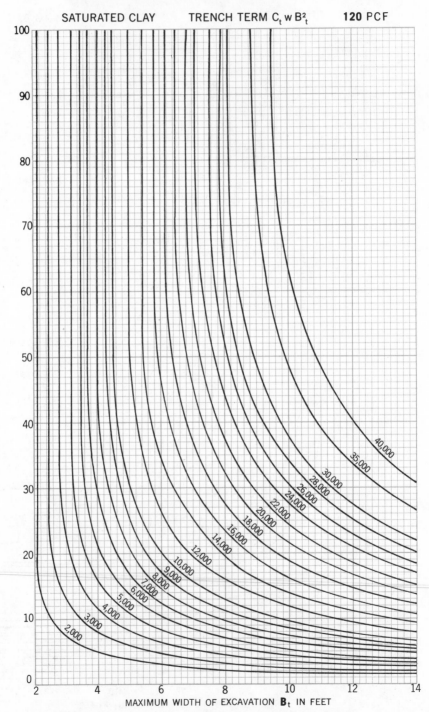

SATURATED CLAY   TRENCH TERM C_t w B^2_t **120** PCF

HEIGHT OF COVER **H** IN FEET

MAXIMUM WIDTH OF EXCAVATION **B**$_t$ IN FEET

For earth weighing other than 120 pounds per cubic foot, multiply loads by w/120.

FIGURE 226

EARTH LOADS ON JACKED OR TUNNELED INSTALLATIONS

SATURATED CLAY   COHESION TERM 2 $C_t B_t$

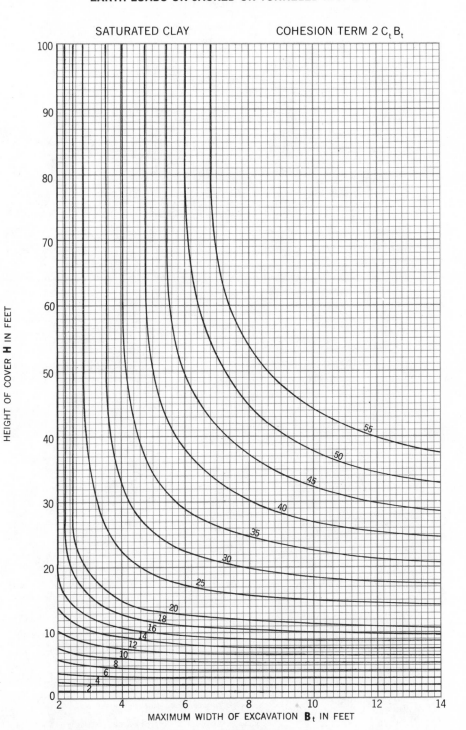

FIGURE 227

TRENCH BEDDINGS
CIRCULAR PIPE

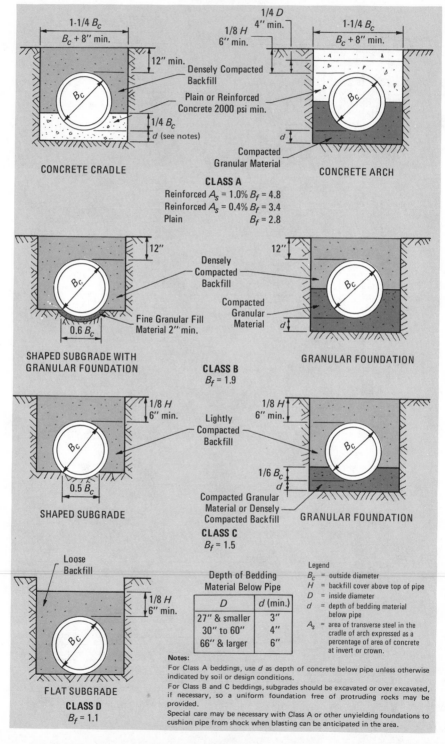

CONCRETE CRADLE

CONCRETE ARCH

CLASS A

Reinforced A_s = 1.0% B_f = 4.8
Reinforced A_s = 0.4% B_f = 3.4
Plain B_f = 2.8

SHAPED SUBGRADE WITH GRANULAR FOUNDATION

GRANULAR FOUNDATION

CLASS B
B_f = 1.9

SHAPED SUBGRADE

GRANULAR FOUNDATION

CLASS C
B_f = 1.5

FLAT SUBGRADE
CLASS D
B_f = 1.1

Depth of Bedding
Material Below Pipe

D	d (min.)
27" & smaller	3"
30" to 60"	4"
66" & larger	6"

Legend
B_c = outside diameter
H = backfill cover above top of pipe
D = inside diameter
d = depth of bedding material below pipe
A_s = area of transverse steel in the cradle of arch expressed as a percentage of area of concrete at invert or crown.

Notes:

For Class A beddings, use d as depth of concrete below pipe unless otherwise indicated by soil or design conditions.

For Class B and C beddings, subgrades should be excavated or over excavated, if necessary, so a uniform foundation free of protruding rocks may be provided.

Special care may be necessary with Class A or other unyielding foundations to cushion pipe from shock when blasting can be anticipated in the area.

FIGURE 228   **TRENCH BEDDINGS**

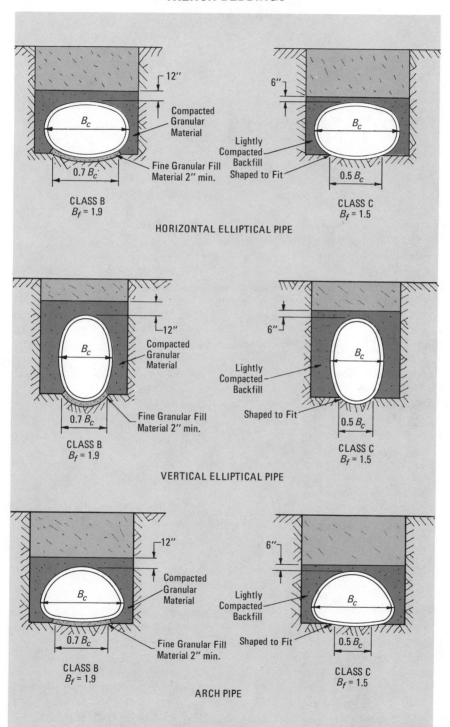

HORIZONTAL ELLIPTICAL PIPE

VERTICAL ELLIPTICAL PIPE

ARCH PIPE

FIGURE 229

EMBANKMENT BEDDINGS
CIRCULAR PIPE

Notes:

For Class B and C beddings, subgrades should be excavated or over excavated, if necessary, so a uniform foundation free of protruding rocks may be provided.

Special care may be necessary with Class A or other unyielding foundations to cushion pipe from shock when blasting can be anticipated in the area.

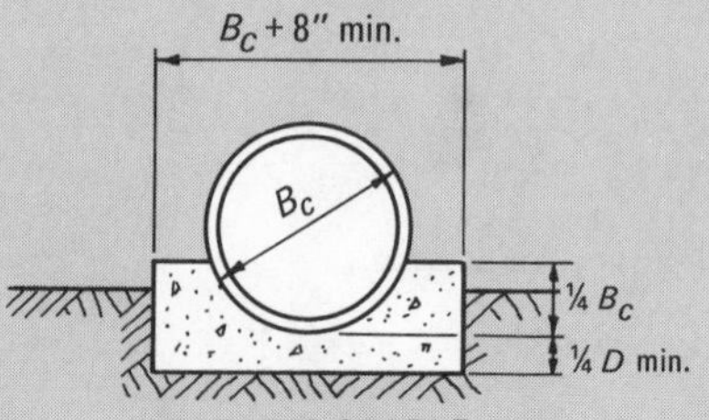

$B_c + 8''$ min.

B_c

¼ B_c

¼ D min.

CONCRETE CRADLE

CLASS A

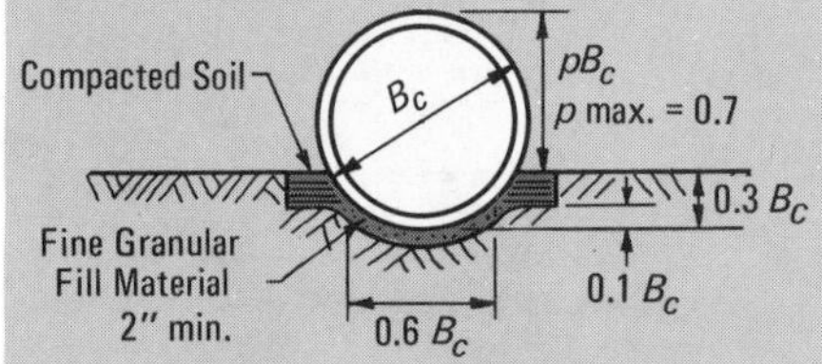

Compacted Soil

B_c

pB_c p max. = 0.7

Fine Granular Fill Material 2" min.

$0.3 B_c$

$0.1 B_c$

$0.6 B_c$

SHAPED SUBGRADE WITH GRANULAR FOUNDATION

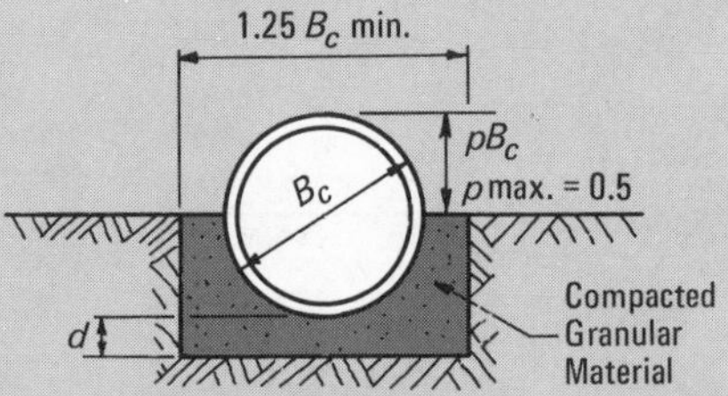

1.25 B_c min.

B_c

pB_c p max. = 0.5

d

Compacted Granular Material

GRANULAR FOUNDATION

CLASS B

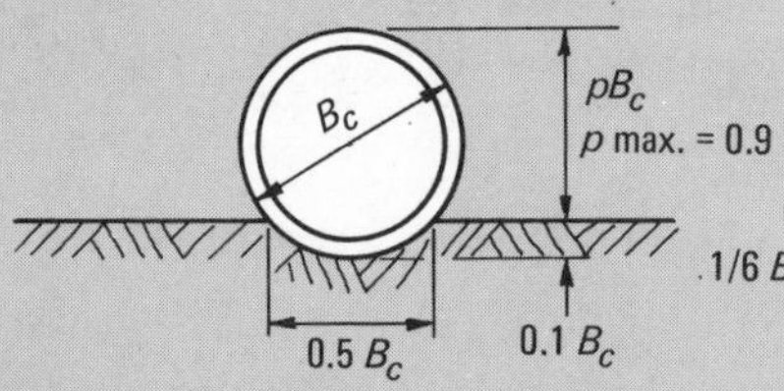

B_c

pB_c p max. = 0.9

$0.5 B_c$

$0.1 B_c$

SHAPED SUBGRADE

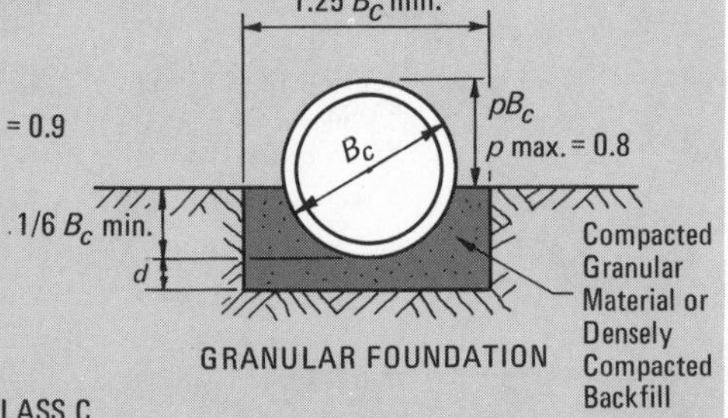

1.25 B_c min.

B_c

pB_c p max. = 0.8

d

1/6 B_c min.

Compacted Granular Material or Densely Compacted Backfill

GRANULAR FOUNDATION

CLASS C

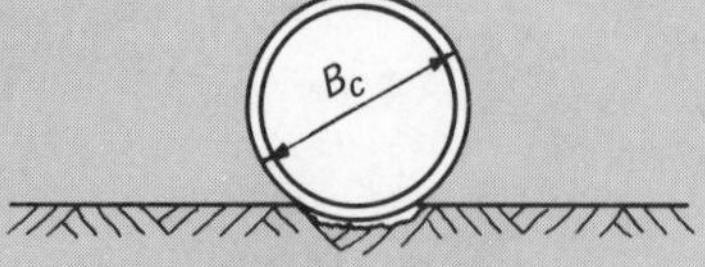

B_c

FLAT SUBGRADE

CLASS D

Depth of Bedding Material Below Pipe

D	d (min.)
27" & smaller	3"
30" to 60"	4"
66" & larger	6"

Legend

B_c = outside diameter
H = backfill cover above top of pipe
D = inside diameter
d = depth of bedding material below pipe

FIGURE 230

EMBANKMENT BEDDINGS

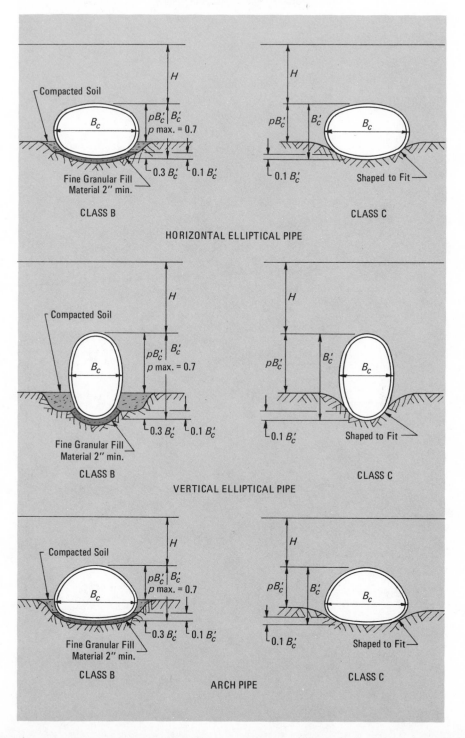

EQUATIONS

EQUATIONS

(1) Manning's Formula

$$Q = \frac{1.486}{n} AR^{2/3}S^{1/2}$$

and

$$V = \frac{1.486}{n} R^{2/3}S^{1/2}$$

(2) Manning's Formula for Full Flow

$$Q = C_1 S^{1/2}$$

(3) Design Flow for Storm Sewers

$$Q = CiA$$

(4) Culvert Headwater Depth Under Outlet Control

$$HW = H + h_o - S_oL$$

(5) Trench Backfill Load

$$W_d = C_d w B_d^2$$

(6) Trench Load Coefficient

$$C_d = \frac{1 - e^{-2K\mu' \frac{H}{B_d}}}{2K\mu'}$$

(7) Positive Projecting Embankment Fill Load

$$W_c = C_c w B_c^2$$

(8) Positive Projecting Embankment Load Coefficient
(Complete Condition)

$$C_c = \frac{e^{2K\mu \frac{H}{B_c}} - 1}{2K\mu} \quad \text{when } H \leq H_e$$

(9) Positive Projecting Embankment Load Coefficient (Incomplete Condition)

$$C_c = \frac{e^{2K\mu\frac{H_e}{B_c}} - 1}{2K\mu} + \left(\frac{H}{B_c} - \frac{H_e}{B_c}\right) e^{2K\mu\frac{H_e}{B_c}} \text{ when } H > H_e$$

(10) Settlement Ratio for Positive Projecting Embankment

$$r_{sd} = \frac{(s_m + s_g) - (s_f + d_c)}{s_m}$$

(11) Negative Projecting Embankment Fill Load

$$W_n = C_n w B_d^2$$

(12) Negative Projecting Embankment Load Coefficient (Complete Condition)

$$C_n = \frac{e^{-2K\mu\frac{H}{B_d}} - 1}{-2K\mu} \text{ when } H \leq H_e$$

(13) Negative Projecting Embankment Load Coefficient (Incomplete Condition)

$$C_n = \frac{e^{-2K\mu\frac{H_e}{B_d}} - 1}{-2K\mu} + \left(\frac{H}{B_d} - \frac{H_e}{B_d}\right) e^{-2K\mu\frac{H_e}{B_d}} \text{ when } H > H_e$$

(14) Settlement Ratio for Negative Projecting Embankment

$$r_{sd} = \frac{s_g - (s_d + s_f + d_c)}{s_d}$$

(15) Induced Trench Fill Load

$$W_i = C_i w B_c^2$$

(16) Induced Trench Load Coefficient (Complete Condition)

$$C_i = \frac{e^{-2K\mu\frac{H}{B_c}} - 1}{-2K\mu} \text{ when } H \leq H_e$$

(17) Induced Trench Load Coefficient (Incomplete Condition)

$$C_i = \frac{e^{-2K\mu\frac{H_e}{B_c}} - 1}{-2K\mu} + \left(\frac{H}{B_c} - \frac{H_e}{B_c}\right) e^{-2K\mu\frac{H_e}{B_c}} \text{ when } H > H_e$$

(18)   Jacked or Tunneled Earth Load
$$W_t = C_t w B_t^2 - 2cC_t B_t$$

(19)   Jacked or Tunneled Load Coefficient
$$C_t = \frac{1 - e^{-2K\mu'\frac{H}{B_t}}}{2K\mu'}$$

(20)   Average Live Load Pressure Intensity on Subsoil Plane
$$w_L = \frac{P(I_f)}{A_{LL}}$$

(21)   Total Live Load
$$W_T = w_L L S_L$$

(22)   Live Load on Pipe
$$W_L = \frac{W_T}{L_e}$$

(23)   Effective Supporting Length
$$L_e = L + 1.75\left(\frac{3B_c}{4}\right)$$

(24)   Aircraft Live Load — Rigid Pavement
$$p_{(H,X)} = \frac{CP}{R_s^2}$$

(25)   Radius of Stiffness for Rigid Pavements
$$R_s = \sqrt[4]{\frac{Eh^3}{12(1 - u^2)k}}$$

(26)   Aircraft Live Load — Flexible Pavement
$$p_{(H,X)} = Cp_o$$

(27)   Radius of Circle of Pressure
$$r = \sqrt{\frac{P}{p_o\pi}}$$

(28)   Railroad Live Load

$$W_L = C p_o B_c I_f$$

(29)   Bedding Factor for Positive Projecting Embankment and Induced Trench

$$B_f = \frac{A}{N - xq}$$

(30)   Lateral Pressure Term (Circular Pipe)

$$q = \frac{pK}{C_c} \left(\frac{H}{B_c} + \frac{p}{2} \right)$$

(31)   Lateral Pressure Term (Elliptical or Arch Pipe)

$$q = \frac{pB'_c K}{C_c B_c^2} \left(H + \frac{pB'_c}{2} \right)$$

(32)   Three-edge Bearing Strength

$$T.E.B. = \frac{W_L + W_E}{B_f} \times F.S.$$

(33)   D-load — Circular Pipe

$$D\text{-}load = \frac{W_L + W_E}{B_f \times D} \times F.S.$$

(34)   D-load — Elliptical and Arch Pipe

$$D\text{-}load = \frac{W_L + W_E}{B_f \times S} \times F.S.$$

GLOSSARY

GLOSSARY OF HYDRAULIC TERMS
(Equations 1 through 4)

A cross-sectional area of flow, square feet

A drainage area, acres

AHW allowable headwater depth at culvert entrance, feet

C coefficient of runoff which is a function of the characteristics of the drainage area

C_1 constant in Manning's Formula for full flow

D height of culvert opening or diameter of pipe, inches or feet

d_c critical depth, feet

H head loss, feet (the difference between the elevation of the entrance pool surface and the outlet tailwater surface)

HW headwater depth at culvert inlet measured from invert of pipe, feet

h_o vertical distance between the culvert invert at the outlet and the hydraulic grade line, feet

k_e entrance head loss coefficient

i rainfall intensity, inches per hour

L length of culvert, feet

n Manning's coefficient of roughness

Q flow in sewer or culvert discharge, cubic feet per second

R hydraulic radius, equals area of flow divided by wetted perimeter, feet

R inside vertical rise of elliptical, arch pipe, or boxes, feet or inches

S inside horizontal span of elliptical, arch pipe, or boxes, feet or inches

S slope of sewer, feet per foot

S_o slope of culvert, feet per foot

TW tailwater depth at culvert outlet measured from invert of pipe, feet

V velocity, feet per second

GLOSSARY OF LOAD TERMS
(Equations 5 through 34)

A a constant corresponding to the shape of the pipe

A_{LL} distributed live load area on subsoil plane at outside top of pipe, square feet

A_s area of transverse steel in a cradle or arch expressed as a percentage of the area of concrete in the cradle at the invert or arch at the crown

B_c outside horizontal span of the pipe, feet

B'_c outside vertical height of the pipe, feet

B_d width of trench at top of pipe, feet

B'_d average of the width of trench at top of pipe and the outside horizontal span of the pipe for negative projecting embankment installations, feet

$$B'_d = \frac{B_d + B_c}{2}$$

B_f bedding factor

B_t maximum width of excavation ahead of pipe or tunnel, feet

C pressure coefficient for live loads

C_c load coefficient for positive projecting embankment installations

C_d load coefficient for trench installations

C_i load coefficient for induced trench installations

C_n load coefficient for negative projecting embankment installations

C_t load coefficient for jacked or tunneled installations

c coefficient of cohesion of undisturbed soil, pounds per square foot

D inside diameter of circular pipe, feet or inches

$D\text{-}load$ the supporting strength of a pipe loaded under three-edge-bearing test conditions expressed in pounds per linear foot per foot of inside diameter or horizontal span

$D_{0.01}$ the maximum three-edge-bearing test load supported by a concrete pipe before a crack occurs having a width of 0.01 inch measured at close intervals, throughout a length of at least 1 foot expressed as D-load.

$D_{ult.}$ the maximum three-edge-bearing test load supported by a pipe, expressed as D-load.

d depth of bedding material below pipe, inches

d_c deflection of the vertical height of the pipe

E modulus of elasticity of concrete, pounds per square inch (4,000,000 psi)

e base of natural logarithms (2.718)

$F.S.$ factor of safety

H height of backfill or fill material above top of pipe, feet

H_e height of the plane of equal settlement above top of pipe, feet

h thickness of rigid pavement

I_f impact factor for live loads

K conjugate ratio for backfill or fill material

k modulus of subgrade reaction, pounds per cubic inch

L length of A_{LL} parallel to longitudinal axis of pipe, feet

L_e effective live load supporting length of pipe, feet

μ coefficient of internal friction of fill material

μ' coefficient of sliding friction between the backfill material and the trench walls

N a parameter which is a function of the distribution of the vertical load and vertical reaction

N' a parameter which is a function of the distribution of the vertical load and the vertical reaction for the concrete cradle method of bedding

P wheel load, pounds

p projection ratio for positive projecting embankment installations; equals vertical distance between the top of the pipe and the natural ground surface divided by the outside vertical height of the pipe

p' projection ratio for negative projecting and induced trench installations; equals vertical distance between the top of the pipe and the top of the trench divided by the trench width (negative projecting) or the height of the induced trench divided by the outside horizontal span of the pipe (induced trench)

p_o live load pressure at the surface, pounds per square inch or pounds per square foot

$p_{(H,X)}$ pressure intensity at any vertical distance, H, and horizontal distance, X, pounds per square inch or pounds per square foot

π 3.1416

q the ratio of total lateral pressure to the total vertical load

R inside vertical rise of elliptical, arch pipe, or boxes feet or inches

R_s radius of stiffness of the concrete pavement, inches or feet

r radius of the circle of pressure at the surface, inches

r_{sd} settlement ratio

S inside horizontal span of elliptical, arch pipe, or boxes feet or inches

S_L outside horizontal span of pipe (B_c) or width of A_{LL} transverse to longitudinal axis of pipe, whichever is less, feet

s_d compression of the fill material in the trench within the height $p'B_d$ for negative projecting embankment installations

s_f settlement of the pipe into its bedding foundation

s_g settlement of the natural ground or compacted fill surface adjacent to the pipe

s_m settlement of the adjacent soil of height pB'_c for positive projecting embankment installations

T.E.B.   three-edge bearing strength, pounds per linear foot

u Poisson's ratio of concrete (0.15)

W_c fill load for positive projecting embankment installations, pounds per linear foot

W_d backfill load for trench installations, pounds per linear foot

W_E earth load, pounds per linear foot

W_i fill load for induced trench installations, pounds per linear foot

W_L live load on pipe, pounds per linear foot

W_n fill load for negative projecting embankment installations, pounds per linear foot

W_p weight of pavement, pounds per linear foot

W_T total live load on pipe, pounds

W_t earth load for jacked or tunneled installations, pounds per linear foot

w unit weight of backfill or fill material, pounds per cubic foot

w_L average pressure intensity of live load on subsoil plane at outside top of pipe, pounds per square foot

x a parameter which is a function of the area of the vertical projection of the pipe over which active lateral pressure is effective

x' a parameter which is a function of the effective lateral support provided by the concrete cradle method of bedding

APPENDIX

TABLE A-1

SQUARE ROOTS OF DECIMAL NUMBER($S^{1/2}$ IN MANNING'S FORMULA)

No.	.−0	.−1	.−2	.−3	.−4	.−5	.−6	.−7	.−8	.−9
.00001	.003162	.003317	.003464	.003606	.003742	.003873	.004000	.004123	.004243	.004359
.00002	.004472	.004583	.004690	.004796	.004899	.005000	.005099	.005196	.005292	.005385
.00003	.005477	.005568	.005657	.005745	.005831	.005916	.006000	.006083	.006164	.006245
.00004	.006325	.006403	.006481	.006557	.006633	.006708	.006782	.006856	.006928	.007000
.00005	.007071	.007141	.007211	.007280	.007348	.007416	.007483	.007550	.007616	.007681
.00006	.007746	.007810	.007874	.007937	.008000	.008062	.008124	.008185	.008246	.008307
.00007	.008367	.008426	.008485	.008544	.008602	.008660	.008718	.008775	.008832	.008888
.00008	.008944	.009000	.009055	.009110	.009165	.009220	.009274	.009327	.009381	.009434
.00009	.009487	.009539	.009592	.009644	.009695	.009747	.009798	.009849	.009899	.009950
.00010	.010000	.010050	.010100	.010149	.010198	.010247	.010296	.010344	.010392	.010440
.0001	.01000	.01049	.01095	.01140	.01183	.01225	.01265	.01304	.01342	.01378
.0002	.01414	.01449	.01483	.01517	.01549	.01581	.01612	.01643	.01673	.01703
.0003	.01732	.01761	.01789	.01817	.01844	.01871	.01897	.01924	.01949	.01975
.0004	.02000	.02025	.02049	.02074	.02098	.02121	.02145	.02168	.02191	.02214
.0005	.02236	.02258	.02280	.02302	.02324	.02345	.02366	.02387	.02408	.02429
.0006	.02449	.02470	.02490	.02510	.02530	.02550	.02569	.02588	.02608	.02627
.0007	.02646	.02665	.02683	.02702	.02720	.02739	.02757	.02775	.02793	.02811
.0008	.02828	.02846	.02864	.02881	.02898	.02915	.02933	.02950	.02966	.02983
.0009	.03000	.03017	.03033	.03050	.03066	.03082	.03098	.03114	.03130	.03146
.0010	.03162	.03178	.03194	.03209	.03225	.03240	.03256	.03271	.03286	.03302
.001	.03162	.03317	.03464	.03606	.03742	.03873	.04000	.04123	.04243	.04359
.002	.04472	.04583	.04690	.04796	.04899	.05000	.05099	.05196	.05292	.05385
.003	.05477	.05568	.05657	.05745	.05831	.05916	.06000	.06083	.06164	.06245
.004	.06325	.06403	.06481	.06557	.06633	.06708	.06782	.06856	.06928	.07000
.005	.07071	.07141	.07211	.07280	.07348	.07416	.07483	.07550	.07616	.07681
.006	.07746	.07810	.07874	.07937	.08000	.08062	.08124	.08185	.08246	.08307
.007	.08367	.08426	.08485	.08544	.08602	.08660	.08718	.08775	.08832	.08888
.008	.08944	.09000	.09055	.09110	.09165	.09220	.09274	.09327	.09381	.09434
.009	.09487	.09539	.09592	.09644	.09695	.09747	.09798	.09849	.09899	.09950
.010	.10000	.10050	.10100	.10149	.10198	.10247	.10296	.10344	.10392	.10440
.01	.1000	.1049	.1095	.1140	.1183	.1225	.1265	.1304	.1342	.1378
.02	.1414	.1449	.1483	.1517	.1549	.1581	.1612	.1643	.1673	.1703
.03	.1732	.1761	.1789	.1817	.1844	.1871	.1897	.1924	.1949	.1975
.04	.2000	.2025	.2049	.2074	.2098	.2121	.2145	.2168	.2191	.2214
.05	.2236	.2258	.2280	.2302	.2324	.2345	.2366	.2387	.2408	.2429
.06	.2449	.2470	.2490	.2510	.2530	.2550	.2569	.2588	.2608	.2627
.07	.2646	.2665	.2683	.2702	.2720	.2739	.2757	.2775	.2793	.2811
.08	.2828	.2846	.2864	.2881	.2898	.2915	.2933	.2950	.2966	.2983
.09	.3000	.3017	.3033	.3050	.3066	.3082	.3098	.3114	.3130	.3146
.10	.3162	.3178	.3194	.3209	.3225	.3240	.3256	.3271	.3286	.3302

TABLE A-2

THREE-EIGHTHS POWERS OF NUMBERS

No.	0	2	4	6	8	No.	0	2	4	6	8
0	.00	.55	.71	.83	.92	50	4.34	4.40	4.46	4.52	4.58
1	1.00	1.07	1.13	1.19	1.25	60	4.64	4.70	4.76	4.81	4.87
2	1.30	1.34	1.39	1.43	1.47	70	4.92	4.97	5.02	5.07	5.12
3	1.51	1.55	1.58	1.62	1.65	80	5.17	5.22	5.27	5.31	5.36
4	1.68	1.71	1.74	1.77	1.80	90	5.41	5.45	5.49	5.54	5.58
5	1.83	1.86	1.88	1.91	1.93	100	5.62	5.67	5.71	5.75	5.79
6	1.96	1.98	2.01	2.03	2.05	110	5.83	5.87	5.91	5.95	5.98
7	2.07	2.10	2.12	2.14	2.16	120	6.02	6.06	6.10	6.13	6.17
8	2.18	2.20	2.22	2.24	2.26	130	6.20	6.24	6.28	6.31	6.35
9	2.28	2.30	2.32	2.34	2.35	140	6.38	6.41	6.45	6.48	6.51
10	2.37	2.39	2.41	2.42	2.44	150	6.55	6.58	6.61	6.64	6.68
11	2.46	2.47	2.49	2.51	2.52	160	6.71	6.74	6.77	6.80	6.83
12	2.54	2.56	2.57	2.59	2.60	170	6.86	6.89	6.92	6.95	6.98
13	2.62	2.63	2.65	2.66	2.68	180	7.01	7.04	7.07	7.10	7.12
14	2.69	2.71	2.72	2.73	2.75	190	7.15	7.18	7.21	7.24	7.27
15	2.76	2.77	2.79	2.80	2.81	200	7.29	7.32	7.35	7.37	7.40
16	2.83	2.84	2.86	2.87	2.88	210	7.43	7.46	7.48	7.51	7.54
17	2.89	2.91	2.92	2.93	2.94	220	7.56	7.58	7.61	7.63	7.66
18	2.96	2.97	2.98	2.99	3.00	230	7.69	7.71	7.73	7.76	7.78
19	3.02	3.03	3.04	3.05	3.06	240	7.81	7.83	7.86	7.88	7.91
20	3.08	3.09	3.10	3.11	3.12	250	7.93	7.95	7.98	8.00	8.02
21	3.13	3.14	3.15	3.17	3.18	260	8.05	8.07	8.09	8.12	8.14
22	3.19	3.20	3.21	3.22	3.23	270	8.16	8.18	8.21	8.23	8.25
23	3.24	3.25	3.26	3.27	3.28	280	8.27	8.30	8.32	8.34	8.36
24	3.29	3.30	3.31	3.32	3.33	290	8.38	8.40	8.43	8.45	8.47
25	3.34	3.35	3.36	3.37	3.38	300	8.49	8.51	8.53	8.55	8.57
26	3.39	3.40	3.41	3.42	3.43	310	8.60	8.62	8.64	8.66	8.68
27	3.44	3.45	3.46	3.47	3.48	320	8.70	8.72	8.74	8.76	8.78
28	3.49	3.50	3.51	3.52	3.53	330	8.80	8.82	8.84	8.86	8.88
29	3.54	3.54	3.55	3.56	3.57	340	8.90	8.92	8.94	8.96	8.98
30	3.58	3.59	3.60	3.61	3.62	350	9.00	9.01	9.03	9.05	9.07
31	3.62	3.63	3.64	3.65	3.66	360	9.09	9.11	9.13	9.15	9.17
32	3.67	3.68	3.69	3.69	3.70	370	9.18	9.20	9.22	9.24	9.26
33	3.71	3.72	3.73	3.74	3.74	380	9.28	9.30	9.31	9.33	9.35
34	3.75	3.76	3.77	3.78	3.79	390	9.37	9.39	9.40	9.42	9.44
35	3.79	3.80	3.81	3.82	3.83	400	9.46	9.48	9.49	9.51	9.53
36	3.83	3.84	3.85	3.86	3.87	410	9.55	9.56	9.58	9.60	9.61
37	3.87	3.88	3.89	3.90	3.91	420	9.63	9.65	9.67	9.68	9.70
38	3.91	3.92	3.93	3.94	3.94	430	9.72	9.73	9.75	9.77	9.78
39	3.95	3.96	3.97	3.97	3.98	440	9.80	9.82	9.83	9.85	9.87
40	3.99	4.00	4.00	4.01	4.02	450	9.88	9.90	9.92	9.93	9.95
41	4.03	4.03	4.04	4.05	4.05	460	9.97	9.98	10.00	10.01	10.03
42	4.06	4.07	4.08	4.08	4.09	470	10.05	10.06	10.08	10.09	10.11
43	4.10	4.10	4.11	4.12	4.13	480	10.13	10.14	10.16	10.17	10.19
44	4.13	4.14	4.15	4.15	4.16	490	10.21	10.22	10.24	10.25	10.27
45	4.17	4.18	4.18	4.19	4.20	500	10.28	10.30	10.31	10.33	10.34
46	4.20	4.21	4.22	4.22	4.23	510	10.36	10.37	10.39	10.41	10.42
47	4.24	4.24	4.25	4.26	4.26	520	10.44	10.45	10.47	10.48	10.50
48	4.27	4.28	4.28	4.29	4.30	530	10.51	10.52	10.54	10.55	10.57
49	4.30	4.31	4.32	4.32	4.33	540	10.58	10.60	10.61	10.63	10.64

TABLE A-3

TWO-THIRDS POWERS OF NUMBERS

No.	.00	.01	.02	.03	.04	.05	.06	.07	.08	.09
.0	.000	.046	.074	.097	.117	.136	.153	.170	.186	.201
.1	.215	.229	.243	.256	.269	.282	.295	.307	.319	.331
.2	.342	.353	.364	.375	.386	.397	.407	.418	.428	.438
.3	.448	.458	.468	.477	.487	.497	.506	.515	.525	.534
.4	.543	.552	.561	.570	.578	.587	.596	.604	.613	.622
.5	.630	.638	.647	.655	.663	.671	.679	687	.695	.703
.6	.711	.719	.727	.735	.743	.750	.758	.765	.773	.781
.7	.788	.796	.803	.811	.818	.825	.832	.840	.847	.855
.8	.862	.869	.876	.883	.890	.897	.904	.911	.918	.925
.9	.932	.939	.946	.953	.960	.966	.973	.980	.987	.993
1.0	1.000	1.007	1.013	1.020	1.027	1.033	1.040	1.046	1.053	1.059
1.1	1.065	1.072	1.078	1.085	1.091	1.097	1.104	1.110	1.117	1.123
1.2	1.129	1.136	1.142	1.148	1.154	1.160	1.167	1.173	1.179	1.185
1.3	1.191	1.197	1.203	1.209	1.215	1.221	1.227	1.233	1.239	1.245
1.4	1.251	1.257	1.263	1.269	1.275	1.281	1.287	1.293	1.299	1.305
1.5	1.310	1.316	1.322	1.328	1.334	1.339	1.345	1.351	1.357	1.362
1.6	1.368	1.374	1.379	1.385	1.391	1.396	1.402	1.408	1.413	1.419
1.7	1.424	1.430	1.436	1.441	1.447	1.452	1.458	1.463	1.469	1.474
1.8	1.480	1.485	1.491	1.496	1.502	1.507	1.513	1.518	1.523	1.529
1.9	1.534	1.539	1.545	1.550	1.556	1.561	1.566	1.571	1.577	1.582
2.0	1.587	1.593	1.598	1.603	1.608	1.613	1.619	1.624	1.629	1.634
2.1	1.639	1.645	1.650	1.655	1.660	1.665	1.671	1.676	1.681	1.686
2.2	1.691	1.697	1.702	1.707	1.712	1.717	1.722	1.727	1.732	1.737
2.3	1.742	1.747	1.752	1.757	1.762	1.767	1.772	1.777	1.782	1.787
2.4	1.792	1.797	1.802	1.807	1.812	1.817	1.822	1.827	1.832	1.837
2.5	1.842	1.847	1.852	1.857	1.862	1.867	1.871	1.876	1.881	1.886
2.6	1.891	1.896	1.900	1.905	1.910	1.915	1.920	1.925	1.929	1.934
2.7	1.939	1.944	1.949	1.953	1.958	1.963	1.968	1.972	1.977	1.982
2.8	1.987	1.992	1.996	2.001	2.006	2.010	2.015	2.020	2.024	2.029
2.9	2.034	2.038	2.043	2.048	2.052	2.057	2.062	2.066	2.071	2.075
3.0	2.080	2.085	2.089	2.094	2.099	2.103	2.108	2.112	2.117	2.122
3.1	2.126	2.131	2.135	2.140	2.144	2.149	2.153	2.158	2.163	2.167
3.2	2.172	2.176	2.180	2.185	2.190	2.194	2.199	2.203	2.208	2.212
3.3	2.217	2.221	2.226	2.230	2.234	2.239	2.243	2.248	2.252	2.257
3.4	2.261	2.265	2.270	2.274	2.279	2.283	2.288	2.292	2.296	2.301
3.5	2.305	2.310	2.314	2.318	2.323	2.327	2.331	2.336	2.340	2.345
3.6	2.349	2.353	2.358	2.362	2.366	2.371	2.375	2.379	2.384	2.388
3.7	2.392	2.397	2.401	2.405	2.409	2.414	2.418	2.422	2.427	2.431
3.8	2.435	2.439	2.444	2.448	2.452	2.457	2.461	2.465	2.469	2.474
3.9	2.478	2.482	2.486	1.490	2.495	2.499	2.503	2.507	2.511	2.516
4.0	2.520	2.524	2.528	2.532	2.537	2.541	2.545	2.549	2.553	2.558
4.1	2.562	2.566	2.570	2.574	2.579	2.583	2.587	2.591	2.595	2.599
4.2	2.603	2.607	2.611	2.616	2.620	2.624	2.628	2.632	2.636	2.640
4.3	2.644	2.648	2.653	2.657	2.661	2.665	2.669	2.673	2.677	2.681
4.4	2.685	2.689	2.693	2.698	2.702	2.706	2.710	2.714	2.718	2.722
4.5	2.726	2.730	2.734	2.738	2.742	2.746	2.750	2.754	2.758	2.762
4.6	2.766	2.770	2.774	2.778	2.782	2.786	2.790	2.794	2.798	2.802
4.7	2.806	2.810	2.814	2.818	2.822	2.826	2.830	2.834	2.838	2.842
4.8	2.846	2.850	2.854	2.858	2.862	2.865	2.869	2.873	2.877	2.881
4.9	2.885	2.889	2.893	2.897	2.901	2.904	2.908	2.912	2.916	2.920

TABLE A-4

EIGHT-THIRDS POWERS OF NUMBERS

No.	.00	.02	.04	.06	.08	No.	.00	.02	.04	.06	.08
0.1	.002	.004	.005	.008	.010	5.1	77.1	77.9	78.7	79.5	80.3
0.2	.014	.018	.022	.028	.034	5.2	81.2	82.0	82.8	83.7	84.5
0.3	.040	.048	.056	.066	.076	5.3	85.4	86.3	87.1	88.0	88.9
0.4	.087	.099	.112	.126	.141	5.4	89.8	90.6	91.5	92.4	93.3
0.5	.157	.175	.193	.213	.234	5.5	94.3	95.2	96.1	97.0	98.0
0.6	.256	.279	.304	.330	.358	5.6	98.9	99.8	101	102	103
0.7	.386	.416	.448	.481	.516	5.7	104	105	106	107	108
0.8	.552	.589	.628	.669	.711	5.8	109	110	111	112	113
0.9	.755	.801	.848	.897	.948	5.9	114	115	116	117	118
1.0	1.000	1.054	1.110	1.168	1.228	6.0	119	120	121	122	123
1.1	1.29	1.35	1.42	1.49	1.55	6.1	124	125	126	128	129
1.2	1.63	1.70	1.77	1.85	1.93	6.2	130	131	132	133	134
1.3	2.01	2.10	2.18	2.27	2.36	6.3	135	137	138	139	140
1.4	2.45	2.55	2.64	2.74	2.84	6.4	141	142	144	145	146
1.5	2.95	3.05	3.16	3.27	3.39	6.5	147	148	150	151	152
1.6	3.50	3.62	3.74	3.86	3.99	6.6	153	155	156	157	158
1.7	4.12	4.25	4.38	4.51	4.65	6.7	160	161	162	163	165
1.8	4.79	4.94	5.08	5.23	5.39	6.8	166	167	169	170	171
1.9	5.54	5.69	5.85	6.02	6.18	6.9	173	174	175	177	178
2.0	6.35	6.52	6.69	6.87	7.05	7.0	179	181	182	183	185
2.1	7.23	7.42	7.60	7.80	7.99	7.1	186	188	189	190	192
2.2	8.19	8.39	8.59	8.80	9.00	7.2	193	195	196	198	199
2.3	9.22	9.43	9.65	9.87	10.10	7.3	201	202	203	205	206
2.4	10.33	10.56	10.79	11.03	11.27	7.4	208	209	211	212	214
2.5	11.51	11.76	12.01	12.26	12.52	7.5	216	217	219	220	222
2.6	12.8	13.0	13.3	13.6	13.9	7.6	223	225	226	228	230
2.7	14.1	14.4	14.7	15.0	15.3	7.7	231	233	234	236	238
2.8	15.6	15.9	16.2	16.5	16.8	7.8	239	241	243	244	246
2.9	17.1	17.4	17.7	18.1	18.4	7.9	248	249	251	253	254
3.0	18.7	19.1	19.4	19.7	20.1	8.0	256	258	259	261	263
3.1	20.4	20.8	21.1	21.5	21.9	8.1	265	266	268	270	272
3.2	22.2	22.6	23.0	23.4	23.7	8.2	273	275	277	279	281
3.3	24.1	24.5	24.9	25.3	25.7	8.3	282	284	286	288	290
3.4	26.1	26.6	27.0	27.4	27.8	8.4	292	293	295	297	299
3.5	28.2	28.7	29.1	29.5	30.0	8.5	301	303	305	307	309
3.6	30.4	30.9	31.4	31.8	32.3	8.6	310	312	314	316	318
3.7	32.7	33.2	33.7	34.2	34.7	8.7	320	322	324	326	328
3.8	35.2	35.7	36.2	36.7	37.2	8.8	330	332	334	336	338
3.9	37.7	38.2	38.7	39.3	39.8	8.9	340	342	344	346	348
4.0	40.3	40.9	41.4	42.0	42.5	9.0	350	353	355	357	359
4.1	43.1	43.6	44.2	44.8	45.3	9.1	361	363	365	367	369
4.2	45.9	46.5	47.1	47.7	48.3	9.2	372	374	376	378	380
4.3	48.9	49.5	50.1	50.7	51.4	9.3	382	385	387	390	391
4.4	52.0	52.6	53.3	53.9	54.5	9.4	394	396	398	400	403
4.5	55.2	55.9	56.5	57.2	57.9	9.5	405	407	409	412	414
4.6	58.5	59.2	59.9	60.6	61.3	9.6	416	419	421	423	426
4.7	62.0	62.7	63.4	64.1	64.8	9.7	428	429	433	435	437
4.8	65.6	66.3	67.0	67.8	68.5	9.8	440	442	445	447	449
4.9	69.3	70.0	70.8	71.6	72.3	9.9	452	454	457	459	462
5.0	73.1	73.9	74.7	75.5	76.3	10.0	464	467	469	472	474

TABLE A-5

SQUARE ROOTS AND CUBE ROOTS OF NUMBERS

No.	Square Root	Cube Root	No.	Square Root	Cube Root	No.	Square Root	Cube Root	No	Square Root	Cube Root
1	1.000	1.000	26	5.099	2.963	51	7.141	3.708	76	8.718	4.236
2	1.414	1.260	27	5.196	3.000	52	7.211	3.733	77	8.775	4.254
3	1.732	1.442	28	5.292	3.037	53	7.280	3.756	78	8.832	4.273
4	2.000	1.587	29	5.385	3.072	54	7.348	3.780	79	8.888	4.291
5	2.236	1.710	30	5.477	3.107	55	7.416	3.803	80	8.944	4.309
6	2.449	1.817	31	5.568	3.141	56	7.483	3.826	81	9.000	4.327
7	2.646	1.913	32	5.657	3.175	57	7.550	3.849	82	9.055	4.345
8	2.828	2.000	33	5.745	3.208	58	7.616	3.871	83	9.110	4.362
9	3.000	2.080	34	5.831	3.240	59	7.681	3.893	84	9.165	4.380
10	3.162	2.154	35	5.916	3.271	60	7.746	3.915	85	9.220	4.397
11	3.317	2.224	36	6.000	3.302	61	7.810	3.937	86	9.274	4.414
12	3.464	2.289	37	6.083	3.332	62	7.874	3.958	87	9.327	4.431
13	3.606	2.351	38	6.164	3.362	63	7.937	3.979	88	9.381	4.448
14	3.742	2.410	39	6.245	3.391	64	8.000	4.000	89	9.434	4.465
15	3.873	2.466	40	6.325	3.420	65	8.062	4.021	90	9.487	4.481
16	4.000	2.520	41	6.403	3.448	66	8.124	4.041	91	9.539	4.498
17	4.123	2.571	42	6.481	3.476	67	8.185	4.062	92	9.592	4.514
18	4.243	2.621	43	6.557	3.503	68	8.246	4.082	93	9.644	4.531
19	4.359	2.668	44	6.633	3.530	69	8.307	4.102	94	9.695	4.547
20	4.472	2.714	45	6.708	3.557	70	8.367	4.121	95	9.747	4.563
21	4.583	2.759	46	6.782	3.583	71	8.426	4.141	96	9.798	4.579
22	4.690	2.802	47	6.856	3.609	72	8.485	4.160	97	9.849	4.595
23	4.796	2.844	48	6.928	3.634	73	8.544	4.179	98	9.900	4.610
24	4.899	2.885	49	7.000	3.659	74	8.602	4.198	99	9.950	4.626
25	5.000	2.924	50	7.071	3.684	75	8.660	4.217	100	10.000	4.642

For Square Roots—moving the decimal point 2 places in the number requires a change of 1 place in the square root.

For Cube Roots—moving the decimal point 3 places in the number requires a change of 1 place in the cube root.

TABLE A-6

DECIMAL EQUIVALENTS OF INCHES AND FEET

Fractions of (Inch)	Foot	Inch Equivalents to Foot Fractions	Fractions of (Inch)	Foot	Inch Equivalents to Foot Fractions	Fractions of (Inch)	Foot	Inch Equivalents to Foot Fractions	Fractions of (Inch)	Foot	Inch Equivalents to Foot Fractions
	.005208	1/16		.255208	3 1/16		.505208	6 1/16		.755208	9 1/16
	.010417	1/8		.260417	3 1/8		.510417	6 1/8		.760417	9 1/8
1/64	.015625	3/16	17/64	.265625	3 3/16	33/64	.515625	6 3/16	49/64	.765625	9 3/16
	.020833	1/4		.270833	3 1/4		.520833	6 1/4		.770833	9 1/4
	.026042	5/16		.276042	3 5/16		.526042	6 5/16		.776042	9 5/16
1/32	.031250	3/8	9/32	.281250	3 3/8	17/32	.531250	6 3/8	25/32	.781250	9 3/8
	.036458	7/16		.286458	3 7/16		.536458	6 7/16		.786458	9 7/16
	.041667	1/2		.291667	3 1/2		.541667	6 1/2		.791667	9 1/2
3/64	.046875	9/16	19/64	.296875	3 9/16	35/64	.546875	6 9/16	51/64	.796875	9 9/16
	.052083	5/8		.302083	3 5/8		.552083	6 5/8		.802083	9 5/8
	.057292	11/16		.307292	3 11/16		.557292	6 11/16		.807292	9 11/16
1/16	.062500	3/4	5/16	.312500	3 3/4	9/16	.562500	6 3/4	13/16	.812500	9 3/4
	.067708	13/16		.317708	3 13/16		.567708	6 13/16		.817708	9 13/16
	.072917	7/8		.322917	3 7/8		.572917	6 7/8		.822917	9 7/8
5/64	.078125	15/16	21/64	.328125	3 15/16	37/64	.578125	6 15/16	53/64	.828125	9 15/16
	.083333	1		.333333	4		.583333	7		.833333	10
	.088542	1 1/16		.338542	4 1/16		.588542	7 1/16		.838542	10 1/16
3/32	.093750	1 1/8	11/32	.343750	4 1/8	19/32	.593750	7 1/8	27/32	.843750	10 1/8
	.098958	1 3/16		.348958	4 3/16		.598958	7 3/16		.848958	10 3/16
	.104167	1 1/4		.354167	4 1/4		.604167	7 1/4		.854167	10 1/4
7/64	.109375	1 5/16	23/64	.359375	4 5/16	39/64	.609375	7 5/16	55/64	.859375	10 5/16
	.114583	1 3/8		.364583	4 3/8		.614583	7 3/8		.864583	10 3/8
	.119792	1 7/16		.369792	4 7/16		.619792	7 7/16		.869792	10 7/16
1/8	.125000	1 1/2	3/8	.375000	4 1/2	5/8	.625000	7 1/2	7/8	.875000	10 1/2
	.130208	1 9/16		.380208	4 9/16		.630208	7 9/16		.880208	10 9/16
	.135417	1 5/8		.385417	4 5/8		.635417	7 5/8		.885417	10 5/8
9/64	.140625	1 11/16	25/64	.390625	4 11/16	41/64	.640625	7 11/16	57/64	.890625	10 11/16
	.145833	1 3/4		.395833	4 3/4		.645833	7 3/4		.895833	10 3/4
	.151042	1 13/16		.401042	4 13/16		.651042	7 13/16		.901042	10 13/16
5/32	.156250	1 7/8	13/32	.406250	4 7/8	21/32	.656250	7 7/8	29/32	.906250	10 7/8
	.161458	1 15/16		.411458	4 15/16		.661458	7 15/16		.911458	10 15/16
	.166667	2		.416667	5		.666667	8		.916667	11
11/64	.171875	2 1/16	27/64	.421875	5 1/16	43/64	.671875	8 1/16	59/64	.921875	11 1/16
	.177083	2 1/8		.427083	5 1/8		.677083	8 1/8		.927083	11 1/8
	.182292	2 3/16		.432292	5 3/16		.682292	8 3/16		.932292	11 3/16
3/16	.187500	2 1/4	7/16	.437500	5 1/4	11/16	.687500	8 1/4	15/16	.937500	11 1/4
	.192708	2 5/16		.442708	5 5/16		.692708	8 5/16		.942708	11 5/16
	.197917	2 3/8		.447917	5 3/8		.697917	8 3/8		.947917	11 3/8
13/64	.203125	2 7/16	29/64	.453125	5 7/16	45/64	.703125	8 7/16	61/64	.953125	11 7/16
	.208333	2 1/2		.458333	5 1/2		.708333	8 1/2		.958333	11 1/2
	.213542	2 9/16		.463542	5 9/16		.713542	8 9/16		.963542	11 9/16
7/32	.218750	2 5/8	15/32	.468750	5 5/8	23/32	.718750	8 5/8	31/32	.968750	11 5/8
	.223958	2 11/16		.473958	5 11/16		.723958	8 11/16		.973958	11 11/16
	.229167	2 3/4		.479167	5 3/4		.729167	8 3/4		.979167	11 3/4
15/64	.234375	2 13/16	31/64	.484375	5 13/16	47/64	.734375	8 13/16	63/64	.984375	11 13/16
	.229583	2 7/8		.489583	5 7/8		.739583	8 7/8		.989583	11 7/8
	.244792	2 15/16		.494792	5 15/16		.744792	8 15/16		.994792	11 15/16
1/4	.2500	3	1/2	.5000	6	3/4	.7500	9	1	1.0000	12

TABLE A-7

VARIOUS POWERS OF PIPE DIAMETERS

Pipe Diameter In.	Ft. (D)	$D^{1/3}$	$D^{2/3}$	$D^{4/3}$	$D^{8/3}$	$D^{5/2}$	$D^{16/3}$	D^4
6	0.50	0.794	0.630	0.397	0.157	0.177	0.025	0.063
8	0.67	0.874	0.763	0.582	0.339	0.363	0.115	0.198
9	0.75	0.909	0.825	0.681	0.464	0.487	0.216	0.316
10	0.83	0.941	0.886	0.784	0.615	0.634	0.378	0.482
12	1.00	1.000	1.000	1.000	1.000	1.000	1.000	1.000
15	1.25	1.077	1.160	1.347	1.813	1.747	3.287	2.441
16	1.33	1.101	1.211	1.468	2.154	2.053	4.638	3.160
18	1.50	1.145	1.310	1.717	2.948	2.756	8.693	5.063
21	1.75	1.205	1.452	2.109	4.447	4.051	19.78	9.379
24	2.00	1.260	1.587	2.520	6.35	5.657	40.32	16.00
27	2.25	1.310	1.717	2.948	8.69	7.594	75.56	25.63
30	2.50	1.357	1.842	3.393	11.51	9.882	132.5	39.06
33	2.75	1.401	1.963	3.853	14.84	12.54	220.3	57.19
36	3.00	1.442	2.080	4.327	18.72	15.59	350.4	81.0
39	3.25	1.481	2.194	4.814	23.17	19.04	537.1	111.6
42	3.50	1.518	2.305	5.314	28.24	22.92	797.5	150.1
45	3.75	1.554	2.414	5.826	33.94	27.23	1152.	197.8
48	4.0	1.587	2.520	6.35	40.32	32.00	1626.	256.0
54	4.5	1.651	2.726	7.43	55.20	42.96	3047.	410.1
60	5.0	1.710	2.924	8.55	73.10	55.90	5344.	625.0
66	5.5	1.765	3.116	9.71	94.25	70.94	8883.	915.1
72	6.0	1.817	3.302	10.90	118.8	88.2	14130	1296
78	6.5	1.866	3.483	12.13	147.1	107.7	21654	1785
84	7.0	1.913	3.659	13.39	179.3	129.6	32148	2401
90	7.5	1.957	3.832	14.68	215.5	154.0	46451	3164
96	8.0	2.000	4.00	16.00	256	181.0	65536	4096
102	8.5	2.041	4.17	17.35	301	210.6	90552	5220
108	9.0	2.080	4.33	18.72	350	243.0	122827	6561
114	9.5	2.118	4.49	20.12	405	278.2	163879	8145
120	10.0	2.154	4.64	21.54	464	316	215443	10000
132	11.0	2.224	4.95	24.46	598	401	358173	14641
144	12.0	2.289	5.24	27.47	755	499	569680	20736
156	13.0	2.351	5.53	30.57	934	609	873031	28561
168	14.0	2.410	5.81	33.74	1140	733	1296200	38416
180	15.0	2.466	6.08	36.99	1370	871	1872800	50625

TABLE A-8

AREAS OF CIRCULAR SECTIONS (Square Feet)

Inches	Feet and inches	0	⅛	¼	⅜	½	⅝	¾	⅞
0	0-0		.0001	.0003	.0008	.0014	.0021	.0031	.0042
1	0-1	.0055	.0069	.0085	.0103	.0123	.0144	.0167	.0192
2	0-2	.0218	.0246	.0276	.0308	.0341	.0376	.0413	.0451
3	0-3	.0491	.0533	.0576	.0621	.0668	.0717	.0767	.0819
4	0-4	.0873	.0928	.0985	.1044	.1104	.1167	.1231	.1296
5	0-5	.1364	.1433	.1503	.1576	.1650	.1726	.1803	.1883
6	0-6	.1963	.2046	.2131	.2217	.2304	.2394	.2485	.2578
7	0-7	.2673	.2769	.2867	.2967	.3068	.3171	.3276	.3382
8	0-8	.3491	.3601	.3712	.3826	.3941	.4057	.4176	.4296
9	0-9	.4418	.4541	.4667	.4794	.4922	.5053	.5185	.5319
10	0-10	.5454	.5591	.5730	.5871	.6013	.6157	.6303	.6450
11	0-11	.6600	.6750	.6903	.7057	.7213	.7371	.7530	.7691
12	1-0	.7854	.8018	.8185	.8353	.8522	.8693	.8866	.9041
13	1-1	.9218	.9396	.9575	.9757	.9940	1.013	1.031	1.050
14	1-2	1.069	1.088	1.108	1.127	1.147	1.167	1.187	1.207
15	1-3	1.227	1.248	1.268	1.289	1.310	1.332	1.353	1.375
16	1-4	1.396	1.418	1.440	1.462	1.485	1.507	1.530	1.553
17	1-5	1.576	1.600	1.623	1.647	1.670	1.694	1.718	1.743
18	1-6	1.767	1.792	1.817	1.842	1.867	1.892	1.917	1.943
19	1-7	1.969	1.995	2.021	2.047	2.074	2.101	2.127	2.154
20	1-8	2.182	2.209	2.237	2.264	2.292	2.320	2.348	2.377
21	1-9	2.405	2.434	2.463	2.492	2.521	2.551	2.580	2.610
22	1-10	2.640	2.670	2.700	2.731	2.761	2.792	2.823	2.854
23	1-11	2.885	2.917	2.948	2.980	3.012	3.044	3.076	3.109
24	2-0	3.142	3.174	3.207	3.241	3.274	3.307	3.341	3.375
25	2-1	3.409	3.443	3.477	3.512	3.547	3.581	3.616	3.652
26	2-2	3.687	3.723	3.758	3.794	3.830	3.866	3.903	3.939
27	2-3	3.976	4.013	4.050	4.087	4.125	4.162	4.200	4.238
28	2-4	4.276	4.314	4.353	4.391	4.430	4.469	4.508	4.547
29	2-5	4.587	4.627	4.666	4.706	4.746	4.787	4.827	4.868
30	2-6	4.909	4.950	4.991	5.032	5.074	5.115	5.157	5.199
31	2-7	5.241	5.284	5.326	5.369	5.412	5.455	5.498	5.541
32	2-8	5.585	5.629	5.673	5.717	5.761	5.805	5.850	5.895
33	2-9	5.940	5.985	6.030	6.075	6.121	6.167	6.213	6.259
34	2-10	6.305	6.351	6.398	6.445	6.492	6.539	6.586	6.634
35	2-11	6.681	6.729	6.777	6.825	6.874	6.922	6.971	7.020
36	3-0	7.069	7.118	7.167	7.217	7.266	7.316	7.366	7.416
37	3-1	7.467	7.517	7.568	7.619	7.670	7.721	7.773	7.824
38	3-2	7.876	7.928	7.980	8.032	8.084	8.137	8.190	8.243
39	3-3	8.296	8.349	8.402	8.456	8.510	8.564	8.618	8.672
40	3-4	8.727	8.781	8.836	8.891	8.946	9.001	9.057	9.113
41	3-5	9.168	9.224	9.281	9.337	9.393	9.450	9.507	9.564
42	3-6	9.621	9.678	9.736	9.794	9.852	9.910	9.968	10.03
43	3-7	10.08	10.14	10.20	10.26	10.32	10.38	10.44	10.50
44	3-8	10.56	10.62	10.68	10.74	10.80	10.86	10.92	10.98
45	3-9	11.04	11.11	11.17	11.23	11.29	11.35	11.42	11.48
46	3-10	11.54	11.60	11.67	11.73	11.79	11.86	11.92	11.98
47	3-11	12.05	12.11	12.18	12.24	12.31	12.37	12.44	12.50
48	4-0	12.57	12.63	12.70	12.76	12.83	12.90	12.96	13.03
49	4-1	13.10	13.16	13.23	13.30	13.36	13.43	13.50	13.57

TABLE A-9

AREAS OF CIRCULAR SEGMENTS

For Ratios of Rise and Chord

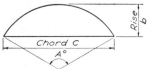

Area = b x C x coefficient

A°	Coefficient	$\frac{b}{C}$	A°	Coefficient	$\frac{b}{C}$	A°	Coefficient	$\frac{b}{C}$	A°	Coefficient	$\frac{b}{C}$
1	.6667	.0022	46	.6722	.1017	91	.6895	.2097	136	.7239	.3373
2	.6667	.0044	47	.6724	.1040	92	.6901	.2122	137	.7249	.3404
3	.6667	.0066	48	.6727	.1063	93	.6906	.2148	138	.7260	.3436
4	.6667	.0087	49	.6729	.1086	94	.6912	.2174	139	.7270	.3469
5	.6667	.0109	50	.6732	.1109	95	.6918	.2200	140	.7281	.3501
6	.6667	.0131	51	.6734	.1131	96	.6924	.2226	141	.7292	.3534
7	.6668	.0153	52	.6737	.1154	97	.6930	.2252	142	.7303	.3567
8	.6668	.0175	53	.6740	.1177	98	.6936	.2279	143	.7314	.3600
9	.6669	.0197	54	.6743	.1200	99	.6942	.2305	144	.7325	.3633
10	.6670	.0218	55	.6746	.1224	100	.6948	.2332	145	.7336	.3666
11	.6670	.0240	56	.6749	.1247	101	.6954	.2358	146	.7348	.3700
12	.6671	.0262	57	.6752	.1270	102	.6961	.2385	147	.7360	.3734
13	.6672	.0284	58	.6755	.1293	103	.6967	.2412	148	.7372	.3768
14	.6672	.0306	59	.6758	.1316	104	.6974	.2439	149	.7384	.3802
15	.6673	.0328	60	.6761	.1340	105	.6980	.2466	150	.7396	.3837
16	.6674	.0350	61	.6764	.1363	106	.6987	.2493	151	.7408	.3871
17	.6674	.0372	62	.6768	.1387	107	.6994	.2520	152	.7421	.3906
18	.6675	.0394	63	.6771	.1410	108	.7001	.2548	153	.7434	.3942
19	.6676	.0416	64	.6775	.1434	109	.7008	.2575	154	.7447	.3977
20	.6677	.0437	65	.6779	.1457	110	.7015	.2603	155	.7460	.4013
21	.6678	.0459	66	.6782	.1481	111	.7022	.2631	156	.7473	.4049
22	.6679	.0481	67	.6786	.1505	112	.7030	.2659	157	.7486	.4085
23	.6680	.0504	68	.6790	.1529	113	.7037	.2687	158	.7500	.4122
24	.6681	.0526	69	.6794	.1553	114	.7045	.2715	159	.7514	.4159
25	.6682	.0548	70	.6797	.1577	115	.7052	.2743	160	.7528	.4196
26	.6684	.0570	71	.6801	.1601	116	.7060	.2772	161	.7542	.4233
27	.6685	.0592	72	.6805	.1625	117	.7068	.2800	162	.7557	.4270
28	.6687	.0614	73	.6809	.1649	118	.7076	.2829	163	.7571	.4308
29	.6688	.0636	74	.6814	.1673	119	.7084	.2858	164	.7586	.4346
30	.6690	.0658	75	.6818	.1697	120	.7092	.2887	165	.7601	.4385
31	.6691	.0681	76	.6822	.1722	121	.7100	.2916	166	.7616	.4424
32	.6693	.0703	77	.6826	.1746	122	.7109	.2945	167	.7632	.4463
33	.6694	.0725	78	.6831	.1771	123	.7117	.2975	168	.7648	.4502
34	.6696	.0747	79	.6835	.1795	124	.7126	.3004	169	.7664	.4542
35	.6698	.0770	80	.6840	.1820	125	.7134	.3034	170	.7680	.4582
36	.6700	.0792	81	.6844	.1845	126	.7143	.3064	171	.7696	.4622
37	.6702	.0814	82	.6849	.1869	127	.7152	.3094	172	.7712	.4663
38	.6704	.0837	83	.6854	.1894	128	.7161	.3124	173	.7729	.4704
39	.6706	.0859	84	.6859	.1919	129	.7170	.3155	174	.7746	.4745
40	.6708	.0882	85	.6864	.1944	130	.7180	.3185	175	.7763	.4787
41	.6710	.0904	86	.6869	.1970	131	.7189	.3216	176	.7781	.4828
42	.6712	.0927	87	.6874	.1995	132	.7199	.3247	177	.7799	.4871
43	.6714	.0949	88	.6879	.2020	133	.7209	.3278	178	.7817	.4914
44	.6717	.0972	89	.6884	.2046	134	.7219	.3309	179	.7835	.4957
45	.6719	.0995	90	.6890	.2071	135	.7229	.3341	180	.7854	.5000

TABLE A-10

AREA, WETTED PERIMETER AND HYDRAULIC RADIUS OF
PARTIALLY FILLED CIRCULAR PIPE

$\frac{d}{D}$	$\frac{area}{D^2}$	$\frac{wet.\ per.}{D}$	$\frac{hyd.\ rad.}{D}$	$\frac{d}{D}$	$\frac{area}{D^2}$	$\frac{wet.\ per.}{D}$	$\frac{hyd.\ rad.}{D}$
0.01	0.0013	0.2003	0.0066	0.51	0.4027	1.5908	0.2531
0.02	0.0037	0.2838	0.0132	0.52	0.4127	1.6108	0.2561
0.03	0.0069	0.3482	0.0197	0.53	0.4227	1.6308	0.2591
0.04	0.0105	0.4027	0.0262	0.54	0.4327	1.6509	0.2620
0.05	0.0147	0.4510	0.0326	0.55	0.4426	1.6710	0.2649
0.06	0.0192	0.4949	0.0389	0.56	0.4526	1.6911	0.2676
0.07	0.0242	0.5355	0.0451	0.57	0.4625	1.7113	0.2703
0.08	0.0294	0.5735	0.0513	0.58	0.4723	1.7315	0.2728
0.09	0.0350	0.6094	0.0574	0.59	0.4822	1.7518	0.2753
0.10	0.0409	0.6435	0.0635	0.60	0.4920	1.7722	0.2776
0.11	0.0470	0.6761	0.0695	0.61	0.5018	1.7926	0.2799
0.12	0.0534	0.7075	0.0754	0.62	0.5115	1.8132	0.2821
0.13	0.0600	0.7377	0.0813	0.63	0.5212	1.8338	0.2842
0.14	0.0668	0.7670	0.0871	0.64	0.5308	1.8546	0.2862
0.15	0.0739	0.7954	0.0929	0.65	0.5404	1.8755	0.2881
0.16	0.0811	0.8230	0.0986	0.66	0.5499	1.8965	0.2899
0.17	0.0885	0.8500	0.1042	0.67	0.5594	1.9177	0.2917
0.18	0.0961	0.8763	0.1097	0.68	0.5687	1.9391	0.2933
0.19	0.1039	0.9020	0.1152	0.69	0.5780	1.9606	0.2948
0.20	0.1118	0.9273	0.1206	0.70	0.5872	1.9823	0.2962
0.21	0.1199	0.9521	0.1259	0.71	0.5964	2.0042	0.2975
0.22	0.1281	0.9764	0.1312	0.72	0.6054	2.0264	0.2987
0.23	0.1365	1.0003	0.1364	0.73	0.6143	2.0488	0.2998
0.24	0.1449	1.0239	0.1416	0.74	0.6231	2.0714	0.3008
0.25	0.1535	1.0472	0.1466	0.75	0.6318	2.0944	0.3017
0.26	0.1623	1.0701	0.1516	0.76	0.6404	2.1176	0.3025
0.27	0.1711	1.0928	0.1566	0.77	0.6489	2.1412	0.3032
0.28	0.1800	1.1152	0.1614	0.78	0.6573	2.1652	0.3037
0.29	0.1890	1.1373	0.1662	0.79	0.6655	2.1895	0.3040
0.30	0.1982	1.1593	0.1709	0.80	0.6736	2.2143	0.3042
0.31	0.2074	1.1810	0.1755	0.81	0.6815	2.2395	0.3044
0.32	0.2167	1.2025	0.1801	0.82	0.6893	2.2653	0.3043
0.33	0.2260	1.2239	0.1848	0.83	0.6969	2.2916	0.3041
0.34	0.2355	1.2451	0.1891	0.84	0.7043	2.3186	0.3038
0.35	0.2450	1.2661	0.1935	0.85	0.7115	2.3462	0.3033
0.36	0.2546	1.2870	0.1978	0.86	0.7186	2.3746	0.3026
0.37	0.2642	1.3078	0.2020	0.87	0.7254	2.4038	0.3017
0.38	0.2739	1.3284	0.2061	0.88	0.7320	2.4341	0.3008
0.39	0.2836	1.3490	0.2102	0.89	0.7384	2.4655	0.2996
0.40	0.2934	1.3694	0.2142	0.90	0.7445	2.4981	0.2980
0.41	0.3032	1.3898	0.2181	0.91	0.7504	2.5322	0.2963
0.42	0.3130	1.4101	0.2220	0.92	0.7560	2.5681	0.2944
0.43	0.3229	1.4303	0.2257	0.93	0.7612	2.6061	0.2922
0.44	0.3328	1.4505	0.2294	0.94	0.7662	2.6467	0.2896
0.45	0.3428	1.4706	0.2331	0.95	0.7707	2.6906	0.2864
0.46	0.3527	1.4907	0.2366	0.96	0.7749	2.7389	0.2830
0.47	0.3627	1.5108	0.2400	0.97	0.7785	2.7934	0.2787
0.48	0.3727	1.5308	0.2434	0.98	0.7816	2.8578	0.2735
0.49	0.3827	1.5508	0.2467	0.99	0.7841	2.9412	0.2665
0.50	0.3927	1.5708	0.2500	1.00	0.7854	3.1416	0.2500

TABLE A-11

HEADWATER DEPTH FOR CIRCULAR
PIPE CULVERTS WITH INLET CONTROL
END SECTION WITH CLOSED TAPER

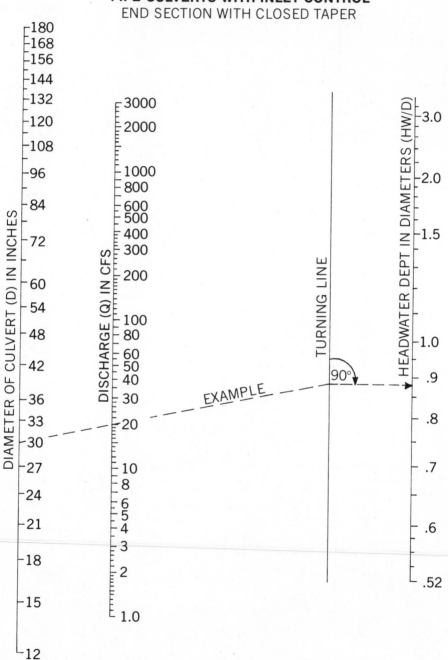

TABLE A-12

TRIGONOMETRIC FORMULAS

TRIGONOMETRIC FUNCTIONS

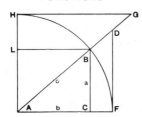

Radius AF $= 1$
$= \sin^2 A + \cos^2 A = \sin A \cosec A$
$= \cos A \sec A = \tan A \cot A$

Sine A $= \dfrac{\cos A}{\cot A} = \dfrac{1}{\cosec A} = \cos A \tan A = \sqrt{1 - \cos^2 A} = BC$

Cosine A $= \dfrac{\sin A}{\tan A} = \dfrac{1}{\sec A} = \sin A \cot A = \sqrt{1 - \sin^2 A} = AC$

Tangent A $= \dfrac{\sin A}{\cos A} = \dfrac{1}{\cot A} = \sin A \sec A$ $= FD$

Cotangent A $= \dfrac{\cos A}{\sin A} = \dfrac{1}{\tan A} = \cos A \cosec A$ $= HG$

Secant A $= \dfrac{\tan A}{\sin A} = \dfrac{1}{\cos A}$ $= AD$

Cosecant A $= \dfrac{\cot A}{\cos A} = \dfrac{1}{\sin A}$ $= AG$

RIGHT ANGLED TRIANGLES

$a^2 = c^2 - b^2$

$b^2 = c^2 - a^2$

$c^2 = a^2 + b^2$

Known	Required					
	A	B	a	b	c	Area
a, b	$\tan A = \dfrac{a}{b}$	$\tan B = \dfrac{b}{a}$			$\sqrt{a^2 + b^2}$	$\dfrac{ab}{2}$
a, c	$\sin A = \dfrac{a}{c}$	$\cos B = \dfrac{a}{c}$		$\sqrt{c^2 - a^2}$		$\dfrac{a\sqrt{c^2 - a^2}}{2}$
A, a		$90° - A$		$a \cot A$	$\dfrac{a}{\sin A}$	$\dfrac{a^2 \cot A}{2}$
A, b		$90° - A$	$b \tan A$		$\dfrac{b}{\cos A}$	$\dfrac{b^2 \tan A}{2}$
A, c		$90° - A$	$c \sin A$	$c \cos A$		$\dfrac{c^2 \sin 2A}{4}$

OBLIQUE ANGLED TRIANGLES

$s = \dfrac{a + b + c}{2}$

$K = \sqrt{\dfrac{(s - a)(s - b)(s - c)}{s}}$

$a^2 = b^2 + c^2 - 2bc \cos A$

$b^2 = a^2 + c^2 - 2ac \cos B$

$c^2 = a^2 + b^2 - 2ab \cos C$

Known	Required					
	A	B	C	b	c	Area
a, b, c	$\tan \frac{1}{2} A = \dfrac{K}{s - a}$	$\tan \frac{1}{2} B = \dfrac{K}{s - b}$	$\tan \frac{1}{2} C = \dfrac{K}{s - c}$			$\sqrt{s(s-a)(s-b)(s-c)}$
a, A, B			$180° - (A + B)$	$\dfrac{a \sin B}{\sin A}$	$\dfrac{a \sin C}{\sin A}$	
a, b, A		$\sin B = \dfrac{b \sin A}{a}$			$\dfrac{b \sin C}{\sin B}$	
a, b, C	$\tan A = \dfrac{a \sin C}{b - a \cos C}$				$\sqrt{a^2 + b^2 - 2ab \cos C}$	$\dfrac{ab \sin C}{2}$

TABLE A-13

PROPERTIES OF THE CIRCLE

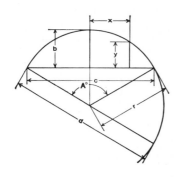

Circumference $= 6.28318\, r = 3.14159\, d$
Diameter $= 0.31831$ circumference
Area $= 3.14159\, r^2$

Arc $a = \dfrac{\pi r A^\circ}{180^\circ} = 0.017453\, r A^\circ$

Angle $A^\circ = \dfrac{180^\circ a}{\pi r} = 57.29578\, \dfrac{a}{r}$

Radius r $= \dfrac{4b^2 + c^2}{8b}$

Chord c $= 2\sqrt{2br - b^2} = 2r\sin\dfrac{A}{2}$

Rise   b $= r - \tfrac{1}{2}\sqrt{4r^2 - c^2} = \dfrac{c}{2}\tan\dfrac{A}{4}$

        $= 2r\sin^2\dfrac{A}{4} = r + y - \sqrt{r^2 - x^2}$

    y $= b - r + \sqrt{r^2 - x^2}$

    x $= \sqrt{r^2 - (r + y - b)^2}$

Diameter of circle of equal periphery as square = 1.27324 side of square
Side of square of equal periphery as circle = 0.78540 diameter of circle
Diameter of circle circumscribed about square = 1.41421 side of square
Side of square inscribed in circle = 0.70711 diameter of circle

---

CIRCULAR SECTOR

r = radius of circle   y = angle ncp in degrees

Area of Sector ncpo = ½ (length of arc nop × r)

    $= $ Area of Circle $\times \dfrac{y}{360}$

    $= 0.0087266 \times r^2 \times y$

CIRCULAR SEGMENT

r = radius of circle   x = chord   b = rise

Area of Segment nop = Area of Sector ncpo — Area of triangle ncp

    $= \dfrac{(\text{Length of arc nop} \times r) - x(r - b)}{2}$

Area of Segment nsp = Area of Circle — Area of Segment nop

VALUES FOR FUNCTIONS OF π

$\pi = 3.14159265359$,   log = 0.4971499

$\pi^2 = 9.8696044$, log = 0.9942997 $\dfrac{1}{\pi} = 0.3183099$, log = $\overline{1}.5028501$ $\sqrt{\dfrac{1}{\pi}} = 0.5641896$, log = $\overline{1}.7514251$

$\pi^3 = 31.0062767$, log = 1.4914496 $\dfrac{1}{\pi^2} = 0.1013212$, log = $\overline{1}.0057003$ $\dfrac{\pi}{180} = 0.0174533$, log = $\overline{2}.2418774$

$\sqrt{\pi} = 1.7724539$, log = 0.2485749 $\dfrac{1}{\pi^3} = 0.0322515$, log = $\overline{2}.5085500$ $\dfrac{180}{\pi} = 57.2957795$, log = 1.7581226

Note: Logs of fractions such as $\overline{1}.5028501$ and $\overline{2}.5085500$ may also be written 9.5028501 − 10 and 8.5085500 − 10 respectively.

COURTESY OF AMERICAN INSTITUTE OF STEEL CONSTRUCTION

TABLE A-14a

PROPERTIES OF GEOMETRIC SECTIONS

SQUARE

Axis of moments through center

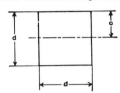

$A = d^2$

$c = \dfrac{d}{2}$

$I = \dfrac{d^4}{12}$

$S = \dfrac{d^3}{6}$

$r = \dfrac{d}{\sqrt{12}} = .288675\,d$

$Z = \dfrac{d^3}{4}$

SQUARE

Axis of moments on base

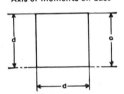

$A = d^2$

$c = d$

$I = \dfrac{d^4}{3}$

$S = \dfrac{d^3}{3}$

$r = \dfrac{d}{\sqrt{3}} = .577350\,d$

SQUARE

Axis of moments on diagonal

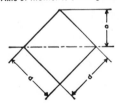

$A = d^2$

$c = \dfrac{d}{\sqrt{2}} = .707107\,d$

$I = \dfrac{d^4}{12}$

$S = \dfrac{d^3}{6\sqrt{2}} = .117851\,d^3$

$r = \dfrac{d}{\sqrt{12}} = .288675\,d$

$Z = \dfrac{2c^3}{3} = \dfrac{d^3}{3\sqrt{2}} = .235702d^3$

RECTANGLE

Axis of moments through center

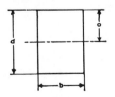

$A = bd$

$c = \dfrac{d}{2}$

$I = \dfrac{bd^3}{12}$

$S = \dfrac{bd^2}{6}$

$r = \dfrac{d}{\sqrt{12}} = .288675\,d$

$Z = \dfrac{bd^2}{4}$

TABLE A-14b

PROPERTIES OF GEOMETRIC SECTIONS

RECTANGLE
Axis of moments on base

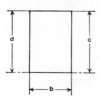

$A = bd$

$c = d$

$I = \dfrac{bd^3}{3}$

$S = \dfrac{bd^2}{3}$

$r = \dfrac{d}{\sqrt{3}} = .577350\, d$

RECTANGLE
Axis of moments on diagonal

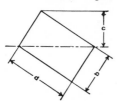

$A = bd$

$c = \dfrac{bd}{\sqrt{b^2 + d^2}}$

$I = \dfrac{b^3 d^3}{6\,(b^2 + d^2)}$

$S = \dfrac{b^2 d^2}{6\sqrt{b^2 + d^2}}$

$r = \dfrac{bd}{\sqrt{6\,(b^2 + d^2)}}$

RECTANGLE
Axis of moments any line
through center of gravity

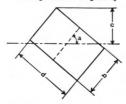

$A = bd$

$c = \dfrac{b \sin a + d \cos a}{2}$

$I = \dfrac{bd\,(b^2 \sin^2 a + d^2 \cos^2 a)}{12}$

$S = \dfrac{bd\,(b^2 \sin^2 a + d^2 \cos^2 a)}{6\,(b \sin a + d \cos a)}$

$r = \sqrt{\dfrac{b^2 \sin^2 a + d^2 \cos^2 a}{12}}$

HOLLOW RECTANGLE
Axis of moments through center

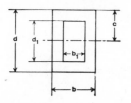

$A = bd - b_1 d_1$

$c = \dfrac{d}{2}$

$I = \dfrac{bd^3 - b_1 d_1^3}{12}$

$S = \dfrac{bd^3 - b_1 d_1^3}{6d}$

$r = \sqrt{\dfrac{bd^3 - b_1 d_1^3}{12\,A}}$

$z = \dfrac{bd^2}{4} - \dfrac{b_1 d_1^2}{4}$

TABLE A-14c

PROPERTIES OF GEOMETRIC SECTIONS

EQUAL RECTANGLES

Axis of moments through center of gravity

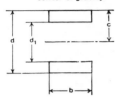

$$A = b(d - d_1)$$

$$c = \frac{d}{2}$$

$$I = \frac{b(d^3 - d_1{}^3)}{12}$$

$$S = \frac{b(d^3 - d_1{}^3)}{6d}$$

$$r = \sqrt{\frac{d^3 - d_1{}^3}{12(d - d_1)}}$$

$$Z = \frac{b}{4}(d^2 - d_1{}^2)$$

UNEQUAL RECTANGLES

Axis of moments through center of gravity

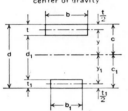

$$A = bt + b_1 t_1$$

$$c = \frac{\frac{1}{2} bt^2 + b_1 t_1 (d - \frac{1}{2} t_1)}{A}$$

$$I = \frac{bt^3}{12} + bty^2 + \frac{b_1 t_1{}^3}{12} + b_1 t_1 y_1{}^2$$

$$S = \frac{I}{c} \qquad S_1 = \frac{I}{c_1}$$

$$= \sqrt{\frac{I}{A}}$$

$$Z = \frac{A}{2} \left[d - \left(\frac{t + t_1}{2} \right) \right]$$

TRIANGLE

Axis of moments through center of gravity

$$A = \frac{bd}{2}$$

$$c = \frac{2d}{3}$$

$$I = \frac{bd^3}{36}$$

$$S = \frac{bd^2}{24}$$

$$r = \frac{d}{\sqrt{18}} = .235702\, d$$

TRIANGLE

Axis of moments on base

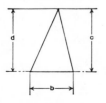

$$A = \frac{bd}{2}$$

$$c = d$$

$$I = \frac{bd^3}{12}$$

$$S = \frac{bd^2}{12}$$

$$r = \frac{d}{\sqrt{6}} = .408248\, d$$

TABLE A-14d

PROPERTIES OF GEOMETRIC SECTIONS

TRAPEZOID

Axis of moments through center of gravity

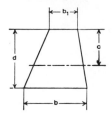

$$A = \frac{d(b + b_1)}{2}$$

$$c = \frac{d(2b + b_1)}{3(b + b_1)}$$

$$I = \frac{d^3(b^2 + 4bb_1 + b_1^2)}{36(b + b_1)}$$

$$S = \frac{d^2(b^2 + 4bb_1 + b_1^2)}{12(2b + b_1)}$$

$$r = \frac{d}{6(b + b_1)}\sqrt{2(b^2 + 4bb_1 + b_1^2)}$$

CIRCLE

Axis of moments through center

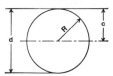

$$A = \frac{\pi d^2}{4} = \pi R^2 = .785398\,d^2 = 3.141593\,R^2$$

$$c = \frac{d}{2} = R$$

$$I = \frac{\pi d^4}{64} = \frac{\pi R^4}{4} = .049087\,d^4 = .785398\,R^4$$

$$S = \frac{\pi d^3}{32} = \frac{\pi R^3}{4} = .098175\,d^3 = .785398\,R^3$$

$$r = \frac{d}{4} = \frac{R}{2}$$

$$Z = \frac{d^3}{6}$$

HOLLOW CIRCLE

Axis of moments through center

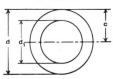

$$A = \frac{\pi(d^2 - d_1^2)}{4} = .785398\,(d^2 - d_1^2)$$

$$c = \frac{d}{2}$$

$$I = \frac{\pi(d^4 - d_1^4)}{64} = .049087\,(d^4 - d_1^4)$$

$$S = \frac{\pi(d^4 - d_1^4)}{32d} = .098175\,\frac{d^4 - d_1^4}{d}$$

$$r = \frac{\sqrt{d^2 + d_1^2}}{4}$$

$$Z = \frac{d^3}{6} - \frac{d_1^3}{6}$$

HALF CIRCLE

Axis of moments through center of gravity

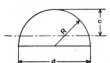

$$A = \frac{\pi R^2}{2} = 1.570796\,R^2$$

$$c = R\left(1 - \frac{4}{3\pi}\right) = .575587\,R$$

$$I = R^4\left(\frac{\pi}{8} - \frac{8}{9\pi}\right) = .109757\,R^4$$

$$S = \frac{R^3}{24}\frac{(9\pi^2 - 64)}{(3\pi - 4)} = .190687\,R^3$$

$$r = R\frac{\sqrt{9\pi^2 - 64}}{6\pi} = .264336\,R$$

TABLE A-14e

PROPERTIES OF GEOMETRIC SECTIONS

PARABOLA

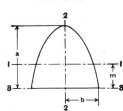

$$A = \frac{4}{3}ab$$

$$m = \frac{2}{5}a$$

$$I_1 = \frac{16}{175}a^3b$$

$$I_2 = \frac{4}{15}ab^3$$

$$I_3 = \frac{32}{105}a^3b$$

HALF PARABOLA

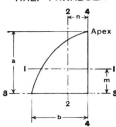

$$A = \frac{2}{3}ab$$

$$m = \frac{2}{5}a$$

$$n = \frac{3}{8}b$$

$$I_1 = \frac{8}{175}a^3b$$

$$I_2 = \frac{19}{480}ab^3$$

$$I_3 = \frac{16}{105}a^3b$$

$$I_4 = \frac{2}{15}ab^3$$

COMPLEMENT OF HALF PARABOLA

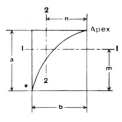

$$A = \frac{1}{3}ab$$

$$m = \frac{7}{10}a$$

$$n = \frac{3}{4}b$$

$$I_1 = \frac{37}{2100}a^3b$$

$$I_2 = \frac{1}{80}ab^3$$

PARABOLIC FILLET IN RIGHT ANGLE

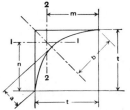

$$a = \frac{t}{2\sqrt{2}}$$

$$b = \frac{t}{\sqrt{2}}$$

$$A = \frac{1}{6}t^2$$

$$m = n = \frac{4}{5}t$$

$$I_1 = I_2 = \frac{11}{2100}t^4$$

TABLE A-14f

PROPERTIES OF GEOMETRIC SECTIONS

* HALF ELLIPSE

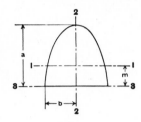

$$A = \frac{1}{2}\pi ab$$

$$m = \frac{4a}{3\pi}$$

$$I_1 = a^3b\left(\frac{\pi}{8} - \frac{8}{9\pi}\right)$$

$$I_2 = \frac{1}{8}\pi ab^3$$

$$I_3 = \frac{1}{8}\pi a^3b$$

* QUARTER ELLIPSE

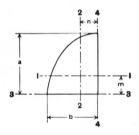

$$A = \frac{1}{4}\pi ab$$

$$m = \frac{4a}{3\pi}$$

$$n = \frac{4b}{3\pi}$$

$$I_1 = a^3b\left(\frac{\pi}{16} - \frac{4}{9\pi}\right)$$

$$I_2 = ab^3\left(\frac{\pi}{16} - \frac{4}{9\pi}\right)$$

$$I_3 = \frac{1}{16}\pi a^3b$$

$$I_4 = \frac{1}{16}\pi ab^3$$

* ELLIPTIC COMPLEMENT

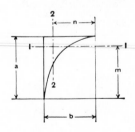

$$A = ab\left(1 - \frac{\pi}{4}\right)$$

$$m = \frac{a}{6\left(1 - \frac{\pi}{4}\right)}$$

$$n = \frac{b}{6\left(1 - \frac{\pi}{4}\right)}$$

$$I_1 = a^3b\left(\frac{1}{3} - \frac{\pi}{16} - \frac{1}{36\left(1 - \frac{\pi}{4}\right)}\right)$$

$$I_2 = ab^3\left(\frac{1}{3} - \frac{\pi}{16} - \frac{1}{36\left(1 - \frac{\pi}{4}\right)}\right)$$

* To obtain properties of half circle, quarter circle and circular complement substitute a = b = R.

TABLE A-15
PROPERTIES OF GEOMETRIC SECTIONS AND STRUCTURAL SHAPES

REGULAR POLYGON

Axis of moments
through center

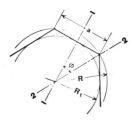

$n = $ Number of sides

$\phi = \dfrac{180°}{n}$

$a = 2\sqrt{R^2 - R_1^2}$

$R = \dfrac{a}{2 \sin \phi}$

$R_1 = \dfrac{a}{2 \tan \phi}$

$A = \dfrac{1}{4} na^2 \cot \phi = \dfrac{1}{2} nR^2 \sin 2\phi = nR_1^2 \tan \phi$

$I_1 = I_2 = \dfrac{A(6R^2 - a^2)}{24} = \dfrac{A(12R_1^2 + a^2)}{48}$

$r_1 = r_2 = \sqrt{\dfrac{6R^2 - a^2}{24}} = \sqrt{\dfrac{12R_1^2 + a^2}{48}}$

ANGLE

Axis of moments through
center of gravity

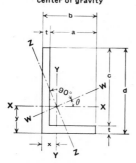

Z-Z is axis of minimum I

$\tan 2\theta = \dfrac{2K}{I_Y - I_X}$

$A = t(b + c) \quad x = \dfrac{b^2 + ct}{2(b + c)} \quad y = \dfrac{d^2 + at}{2(b + c)}$

$K = $ Product of Inertia about X-X & Y-Y

$= \dfrac{abcdt}{+ \ 4(b + c)}$

$I_X = \dfrac{1}{3}\left(t(d - y)^3 + by^3 - a(y - t)^3 \right)$

$I_Y = \dfrac{1}{3}\left(t(b - x)^3 + dx^3 - c(x - t)^3 \right)$

$I_z = I_X \sin^2\theta + I_Y \cos^2\theta + K \sin 2\theta$

$I_w = I_X \cos^2\theta + I_Y \sin^2\theta - K \sin 2\theta$

K is negative when heel of angle, with respect to c. g., is in 1st or 3rd quadrant, positive when in 2nd or 4th quadrant.

BEAMS AND CHANNELS

Transverse force oblique
through center of gravity

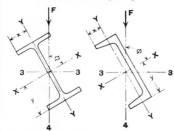

$I_3 = I_X \sin^2\phi + I_Y \cos^2\phi$

$I_4 = I_X \cos^2\phi + I_Y \sin^2\phi$

$f_b = M\left(\dfrac{y}{I_X} \sin\phi + \dfrac{x}{I_Y} \cos\phi \right)$

where M is bending moment due to force F.

TABLE A-16

FOUR PLACE LOGARITHM TABLES

No.	0	1	2	3	4	5	6	7	8	9
10	0000	0043	0086	0128	0170	0212	0253	0294	0334	0374
11	0414	0453	0492	0531	0569	0607	0645	0682	0719	0755
12	0792	0828	0864	0899	0934	0969	1004	1038	1072	1106
13	1139	1173	1206	1239	1271	1303	1335	1367	1399	1430
14	1461	1492	1523	1553	1584	1614	1644	1673	1703	1732
15	1761	1790	1818	1847	1875	1903	1931	1959	1987	2014
16	2041	2068	2095	2122	2148	2175	2201	2227	2253	2279
17	2304	2330	2355	2380	2405	2430	2455	2480	2504	2529
18	2553	2577	2601	2625	2648	2672	2695	2718	2742	2765
19	2788	2810	2833	2856	2878	2900	2923	2945	2967	2989
20	3010	3032	3054	3075	3096	3118	3139	3160	3181	3201
21	3222	3243	3263	3284	3304	3324	3345	3365	3385	3404
22	3424	3444	3464	3483	3502	3522	3541	3560	3579	3598
23	3617	3636	3655	3674	3692	3711	3729	3747	3766	3784
24	3802	3820	3838	3856	3874	3892	3909	3927	3945	3962
25	3979	3997	4014	4031	4048	4065	4082	4099	4116	4133
26	4150	4166	4183	4200	4216	4232	4249	4265	4281	4298
27	4314	4330	4346	4362	4378	4393	4409	4425	4440	4456
28	4472	4487	4502	4518	4533	4548	4564	4579	4594	4609
29	4624	4639	4654	4669	4683	4698	4713	4728	4742	4757
30	4771	4786	4800	4814	4829	4843	4857	4871	4886	4900
31	4914	4928	4942	4955	4969	4983	4997	5011	5024	5038
32	5051	5065	5079	5092	5105	5119	5132	5145	5159	5172
33	5185	5198	5211	5224	5237	5250	5263	5276	5289	5302
34	5315	5328	5340	5353	5366	5378	5391	5403	5416	5428
35	5441	5453	5465	5478	5498	5502	5514	5527	5539	5551
36	5563	5575	5587	5599	5611	5623	5635	5647	5658	5670
37	5682	5694	5705	5717	5729	5740	5752	5763	5775	5786
38	5798	5809	5821	5832	5843	5855	5866	5877	5888	5899
39	5911	5922	5933	5944	5955	5966	5977	5988	5999	6010
40	6021	6031	6042	6053	6064	6075	6085	6096	6107	6117
41	6128	6138	6149	6160	6170	6180	6191	6201	6212	6222
42	6232	6243	6253	6263	6274	6284	6294	6304	6314	6325
43	6335	6345	6355	6365	6375	6385	6395	6405	6415	6425
44	6435	6444	6454	6464	6474	6484	6493	6503	6513	6522
45	6532	6542	6551	6561	6571	6580	6590	6599	6609	6618
46	6628	6637	6646	6656	6665	6675	6684	6693	6702	6712
47	6721	6730	6739	6749	6758	6767	6776	6785	6794	6803
48	6812	6821	6830	6839	6848	6857	6866	6875	6884	6893
49	6902	6911	6920	6928	6937	6946	6955	6964	6972	6981
50	6990	6998	7007	7016	7024	7033	7042	7050	7059	7067
51	7076	7084	7093	7101	7110	7118	7126	7135	7143	7152
52	7160	7168	7177	7185	7193	7202	7210	7218	7226	7235
53	7243	7251	7259	7267	7275	7284	7292	7300	7308	7316
54	7324	7332	7340	7348	7356	7364	7372	7380	7388	7396
55	7404	7412	7419	7427	7435	7443	7451	7459	7466	7474
56	7482	7490	7497	7505	7513	7520	7528	7536	7543	7551
57	7559	7566	7574	7582	7589	7597	7604	7612	7619	7627
58	7634	7642	7649	7657	7664	7672	7679	7686	7694	7701
59	7709	7716	7723	7731	7738	7745	7752	7760	7767	7774
60	7782	7789	7796	7803	7810	7818	7825	7832	7839	7846
61	7853	7860	7868	7875	7882	7889	7896	7903	7910	7917
62	7924	7931	7938	7945	7952	7959	7966	7973	7980	7987
63	7993	8000	8007	8014	8021	8028	8035	8041	8048	8055
64	8062	8069	8075	8082	8089	8096	8102	8109	8116	8122
65	8129	8136	8142	8149	8156	8162	8169	8176	8182	8189
66	8195	8202	8209	8215	8222	8228	8235	8241	8248	8254
67	8261	8267	8274	8280	8287	8293	8299	8306	8312	8319
68	8325	8331	8338	8344	8351	8357	8363	8370	8376	8382
69	8388	8395	8401	8407	8414	8420	8426	8432	8439	8445
70	8451	8457	8463	8470	8476	8482	8488	8494	8500	8506
71	8513	8519	8525	8531	8537	8543	8549	8555	8561	8567
72	8573	8579	8585	8591	8597	8603	8609	8615	8621	8627
73	8633	8639	8645	8651	8657	8663	8669	8675	8681	8686
74	8692	8698	8704	8710	8716	8722	8727	8733	8739	8745
75	8751	8756	8762	8768	8774	8779	8785	8791	8797	8802
76	8808	8814	8820	8825	8831	8837	8842	8848	8854	8859
77	8865	8871	8876	8882	8887	8893	8899	8904	8910	8915
78	8921	8927	8932	8938	8943	8949	8954	8960	8965	8971
79	8976	8982	8987	8993	8998	9004	9009	9015	9020	9025
80	9031	9036	9042	9047	9053	9058	9063	9069	9074	9079
81	9085	9090	9096	9101	9106	9112	9117	9122	9128	9133
82	9138	9143	9149	9154	9159	9165	9170	9175	9180	9186
83	9191	9196	9201	9206	9212	9217	9222	9227	9232	9238
84	9243	9248	9253	9258	9263	9269	9274	9279	9284	9289
85	9294	9299	9304	9309	9315	9320	9325	9330	9335	9340
86	9345	9350	9355	9360	9365	9370	9375	9380	9385	9390
87	9395	9400	9405	9410	9415	9420	9425	9430	9435	9440
88	9445	9450	9455	9460	9465	9469	9474	9479	9484	9489
89	9494	9499	9504	9509	9513	9518	9523	9528	9533	9538
90	9542	9547	9552	9557	9562	9566	9571	9576	9581	9586
91	9590	9595	9600	9605	9609	9614	9619	9624	9628	9633
92	9638	9643	9647	9652	9657	9661	9666	9671	9675	9680
93	9685	9689	9694	9699	9703	9708	9713	9717	9722	9727
94	9731	9736	9741	9745	9750	9754	9759	9763	9768	9773
95	9777	9782	9786	9791	9795	9800	9805	9809	9814	9818
96	9823	9827	9832	9836	9841	9845	9850	9854	9859	9863
97	9868	9872	9877	9881	9886	9890	9894	9899	9903	9908
98	9912	9917	9921	9926	9930	9934	9939	9943	9948	9952
99	9956	9961	9965	9969	9974	9978	9983	9987	9991	9996

TABLE A-17a

FREQUENTLY USED CONVERSION FACTORS

TO CONVERT	INTO	MULTIPLY BY	TO CONVERT	INTO	MULTIPLY BY
A			cubic meters	cu incnes	61,023.0
acres	sq feet	43,560.0	cubic meters	cu yards	1.308
acres	sq meters	4,047	cubic meters	gallons (U.S. liq.)	264.2
acres	sq miles	1.562×10^{-3}	cubic meters	liters	1,000.0
acres	sq yards	4,840.	cubic meters	pints (U.S. liq.)	2,113.0
acre-feet	cu feet	43,560.0	cubic meters	quarts (U.S. liq.)	1,057.
acre-feet	gallons	3.259×10^{5}	cubic yards	cu cms	7.646×10^{5}
atmospheres	cms of mercury	76.0	cubic yards	cu feet	27.0
atmospheres	ft of water (at 4°C)	33.90	cubic yards	cu inches	46,656.0
atmospheres	in. of mercury (at 0°C)	29.92	cubic yards	cu meters	0.7646
atmospheres	kgs/sq cm	1.0333	cubic yards	gallons (U.S. liq.)	202.0
atmospheres	kgs/sq meter	10,332.	cubic yards	liters	764.6
atmospheres	pounds/sq in	14.70	cubic yards	pints (U.S. liq.)	1,615.9
			cubic yards	quarts (U.S. liq.)	807.9
C			cubic yards/min	cubic ft/sec	0.45
Centigrade	Fahrenheit	(C°x9/5)+32	cubic yards/min	gallons/sec	3.367
centiliters	liters	0.01	cubic yards/min	liters/sec	12.74
centimeters	feet	3.281×10^{-2}			
centimeters	inches	0.3937	**D**		
centimeters	kilometers	10^{-5}			
centimeters	meters	0.01	days	seconds	86,400.0
centimeters	miles	6.214×10^{-6}	decigrams	grams	0.1
centimeters	millimeters	10.0	deciliters	liters	0.1
centimeters	yards	1.094×10^{-2}	decimeters	meters	0.1
centimeters of mercury	atmospheres	0.01316	degrees (angle)	quadrants	0.01111
centimeters of mercury	feet of water	0.4461	degrees (angle)	radians	0.01745
centimeters of mercury	kgs/sq meter	136.0	degrees (angle)	seconds	3,600.0
centimeters of mercury	pounds/sq ft	27.85	dekagrams	grams	10.0
centimeters of mercury	pounds/sq in	0.1934	dekaliters	liters	10.0
centimeters/sec	feet/min	1.1969	dekameters	meters	10.0
centimeters/sec	feet/sec	0.03281			
centimeters/sec	kilometers/hr	0.036	**F**		
centimeters/sec	meters/min	0.6			
centimeters/sec	miles/hr	0.02237	feet	centimeters	30.48
centimeters/sec	miles/min	3.728×10^{-4}	feet	kilometers	3.048×10^{-4}
centimeters/sec/sec	feet/sec/sec	0.03281	feet	meters	0.3048
centimeters/sec/sec	kms/hr/sec	0.036	feet	miles (naut.)	1.645×10^{-4}
centimeters/sec/sec	meters/sec/sec	0.01	feet	miles (stat.)	1.894×10^{-4}
centimeters/sec/sec	miles/hr/sec	0.02237	feet	millimeters	304.8
Chain	Inches	792.00	feet	mils	1.2×10^{4}
Chain	meters	20.12	feet of water	atmospheres	0.02950
Chains (suveyors'			feet of water	in. of mercury	0.8826
or Gunter's)	yards	22.00	feet of water	kgs/sq cm	0.03048
Circumference	Radians	6.283	feet of water	kgs/sq meter	304.8
cubic centimeters	cu feet	3.531×10^{-5}	feet of water	pounds/sq ft	62.43
cubic centimeters	cu inches	0.06102	feet of water	pounds/sq in	0.4335
cubic centimeters	cu meters	10^{-6}	feet/min	cms/sec	0.5080
cubic centimeters	cu yards	1.308×10^{-6}	feet/min	feet/sec	0.01667
cubic centimeters	gallons (U.S. liq.)	2.642×10^{-4}	feet/min	kms/hr	0.01829
cubic centimeters	liters	0.001	feet/min	meters/min	0.3048
cubic centimeters	pints (U.S. liq.)	2.113×10^{-3}	feet/min	miles/hr	0.01136
cubic centimeters	quarts (U.S. liq.)	1.057×10^{-3}	feet/sec	cms/sec	30.48
cubic feet	cu cms	28,320.0	feet/sec	kms/hr	1.097
cubic feet	cu inches	1,728.0	feet/sec	knots	0.5921
cubic feet	cu meters	0.02832	feet/sec	meters/min	18.29
cubic feet	cu yards	0.03704	feet/sec	miles/hr	0.6818
cubic feet	gallons (U.S. liq.)	7.48052	feet/sec	miles/min	0.01136
cubic feet	liters	28.32	feet/sec/sec	cms/sec/sec	30.48
cubic feet	pints (U.S. liq.)	59.84	feet/sec/sec	kms/hr/sec	1.097
cubic feet	quarts (U.S. liq.)	29.92	feet/sec/sec	meters/sec/sec	0.3048
cubic feet/min	cu cms/sec	472.0	feet/sec/sec	miles/hr/sec	0.6818
cubic feet/min	gallons/sec	0.1247	furlongs	miles (U.S.)	0.125
cubic feet/min	liters/sec	0.4720	furlongs	feet	660.0
cubic feet/min	pounds of water/min	62.43			
cubic feet/sec	gallons/min	448.831	**G**		
cubic inches	cu cms	16.39	gallons	cu cms	3,785.0
cubic inches	cu feet	5.787×10^{-4}	gallons	cu feet	0.1337
cubic inches	cu meters	1.639×10^{-5}	gallons	cu inches	231.0
cubic inches	cu yards	2.143×10^{-5}	gallons	cu meters	3.785×10^{-3}
cubic inches	gallons	4.329×10^{-3}	gallons	cu yards	4.951×10^{-3}
cubic inches	liters	0.01639	gallons	liters	3.785
cubic inches	pints (U.S. liq.)	0.03463	gallons (liq. Br. Imp.)	gallons (U.S. liq.)	1.20095
cubic inches	quarts (U.S. liq.)	0.01732	gallons (U.S.)	gallons (Imp.)	0.83267
cubic meters	cu cms	10^{6}	gallons of water	pounds of water	8.3453
cubic meters	cu feet	35.31	gallons/min	cu ft/sec	2.228×10^{-3}

TABLE A-17b

FREQUENTLY USED CONVERSION FACTORS

TO CONVERT	INTO	MULTIPLY BY	TO CONVERT	INTO	MULTIPLY BY
gallons/min	cu ft/hr	8.0208	kilometers/hr	feet/sec	0.9113
gallons/day	cu ft/sec	1.5472×10^{-6}	kilometers/hr	knots	0.5396
grains (troy)	grams	0.06480	kilometers/hr	meters/min	16.67
grains (troy)	ounces (avdp)	2.0833×10^{-3}	kilometers/hr	miles/hr	0.6214
grams	grains	15.43	knots	feet/hr	6,080.
grams	kilograms	0.001	knots	kilometers/hr	1.8532
grams	milligrams	1,000.	knots	nautical miles/hr	1.0
grams	ounces (avdp)	0.03527	knots	statute miles/hr	1.151
grams	ounces (troy)	0.03215	knots	yards/hr	2.027.
grams	pounds	2.205×10^{-3}	knots	feet/sec	1.689
grams/cm	pounds/inch	5.600×10^{-3}		**L**	
grams/cu cm	pounds/cu ft	62.43			
grams/cu cm	pounds/cu in	0.03613	links (engineer's)	inches	12.0
grams/liter	pounds/cu ft	0.062427	links (surveyor's)	inches	7.92
grams/sq cm	pounds/sq ft	2.0481	liters	bushels (U. S. dry)	0.02838
	H		liters	cu cm	1,000.0
			liters	cu feet	0.03531
hectograms	grams	100.0	liters	cu inches	61.02
hectoliters	liters	100.0	liters	cu meters	0.001
hectometers	meters	100.0	liters	cu yards	1.308×10^{-3}
hours	days	4.167×10^{-2}	liters	gallons (U.S. liq.)	0.2642
hours	weeks	5.952×10^{-3}	liters	pints (U.S. liq.)	2.113
	I		liters	quarts (U.S. liq.)	1.057
			liters/min	cu ft/sec	5.886×10^{-4}
inches	centimeters	2.540	liters/min	gals/sec	4.403×10^{-3}
inches	meters	2.540×10^{-2}		**M**	
inches	miles	1.578×10^{-5}			
inches	millimeters	25.40	meters	centimeters	100.0
inches	mils	1,000.0	meters	feet	3.281
inches	yards	2.778×10^{-2}	meters	inches	39.37
inches of mercury	atmospheres	0.03342	meters	kilometers	0.001
inches of mercury	feet of water	1.133	meters	miles (naut.)	5.396×10^{-4}
inches of mercury	kgs/sq cm	0.03453	meters	miles (stat.)	6.214×10^{-4}
inches of mercury	kgs/sq meter	345.3	meters	millimeters	1,000.0
inches of mercury	pounds/sq ft	70.73	meters	yards	1.094
inches of mercury	pounds/sq in	0.4912	meters/min	cms/sec	1.667
inches of water (at 4°C)	atmospheres	2.458×10^{-3}	meters/min	feet/min	3.281
inches of water (at 4°C)	inches of mercury	0.07355	meters/min	feet/sec	0.05468
inches of water (at 4°C)	kgs/sq cm	2.540×10^{-3}	meters/min	knots	0.03238
inches of water (at 4°C)	ounces/sq in	0.5781	meters/min	miles/hr	0.03728
inches of water (at 4°C)	pounds/sq ft	5.204	meters/sec	feet/min	196.8
inches of water (at 4°C)	pounds/sq in	0.03613	meters/sec	feet/sec	3.281
	K		meters/sec	kilometers/hr	3.6
			meters/sec	kilometers/min	0.06
kilograms	dynes	980,665.	meters/sec	miles/hr	2.237
kilograms	grams	1,000.0	meters/sec	miles/min	0.03728
kilograms	pounds	2.205	micrograms	grams	10^{-6}
kilograms	tons (long)	9.842×10^{-4}	microliters	liters	10^{-6}
kilograms	tons (short)	1.102×10^{-3}	microns	meters	1×10^{-6}
kilograms/cu meter	grams/cu cm	0.001	miles (naut.)	feet	6,080.27
kilograms/cu meter	pounds/cu ft	0.06243	miles (naut.)	kilometers	1.853
kilograms/cu meter	pounds/cu in	3.613×10^{-5}	miles (naut.)	meters	1,853.
kilograms/cu meter	pounds/mil-foot	3.405×10^{-10}	miles (naut.)	miles (statute)	1.1516
kilograms/meter	pounds/ft	0.6720	miles (naut.)	yards	2,027.
kilograms/sq cm	atmospheres	0.9678	miles (statute)	centimeters	1.609×10^{5}
kilograms/sq cm	feet of water	32.81	miles (statute)	feet	5,280.
kilograms/sq cm	inches of mercury	28.96	miles (statute)	inches	6.336×10^{4}
kilograms/sq cm	pounds/sq ft	2,048.	miles (statute)	kilometers	1.609
kilograms/sq cm	pounds/sq in	14.22	miles (statute)	meters	1,609.
kilograms/sq meter	atmospheres	9.678×10^{-5}	miles (statute)	miles (naut.)	0.8684
kilograms/sq meter	feet of water	3.281×10^{-2}	miles (statute)	yards	1,760.
kilograms/sq meter	inches of mercury	2.896×10^{-2}	miles/hr	cms/sec	44.70
kilograms/sq meter	pounds/sq ft	0.2048	miles/hr	feet/min	88.
kilograms/sq meter	pounds/sq in	1.422×10^{-3}	miles/hr	feet/sec	1.467
kilograms/sq mm	kgs/sq meter	10^{6}	miles/hr	kms/hr	1.609
kiloliters	liters	1,000.0	miles/hr	kms/min	0.02682
kilometers	centimeters	10^{5}	miles/hr	knots	0.8684
kilometers	feet	3,281.	miles/hr	meters/min	26.82
kilometers	inches	3.937×10^{4}	miles/hr	miles/min	0.1667
kilometers	meters	1,000.0	miles/min	cms/sec	2,682.
kilometers	miles	0.6214	miles/min	feet/sec	88.
kilometers	millimeters	10^{6}	miles/min	kms/min	1.609
kilometers	yards	1,094.	miles/min	knots/min	0.8684
kilometers/hr	cms/sec	27.78	miles/min	miles/hr	60.0
kilometers/hr	feet/min	54.68	mil-feet	cu inches	9.425×10^{-6}

TABLE A-17c
FREQUENTLY USED CONVERSION FACTORS

TO CONVERT	INTO	MULTIPLY BY	TO CONVERT	INTO	MULTIPLY BY
milliers	kilograms	1,000.	pounds/sq ft	atmospheres	4.725×10^{-4}
Millimicrons	meters	1×10^{-9}	pounds/sq ft	feet of water	0.01602
milligrams	grams	0.001	pounds/sq ft	inches of mercury	0.01414
milliliters	liters	0.001	pounds/sq ft	kgs/sq meter	4.882
millimeters	centimeters	0.1	pounds/sq in.	atmospheres	0.06804
millimeters	feet	3.281×10^{-3}	pounds/sq in.	feet of water	2.307
millimeters	inches	0.03937	pounds/sq in.	inches of mercury	2.036
millimeters	kilometers	10^{-6}	pounds/sq in.	kgs/sq meter	703.1
millimeters	meters	0.001	pounds/sq in	pounds/sq ft	144.0
millimeters	miles	6.214×10^{-7}			
millimeters	yards	1.094×10^{-3}	**Q**		
million gals/day	cu ft/sec	1.54723	quadrants (angle)	degrees	90.0
mils	centimeters	2.540×10^{-3}	quadrants (angle)	minutes	5,400.0
mils	feet	8.333×10^{-5}	quadrants (angle)	radians	1.571
mils	inches	0.001	quadrants (angle)	seconds	3.24×10^{5}
mils	kilometers	2.540×10^{-8}			
mils	yards	2.778×10^{-5}	**R**		
minutes (angles)	degrees	0.01667			
myriagrams	kilograms	10.0	radians	degrees	57.30
myriameters	kilometers	10.0	radians	minutes	3,438.
myriawatts	kilowatts	10.0	radians	quadrants	0.6366
			radians	seconds	2.063×10^{5}
O			rods	chain (Gunters)	.25
			rods	meters	5.029
ounces	drams	16.0	rods (Surveyors' meas.)	yards	5.5
ounces	grains	437.5	rods	feet	16.5
ounces	grams	28.349527			
ounces	pounds	0.0625	**S**		
ounces	ounces (troy)	0.9115			
ounces	tons (long)	2.790×10^{-5}	square centimeters	sq feet	1.076×10^{-3}
ounces	tons (metric)	2.835×10^{-5}	square centimeters	sq inches	0.1550
ounces (fluid)	cu inches	1.805	square centimeters	sq meters	0.0001
ounces (fluid)	liters	0.02957	square centimeters	sq miles	3.861×10^{-11}
ounces (troy)	grains	480.0	square centimeters	sq millimeters	100.0
ounces (troy)	grams	31.103481	square centimeters	sq yards	1.196×10^{-4}
ounces (troy)	ounces (avdp.)	1.09714	square feet	acres	2.296×10^{-5}
ounces (troy)	pounds (troy)	0.08333	square feet	sq cms	929.0
ounces/sq in.	pounds/sq in.	0.0625	square feet	sq inches	144.0
			square feet	sq meters	0.09290
P			square feet	sq miles	3.587×10^{-8}
			square feet	sq millimeters	9.290×10^{4}
pints (dry)	cu inches	33.60	square feet	sq yards	0.1111
pints (liq.)	cu cms	473.2	square inches	sq cms	6.452
pints (liq.)	cu feet	0.01671	square inches	sq feet	6.944×10^{-3}
pints (liq.)	cu inches	28.87	square inches	sq millimeters	645.2
pints (liq.)	cu meters	4.732×10^{-4}	square inches	sq yards	7.716×10^{-4}
pints (liq.)	cu yards	6.189×10^{-4}	square kilometers	acres	247.1
pints (liq.)	gallons	0.125	square kilometers	sq cms	10^{10}
pints (liq.)	liters	0.4732	square kilometers	sq ft	10.76×10^{6}
pints (liq.)	quarts (liq.)	0.5	square kilometers	sq inches	1.550×10^{9}
Pounds (advp)	ounces (troy)	14.5833	square kilometers	sq meters	10^{6}
pounds	drams	256.	square kilometers	sq miles	0.3861
pounds	grams	453.5924	square kilometers	sq yards	1.196×10^{6}
pounds	kilograms	0.4536	square meters	acres	2.471×10^{-4}
pounds	ounces	16.0	square meters	sq cms	10^{4}
pounds	ounces (troy)	14.5833	square meters	sq feet	10.76
pounds	pounds (troy)	1.21528	square meters	sq inches	1,550.
pounds	tons (short)	0.0005	square meters	sq miles	3.861×10^{-7}
pounds (troy)	ounces (avdp.)	13.1657	square meters	sq millimeters	10^{6}
pounds (troy)	ounces (troy)	12.0	square meters	sq yards	1.196
pounds (troy)	pounds (avdp.)	0.822857	square miles	acres	640.0
pounds (troy)	tons (long)	3.6735×10^{-4}	square miles	sq feet	27.88×10^{6}
pounds (troy)	tons (metric)	3.7324×10^{-4}	square miles	sq kms	2.590
pounds (troy)	tons (short)	4.1143×10^{-4}	square miles	sq meters	2.590×10^{6}
pounds of water	cu feet	0.01602	square miles	sq yards	3.098×10^{6}
pounds of water	cu inches	27.68	square millimeters	sq cms	0.01
pounds of water	gallons	0.1198	square millimeters	sq feet	1.076×10^{-5}
pounds/cu ft	grams/cu cm	0.01602	square millimeters	sq inches	1.550×10^{-3}
pounds/cu ft	kgs/cu meter	16.02	square mils	sq cms	6.452×10^{-6}
pounds/cu ft	pounds/cu in.	5.787×10^{-4}	square mils	sq inches	10^{-6}
pounds/cu in	gms/cu cm	27.68	square yards	acres	2.066×10^{-4}
pounds/cu in	kgs/cu meter	2.768×10^{4}	square yards	sq cms	8,361.
pounds/cu in	pounds/cu ft	1,728.	square yards	sq feet	9.0
pounds/ft	kgs/meter	1.488	square yards	sq inches	1,296.
pounds/in.	gms/cm	178.6	square yards	sq meters	0.8361

TABLE A-17d
FREQUENTLY USED CONVERSION FACTORS

TO CONVERT	INTO	MULTIPLY BY	TO CONVERT	INTO	MULTIPLY BY
square yards	sq miles	3.288×10^{-7}	tons (short)	ounces (troy)	29,166.66
square yards	sq millimeters	8.361×10^{5}	tons (short)	pounds	2,000.
			tons (short)	pounds (troy)	2,430.56
T			tons (short)	tons (long)	0.89287
temperature (°C)+273	absolute temperature (°C)	1.0	tons (short)	tons (metric)	0.9078
			tons (short)/sq ft	kgs/sq meter	9,765.
temperature (°C)+17.78	temperature (°F)	1.8	tons (short)/sq ft	pounds/sq in.	2,000.
			tons of water/24 hrs	pounds of water/hr	83.333
temperature (°F)+460	absolute temperature (°F)	1.0	tons of water/24 hrs	gallons/min	0.16643
			tons of water/24 hrs	cu ft/hr	1.3349
temperature (°F)−32	temperature (°C)	5/9			
tons (long)	kilograms	1,016.	**Y**		
tons (long)	pounds	2,240.	yards	centimeters	91.44
tons (long)	tons (short)	1.120	yards	kilometers	9.144×10^{-4}
tons (metric)	kilograms	1,000.	yards	meters	0.9144
tons (metric)	pounds	2,205.	yards	miles (naut.)	4.934×10^{-4}
tons (short)	kilograms	907.1848	yards	miles (stat.)	5.682×10^{-4}
tons (short)	ounces	32,000.	yards	millimeters	914.4

TABLE A-18
METRIC CONVERSION OF DIAMETER

in	mm	in	mm	in	mm	in	mm
6	150	30	750	57	1425	96	2400
8	200	33	825	60	1500	102	2550
10	250	36	900	63	1575	108	2700
12	300	39	975	66	1650	114	2850
15	375	42	1050	69	1725	120	3000
18	450	45	1125	72	1800	132	3300
21	525	48	1200	78	1950	144	3600
24	600	51	1275	84	2100	156	3900
27	675	54	1350	90	2250	168	4200

TABLE A-19
METRIC CONVERSION OF WALL THICKNESS

in	mm	in	mm	in	mm	in	mm
1	25	3-1/8	79	5	125	8	200
1-1/2	38	3-1/4	82	5-1/4	131	8-1/2	213
2	50	3-1/2	88	5-1/2	138	9	225
2-1/4	56	3-3/4	94	5-3/4	144	9-1/2	238
2-3/8	59	3-7/8	98	6	150	10	250
2-1/2	63	4	100	6-1/4	156	10-1/2	263
2-5/8	66	4-1/8	103	6-1/2	163	11	275
2-3/4	69	4-1/4	106	6-3/4	169	11-1/2	288
2-7/8	72	4-1/2	113	7	175	12	300
3	75	4-3/4	119	7-1/2	188	12-1/2	313

CONDENSED
BIBLIOGRAPHY

CONDENSED BIBLIOGRAPHY

"Airport Drainage," Federal Aviation Agency, AC 150/5320-5A, U. S. Government Printing Office, Washington, D. C. (1965).

Applied Hydrology, R. K. Linsley, Jr., M. A. Kohler, and J. L. H. Paulhaus, McGraw-Hill Book Co., Inc., New York (1949).

"California Culvert Practice," Second Edition, Div. Highways, Department of Public Works, State of California (1960).

"Capacity Charts for the Hydraulic Design of Highway Culverts," Bureau of Public Roads, Hydr. Eng. Circular No. 10, U. S. Government Printing Office, Washington, D. C. (1965).

"Computerized Design of Precast Reinforced Box Culverts," La Tona, R. W., Heger, F. J., and Bealey, M., Highway Research Record 443, 1973.

Concrete Pipe Handbook, American Concrete Pipe Association, Arlington, Virginia (1967).

Concrete Sewers, Portland Cement Association, Chicago, Illinois.

"Conduit Strengths and Trenching Requirements," H. M. Reitz, M. G. Spangler, H. L. White, J. G. Hendrickson, Jr., and H. H. Benjes, Washington University Conf. Syllabus, St. Louis, Missouri (1958).

"Design and Construction of Sanitary and Storm Sewers," *WPCF Manual of Practice No. 9, ASCE Manuals and Reports on Engineering Practice No. 37,* Water Pollution Control Federation, Washington, D. C.

"Design Data Series," American Concrete Pipe Association, Arlington, Virginia (1969).

"Electronic Computer Program for Hydraulic Analysis of Circular Culverts," Bureau of Public Roads, BPR Program HY-1, U. S. Government Printing Office, Washington, D. C. (1965).

Engineering Hydraulics, John Wiley & Sons, Inc., New York.

"Generalized Estimates of Probable Maximum Precipitation for the United States West of the 105th Meridian for Areas to 400 Sq. Miles and Durations to 24 Hr.," Weather Bureau, Technical Paper No. 38, U.S. Government Printing Office, Washington, D. C. (1960).

Handbook of Applied Hydraulics, McGraw-Hill Book Co., Inc., New York.

Handbook of Concrete Culvert Pipe Hydraulics, Portland Cement Association, Chicago, Illinois (1964).

Handbook of Hydraulics, H. W. King and E. F. Brater, 5th Edition, McGraw-Hill Book Co., Inc., New York (1963).

"Hydraulic Charts for the Selection of Highway Culverts," Bureau of Public Roads, Hydraulic Engineering Circular No. 5, U. S. Government Printing Office, Washington, D. C. (1965).

Hydraulics of Culverts, J. G. Hendrickson, Jr., American Concrete Pipe Association, Arlington, Virginia (1964).

"Hydrology," *Manual of Practice No. 28,* American Society of Civil Engineers, New York (1949).

Hydrology for Engineers, R. K. Linsley, Jr., M. A. Kohler, and J. L. H. Paulhaus, McGraw-Hill Book Co., Inc., New York (1958).

"Loads on Pipe in Wide Ditches," W. J. Schlick, Iowa Eng. Exp. Sta., Bulletin No. 108 (1932).

"Municipal Requirements for Sewer Infiltration," *Public Works,* 96, 6, 158 (1965).

"Negative Projecting Conduits," M. G. Spangler and W. J. Schlick, Iowa Engineering Experiment Station, Engineering Report No. 14 (1952-53).

"Nomenclature for Hydraulics," *Manual of Engineering Practice No. 43,* American Society of Civil Engineers, New York (1962).

"Rainfall Frequency Atlas of the United States for Durations from 30-Min. to 24-Hr. and Return Periods from 1 to 100 Yr.," Weather Bureau, Technical Paper No. 40, U. S. Government Printing Office, Washington, D. C. (1961).

"Rainfall Intensity-Frequency Data," D. L. Yarnell, Department of Agriculture, Misc. Publication No. 204, U. S. Government Printing Office, Washington, D. C. (1935).

"Rainfall Intensity-Frequency Regime," Weather Bureau, Technical Paper No. 29, U. S. Government Printing Office, Washington, D. C.: Part 1 — Ohio Valley (1957); Part 2 — Southeastern U. S. (1958); Part 3 — Middle Atlantic Region (1958); Part 4 — Northeastern U. S. (1959); Part 5 — Great Lakes Region (1960).

"Reinforced Concrete Pipe Culverts — Criteria for Structural Design and Installation," Bureau of Public Roads, U. S. Government Printing Office, Washington, D. C. (1963).

"Relation between Rainfall and Runoff from Small Urban Areas," W. W. Horner and F. L. Flynt, *Trans. Amer. Soc. Civil Engr.,* 101, 140 (1936).

Soil Mechanics in Engineering Practice, John Wiley & Sons, Inc., New York (1966). K. Terzaghi and R. R. Peck.

Soils Engineering, M. G. Spangler, 2nd Edition, International Textbook Co., Scranton, Pa. (1960).

"Structural Characteristics of Reinforced Concrete Elliptical Sewer and Culvert Pipe," H. V. Swanson and M. D. Reed, Publ. No. 1240, Highway Research Board, Washington, D. C. (1964).

"Structural Design of Precast Concrete Box Sections for Zero to Deep Earth Cover Conditions and Surface Wheel Loads," Heger, F. J., and Long, K. N., ASTM Special Technical Publication STP 630, 1977.

"Test Program for Evaluation of Design Method and Standard Design for Precast Concrete Box Culvert with Welded Wire Fabric Reinforcing," Heger, F. J., Boring, M. R., and Bealey, M., Highway Research Record 518, 1974.

"The Supporting Strength of Rigid Pipe Culverts," Iowa Engineering Experiment Station, M. G. Spangler, Bulletin No. 112 (1933).

"The Theory of External Loads on Closed Conduits in the Light of the Latest Experiments," A. Marston, Iowa Engineering Experiment Station, Bulletin No. 96 (1930).

"Vertical Pressure on Culverts Under Wheel Loads on Concrete Pavement Slabs," Portland Cement Association, Publ. No. ST-65, Skokie, Illinois (1951).